Copy #1

FROM

YOUR CONGRESSMAN
OAKLEY HUNTER
TWELFTH DISTRICT, CALIFORNIA

83D CONGRESS, 2D SESSION, HOUSE DOCUMENT NO. 280

THE YEARBOOK OF AGRICULTURE · 1954

THE UNITED STATES GOVERNMENT PRINTING OFFICE

Marketing

THE YEARBOOK OF AGRICULTURE • 1954

THE UNITED STATES DEPARTMENT OF AGRICULTURE

FOR SALE BY THE SUPERINTENDENT OF DOCUMENTS,
WASHINGTON 25, D. C., PRICE $1.75 (CLOTH)

The Yearbook Committee

Agricultural Marketing Service: ARTHUR E. BROWNE, WILLIAM C. CROW, ROY W. LENNARTSON, STERLING R. NEWELL, HERMAN M. SOUTHWORTH, HARRY C. TRELOGAN, *chairman,* FREDERICK V. WAUGH, O. V. WELLS

Agricultural Research Service: E. C. ELTING, W. T. PENTZER, GERTRUDE S. WEISS

Farmer Cooperative Service: JOSEPH G. KNAPP

Office of Information: ALFRED STEFFERUD, *editor*

Foreword *by the Secretary of Agriculture*

I write these words in a time of uncertainty. No one can foresee the results of recent economic and international developments. We can see, though, the need to understand the underlying trends and to use them to advantage. After the war our export markets expanded greatly and then shrank. Marketing became much more costly. The need grew for bigger and more stable markets at home and abroad and for more efficient methods of storing, transporting, and distributing the products of our farms. Those problems concern every farmer, every processor, every distributor, every family in the United States.

Our marketing system is intricate. It is sensitive to many economic and international developments. It includes millions of processors and dealers, each making his own plans. When one first looks at such a complex system, he may easily get an impression of disorder in it.

Yet there is a guiding principle. Adam Smith, a Scottish political economist of the eighteenth century, pointed out that the individual producers and businessmen, acting in their own self-interest as they make their countless separate decisions to buy or sell or hold or ship, are led as if by an invisible hand to benefit the general public. The principle is one of beneficial competition. When all buyers and sellers have accurate information, the process of competition can help the farmer and the consumer.

In practice, however, competition often is imperfect and our factual information is far from complete. Adjustments therefore often are slow, and Government—local, State, and Federal—is asked to help, to speed things up, to supplement individual efforts with broader measures. All need to work together to improve the marketing process.

The challenge to our American system is to maintain both freedom and order—to assure the flexibility that stimulates progress and the stability that promotes steady employment and purchasing power.

To that challenge we in the Department of Agriculture have increasingly turned our thoughts and efforts. Greater emphasis than ever before has been placed on marketing as a mainspring of our national and individual lives. I am confident that we shall meet that challenge—that all of us, fully informed as to the scope and demands of marketing, will reach our goal of stable well-being.

So, I bespeak a continuing search for the facts needed for understanding fully our economic problems, especially the problems of marketing. To that search this Yearbook is a contribution.

Ezra Taft Benson.

Preface *by the Editor*

The purpose of this book is to give information about the dynamic business that brings American farm products to their users. The information should help many persons: The farmer, to make more money; the housewife, to buy better; the wholesaler, retailer, and all the others who handle farm products, to give better service; the administrator and student of agriculture, to get a broader view of the structure of this large sector of our economy, within which so many agricultural problems come to focus.

Our purpose is not to outline an official program, for that has never been a function of the Yearbooks of Agriculture. Analysis is to be found herein, yes, and some discussion of controversial issues, because marketing involves competitions, tensions, and differences of opinion. The contributors were free to develop their assignments as they thought best.

They explain, discuss, and describe, but they were not asked to support a prescribed case or cause. The reader is left free to draw his own conclusions from the facts, estimates, and arguments we set forth.

Many questions are not answered, at least not fully: In a fast-changing field like marketing it is impossible to do so, and it would not be right to pretend that we could.

A related volume is *Crops in Peace and War*, the 1950–1951 Yearbook of Agriculture, which describes the many uses to which farm products are put and alternative uses in times of overproduction or scarcity. The two books are intended as guides to the thinking of citizens about agricultural stability.

The chapters of this book are organized to give first a general view of the components of the marketing system and its importance, then a description of its major parts, and finally discussions of its many problems. An Atlas of Marketing pictures the handling of some of our main products.

The whole book, we think, is worth reading by everyone who is interested in learning more about this vital, everyday subject, but to those who want only a basic introduction we recommend especially the chapters that begin on pages 3, 11, 52, 72, 164, 195, 211, and 395.

The book was planned and outlined in the spring of 1952. Most of the writing was done in 1952 and early 1953. Congress appropriated funds for publishing it in May 1953. The proofs were approved in May 1954.

Special acknowledgment is made of the work of Catherine F. George, the editor's assistant.

Grateful acknowledgment also is made of the interest of persons in the Congress and elsewhere which insured the continued publication of the Yearbooks.

Alfred Stefferud.

Contents:

Marketing

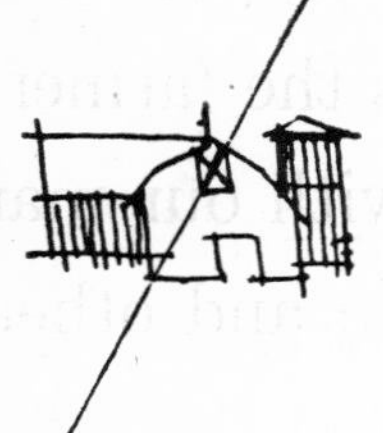

The Basis

The basis of marketing is this: Farm goods must be stored, transported, processed, and delivered in the form, at the time, and to the places that consumers desire. Those functions are performed more and more by specialists and less and less by farmers. Their competition for your dollar encourages efficiency—and conflict. The price of goods processed or made from American farm products in recent years has run about two and one-half or three times the farmers' cash receipts. Is something wrong, then, with our marketing system? An answer to that question and others like it rests on an understanding of marketing, which can be said to begin at the farm gate. A brief first look discloses the many things that happen afterward: Assembling the raw commodities, transportation, preparation for use, storage, shifting and sharing risks, change in ownership, pricing and exchange, wholesaling and retailing. They are described in detail later. More than a million American firms engage in those activities; they employ 10 million workers.

Marketing: What Is It? Why Is It?

Marketing is part and parcel of the modern productive process, the part at the end that gives point and purpose to all that has gone before.

Marketing is getting the product to the consumer.

And it is the product, too: The bread from the wheat, the cloth from the cotton, the steak from the beef, the salad from the lettuce. It is service and utility: The stores that sell the food and clothing, the railroads and trucks that carry the goods, and banks, elevators, markets. It is people and work.

Wheat that is put in an elevator in Kansas is of no use to the housewife in Atlanta who wants to make rolls for dinner. Cattle on a Texas ranch are not steaks in New York. Cotton at a gin in Alabama is not a dress at a party in Dubuque.

This is the basic fact with which we start our exploration of agricultural marketing: The goods that farmers grow and sell must be stored, transported, processed, and delivered in the form and at the time and to the places that consumers desire.

The storing, transporting, processing, and delivery are the simpler parts of marketing. Farmers in an earlier day often did them when they sold directly to customers. Some people still buy some products from some farmers, especially in small towns and rural communities. But specialization is the general rule today. Fewer and fewer farmers sell directly to consumers. Rather, each function that occurs in marketing or between the time the farmer first offers his products for sale and the final purchase—each function is performed by agencies or persons who have some particular advantage or skill.

Specialization—the division of labor—itself creates a series of activities in the marketing process. As the process becomes increasingly complex, as more and more steps come between the farmer and the buyer, agencies or individuals appear whose only business is to facilitate exchange of ownership—commodity exchanges, brokers, commission houses. Many-sided questions also arise as to the division of supplies

281437°—54——2

among buyers, of returns among those who contribute to the final product, and of providing guidance to farmers and producers as to future plans for what, when, and how much.

We seem to have come to accept this specialization without much question even though Americans prided themselves not long ago on being jacks-of-all-trades, personally able to do anything that was necessary.

The reason lies in the efficiency of the new way and the need to divide up the tasks as a means to the smooth operation of the new mechanized system. Even though the soil and climate in places in Louisiana and a few other States are most favorable for growing early strawberries, any farmer there could not afford to produce on a commercial scale if he himself had to carry the strawberries to Pittsburgh and peddle them from house to house. Adapting farm production to the various possibilities of soil and weather over our vast country depends chiefly on adequate transportation and on handling and sales agencies that do the job at reasonable cost.

Or if early strawberries are too narrow an example, consider any of the great staple commodities—oranges, which need the climate of the far South, the great corn and livestock business built upon the rich soils and temperate climate of the Corn Belt; or the volume, methods, and location of wheat production in the Great Plains. The existence of such types of agriculture, the organization of the farms within the areas, and the year-to-year changes in the farmers' decisions as to what to do rest on a highly geared marketing system made up of thousands of separate agencies, each essentially independent but together one closely knit, flexible system.

Creameries, elevators, packing sheds, canneries, tobacco warehouses, cotton gins; local buyers, assemblers, auction markets; trucklines, railroads, and air-cargo companies; commission houses, brokers, organized exchanges, credit institutions; packing plants, flour and textile mills, cigarette factories; wholesalers, jobbers, exporters, converters, factory sales representatives; independent and chain groceries, specialized clothing and the general department stores, mail-order houses, drugstores, restaurants—those are the kinds of agencies that move farm products to consumers over the United States and the rest of the world.

Our modern marketing system has several functions:

From one standpoint, its function is to move the desired varieties of farm and food products to consumers in the desired forms and conditions at the lowest possible cost.

From another standpoint, its function is to make a living for people working in it and to yield reasonable returns to the capital and management skills devoted to it.

And in a dynamic economy such as the one we live in, the marketing system also has the function of finding and developing new markets—new, that is, in the sense of moving new products, better products, or more of the old products, either at home or abroad.

These three functions do not necessarily conflict with each other. In fact, in an economy based on free enterprise and competition they lead to the same end.

But one should not think there are no conflicts of interest in marketing. Competition itself is a form of conflict between agencies engaged in the same line of business. Conflicts occur also between products and between prime producers (that is, farmers) and the marketing agencies. After all, the incomes of consumers and their stomachs are limited.

What farmers want from the marketing system is expressed perhaps as well as anywhere in the preambles to State laws that authorized farm cooperatives in the 1920's. That is, the objective is to "encourage the intelligent and orderly marketing of agricultural products . . . to eliminate speculation and waste . . . to make the distribution of agricultural products between producer and consumer as direct as can be efficiently done; and to stabilize the marketing of agricultural products."

To good salesmen the American market is big, exciting, different. It is up to them to make the most of it, to catch the consumer's attention, to sell. Their efforts lead to advertising and the development of new services and products in an attempt to get a larger part of an established market and to enlarge the total market. Farm products and the commodities processed from them—food, clothing, industrial materials of many kinds—get their share of this selling effort.

The immediate interests of food processors and textile manufacturers and others like them and of those who wholesale and retail the products are closely related. In many industries, in fact, the advertising and related sales activities of manufacturers and retailers are so closely tied together as to be one. But in the food and clothing fields, in which the larger part of the trade is in staple, nonbranded items, a sharp line still divides the sales activities of the intermediate handlers and the retailers who make most of the day-to-day sales effort.

The average American consumer expects the marketing system to keep the goods flowing continuously into the retail outlets handiest to him, preferably at prices that allow him a rising standard of living. That goal requires just as much of the farmers as it does of the marketing system.

American farm products also move into foreign markets. In them, too, despite an intervening web of trade difficulties that can sometimes considerably modify the free-market demand, the basic marketing function is to find and serve the final user.

Some people seem to regard marketing as a merely passive act and the function of the marketing agencies as merely to stand ready to supply demands. But in a growing, dynamic economy, in which competition is the chief coordinator, marketing agencies try always to create new or larger demands for their products. Some uncertainty may result, but that is one of the chief factors in economic growth.

Farmers want maximum returns over costs. So do the marketing agencies. The workers engaged in marketing want better wages. But the buyer's dollar must cover returns to producers and all the marketing interests. The competition for a larger share of the dollar on the part of farmers and everyone else along the line is the factor that does most to select and force efficiency among producers and marketing agencies—efficiency here being the ability to meet the specific demands that consumers are willing to translate into actual purchases. Therein lie most of the conflicts in marketing.

The market for goods processed or fabricated from American farm commodities runs some two and one-half to three times farmers' cash receipts—in recent years, perhaps as much as 85 billion to 90 billion dollars (including the wholesale value of farm export commodities in the foreign market) compared to annual cash sales of 30 billion to 33 billion dollars. In recent years, farmers have received 45 to 50 cents of each dollar Americans spent for food at retail, 25 cents out of each dollar spent for food in restaurants, and 12 to 15 cents out of each dollar spent for ordinary clothing, household textiles, and tobacco products at retail.

Such details and the tendency of marketing costs to hold steady or even go up when farm prices are falling lead thinking people to ask: Is enough effort being concentrated on selling the basic products, or are sales activities increasingly creating a demand for more and more services?—that is, for services like packaging, refrigeration, pre-preparation, and pleasant shopping conditions. Does the existence of inflexible marketing costs so far separate farmers and consumers as to weaken the traditional guidance functions of the marketing process? To what extent has concentration or organization of the various agencies or elements within the marketing system changed the relative bargaining strength of farmers?

We leave for later consideration the answers to those questions and the many changes and improvements that are going forward in marketing. It is enough in this introduction to explain why we have marketing and to indicate its nature and the framework within which its problems are set.

The demand for farm products is a derived demand—that is, the demand works backward from the consumer to the retailer to the wholesaler to the processor to the assembler to the farmer. A long chain of agencies or functions intervene between the average farmer and the final users of his products. Because the demand for farm products is closely keyed to the consumer's dollar, imperfections or disturbances in marketing often fall hardest on the farmer—a tendency reinforced by the fact that many marketing costs are relatively inflexible.

Regardless of the problems and inequalities, though, American farmers and the business agencies which handle, process, and sell their commodities have a strong common interest. They do need to understand (as do the rest of us) the marketing process better, because understanding is one of the main routes to improvement. (*O. V. Wells.*)

And What Are Its Parts?

Before we get farther along, let us get a quick bird's-eye view of the elements of agricultural marketing as a basis for detailed explanations later.

Marketing itself may be said to begin at the farm gate. One of its first steps is assembling the raw commodities. It may begin with country buyers or at the local creamery, country elevator, buying station, cotton gin, cotton or fruit warehouse, or local processing plant. It may begin at interior or central stockyards, elevators, or warehouses. It may begin when farmers offer their products for direct sale at farmers' markets or large retail outlets.

Transportation becomes a major factor at the start of assembling and continues to be important throughout almost all phases of marketing. A network of railways, waterways, airways, highways, assembly yards and transfer points, manned around the clock by truck drivers and engineers, conductors and captains, pilots, trainmen, dispatchers, and signalmen, carries the goods to intermediate processing and distribution points and to final markets.

Most agricultural commodities are processed in some way. Some fruits and vegetables are canned. Meat animals are slaughtered, cut up, and chilled. Wheat is ground, and the flour is baked into bread. Soybeans are crushed, and the oil is made into margarine and shortening; the meal is used for livestock feed or refined for high-protein flour. Cotton is spun into thread and yarn; the yarn goes into cloth, and the cloth into shirts and dresses and sheets. Byproducts of many agricultural products yield glycerin, furfural, fatty acids, enzymes, hormones, and many other chemicals.

A related function is packaging. Its primary purpose is to place the products in convenient forms for shipment, storage, or sale. Prepackaging of perishable products before they are put on retail display is a new, fast-growing development.

Because agricultural production is seasonal, the products have to be stored for orderly distribution later. The storage function involves risks—risks of deterioration of products in storage and risks of fluctuating market prices. Fairly elaborate precautions are taken to guard against any deterioration of products from excessive moisture, heat, contaminating metals, bacteria and fungi, insects, and rodents and against loss from fire and theft.

Whether a stored commodity is held by a farmer, a warehouseman, a processor, a wholesaler, or a retailer, the risk of a drop in the market price is always present. Various devices are used to shift the risk or to spread the risk.

For certain commodities, such as wheat and cotton, the farmers can get Government nonrecourse loans. The farmers can redeem the loans and sell when prices are good. Or they may permit the Government to take title to the commodity at the loan-maturity date; then the farmers have received the benefit of the full loan value. The Government assumes all market price risk below the loan value.

Another device is to sell products for later delivery. A wheat miller might sell flour to bakeries for later delivery at the price prevailing when he bought the wheat. The deferred delivery period might be 30 days to 6 months, depending on buyers' needs and willingness to run the risk of falling prices.

A more widely used device is the buying and selling of futures contracts on the commodities exchange. All individuals or firms holding agricultural commodities for which futures markets are available may guard—"hedge"—against price changes in that way. Essential marketing services are performed by the people who run the futures exchange and enforce its trading rules, the brokers who act as agents on the floor of the exchange, and the speculators who assume the risks and thus make hedging possible.

Retailers are protected to a degree against change in price by the practice of pricing goods on the basis of a specific markup over the acquisition cost. The practice is not always feasible on a highly competitive market; customers may not pay the price. Pricing goods for rapid turnover is another way in which retail distributors can reduce price risks.

Another major role of marketing relates to change in ownership. Agricultural goods, like most other goods, have value only in terms of their usefulness—utility—to consumers. The pricing and exchange functions associated with possession are the heart of marketing.

Pricing is the determination of market values in terms of money. Buyers and sellers at a given time agree on a common evaluation. Prices may vary from day to day or hour to hour, depending on demand and supply. But in time prices of different commodities seek different levels in accordance with the relative utilities of the commodities and their costs. A ton of wheat contains more nutrients than a ton of hay and costs more to produce. Thus the price of a ton of wheat ordinarily is about three times the price of a ton of hay.

Exchange involves the transfer of ownership—goods for money or goods for goods. Most exchange transactions are concluded with the payment of money, although some barter exchange is practiced among countries having centrally controlled trading agencies.

Many people and agencies are engaged in the exchange of agricultural products. The courts stand ready to enforce rules of fair dealing. Commercial banks provide credit for the shipment of products and to finance processing and storage. The futures market is available to help in spreading the market price risk. Several auxiliary services are performed to facilitate pricing and exchange, including sanitary inspection, dissemination of market news, and market forecasting.

Another service is the grading of products by recognized standards of quality. Grading helps farmers get fair prices for their products. It also permits commercial buyers to make purchases of such products as milk, butter, eggs, and meat on a basis of quality and price.

Wholesaling and retailing, two essential services, are performed on the widest scale possible. They reach every community.

Wholesale assembly and distribution particularly is a key activity in the whole marketing system, since the wholesale market represents the focal point in the flow of goods from producer to consumer.

Price changes and the surpluses or shortages of specific products are often first noted in wholesale channels. The wholesaler to a certain extent regulates the market price. If more pork is offered through trade channels than consumers will take at a given price, the wholesaler promptly reduces his price bid to packinghouses; prices paid for live hogs on the one hand, and for wholesale cuts of pork on the other, will decline. Reduced prices to consumers are thus made possible, and a larger supply of pork will be absorbed. An opposite action will occur, with rising prices to producers and consumers, when pork becomes scarce.

Besides assembling a wide assortment of products, the wholesaler also may extend short-term credit to buyers. Often he assists retailers in solving merchandising problems. Sometimes wholesalers prepackage products.

Retailing is the final link in the distribution chain. Several hundred thousand retail foodstores and additional thousands of department, dry goods, and cigar stores and other specialty stores throughout the country satisfy day-to-day consumer requirements for food and other products of agricultural origin.

Retailing has undergone dynamic change in a few decades. Regional and national chainstore organizations have grown rapidly. In our automobile age, retail stores have become fewer and larger. They also have enlarged their services to buyers.

Retailers, wholesalers, processors, farmer cooperatives, and farm organizations and trade associations are engaged in merchandising farm products. Merchandising, defined by the American Marketing Association as "the planning involved in marketing the right merchandise or service at the right place, at the right time, in the right quantities, and at the right price," involves promotional activities—attractive packaging and display, advertising, product differentiation in an effort to establish customer loyalty for brand names, competitive pricing, and personal salesmanship. A great deal of thought, effort, and money goes into this activity; without it, some of the variety, freshness, and appeal of agricultural products now available to consumers would be lacking. (*Robert M. Walsh.*)

What Can It Do for Us?

Statisticians predict that the population of the United States will continue to grow rapidly. They expect more than 200 million people by 1975—one-third more than in 1950. Food supply will be a vital factor in determining where and how the people will live and how well they will live. Indeed, if the trend toward better eating of the past 25 years continues, we will require by 1975 not just 33 percent more food, but around 45 percent more—measuring the amount in value terms that reflect quality preferences and the added services that consumers want.

A glance backward points up the magnitude of the development.

The population of the United States in 1800 was 5 million persons, almost all of whom lived east of the Appalachians. About 95 percent lived on farms. The few urban communities were eastern seaport towns, whose inhabitants were fed from the produce of nearby farms. By 1900, population was more than 75 million, 30 million of whom lived in urban communities scattered between the Atlantic and the Pacific. The population of three cities exceeded a million, and the population of 33 others exceeded 100,000.

By 1950 the population had again doubled, exceeding 150 million, of whom nearly 100 millions lived in cities. The number of people living on farms actually started downward in this half century, falling from 32.5 in 1916 to 25 million in 1950. Cities continued to grow in size and number; in 1950 there were 151 metropolitan areas of more than 100,000 population, of which 14 had more than a million inhabitants. The largest—New York-northeastern New Jersey—was almost 13 million. By then the railroads were supplemented by an even vaster system of highways over which fleets of trucks carried an uncounted but enormous volume of long- and short-haul traffic, including large quantities of foods and other farm products.

Whereas at the beginning of this Nation's history 9 out of 10 people lived on farms, today the number is fewer than 1 in 6. And whereas at the beginning of our history nearly every family raised its own food or bought it directly from the producer, today the number of people engaged primarily in marketing food—in getting it from the farmers to consumers—approaches that engaged in producing the food in the first place. The total cost of processing and distributing the food after it leaves the farm exceeds the amount the farmers get. Food marketing is the business of some of our largest industries, and of several of our largest corporations—the meatpackers, grain dealers, flour millers, canners, chainstore companies. Even so, the combined job of producing food in the United States today and getting it to consumers requires less than one-fifth of our total productive effort.

Historically, the great increases in our food supplies have come through opening new lands to cultivation. By now this source of new production is about gone. Further increases will have to come mainly through getting more output from our present farming acreage. The experience of recent decades has demonstrated how this can be done—through technological advances in production, through further specialization, and the shifting of land from extensive to more intensive types of farming.

The marketing system, too, can help to increase food supplies. It can help first of all by adapting facilities and trade channels to the new patterns of production that will be needed. The need in the future will be to facilitate changes in the use of existing land. When farmers in an area shift to new lines of production that permit more intensive use of their resources, they will need new market facilities to handle their products and new trade channels to give them access to the national market.

The marketing system can help also to achieve fuller use of the foods that are produced. It can cut down on deterioration and spoilage of foods through the new and better methods of packing, processing, handling, and storage. It can find byproduct uses for food materials that now are wasted.

The marketing system itself will have greatly increased volumes to distribute, with increasing needs and opportunities for improved methods of operation, for shortcuts that eliminate unnecessary handling, for improved design of facilities, for ways to mechanize operations both to speed them up and to reduce the labor costs involved, for management methods that overcome lost motion and prevent wrong decisions, for improvements in the organization of markets to facilitate smoother and faster flow of products through trade channels.

The transportation system obviously will have a greatly increased volume. It will have to carry not only the additional food, but all the other products needed for a larger population. Historically, its task in expanding food supply has been the extension, first of river and canal lines, then of railroads, more recently of motortruck highways and airlines to open up new territories to production. The need of the future will be instead to haul a greater volume over existing routes. Traffic congestion on highways and in some instances on railroads is already a recognized problem. A great deal of ingenuity and imagination will be needed to overcome it. Fully as much effort will need to be directed toward improving local hauling within metropolitan areas as toward improving over-the-road movement. If the present shift of city people to the suburbs continues, more transportation and a more complex pattern of transportation will be required to distribute the foods throughout the spreading residential areas.

Communications facilities will face a similar problem. Our free-enterprise system works through millions of daily decisions of independent farmers, businessmen, and consumers throughout the country—decisions to buy or sell, to ship, process, or store the countless products of our farms. Our whole economy is a demonstration of the efficiency of such a system. But in order to achieve this efficiency, the thousands of independent operators must have continuously available information on which to base intelligent decisions. And each one must have quick and ready access to all the others with whom he must deal in translating his decisions into action. This means highly complex and highly organized communications.

We have developed effective systems for this in the United States. But here again the great increase in traffic will require continuing application of ingenuity and imagination in devising quicker, simpler, more effective ways of assembling, summarizing, and disseminating market information, in organizing buying and selling more efficiently, in facilitating contact between operators at distant points in the marketing system. We will need, for example, to improve and extend the use of the grading systems that provide a common, precise language of trade. We will need to devise more compact systems of shorthand notation that permit packing more information in brief messages. New arrangements for direct dialing of long-distance telephone calls illustrate a type of improvement for speeding up communications.

We can also anticipate a great increase in the role of processing and storage in the food-supply system of the future. Processing and storage permit fuller use of the production possibilities of areas with seasonal disadvantages. They also reduce the burden upon transportation, partly by reducing the bulk of commodities that must be shipped, partly by spreading the shipping season out over the year instead of having it concentrated at harvesttime. Lack of storage facilities has hampered the marketing of various commodities from time to time in recent years.

Meanwhile the frozen-food industry furnishes a current example of how new methods of processing and distribution can draw upon new producing areas, expand year-around market outlets, and offer consumers both a better product and greater convenience.

The latter point can be generalized. With changing patterns of living and continuing increases in consumer incomes, there will be opportunities throughout the marketing system for developing additional services that will contribute to higher living standards. Recent history is full of developments of this kind—improvements in packaging, putting up foods in ready-to-use form, partly or wholly precooked products.

Food distribution over the next 25 years may not, on the whole, be a spectacular industry like television, although it will likely include isolated spectacular developments, like that of frozen concentrated orange juice over the past few years. It will, however, be an expanding industry. It will face many difficult responsibilities if it is to fulfill its role of furnishing food to an increasing population with rising standards of consumption. Certainly it will be an industry in which there is abundant opportunity for ingenuity and initiative. (*Herman Southworth.*)

How Efficient Is Our Marketing System?

Engineers say that no machine can be 100 percent efficient. There is always some friction, some loss of power. Any machine produces less energy than it consumes.

But the laws of economics differ from the laws of physics, although it is true that the economist must reckon with friction and waste. We expect our marketing machine to have an efficiency of more than 100 percent—we expect the finished goods and services to be worth more to the consumer than the value of the raw farm products plus the value of the labor and capital used to process, transport, and distribute them. Our standard is not physical energy—it is value, whether measured in money terms or in such broader terms as "satisfaction" or "utility."

From that viewpoint, no one would doubt that processing, transportation, and trade add greatly to the value of farm products. A billion-bushel crop of wheat would not be worth much if it were stored permanently on the farm. But the flour and bread made from our wheat are extremely valuable when they are made available to consumers at home and abroad. Who would doubt that the value of wheat is raised by more than the cost of the materials, labor, and capital that are used in marketing?

Why, then, do farmers and consumers ask, "Is our marketing efficient?" What do they mean by the question? Probably they want to know at least three things: Is our marketing machinery too complicated? Is technological progress in marketing keeping pace with that in farming and in business? Is it possible to reduce waste, overlapping and duplication, and monopolistic practices so that the job can be done at less expense?

We do not have the full answer to the three questions. But we shall discuss them as well as we can on the basis of information at hand.

First, our marketing machinery probably is not too complicated. It takes elaborate machinery to do the job efficiently in the United States today. Simple and direct arrangements, such as roadside stands, parcel post, door-to-door peddling, and retail farmers' markets have a minor place in our modern economy. As farming becomes specialized, and especially as distant producing areas are developed, it becomes impracticable for most farmers to deal directly with consumers. So the modern farmer usually sells to a local buyer. Then the farmer loses track of the goods he produced. He knows that they are commonly resold many times and that many middlemen are involved.

This may seem complicated and mysterious. It is complicated, but it need not be mysterious. A watch is a complicated mechanism, but there is no great mystery about it. Few would object because a modern watch is more complicated than an hourglass or than a sundial—at least not if the watch runs well. Nor should we object to a complicated system of marketing if the parts are well coordinated.

The parts of the agricultural marketing system include about 10 million workers, almost 100 thousand processing plants, more than 200 thousand miles of railroads, 3 million miles of highways, 90 thousand wholesale establishments, and 1 million retail stores, restaurants, and eating places.

They include many other things, too—the commodity exchanges, banks, cooperative associations, and so on.

That system has developed almost entirely as a result of competition and free enterprise. Each business unit must make its own way. The weak parts of the machine are gradually replaced by stronger ones. Presumably the changes resulting from competition tend toward greater efficiency. Otherwise they would not be made.

The complexity of marketing comes mainly from specialization. Middlemen are specialists. They include those who buy and sell—and also truck drivers, chemists, brokers, bankers, and many other experts. It is through specialization that industry in this country has been able to develop mass production and mass distribution. Almost all our industries are becoming more and more specialized. Take steel, or automobiles, as an example. Today those industries are more complicated than they were 50 years ago. They are also much more efficient.

Primitive simplicity is not necessarily a sign of modern efficiency.

Second, technological progress is occurring in agricultural marketing as elsewhere. Consider the railway refrigerator car, the modern motortruck, canning and quick-freezing, the chainstore. There have been many important developments in the technology of marketing during the past 50 years. They are less spectacular than the airplane and the atomic bomb, but they probably affect most of our citizens more directly. One big, sudden change would have made any of us sit up and take notice. But actually every year and every month there have been small changes.

One might argue that many technological developments in marketing do not reduce costs—that some of them may increase costs. Good transportation has increased the average distance of shipments to market. It has raised the amount and cost of transportation used to market farm products. But it has also made it possible for each area of the country to specialize in the production of a few commodities to which it is best suited. And it has widened the area of price competition.

Again, some developments in processing and packaging have been aimed at giving the consumer a more satisfactory product, rather than at lowering the price. Is that efficient? If not, should we try to reverse the trend and to teach young housewives to bake their own bread or to spin their own yarn? We should not take too restricted a definition of efficiency. If all we wanted were to reduce the amount of money spent in marketing food, we should all have gardens, pigs, and chickens. Then the marketing of food would cost very little because there would be little of it.

It is impossible to separate the efficiency of marketing from the efficiency of the whole process of production, distribution, and consumption.

We use our economic resources efficiently if—and only if—we raise our standards of living as high as we can—that is, if we get as much as possible of what we want. With rising levels of real income, our families have been able to afford highly processed foods and even restaurant-cooked foods. If they want such foods and can afford them, everyone gains if they are supplied. True, some consumers may prefer the simple, unprocessed, bulk foods, and may have to pay the extra price for packages and services if this represents the going method of sale. But, on the whole, the trend toward greater processing and packaging has doubtless been in response to a real demand, and is thus a sign of efficiency rather than the reverse.

Our statistics are not adequate to measure precisely the changes in the efficiency of food marketing. But the statistics that we have suggest that substantial improvements have been made.

The Agricultural Marketing Service regularly publishes the retail value of a typical market basket for food and also its farm value—that is, the payments to farmers for the farm products used to make the foods in the basket. In 1913–1915 the farmer got an average of 45 cents from each dollar spent for the basket of food. In 1953 also he got 45 cents. But remember that foods are now shipped longer distances and that retail prices cover more services than they did then. The figures suggest that the efficiency of food marketing has increased considerably.

In 1953, because of the growth of population and higher per capita consumption, we consumed about one-third more food than in 1935–1939. Between 1935 and 1953, employment in food marketing went up less than one-fourth—an indication that the average person in our marketing system was handling more food.

An answer to the third question is that there is room for improvements in the efficiency of agricultural marketing. Waste, overlapping and duplication, and monopolistic practices do exist in agricultural marketing. We need better research, better education, and better governmental services to make agricultural marketing as efficient as it might be.

We know, for example, that specific jobs—packing celery, or loading boxes in a freight car—are done in many ways. Some methods are better than others; they take less labor and turn out better products. Even with all the research and education in methods of farming, not all farmers follow—or even know—the most efficient methods of loading hay or feeding chickens. In much the same way, there is room for much improvement in the methods used by individual companies to do particular jobs in marketing.

Some parts of the country have too many small processing plants, many with obsolete machinery and equipment and with unnecessarily high costs of operation—facts that have been shown by many studies of cotton gins, creameries, and grain elevators.

Many of our large city markets for fruits and vegetables are poorly located, lack the modern facilities and equipment, and are so operated as to require excessive rehandling, delay, and waste.

Improvements in efficiency come gradually in an economy that is dominated by free enterprise and competition. A main job of the Department of Agriculture and the State colleges is to help speed up the process by discovering new techniques and by making information available to all those who can use it.

Of course, there is some waste in the competitive processes. Some savings could be made in many cases by eliminating competition—for example, by letting one large packing plant buy all the hogs in a producing area, or by letting one milk company serve all the consumers in a small city. But that course would confront us either with private monopoly or with Government control. Our main reliance in the United States has always been upon free, informed competition.

An efficient marketing system is one that gives the public as nearly as possible what it wants. The present system could no doubt be improved to give greater satisfaction to the farmers, to dealers, and to consumers. But those improvements will continue to come gradually, and they will continue to be made mainly by private industry. The Government helps this process along by providing research and education and by enforcing those laws that define fair methods of competition.

Although in this country we rely mainly on competition, in recent years we have asked our Government to take a more active hand in pricing. Farm prices are supported. Transportation rates are regulated. Marketing agreements and orders are enforced. In many States it is illegal to sell certain trade-marked goods at retail prices below those established by the manufacturer. As our marketing system becomes more and more complex, it is likely that we will call upon our

Government for more and more services and more and more regulation. Will this replace our free enterprise with a sort of creeping socialism? It need not do so. But to avoid it we must be intelligent enough to make sure that our laws and our programs are designed to foster and protect competition and to promote efficiency. Such Government services as market news and official inspection for grades have helped competition and have fostered efficiency. So has the enforcement of honest trade practices. Efficiency and fair competition are not things that come about automatically. In modern society they come only with accurate market news, with public inspection, and with the enforcement of many rules of trading.

The services and rules are changed from time to time, as they must be to keep pace with changes in industry and in the scope and character of competition. Business rules do change, just as do the rules that govern any other form of competition.

The purpose of economic life is to use our resources in such a way as to provide us all with as satisfactory a living as possible. The economist often defines maximum efficiency as "the optimum use of economic resources." But that is only a phrase. What is the optimum use of resources? The economist alone cannot give a satisfactory definition. It is the voters who decide in a democracy what priorities to give to the use of resources. The economist can only give information and help the citizens see what their real choices are. He can, for example, show the possibility of reducing the labor required to market perishable foods in New York City. He can perhaps suggest alternative jobs for those who would be displaced. But he alone cannot prove what use of labor is best.

Nor can the economist prove that competitive pricing alone is either necessary or sufficient to assure the best use of our resources. The teaching of school children is not left to competition alone. Neither is the care of the aged, nor the setting of freight rates, nor the pricing of milk. Competition will, and should, doubtless be the main guide to improvements in agricultural marketing, but the nature and scope of competition will be responsive to public wants—and should be. (*Frederick V. Waugh.*)

How Much Does Marketing Cost Us?

The bill for marketing farm goods amounted to an estimated 50 billion dollars in 1953. That figure covers all costs and profits, including taxes paid by marketing agencies. It represented about a seventh of our gross national product in 1953 and almost a fourth of consumer expenditures for all goods and services.

LET US EXAMINE the composition of this 50-billion-dollar bill.

Almost 30 billion dollars are charges for marketing food. The remainder goes for alcoholic beverages and nonfood products made from tobacco, cotton, wool, and leather.

About 5 billion dollars, or 10 percent, are taken by excise taxes on tobacco products and alcoholic beverages. On those products excise taxes levied by Federal, State, and local governments are nearly as large as all other marketing charges. Property and income taxes, fees, and licenses paid by marketing agencies also are a significant part of the marketing bill.

Wages and salaries paid by marketing agencies are the largest single item. What we might call "direct labor costs" have taken 45 to 50 percent of the total food-marketing bill in recent years. Transportation charges account for perhaps another 10 percent of the total. Packages and containers take about 5 percent. Other marketing costs include rents, utilities, advertising and other selling expenses, administrative expenses, maintenance and depreciation allowances on plant and equipment, the interest on borrowed capital, and the property taxes. The remainder represents profits to the marketing agencies.

When the public becomes concerned about that farmer-consumer price spread, the middlemen sometimes become scapegoats. We have no recent statistics that give the total profits of all marketing firms or middlemen.

The Department of Agriculture estimated that profits of all food-marketing agencies in 1939 amounted to 8 percent of the total charges made for marketing food products and about 5 percent of the consumer's food dollar. Profit series for groups of large food processors and retail food chains that are compiled from earnings statements reported by those companies indicate that in recent years profits per dollar of sales are about the same as those in 1939. If income and excess profit taxes are deducted, profit rates per dollar of sales appear to be substantially lower than in 1939. Dollar sales, of course, are much greater now than prewar; and profit per dollar of sales is not a measure of profits per dollar invested.

Profits thus do not make up a major proportion of the total farmer-consumer spread. A 50-percent reduction in profits would mean a much smaller percentage reduction in total marketing charges. If any substantial savings in marketing charges are to be realized, reductions must be made in operating costs as well as in profits. That is not to imply that middlemen's profits are too low or too high. In making such a judgment, one should consider returns on invested capital in marketing firms in relation to returns on invested capital in other comparable industries. If the returns are comparable, needed capital will be attracted to agricultural marketing.

Payments for many different marketing services (such as local assembly, storage, transportation, processing, wholesaling, and retailing) are all contained in the total marketing bill.

Charges for retailing represent the largest single part. The costs of processing, or manufacturing, farm products come next. Other services take smaller parts of the total.

The importance of these functions may be illustrated by the proportion of workers in each of the activities. More than half of all workers engaged in marketing food are employed in retailing. That includes family labor and self-employed proprietors, who are fairly numerous in retailing. Not all of these workers are in retail foodstores. A large number of them are in restaurants and eating places. Although a smaller proportion of food is bought in the form of meals, labor requirements per unit are very much greater than in retail foodstores.

Labor in processing food accounts for about 25 percent of the total number. Wholesaling, transportation, local assembly, and other activities make up the other 15 to 20 percent.

The importance of the different services in the total farm-retail price spread varies greatly by commodities. Charges for baking bread, for instance, are more than half of the total price spread for bread.

Processing is usually the most costly service for such products as bakery goods, evaporated milk, the prepared cereals, canned fruits and vegetables, and other highly processed products. For other farm products—fresh meat, poultry, eggs—for which processing is of less importance and transportation charges are relatively low, retailing is the most expensive operation. For some fresh fruits and vegetables that require long hauls and protective services, such as refrigerator cars, transportation may be as costly as any other marketing service. These comparisons are all based on farm-to-retail-store spreads. When any of these products are bought as meals, retailing usually is the most costly service.

FARMERS RECEIVED an estimated one-third of consumers' expenditures for farm products in 1953. The farmer's share is not constant from year to year nor is it the same for all commodities. Before giving any specific illustrations of price-spread data, some pitfalls in comparing farm and retail prices might be mentioned. Simple comparisons of retail prices and farm prices for the same unit generally give misleading and inaccurate conclusions.

For example, a common error is to compare retail prices per pound of Choice grade round steak with the average price per pound received by farmers for all beef cattle. The comparison would be valid only if 100 pounds of beef cattle sold by farmers yielded 100 pounds of Choice round steak. Actually, from 100 pounds of the average beef animal sold by farmers, less than 50 pounds of edible meat is obtained, and that amount includes much meat that sells at a lower retail price than round steak. Furthermore, the average grade of all beef animals sold by farmers is lower than Choice.

Another example of an erroneous price comparison is to compare the average price received by Iowa farmers for all eggs with the retail price of Extra Large Grade A eggs in New York City. Even if farm and retail prices for the same grade and size were compared, this price spread would not be representative of eggs marketed by all farmers. Transportation charges, for example, are considerably less for eggs moving from central New Jersey to the New York market than for eggs coming from Iowa.

Price-spread series of the Department of Agriculture attempt to measure the spread between the retail cost to the consumer and payment received by farmers for equivalent quantities of the product. The equivalent amounts are derived from adjustments for losses by waste and shrinkage during the marketing process and for the value of nonedible byproducts. For example, the farm-retail price spread and farmer's share for white flour is based on a comparison of the average retail price paid by consumers for a 5-pound package of flour with the average price received by farmers for an equivalent quantity of wheat—about 7.04 pounds. For both meat products and products made from grain, the farm value is adjusted to allow for the proportion of the farm product represented by the value of byproducts, such as hides or millfeeds, that are obtained in processing the products.

For food products as a whole, farmers in recent years have received a little less than half of what consumers paid in the retail store. (For all expenditures on food the share received by farmers is lower because of added costs of meals "eaten out.") This farmer's share of the retail-store price compares with about 15 percent for tobacco and textile products. For alcoholic beverages the share may be as low as 5 percent, although only rough estimates are available.

By food commodity groups, the farmer's share of the consumer's food dollar in 1953 varied from 69 percent for poultry and eggs and 63 percent for meat products to 22 percent for bakery and cereal products and 20 percent for processed fruits and vegetables.

Similar comparisons can be made for nonfood products. The farm value of the cotton in men's business shirts or women's street dresses is a smaller part of the retail price than it is in such articles as overalls, towels, and bedsheets.

WHAT ACCOUNTS for these differences in the farmer's share of the retail price? No one reason or group of reasons that can be cited will apply in the same way to all products.

The most obvious factor is the amount of processing or manufacturing that is done after the product leaves the farm. If the form or shape of the commodity is substantially changed between the time it leaves the farm and reaches the consumer, it is logical to expect that marketing charges will be increased and the farmer's share will be proportionately smaller. Perishable products and bulky products that are shipped long distances tend to have higher marketing charges and a lower farmer's share. Food products for which the retail price is higher per pound generally have a higher farmer's share. For example, in 1953 the farm value of a pound of butter was 67 percent of the average retail price compared with 31 percent for margarine, although the farm-retail price spread was slightly higher for butter than for margarine.

The proportion of consumer expenditures for farm products that is received by farmers does not remain constant from year to year. During depressions the farm share is low. When the country is prosperous, the farm share tends to be much higher. In general, farm prices tend to fluctuate more than marketing charges so that in depressions, when farm prices are low, they are also a proportionately smaller part of the retail price. For a "market basket" that contains average amounts of farm foods bought by consumers, the farm value varied from 32 percent of the retail-store cost in 1932 and 1933 and an average of 40 percent in 1935–1939 to a high of 53 percent in 1945, and back to 45 percent in 1953.

Probably too great an emphasis is placed on variations in farmers' shares. Most important are the returns to farmers in relation to actual costs of farm production.

THE MARKETING BILL is increasing relative to returns received by farmers. Fluctuations in economic conditions may affect this relationship, but marketing margins in general tend to represent a larger and larger part of consumer expenditures for farm goods.

With an expanding industrial economy, more marketing services are required relative to farm production. The increased services require more workers, more trucks, more railroad cars, more processing facilities, more frozen-food cabinets and other storage facilities. The result is a larger total bill for marketing farm products.

More full-time workers were engaged in 1953 in marketing farm products than in producing them. During the past 20 years the number of workers in agriculture has gone down about 30 percent, while the number in marketing may have increased by as much as a third.

Changes in our rural-urban population balance are increasing the total marketing services required to move farm products from producer to ultimate consumers in the form and at the time desired. The percentage of the population living on farms is declining. Farmers usually buy less of their food than other groups in the population, so that need for marketing services is expanded as more people move to cities. As the city population grows and as farm production becomes more specialized geographically, transportation requirements are increased.

Technological progress has had a great impact on the marketing of farm products. In many instances, gains in efficiency have resulted in reducing marketing costs. But improved technology has also resulted in making many processed and ready-to-eat foods available to consumers in retail stores, so that housewives have transferred many chores from their kitchens to factories. Even though such developments may increase marketing charges relative to farm prices, they may also benefit farmers by widening the market for their products.

Marketing charges or price spreads may increase because more marketing services are provided or because of higher costs of performing the same services. In both cases, the farmer's share may be lower if there are no corresponding increases in farm prices. Net returns to farmers may be affected differently, however, if consumers in the first case are willing to pay a higher price for the same quantity of product because of the additional marketing services.

Our discussion thus far has related to a 50-billion-dollar bill for marketing domestically produced farm products that are purchased by United States consumers. Actually, the proportion of our gross national product or national income represented by *all* marketing activities related to agriculture and agricultural products is significantly larger than the 50 billion dollars would indicate.

In the first place, some of the income received by farmers is actually a payment for marketing services rather than production. Average farm prices and farm income are based upon cash receipts by farmers at whatever point in the marketing system a farmer sells his product. If it can be assumed that farm production stops when a crop is harvested or when livestock and livestock products are ready for sale in the local market, farmers frequently perform some marketing services such as storage, grading, sorting, packing, or hauling to local markets. Although direct farmer-consumer selling is declining in importance, some farmers do perform the entire function of marketing by selling milk, eggs, fruits, vegetables, and other produce directly to consumers.

This marketing bill was estimated only for the major groups of consumer items that are derived principally from agricultural products. Not included in any of these groups are many nonfood products like paints and soap manufactured mainly from fats and oils. An automobile may have farm products as raw materials in its upholstery, cushions, tires, paint, and several other parts. The expanding plastics industry uses many farm products for its raw materials. Most consumer goods probably contain an agricultural product or a part of one in one form or another. It would not be possible to arrive at an exact estimate of the part of consumer expenditures for all of these various products that should be allocated to marketing charges for the agricultural products contained therein.

Consumers also buy food products, clothing, and other items that are derived from imported agricultural products. For the most part, the processing and distributing of these imported products are carried out by our own marketing agencies. This increases the share of our gross national product represented by marketing activities. In addition, agricultural produce for export is transported to shipping points and it may even be processed before export. A part of our marketing activities is included in the purchases of food, clothing, and other products for military use by the Federal Government.

Marketing and charges made for marketing are important to the farmer both as a seller of agricultural products and as a purchaser of items for farm production and family living. With increasing mechanization and specialization of farm operations, farmers are more and more dependent on the market place to supply them with items used in farm production and an outlet or market for their produce. Presumably, our marketing bill of 50 billion dollars would include most of the marketing charges paid by farmers in buying food, clothing, and other items for family living but would include nothing related to production items.

An accurate estimate of a total marketing bill that would account for all of these marketing activities related to agriculture and agricultural products would be a tedious, if not impossible, task. No exact estimate of these total marketing charges is needed to demonstrate the significant role of marketing in our economy and its importance to both farmers and consumers. (*Kenneth E. Ogren.*)

What Are the Problems We Face?

A cartoonist recently pictured a farmer coming out of the county public library saying, "With this new-fangled farming, Lem, I gotta study world conditions, domestic economy, eating trends, and census statistics before I do my spring planting."

True enough. The farmer cannot prosper by producing white eggs if the consumer wants brown ones, fat hogs for lard if the housewife wants lean bacon, or more cereals when the consumer wants fruits and vegetables or meats.

Improvements in the heating of houses have changed the kinds and amount of clothing people buy. When automobiles and tractors replaced horses, a considerable part of the market for hay, oats, and horses was lost. When the First World War began, the European market for cotton disappeared, and the price of cotton to the American farmer dropped to as low as 5 cents a pound. Sales of all products in the Cotton Belt declined, banks failed, and growers had to curtail their production of cotton.

If lambs are relatively higher in price than wool, farmers must turn to the mutton breeds of sheep. If consumers develop a taste for red sweet-potatoes, production shifts from white ones. If millers will pay more for wheat high in protein, the areas that are adapted to producing high-protein varieties will grow more of it. If more hogs are grown than the market will absorb at a reasonable price, the production of hogs must be curtailed, whether the situation is due to a shift in the tastes of consumers, the loss of a foreign market, a decline in purchasing power, or an excessive quantity of meat on the market. Hence, before deciding what to produce the farmer must know a great deal about world conditions, storage stocks, the domestic economy, and production trends: He must know what kind of market he can expect to have.

281437°—54——3

Changing techniques of production also bring new marketing problems. The shift from a self-sufficient agriculture to production in specialized areas made it possible for each area to grow the products for which its climate and soil were best suited and to acquire expensive equipment and specialized skill to produce more efficiently. The change brought tremendous increases in food production and lowered production costs. Yet the changes created a multitude of marketing problems—the necessity of transporting the goods over long distances, the difficulty of trading with people too far away to see the product, repeated handling of products between producers and consumers, the need for money and credit, greater risk, and greater interdependence of various groups.

The continued farm mechanization makes it possible to produce increasing amounts of food with less labor, but the new machines throw more tasks on the marketing system. Mechanical grain harvesting makes it necessary for more grain elevators to install drying equipment. Rapid harvesting in an area throws the grain on the market in a shorter time and so places a greater burden on the elevator and on the supply of railroad cars. During the wheat harvest it is not unusual for hundreds of elevators to be blocked. Grain may be piled on the ground, and sometimes terminal markets are embargoed because facilities there cannot handle the grain as fast as the cars arrive.

The introduction of the mechanical cotton picker helped many farmers with the harvesting of their cotton, but the pickers also picked more trash than the manual laborer. Improved gin and ginning processes had to find ways to remove the trash.

THE PRODUCTION of new products in an area depends on the soil and climate and on the establishment of marketing facilities to handle them. In one southern county where cotton production had long been the chief agricultural enterprise, research specialists at the State experiment station determined that unusually good tomatoes and green beans could be grown. Yet nearly two decades passed before the county shifted to them because there was no market for them. The county had facilities for handling cotton, but none for tomatoes and beans.

A large assembly market for fruits and vegetables was established 170 miles away in another State. A few growers in the county began the commercial production of tomatoes and beans, which they trucked to that market and sold at good prices. The following year more of the new products were grown and taken to the market. By the third year the growers had made enough contacts with buyers at the market that some buyers sent their trucks into this producing area for loads of tomatoes and beans. Sales were made on the basis of prices established in the distant market. Production continued to increase until the volume was enough to justify establishing marketing facilities in the county. Shortly thereafter, the income of the county from the tomatoes and beans exceeded its income from cotton.

Areas in which the production of broiler chickens has expanded have found that adequate processing facilities had to be built first. Before funds can be obtained for financing the production and marketing of new crops, bankers have to become acquainted with the new industry.

In many places an interest has developed in sending products through the marketing channel in a new form. Poultry that is killed, dressed, eviscerated, and cut up in the producing area

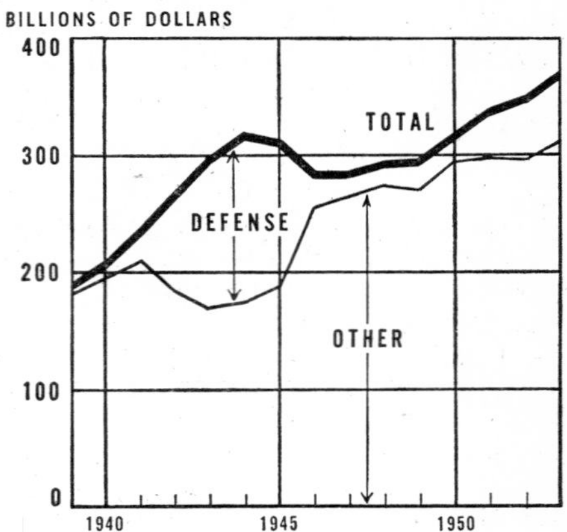

rather than moved through the marketing channel in live form can mean important economies in marketing. But first it is necessary to make changes throughout the marketing system and to change the buying habits and attitudes of consumers.

Persons interested in food freezing reasoned that if products were harvested when they reached the ideal stage of maturity and were promptly frozen, they could be moved through the marketing channel without loss of quality. But first it was necessary to learn how to freeze a product without changing its flavor. Then somebody learned that some varieties were better suited for freezing than others. There remained the problem of getting proper facilities from one end of the marketing channel to another for handling frozen foods. Railroad cars and trucks that could hold temperatures below zero were needed. Refrigerated warehouses were required for holding the products from the harvest period to be fed into the market gradually. Wholesale frozen-food distributors with low-temperature storage had to be established, and retailers had to be sold on the idea of installing freezers to handle the new products.

The industry started by making use

INDEX OF UNITED STATES PRODUCTION AND PRICES, 1913–53

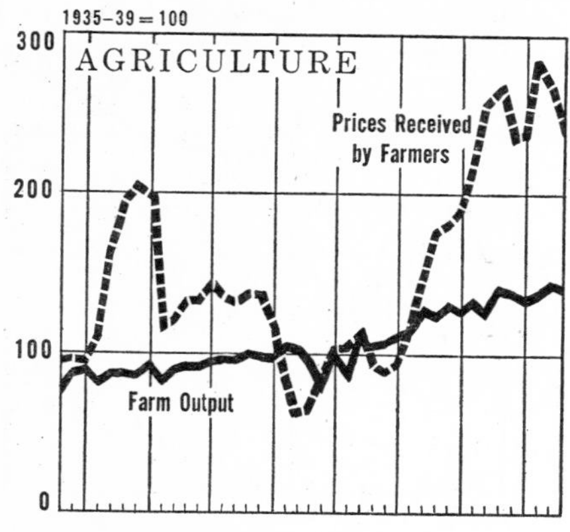

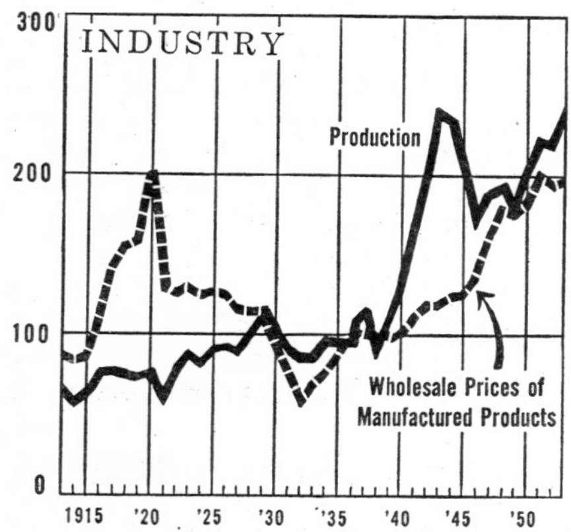

of the best facilities available. Refrigerator cars and trucks were improved. Wholesale distributors usually began to operate in public refrigerated warehouses. Some new warehouses were built. New wholesale plants were established. Many of the wholesalers broke cases in order to be able to deliver a fairly complete line to retailers without exceeding the capacity of their refrigerated cases. Millions of consumers purchased home freezers or else stored the frozen food in their refrigerators. Thus a new industry was born.

Rising transportation costs change production and marketing patterns. An increase of 10 percent in freight rates may increase the cost of transporting 100 pounds of food from California to New York by 15 cents but increase the transportation bill from some area closer to New York by only 3 cents. Such increases have the effect of pushing a producing area farther away from its markets and giving a relative advantage to producers nearer at hand. If freight rates go too high, products of one area may no longer be able to compete in a distant market. Then growers in such an area must find some way to reduce that transportation bill by trimming products (such as cauliflower) before they are shipped or perhaps by processing them so it will be possible to get more in a car. The only alternatives are to find other markets, to shift to the production of other commodities, or to find some other method of transportation that will move the products at less cost.

Our marketing problems are numerous—and difficult. They will not stay solved. Yet the welfare of farmers who produce for market depends upon their solution. A high standard of living for the millions of consumers, who cannot grow their own food or even see the farm where it is grown, is impossible without an efficient marketing system. Marketing agencies cannot stay in business without finding solutions to marketing problems and making the necessary changes in their operations. This land cannot support its present population and the increases to come without producing food where it can be produced best, and such specialized production is impossible without a complicated marketing system which must be continually improved.

Hence, the farmer was on the right track when he said: "With this newfangled farming I gotta study world conditions, domestic economy, eating trends, and census statistics before I do my spring planting." (*William C. Crow.*)

Sale Off Farms

The sale of products off the farm is the first step in marketing. The farmer has a choice of several outlets for his goods. If he sells directly to consumers he may get a good price for his products but he must expend much extra time and effort in selling and he must operate his farm so as to maintain a fairly consistent supply. A variety of local intermediaries will buy the farmer's goods and perform important services for him, such as assembly, storage, and transportation. The farmer must decide if the services are worth the price. A producer of a perishable or bulky product may want to sell directly to a local processor. He must produce the quantity and quality of goods the processor wants and deliver them—and therefore plant and harvest them—at the time the processor specifies. A producer of livestock, say, may sell directly to a terminal market. He must transport and protect the goods on their way to the market and assume the risks and costs involved. Here we introduce the factors the farmer must consider in making his choice.

Farmers As Their Own Salesmen

In order to get a larger part of the price paid by consumers for farm products, farm families sometimes take over the functions of wholesalers and retailers.

Such direct marketing is practiced most widely when farm prices are low or declining rapidly or when the farm unit is relatively small and located near areas of heavy population and traffic.

For example: Direct selling of citrus products in Florida received more attention in 1947 and 1948, when the reported production cost was 55 cents a crate and the return from fruit was only 38 cents a box. Fewer growers attempted to sell directly in 1950–1951, when the cost of production was 58 cents and the farm return for citrus products was $1.28 a box.

Most farmers regard direct marketing of any type as an emergency measure rather than a permanent business enterprise. Many growers have experimented with selling their products by organizing delivery routes in cities, soliciting and filling orders by mail or express delivery, and by selling at retail at a curb. But when farm prices advanced, most of them have abandoned the practices for various reasons: The constant regrading to meet the standard required by consumers, the adjustments in production practices called for when one serves a select trade over a long period, and the relatively high cost of packaging and sales of smaller units.

Of the many direct marketing practices that can be followed by farm families, the most practical seems to be the roadside stand located on or near the farm and operated on a regular schedule as one part of the farm enterprise.

A wide variation exists in the types of facilities, products, and services provided by farmers' roadside markets. Some are only a sign saying that one or more food items can be obtained at the farmhouse or other farm building. At the other extreme are stands that have many products.

An example of the latter type is the Eckert Orchard Association in Bellville, Ill. Originally established to sell apples and peaches and other products grown on the Eckert farm, the business has expanded over the years. The Eckert family now has an enlarged orchard and farm business. It also operates a slaughterhouse, a packing shed, a processing plant for fruit products, and a cold-storage house and carries on a wholesaling business. A complete retail foodstore on the site of their original roadside market continues to provide a direct outlet for much of their own farm production. The total dollar volume of an operation of this size is high, particularly when compared with the average farm roadside market return of 2,357 dollars from sales of homegrown products.

There is no set rule for types of facilities needed in operating a farmer's roadside market. The chart, which sets forth the reported relation of market facilities to volume of sales in three States in 1949–1952, indicates, however, that sales are higher when some permanent or semipermanent type of building and facilities are available for the convenience of customers.

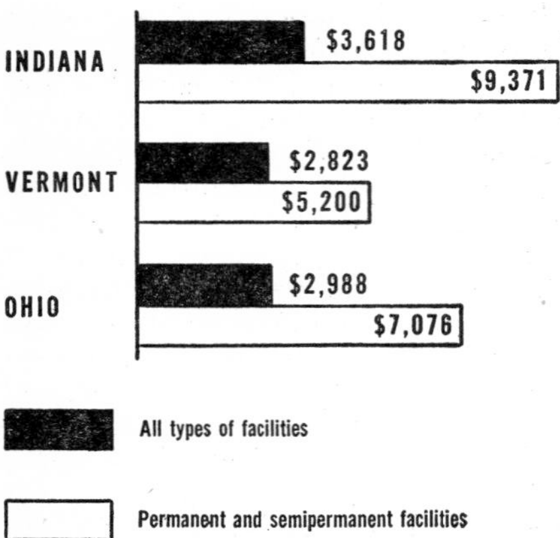

Reports and surveys by experiment stations in several States where this type of marketing is sizable provide guides for establishing a farm market. Advantages of price and quality of product and the personal services that can be offered often compensate customers for the lack of convenience in location of most roadside enterprises.

Markets operated by farmers are usually specialized. Nearly 85 percent of the volume sales are in fresh fruit and vegetables. Other products sold usually require little processing and include such commodities as poultry and eggs, maple products, and honey.

Roadside markets are patronized most heavily during the home canning and freezing seasons, June through September. August is generally the best month for sales.

Sales volume is concentrated into Saturday and Sunday, although markets are usually open 7 days a week. A typical workday at successful markets is 12 hours, 8 a. m. to 8 p. m.

Higher volume markets are located on the right side of the highway entering a city or town of at least 5,000 population. Preferably they are situated on a heavily traveled State or national highway about 3 (but no more than 12) miles from the town.

Market facilities do not need to be elaborate or expensive. The major requirement is an adequate parking area that provides for convenient and safe entry and exit. The largest sales are made at markets that provide parking space for at least 14 cars.

Labor costs are the largest single item of operating expenses (70 percent) and are typically 22 percent of total sales, as is indicated in the table. Most of the work is usually done by the farm family. Containers, the next most costly item, typically account for 13 percent of operating cost and total 4 percent of sales.

Persons staffing the market are more important than the nature of the buildings and the facilities in encouraging repeat sales. These persons should have some training or experience in handling and display methods and in dealing with the public.

More specific recommendations that can serve as guides to the present or would-be operators of roadside stands have been reported in a number of

OPERATING EXPENSES OF 29 INDIANA ROADSIDE MARKETS, 1949

Costs and receipts	Dollars	Percentage of annual sales
Average total sales	5,647	100
Operating costs:		
Total labor [1]	1,274	22
Containers	245	4
Buildings and equipment	51	1
Electricity and telephone	55	1
Advertising	116	2
Insurance	38	1
Miscellaneous [2]	55	1
Total operating costs	1,834	32
Cost of produce purchased for resale	941	17
Total operating and produce costs	2,775	49
Gross returns for farm produce	2,872	51

[1] Includes $582 hired and $692 family labor.

[2] Includes fuel, rent, taxes, etc.

Source: Kohls, R. L., Gaylord, F. C., and Orth, C. M.: Roadside Marketing in Indiana, Station Bulletin 577, Aug. 1952, Purdue University, Lafayette, Ind.

publications. Among them are: *Facts About Roadside Marketing in Ohio*, by R. C. Scott and T. W. Leed, Bulletin 225, July 1951, Ohio State University, Columbus, Ohio; *Roadside Marketing in Indiana*, by R. L. Kohls, F. C. Gaylord, and C. M. Orth, Station Bulletin 577, Purdue University, Lafayette, Ind.; *Roadside Marketing in Vermont*, by E. J. Tadejewski, Bulletin 553, November 1949, University of Vermont, Burlington, Vt.; *Selling Through Roadside Stands*, by W. Wallace, Extension Circular, University of Rhode Island, Kingston, R. I.; *Roadside Marketing of Fruits and Vegetables*, by A. W. Van Dyke, Extension Bulletin 418, April 1950, University of Connecticut, Storrs, Conn.; *Selling Farm Products Through Roadside Markets*, by M. C. Bond, Extension Bulletin 466, 1941, Cornell University, Ithaca, N. Y.

It seems to be generally true that the profitability of the roadside business depends on repeat sales, which result from customers' satisfaction.

THE FACTORS that seem to reflect value are quality, convenience, and price.

Initial and repeat sales of perishable products depend on the total appearance of all displays and (even more) the apparent freshness of each item selected. People buy by seeing. That does not mean that only the fancy or highest quality products should be sold. The operator, rather, should exercise care in selecting and grading the products in each display. It is entirely practical to have two grades of each commodity on display.

The needs of different individuals vary considerably. Maximum sales can be realized only when customers have a chance to select from a wide range of quantities and sizes—not only large units as pecks, half bushels, and bushels of a given commodity, but smaller prepacked containers and bulk displays for customers who want to buy smaller amounts.

The height, size, and location of the tables on which products are displayed should be such that each item is easy to reach. Orderly arrangement also reduces congestion in the aisles even during maximum traffic periods. A carry-out service for customers provides personal attention, which can increase sales.

Because customers stopping at farm roadside markets represent a wide cross-section of incomes, it is good practice to price plainly each quality, container, and bulk display. The greatest volume of sales at roadside markets is achieved by the operators who generally price their perishables somewhat under the price of similar commodities in nearby retail stores. It would seem advisable to keep informed of what local prices are at all times by checking market reports and foodstore advertising.

In Connecticut the practice is to

price small units in even numbers (such as 20 or 30 cents) as opposed to the usual retail store practice of odd-cent pricing. Pricing, however, should be considered as a tool of merchandising. A flexible system that encourages volume movement is preferred to a rigid or set price pattern, particularly for perishable commodities.

Some successful roadside markets have been located considerable distances from trade centers and on highways where there is little traffic, but that is the exception, not the rule. A location on a heavily traveled highway and on the right side of the road for traffic returning to the city has proved to be the best first step to building a successful market business.

An operator who has a choice of building on two highways might well determine which has the heavier traffic by checking with the department of highways in his State. The market preferably should be located on a straightaway in the road rather than on a curve for reasons of safety and visibility.

The potential customer should be advised in advance how far ahead the market is and what items are featured there. A legible sign, whose lettering and background are in contrasting colors, should be provided. One sign might well be about 300 feet beyond the stand. Another sign, also prominent and easy to read, should be placed in front of the stand. Operators of stands should check, however, whether county ordinances prescribe the size of signs and their number and distance from a business. Even if there are no such ordinances, one might well consider the possibility that too many signs detract from attractiveness and effectiveness.

The size of the letters in the signs is important. The table indicates the size that provides maximum legibility at given distances. It is recommended that the letters be at least five times as high as they are wide. To be most effective, the number of words on any sign should be kept to a minimum.

VISIBILITY OF SIGN LETTERS ON THE HIGHWAYS

Heights of letters	*Maximum distance easily visible*	*Approximate time visible at 35 m. p. m.*
Inches	*Feet*	*Seconds*
1	25	½
2	50	1
3	80	1½
4	110	2
5	140	2¾
6	170	3⅓

Source: Bond, M. C.: Selling Farm Products Through Roadside Markets, Agr. Ext. Bulletin 466 (1941), Cornell University, Ithaca, N. Y.

Costs and the expectation of increased traffic will govern the need for utilizing other methods of advertising, such as newspaper, magazine, radio, or television. Any of those methods, while desirable, probably would not be suitable for the average roadside market operation because of costs.

Printing the name of the market on containers for identification and future customer reference is a low-cost advertising device that can be used by nearly all operators.

MANY PEOPLE do not plan purchases, especially those they make at roadside markets. Proper preparation of displays, therefore, can increase sales. Outside displays are almost a must at roadside stands, but all the produce should have some protection because it will have to bear close inspection as to freshness and color.

Some general rules for good display can be given.

Prepare goods properly. All items should be clean and fresh. Wash most vegetable items after they have been properly trimmed to remove all damaged or diseased parts.

Prepackage at least some of the products to offer customers wider selection, increase unit sales, and reduce time and labor costs during heavy traffic hours. A wide variety of containers, trays, boxes, and bands is available for packing many products. The total cost should be little more than the difference between newer packaging materials and the types traditionally used.

Plan displays in advance. Prepare for the best use of available space and avoid confusion during busy hours. Planning of displays can help in three other ways: Products in short supply can be arranged to give the appearance of plenty, which indicates to the average customer better selection and lower prices; alternating products of different colors makes each product stand out and invites individual attention by customers; a continuous row of the same product running from front to back provides better utilization of space and avoids inconveniencing customers by making them reach too far back.

Rotation of stock is necessary to avoid excessive spoilage. When refilling displays, always move older merchandise toward the front. Remove all damaged, diseased, or dull-appearing items immediately.

Mark prices plainly. Some customers may be unwilling to ask about prices. Plainly pricing each product and container on display creates confidence in customers. Also, if products have been sized and graded, it is easily indicated that prices at the stand denote real differences in quality.

Safeguard the quality of the products. Not many operators can afford to provide refrigerated displays for perishable products at a stand that is only open a few months in the year. But all the perishable products should have some protection. A walk-in type of refrigerator is useful for holding reserve stocks. Outside displays can be shaded by a canopy. Vegetables should be sprinkled occasionally to keep them moist and fresh. (*W. F. Lomasney.*)

The farmer who thinks he can boost his income by selling some of his products to the people whose cars whiz past his place should consider a number of questions before he embarks on such a project.

Is his farm close enough to large groups of consumers? What kinds of products can best be sold directly?

What about additional outlays, such as those for packaging, waiting on customers, delivery, and time spent in making collections? Will he have to make changes in his farm operations? Are more time and labor involved?

Will he like the direct contact with consumers? Which gives him more satisfaction, dealing with people or devoting all his efforts to producing the crops or livestock on the farm? Is he willing to take some time from the usual farm operations so he can pay some attention to the details of packaging, wrapping small quantities, running a delivery route, making change, and being a salesman?

Most of the answers to the questions can be given only by the farmer himself on the basis of his own observations.

Many farmers have found that the total income from their farms has been greater when they concentrated on a limited number of commodities and spent their efforts in planning and operating the farms, leaving the selling to merchandising specialists. But some farmers in special locations can organize their farms so as to produce and sell their products successfully.

To do that the farmer must operate his farm in a way different from that of the grower producing for the wholesale market. If he runs a roadside stand selling fruit and vegetables, he will need a succession of plantings so that the persons who depend on him for their regular supply will not be disappointed.

That involves some additional costs. A member of the family or some person must be assigned to tend the stand during the period when people wish to buy. A pleasing personality, the ability to point out the good qualities of the products for sale, neatness, and courtesy are essential in such a salesperson.

Self-harvesting, a variation of such selling, is sometimes practiced in areas close to towns or cities. In periods when fruits or vegetables are at their best for harvesting, some farmers arrange to have buyers come to the farm and do their own harvesting of berries, peaches, apples, and vegetables. The practice saves the farmer considerable labor, although harvesting by inexperienced persons might damage the plants. The consumers often like to do it because it saves them some money and gives them an outing.

Approximately 18 percent of the eggs sold in Massachusetts are sold directly to consumers—about 4 percent at roadside stands, 6 percent at the farm, and 8 percent by direct delivery.

Research workers in Indiana studied methods of selling eggs there and in Athens, Ga.; Baltimore, Md.; Columbus, Ohio; Des Moines, Iowa; Ithaca, N. Y.; and Peoria, Ill. Direct sales by farmers to consumers in those cities varied from 15 percent in one city to 26 percent in another. The average was about 22 percent.

In New Hampshire approximately 28 percent of the milk distributed for consumption within the State in 1952 was sold by the producer-distributors. About 12 percent of the farms in Massachusetts reported distributing their own milk.

A farmer who is not occupied full time in large-scale production or one who likes to meet people may develop a retail route and obtain the highest unit price for his products by direct delivery to the consumer. For a year-around business, dairy and poultry products lend themselves well to this type of business. Special products give greatest satisfaction to discriminating consumers when they are harvested and delivered at their peak of ripeness. Catering to the demands of different families and delivering on a regular basis might build an outlet for some products.

Farmers' retail markets have a long history. A trading post was operated in Albany in 1621. Governor John Winthrop of the Massachusetts Colony named every Thursday as market day in Boston. Roads were poor and the products offered for sale came from farms 5 to 10 miles away.

A survey by the Department of Agriculture showed that there were 291 farmers' retail markets in 1946—143 in the Northeast, 36 in the South, 100 in the Central States, and 12 in the West.

Like them are farm women's markets, of which there were 212 in 1946—13 in the Northeast, 188 in the South, 8 in the Central States, and 3 in the West.

Farm women's markets can be established in towns with a relatively small population. Seventy-seven were located in towns of less than 5,000. (*L. A. Bevan.*)

Selling Through Local Middlemen

Farmers use many kinds of local middlemen in selling their products.

Among them are hucksters, retail merchants, hotels, and restaurants. Many buy dairy products, poultry and eggs, and fruits and vegetables from farmers for resale. They siphon off, in effect, enough of those products to meet local needs before the rest is sent on to wholesale markets.

Notwithstanding the impacts of far-reaching developments in marketing methods, the local middlemen continue to occupy an important place in the marketing of farm products. The changes they are encountering, however, emphasize the need for flexibility in their operations if they are to keep pace with the technical evolution in marketing.

Hucksters buy fruits and vegetables, eggs, poultry, and a few other products from farmers and distribute them from their trucks to consumers. They maintain regular routes and establish sources of supply and customers. Requirements as to quality are about the same as those of other local outlets.

Some retail merchants also serve as local assemblers and ship surplus farm products on to the wholesale markets. The practice has been declining in importance, however, with the development of highly commercialized agricultural production and of specialized market outlets.

Hotels and restaurants are mostly specialty outlets. To operate most effectively they deal with the farmers who can furnish the amount and kind of goods their customers require.

Frozen-food locker plants are one of the more recent developments that furnish farmers outlets in some communities for the local sale of livestock products and homegrown fruits. Livestock often is slaughtered for patrons at the plants and surplus amounts are sold to other locker patrons and at times to the general public.

Local intermediaries who move farm products on to wholesale markets include resident buyers, traveling buyers, order buyers, and the merchant truckers.

One of the most common types is the resident buyer. Often he owns or operates a local marketing facility—a grain elevator, warehouse, fruit packing plant, or a farm-supply business, through which he buys farm products as a sideline. He operates independently or as a representative of other firms. In August 1948, for example, 36 percent of the eggs sold in the North Central States were purchased by local egg and produce dealers, 24 percent were sold at retail stores, 16 percent went to truckers and outside buyers, 10 percent were sold through cooperatives, and 14 percent went to other agencies.

Traveling buyers, who operate independently or as representatives of terminal buyers or firms operating at local shipping points, travel from one producing district to another as crops mature. Purchases are made in trucklots or carlots from the producers. That procedure is followed for fruit and vegetable crops—the produce in which they specialize. Men engaged in buying citrus fruit in Florida during the winter, for example, follow the peach crop from Georgia to South Carolina, and later move on to northern producing districts.

In the fruit and vegetable industry, the "grower-shipper" also has increased in prominence since 1930. Many of them are former cash buyers whose interests as producers have gradually increased. They pack and market products produced by their neighbors, generally for a fixed packing charge and marketing commission. Sometimes farmers form a cooperative to take over the business as it expands.

Order buyers function as shipping-point brokers for chainstores or terminal wholesale buyers at country points. Specialized resident or traveling buyers who may be salaried employees or operate on commission are included in this group. They buy for cash the kind and grade of produce their customers demand.

Some products, like potatoes, are purchased directly from the producer. Western apples, citrus fruit, and California grapes are more likely to be obtained from local packinghouse operators. Order buyers also represent cotton mills, meat plants, grain wholesale houses, oil mills, and other processors and distributors. The greater part of their purchases is made from resident buyers, and the farmer's contact with them is limited.

Merchant truckers purchase eggs, fruits and vegetables, and livestock at the farm and at shipping-point markets at auction or at private sale. This type of buyer is most prominent during periods of depression when prices of farm products are low and regular employment is hard to get. A few are bargain hunters and have been regarded as financially unreliable, but most perform the useful service of

MARKET OUTLETS FOR EGGS IN NORTH CENTRAL STATES, 1948

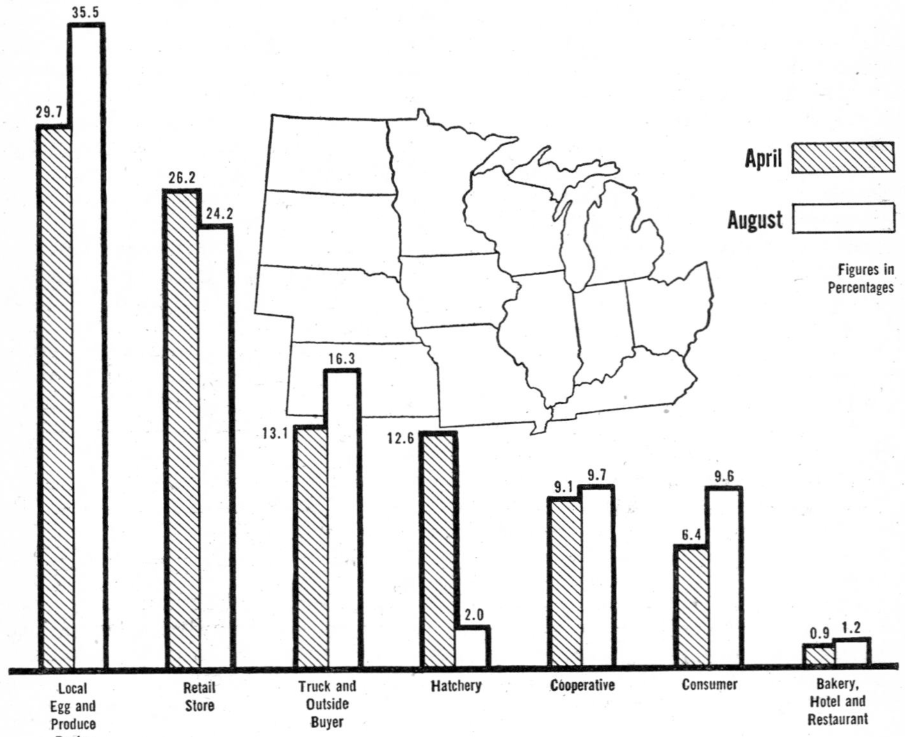

assembling farm products and transporting them to consuming markets.

The buyers who serve terminal markets generally have a number of outlets for the products they buy. The operator of an apple packinghouse in the Pacific Northwest, for example, may sell regularly to a certain order buyer, representing a chainstore or distant wholesaler; he may have a joint-account arrangement with some wholesaler in Chicago, which requires him to deliver one or more carloads each week; and he probably is represented by brokers in several markets. The grain-elevator operator usually depends on one wholesale grain firm in one, two or three central markets.

Traveling buyers regularly represent agencies in the terminal market or agencies that have established terminal connections. Local buyers of livestock, wool, or poultry products and merchant truckers generally have regular customers in distant markets, or represent or are represented by terminal firms.

All these intermediaries are the first step in the progress of farm products to the consumer. As such, they must have dependable outlets, which carry the goods a second step on their way.

Farmers also have set up their own marketing facilities and agencies in many parts of the United States. They function, in effect, as their own local intermediaries in starting farm products on the way to consumers.

Farmers owned and operated approximately 6,700 local cooperative marketing agencies in the United States in 1953. Through them they engaged in marketing at local concentration points.

Many of these associations engaged in more than one type of business. In rounded figures, however, the numbers handling various farm products were: Grain, 2,200; dairy products, 1,900; fruit and vegetables, 800; poultry products, 700; livestock and livestock products, 650; and cotton products, 550. Smaller numbers of associations served producers of beans, peas, nuts, rice, sugar products, tobacco, wool and mohair, and other specialty items.

About 2.5 million farmers used their own cooperatives as local outlets for some or all of their products in 1953—about 3 billion dollars' worth of goods.

AUCTION MARKETS have had an important influence on the operations of local market intermediaries, especially those who handle livestock, fruits and vegetables, tobacco, and poultry and eggs. More than 90 percent of the tobacco grown in this country is marketed through the auctions, and the amount of other products sold through auctions is substantial. Some are owned by the middlemen. In others ownership is specialized, and farmers who use them pay fees for the services.

Auctions operate on a commission basis. Livestock auctions as a rule are located in regions far removed from terminal market outlets. Country-point fruit and vegetable auctions primarily are used by representatives of chainstores, speculators, and trucker-buyers.

Local middlemen who keep abreast of market developments and who maintain flexibility in their operations perform needed services for many types of farmers.

Those services include assembling farm products, separating them into market grades, preparing them for market, and storing and transporting them to market centers. The middlemen used to furnish credit, but that function has declined in importance since the establishment of the production credit associations and greater availability of private sources of credit. For some products, however, it still is important. Feed companies, for example, are active in financing the production of broilers and turkeys and consequently influence the channels used in the local marketing of those items.

The services are used by most farmers for at least some of the products they sell. Farmers with large acreages and production are likely to deal directly with terminal wholesalers and other buyers, but the local intermediary provides an important outlet for many family farms. (*Andrew W. McKay, Martin A. Abrahamsen.*)

Selling to Processors

Often farm products have to be processed in one form or another near the farms where they were produced. Perishable products, like strawberries, must be preserved quickly. Bulky products, like rough rice and sugar beets, sometimes must be reduced to a form that can be shipped economically. Therefore some farmers usually market products directly through processors or manufacturers.

Processing itself is more or less complicated and specialized, and so most farmers cannot process their products themselves.

There is a certain amount of custom processing, such as the operation of cotton gins and oil mills, but that is more nearly a preliminary processing than the making of the end product. As a general rule, processors buy or otherwise take title to the product in order to have freedom and flexibility in their production and sales operations.

When conditions dictate that farmers dispose of products directly to processors, it is common practice and highly desirable for the farmers to deal directly with the processors. Direct negotiations may tend to prevail in all instances except where the processor is located at a great distance or where the processor may be so large and well organized that farmers are unable to bargain satisfactorily. Livestock mostly are processed at some distance from the producing area. Consequently the farmer ordinarily sells to the meatpacker through an agent, be it a commission house or a local buyer.

Dairy farmers sometimes have found that individually they cannot negotiate satisfactorily for the sale of milk directly with the large distributors. Consequently the marketing of milk is organized largely on a cooperative basis. A milk producer must arrange in advance for an outlet for his milk. There is no time for negotiating once the milk is produced and delivered.

But farmers have many opportunities to deal directly with processors. Some dairy farmers sell milk for manufacturing into cheese or condensed and evaporated milk; fruit and vegetable producers often sell their products directly to the canners, preservers, or freezers; rice producers may sell to the millers; alfalfa growers sometimes market their crop to dehydrators; and broiler producers often sell directly to processors.

The location of the processing facilities and consequently all the selling arrangements are affected by the concentration of production. A farmer who produces cream in Minnesota ordinarily sells directly to a local creamery, but in Nebraska, for example, the producer of cream ordinarily sells to a local agent who subsequently ships the cream to a centralized creamery.

If the supply of raw material is large enough, a number of processors ordinarily will be available, and the farmer may have several competing outlets to which he may sell.

Among meatpackers there is a trend toward processing nearer the production areas. Livestock need feed and water while in transit. The shrink, sickness, and death that may occur when animals are moved are factors that encourage slaughter near production areas, although factors like freight rates and the kosher trade may encourage the shipment of live animals instead of meat to consuming centers. The same is true in poultry processing.

Farmers who produce commodities that must be processed quickly want to be sure of at least one outlet or market beforehand. If several possible markets are at hand, or if the product is less perishable, the farmer's need to insure an outlet before production or delivery is less great. Rough rice must be milled to remove bulk, but rice is not highly perishable; consequently, growers have more flexibility in arranging marketing outlets. Cotton must be ginned, but numerous gins are available and the harvest season is reasonably long; consequently few definite arrangements are made in advance. Even for livestock, which are ordinarily marketed through an agent, some flexibility exists in the time and method of marketing.

Processors are aware of the need to arrange sources of supplies. Many products are seasonal, and some processors can operate only for short periods. The mutual dependence of farmer and processor leads to negotiation, general understanding, contracts.

Written contracts for the production of specific crops for a specific market have become customary in the vegetable processing and sugar beet industries. So the processor can insure his supply of raw material, the contract ordinarily provides for the production of a stated number of acres. To protect himself from an oversupply, however, the processor may require that he be obligated to accept only the total production from the specified number of acres at a stated yield. In order to be insured of an economical outlet, farmers must know the price to be received for the product. All such details farmers and processors set forth before the crop is planted.

Milk is sold in accordance with certain mutual arrangements, but there is not necessarily a written contract. Neither is the exact price to be paid stipulated in advance, but the method for computing the price may be agreed upon. The milk producers' cooperatives may affect the method used. Moreover, milk prices in many fluid milk market areas have come to be determined or regulated under Federal and State milk orders.

Quality also is a big factor. Often the processor cannot improve on the quality of the raw material he gets; he must do the best he can with what is delivered to him. In processing vegetables, for instance, many processors sell under a brand name or label and desire a uniform product to meet consumers' expectations. Because lower grade products are sometimes unsalable, processors generally are keenly aware of quality.

Processors therefore may insist that the farmer produce a specific variety or size of product and deliver it at a certain degree of maturity. Grades will ordinarily be specified with varying prices, depending on the grade delivered. To insure that a particular type of seed is used and that insects and disease are controlled, the contract may specify that the processor furnish the seed and perform all spraying and dusting operations. The method of harvesting sometimes affects quality, and processors may undertake to harvest the crop, particularly if specialized and expensive equipment is required. The extent of such provisions in farmer-processor contracts varies with the dependence of each upon the other for a market or for a source of raw material.

Many processors keep in touch with farmers through field agents, servicemen, plant managers, or some other representatives, who visit the farmers and give advice on production problems. They may also arrange sources of supply and write contracts. They maintain good relations between farmer and processor. They are interested in quantity as well as quality. A field agent visits a dairy farmer immediately if a problem of disease or high bacteria count has arisen. Spray schedules, thinning requirements in order to attain size, and general production problems are among the concerns of field agents in the fruit and vegetable industries.

Another point to be settled between the farmer and processor is the time the product will be ready. Farmers want as big a yield as possible at a stated return per unit. Processors want to operate at capacity for as long a season as possible. To satisfy both parties, it is necessary ordinarily to make arrangements as to time of planting, harvesting, or delivery of the product. Some products that do not need to be processed immediately, such as sugar beets, may be harvested when mature and held for a time before processing. But even then sugar factories provide a delivery schedule in an attempt to achieve efficiency of labor and equipment utilization and to maintain a source of supply for capacity operation over an extended period.

These factors represent the most serious points for negotiation between the farmer and processor. A processor may desire that a product be harvested on a given day; farmers are conscious of the fact that if the crop is allowed to grow for a few more days the yield may be increased. Farmers who enter into contracts for the production of crops for sale to processors should consider such factors and reach an understanding in advance of production.

It has happened that processors cannot interest farmers in producing the crop under such conditions or for other reasons cannot insure an adequate supply. The processors then may have to discontinue operations, move elsewhere, or themselves become producers. A few very large vegetable and fruit processors have followed this route. In the broiler industry, processors are engaged rather heavily in the production of broilers to provide a source of supply. An extreme example is the Hawaiian pineapple industry, where the processors grow nearly all of the pineapple.

Processors seem to be reaching further and further into the production process: They have been growing more products on their own. They are entering into the production schedules on individual farms. Packers are feeding more livestock. Feed dealers are entering into broiler production by mutual arrangements with farmers. Canners and freezers are moving further into the production for fruits and vegetables through contracts with farmers. Moreover, processors have sometimes found that financing is necessary to induce farmers to produce the required volume of raw products.

An example is the big commercial broiler industry, in which financing has come to be highly developed. The processor or the feed dealer or manufacturer often supplies the feed for growing the broilers. Chicks, medicines, and equipment may be furnished on credit, under contract. Under some plans the title to the broilers remains with the creditor, and the farmer performs only the service of feeding and caring for the birds. It should be remembered that when farmers undertake production plans that include financing, the farmer is tied more or less to the financial agent or credit source in marketing his product.

In order to protect his investment, the financing agent may insist that farmers market the product in a particular manner, perhaps at a specified time and in some cases through a particular processor. Indeed, the marketing may be taken over by the creditor. Such factors depend on who does the financing, the extent of financial burden, and the difficulty involved in marketing. In Georgia, for example, in 1951, more than 98 out of 100 broiler producers operated on a credit or contractual basis, and many marketing practices developed out of the feed dealers' financial interest or investment in the finished broiler.

In the Shenandoah area and in North Carolina in 1952 about 90 percent of the broilers were grown by farmers who depended on feed dealers for credit to cover production costs. To protect themselves against the credit risk, the usual practice was for feed dealers to retain title to the broilers.

The size or scale of processing facilities and the capital that is required to operate undoubtedly influence the farmer-processor relationship and their methods of doing business. The large operations with diversified products result in less dependence on one product. Small processing plants are slowly giving way to larger ones, often involving well-integrated processing operations. Present-day demands result in the need for more modern facilities with increased capital requirements.

In the pine-gum industry, for example, the processing was accomplished 20 years ago in nearly 1,000 fire stills. Today crude pine gum is processed in about 25 centralized processing plants. In 1954 there were only one-fourth as many cotton gins as in 1915.

The marketing of farm products through processors has come to be big business. With changing consumer demands, perhaps the farmer in the future will be even more dependent on the processor. It hinges largely on the alternative markets available to him. (*Floyd F. Hedlund.*)

Selling Directly to Terminal Markets

A farmer may sell some of his products at a terminal market, where commodities are brought from a rather large area for sale and where functions like processing, storage, and distribution are performed.

At railroad centers between areas of livestock production and population centers, terminal livestock markets developed when railroads provided the only economical method of transportation.

Meatpacking plants, large and small, were established at the livestock markets—the stockyards, located chiefly in the great meat-producing area from Buffalo to Pittsburgh in the East to Denver in the West. A large part of the packing industry finds it economically desirable to operate in the stockyard centers.

For some products, terminal markets have never developed. For other products, dealers rather than farmers use them. Farmers commonly use the terminal markets for livestock but not for grain.

A FARMER who can choose between a terminal market or another outlet for his products may make his decision on the basis of availability of a terminal market, convenience, or habit. He may also compare the prices he will receive in the two alternative markets. To do that, he must have market quotations and a fairly good idea of how his product will grade.

Then he must consider what he must do to reach each market: Arrange for transportation and possibly protection of his produce on the way to market; assume risks until the goods are sold; arrange for a sales agent in the market; and incur the necessary costs involved in getting his product to the market. The transportation may be by railroad or truck. A farmer close to the market may use his own truck.

One question is: Does he have the quantity to sell that fits the unit of transportation—that is, a carload or a truckload? In marketing grain, he usually settles the matter by selling to the local elevator, which assembles carloads.

Related to transportation is the question of protection en route to market. Fruits and vegetables, for example, may require protection against too high or too low temperatures. The transportation agencies will furnish such services if requested at a regular schedule of fees.

RISKS include chances of physical damage, which may be reduced by adequate protection. Sometimes insurance against loss from physical damage may be purchased.

The risks of price changes must be assumed for most commodities that farmers ship to terminal markets. The greater the distance and the longer the time involved in reaching the market, the greater are the risks. The possibility also exists that the price will rise while the goods are en route. On a rising market there might be an advantage in selling to the more distant market.

All terminal markets have commission men and sellers' agents, who compete for business. The problem is to select one in whom the shipper has confidence. (A further discussion of this point begins on page 280.) Over the years close relationships have been built up between many farmers and their sales agents. The agent looks after the commodity upon arrival, makes the sale, and collects and remits the proceeds to the shipper.

The farmer normally bears all costs until his products are sold. These include transportation, the shrinkage in weight in transit, special payments for protection while en route, insurance against damage in transit if this is not included in the transportation charge, and the selling and other charges made in the terminal markets.

SOME COSTS are incurred in any method of marketing. The farmer should determine costs for each alternative outlet. From comparisons of costs and prices in each outlet he will get an idea as to the comparative net returns. (*L. J. Norton.*)

281437°—54——4

Central Markets

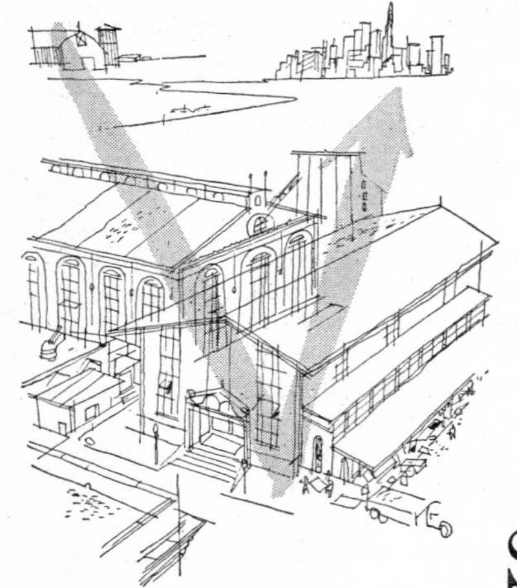

Somewhere between the farmer and the consumer most farm products must be brought together before they are forwarded to wholesale and retail stores. The assembling of many commodities takes place at the great terminal markets, which are equipped to receive, unload, store, and reship the large volume and variety of goods which flow to them by rail, boat, and truck. The essential core of the service of any terminal market is to provide a broad outlet for products and to establish the value of the commodity. For some products sale in a terminal market has been economic;

for others, it has not. The development of the motortruck, good highways, and radio after the First World War lessened the advantage of physically concentrating the products at central markets. Some farmers and dealers found they could reduce their costs by bypassing the terminals. But the trading facilities of a decentralized market must be as good as those of the central market lest the individual sellers and buyers suffer from unfair practices and prices.

The Place of Terminal Markets

The location of terminal markets is essentially a function of transportation.

Before 1850, when water transportation was relied upon chiefly for moving the surplus products of the region between the Alleghenies and the Mississippi River to the East and South, terminal markets were located on an east-west axis along the Ohio and Potomac Rivers, and at each end of the Great Lakes. Along the rivers—from west to east—were St. Louis, Cincinnati, Wheeling, W. Va., Philadelphia, and Baltimore. Through them went surplus corn and hog products to the cotton-raising South. Along the Great Lakes from Chicago to Buffalo and the eastern consuming markets went wheat and salted beef and pork.

When the rails pushed west of the Mississippi River, the terminal markets shifted to a north-south axis, taking on the pattern they have today. From north to south the principal terminal markets are: Minneapolis and St. Paul, Chicago, Omaha, Denver, St. Louis, Kansas City, and Fort Worth. Through them shuttle the products of the region west of the Mississippi and Missouri Rivers to the densely populated States of the North and East.

Only with respect to foreign trade may the seaports be considered as terminals. For domestic trade they are essentially consuming markets except as to reshipments, chiefly by truck, to the nearby territory.

Terminal markets are equipped with facilities for receiving, unloading, reshipping, and warehousing the great volume and variety of products which flow to them by rail, boat, and truck.

After the products are unloaded there is the further task of concentrating them into local wholesale and jobbing market places within the terminal. That involves an expensive trucking operation from the scattered unloading tracks and yards of the different rail carriers over congested city streets into even more congested market places. The work of concentrating into the market places may be simplified in the case of livestock by unloading directly into a central stockyard; or, as in the case of grain by using an elevator.

The adjusting of supply and demand is a main function of terminal markets. Not all the adjustment takes place in the terminal market, because control is exercised also from the shipping point in the country. Adjustment takes place through the buying and selling activities of merchants, processors, brokers, and the selling agents present in the market—agencies that reflect the demand of final consumers back to the shipping points. Their activities also move the part of the supply not needed for local consumption into secondary consuming markets, to processing industries, and into export. Adjustment to demand takes place qualitatively also through inspection, grading, cleaning, repacking, or otherwise conditioning the product to make it even more acceptable to the consumer.

Terminal marketing includes the function of pricing. Market prices are determined through buying and selling activities when they are conducted by large numbers of buyers and sellers in a competitive market in which the product is moving in large volume and in a variety of grades. Because it is this type of trading that goes on in terminal markets, the prices currently prevailing there are accepted as representative, or base, prices, which can be used in quoting prices to country shippers or to buyers in other markets.

Determination of price is not only and always a function of buying and selling at terminal markets. Control tends to shift toward the shipping points in the producing areas when supplies are generally short. Buyers move closer to the supply areas to compete. Limits may be set on the free action of the market also by the organization of producers to control supply and by the stabilizing activities of the Federal Government.

Lines of communication reach out from the terminal market to every part of the producing area from which it draws supplies. Other lines extend to all the large consuming markets in this country and foreign countries. Traders could not operate intelligently without knowing what is happening in the growing areas and the markets.

Terminal markets by definition are free, open, and competitive. Whatever regulation is imposed on trading practices is chiefly concerned with maintaining open-market competition and restraining unfair or restrictive operations that might result in monopolistic control.

Regulation is of two kinds. First, the regulation that the operators themselves impose through the rules of exchanges, auction markets, or trade associations. The rules are aimed mainly at protecting the operators from each other, but they also protect the public interest to the extent that they give effect to the provisions of the common law with respect to contracts and any statutory enactments affecting their particular trade. Besides the formal rules are practices that are sanctioned by custom but may not be covered in any written code.

The second type is governmental control over weights and measures, inspection for grade, sanitary controls, and controls aimed at unfair or monopolistic trading practices. In markets organized under the rules of a trading exchange, the major function of the governmental authority may be said to be that of enforcing the rules of the exchange when the members themselves fail to do so.

THE MARKETING STRUCTURE of terminal markets has both an external and an internal aspect. Externally the structure has a geographical character. Internally it is institutional.

The market center is a focal point to which commodities flow from a tributary supply area and from which supplies not needed for local use move out to a tributary area of distribution. It is possible to plot on a map the tributary areas in terms of the particular commodities.

Two or even more markets may be in competition in supplying the same commodity to a consuming area. The competition involves the area between markets and also large areas beyond the competing markets to which they all have access. For certain commodities it is increasingly true that competition with a distant terminal market is set up by a local market in the producing area, which reflects the demand of a local processing industry or of a distant consuming market.

The economic factors that determine these market areas seem to be the nature of the product and the demand for it, prices and price policies, transportation rates and services, communications, financial services, warehousing services and the local market demand in the producing area.

The internal structure of the terminal market for the various major commodities generally is much the same. There are wholesale merchants who take title, various kinds of agents and the brokers who represent their principals, and also varying degrees of organized trading and regulation.

DATING FROM the 1890's or earlier was a movement toward integration in buying, selling, handling, and processing grain. The movement was marked by the encroachment of the terminal grain elevator on the merchandising functions of the grain commission firm. The processing industry likewise integrated the processing function with large-scale buying through its own terminal and elevator facilities.

The large-scale cooperative marketing organization has appeared more recently. Equipped with important terminal facilities, engaged in both warehousing and processing, and affiliated with a wide-flung organization of country elevators, the cooperative is a large merchandiser of grain and feed and an effective competitor of the corporate terminal and line elevator companies.

Grain commission firms by reason of their numerical strength are in control of the organized boards of trade and grain exchanges. They handle a large volume of business from the country. The cash grain trade in these markets is also well established and in "strong hands."

In a class by itself, integrating a function of price stabilization with the wholesale market operations, is the Government-owned Commodity Credit Corporation. The Corporation, which takes over grain from farmers as a result of its lending operations, may also enter the market on its own initiative to buy or to sell grain, although it rarely engages in these open-market operations. It does not operate for profit, but its activities often have an important effect on the course of prices.

THE FUNCTION of physical concentration of grain in the terminal markets, except to supply processing industries, probably is less important than formerly. Storage capacity at interior primary markets and at the ports has increased more rapidly than in the terminals. Large amounts of grain, which formerly would have been forced into the terminals, are held for the account of the Commodity Credit Corporation at country storage points, some of it on farms.

The accompanying chart shows for the principal grains the receipts at primary (terminal) markets as a percentage of total sales by farmers from 1924 to 1952. The trend was downward for wheat, corn, and oats. Receipts of barley in 1934, 1936, 1942, 1943, and 1944 were inflated by heavy imports. Imports of barley were also substantial during 1948–1951.

Besides the activities of the Commodity Credit Corporation, a number of factors, some of them of long standing, account for this diversion of grain away from the terminals. They are the readjustment of regional freight rates and the rise in the level of rail freight rates; the importance of exports during and immediately following both world wars; the rise of farmers' cooperatives; changes in feeding practices; and decentralization in the manufacture of flour, feed, and cereals. Decentraliza-

RECEIPTS AT PRIMARY MARKETS AS PERCENTAGE OF SALES BY FARMERS, CROP YEARS 1924–51

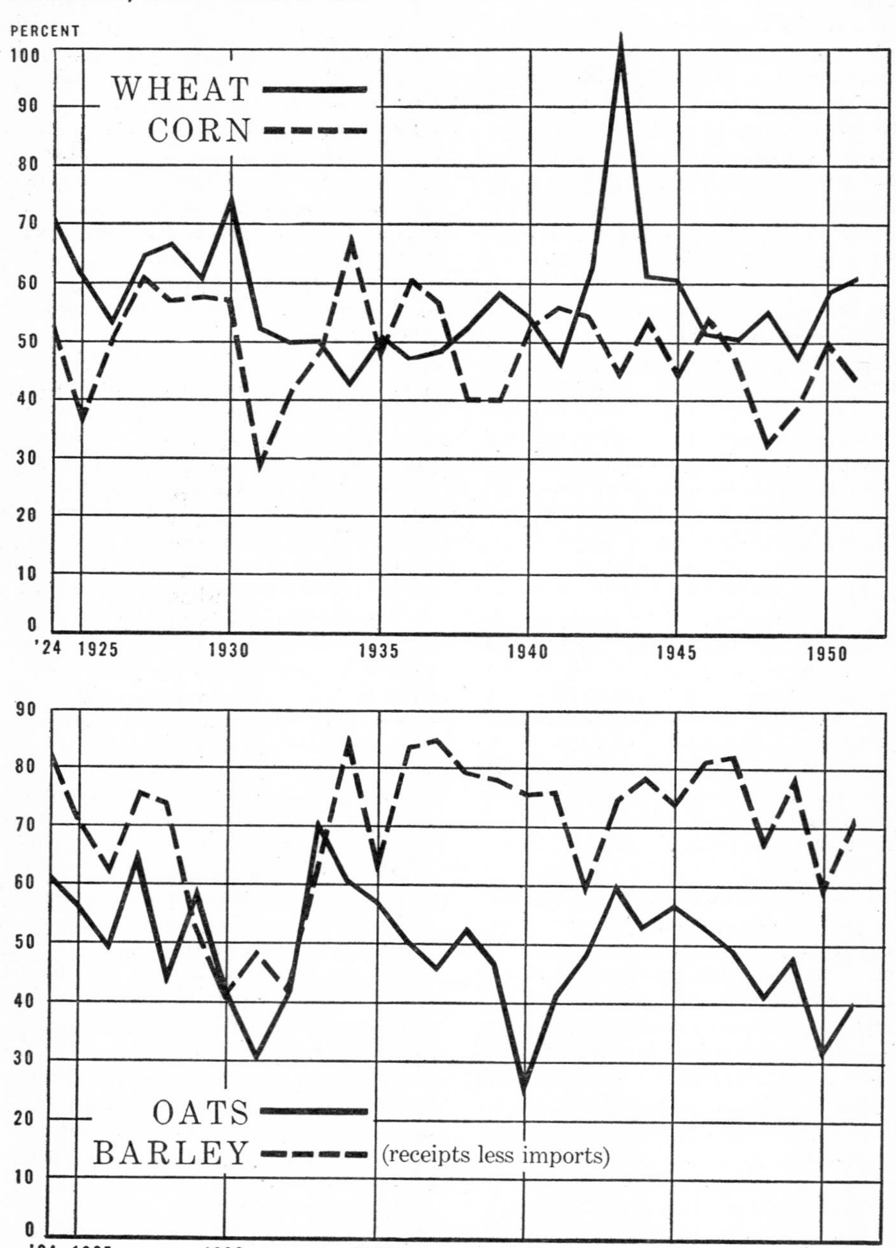

tion to some extent has been toward the producing areas and toward regions in which dairying is the principal industry.

While the concentration of grain at the terminals may be less important than it once was, the function of terminal markets as transaction centers has not been impaired to the same extent. Direct movements of grain in the domestic market and into export are still largely controlled by the buying and selling of operators in the terminal. Prices made in the cash markets continue to be accepted as the best measure of current values. Prices quoted on the futures market provide the only available means of discounting the factors that may affect future values.

THE CONCENTRATION OF LIVESTOCK for slaughter at large terminal markets based on rail and motortruck transportation began in the 1860's and 1870's.

The opening of the Union Stockyards in Chicago in 1865 was significant of the shift from the cattle drive and water transport. The introduction of refrigerator cars in the 1860's made it possible to ship fresh meat to the East and brought a shift of livestock slaughter from the eastern consuming markets to midwestern points at which livestock could be concentrated by rail. This pattern remained substantially unchanged until about 1920.

The main livestock terminals are South St. Paul, Sioux City, Omaha, Denver, Milwaukee, Chicago, Indianapolis, East St. Louis, St. Joseph, Kansas City, Wichita, and Fort Worth. South St. Paul and Sioux City are primarily hog markets. Denver and Omaha are important for sheep and lambs. Kansas City is a big feeder-cattle market. Chicago is a general market handling all kinds of livestock.

Formerly, each of these markets had its own sources of supply. Prices were kept in line by the differential cost of reaching the respective markets and by the effective demand of packing plants located at the terminals. Surplus stock might be moved from one market to another if prices went too low, but the major markets were kept in a general balance by the buying of the large packing companies that distributed their products nationally.

During and immediately after the First World War this pattern began to be disrupted by the growth of packing plants in the producing areas, principally in Iowa, southern Minnesota, and eastern North Dakota. Freight rates gave these interior points an advantage over the established markets in shipping dressed meat to eastern consuming markets. Increases in the level of freight rates, which coincided with a drop in livestock prices in the early 1920's and again in the 1930's, made the farmer want to sell nearer home. Highway improvement and increased use of motortrucks facilitated the marketing of hogs, and later of cattle, at local packing plants and concentration yards. The net result has been a general decentralization of livestock marketing in the region between the Mississippi and Missouri Rivers.

Large numbers of livestock continue to be concentrated in the terminal markets to supply the packing plants of the larger packing companies.

Moreover, the growth of population in the cities in which the plants are located provides a large local demand. Buying by the terminal market packers, however, has shifted largely to country points.

The movement of the stocker and feeder type of animals into these markets also has been reduced by the growth in recent years of local livestock auctions in the Corn and Hog Belt.

Changes in the institutional organization of terminal livestock markets have been minor. Cooperative commission firms owned by farmers have become active since 1920 and have been financially successful. They operate in a manner similar to the regular commission firm.

Much of the financing of the breeding and feeding of livestock, especially in the Corn Belt, has been taken over

CARLOT DIVERSIONS FOR SELECTED COMMODITIES ARRIVING PRINCIPALLY BY RAIL ON THE CHICAGO MARKET, 1939, 1952

	Arrivals			Rail unloads	Percentage diverted
1939	*Rail*	*Truck*	*Total*		
Apples (Washington)	2,883	....	2,883	1,870	34.5
Carrots	4,367	258	4,625	1,281	70.7
Grapefruit	3,579	12	3,591	2,646	26.1
Grapes	7,378	159	7,537	2,065	72.1
Lettuce	13,915	262	14,177	4,382	68.5
Oranges (California)	6,597	....	6,597	3,546	47.0
Watermelons	2,877	62	2,939	1,514	47.4
Total	41,596	753	42,349	17,304	58.4
Percentage of total market	32.8	6.4	32.5	30.0	42.3
Potatoes	31,842	84	31,926	16,507	48.1
Percentage of total market	25.1	....	25.2	23.8	26.7
1952					
Apples (Washington)	3,375	....	3,375	1,465	55.9
Carrots	5,356	417	5,773	2,272	57.4
Grapes	4,753	84	4,837	2,131	55.3
Lettuce	12,619	316	12,935	5,486	56.3
Oranges (California)	3,564	....	3,564	2,379	33.3
Watermelons	3,661	237	3,898	1,961	46.4
Total	33,328	1,054	34,382	15,694	50.6
Percentage of total market	30.4	5.8	26.5	26.3	35.2
Potatoes	30,478	439	30,917	14,151	53.4
Percentage of total market	27.8	2.7	24.0	23.7	32.7

Data from annual reports of Market News Service.

by the banks for cooperatives and by local production credit associations. Such financing was formerly done by commission firms and livestock banks.

PRICES OF LIVESTOCK are determined in the open market by the action of buyers and sellers. Values must be arrived at by actual inspection of the animals by the buyer. Salesmen of commission firms and the buyers for packers are expert judges of quality. They have information about the current supply of animals of a given species and quality and about general conditions of supply and demand. Buyers for the different terminal packers compete with each other and with the trader and order buyer for the farmer's cattle or hogs. The price arrived at reflects the supply and demand conditions in a single market and in all the large markets in which the national packers are buying. If the price goes too high in one market by reason of a short supply, packer buying is shifted to another market in which a lower price prevails. Prices in the terminal markets thus are kept more or less in line for the different grades and kinds of livestock.

Decentralization in the packing industry has somewhat complicated the price-making process. It has increased the cost of buying for the terminal packer and has made price comparison more difficult for the farmer. Extension of the Market News

Service and improvement in quality of service to cover the local markets would seem to be necessary to keep them in line with prices prevailing in the terminal markets.

TERMINAL MARKETS for fruits and vegetables are of more recent origin than the terminal markets for grain and livestock. The extension of railroads, the development of the refrigerator car, and the invention of a process for the making of artificial ice brought them into existence.

Those improvements and relatively low freight rates permitted production of the specialized crops so as to adjust to the most favorable combination of natural factors without much regard for the distance from the consuming market. The concentration by rail and water of fruits and vegetables at large cities gave rise to the terminal markets as we have them today.

Fruits and vegetables, being largely unstandardized, in the beginning had to be concentrated physically in a market place in the city for the convenience of wholesale buyers, who bought by inspection. Parts of a city street next to rail or water transportation were taken over for the purpose. More elaborate facilities later were constructed, with stores or stalls for the merchants, unloading platforms, refrigerated storage space, and wide approaches to give easy access and room for standing trucks until they could be unloaded.

The handling of fruits and vegetables requires an elaborate organization of terminal rail facilities: Hold-yards where cars can be held pending reconsignment or unloading; the inspection tracks, where the cars can be inspected before sale; and the unloading tracks, where cars can be unloaded into trucks that haul the contents into the jobbing market.

With the growth of long-haul truck transportation, the jobbing markets have had to develop truck terminals.

Most of the produce formerly went through the commission firm, but now commission firms are operating as receivers or jobbers or are out of business. Produce that came to market mostly on an ungraded basis had to be sold by inspection in the terminal market. The grower was forced to consign and take the risk of the market.

Abuses that crept into this trade weakened the confidence of the grower in the commission firm.

Improved grading and packaging enabled a buyer to make purchases by wire at country points on the basis of country-point inspection and grade description. The growth of growers' cooperatives and improved financing made the growers reluctant to take the full risk of consignment selling in distant markets. Rapid growth in consumption of fruits and vegetables put a premium on getting adequate supplies. Buying at wholesale tended to shift to the country shipping point. The commission firm was forced to become a merchant in its own right.

Brokers have become important in this trade because they can facilitate sales over wide areas when representing the country shipper. On well graded and well packaged commodities, the activity of the broker may operate to effect direct sales from the shipping point to smaller consuming markets.

The broker may act as the selling agent for a growers' association. His services are also used by the country shipper in placing cars on the auction.

One finds both buying and selling brokers in the midwestern markets. The buying broker typically represents the wholesaler in eastern consuming markets. The selling broker may represent the country shipper or the terminal carlot receiver.

DISTRIBUTORS operate at shipping points and in the terminals. Some of them are large, integrated organizations that sell in all the main consuming markets of the United States and Canada. They operate much as the broker does, but their relationship with the grower or the growers' association

CARLOT DIVERSIONS FOR SELECTED STATES AT THE CHICAGO MARKET, 1939, 1952

	Percentage of total rail arrivals		*Percentage of total unloads*		*Percentage of State unloads by truck*		*Percentage of rail arrivals diverted*		*Percentage of total diversions*	
	1939	*1952*	*1939*	*1952*	*1939*	*1952*	*1939*	*1952*	*1939*	*1952*
Distant States—little use of truck:										
Arizona	4.2	6.5	1.8	3.8	0	(1)	71.2	41.0	6.2	8.6
California	35.5	38.0	32.2	25.6	0	0.6	59.1	51.7	46.3	43.1
Idaho	7.8	7.6	7.4	5.7	0	(1)	39.3	53.0	5.2	8.8
Minnesota	3.0	3.6	1.7	2.2	(1)	2.4	62.7	58.0	3.8	4.8
North Dakota	3.3	5.4	1.6	3.2	0	0	70.0	57.6	4.5	6.8
Texas	6.3	6.3	6.8	5.3	(1)	3.9	31.1	42.0	3.4	5.8
Washington	3.4	5.7	3.4	3.4	0	(1)	38.2	56.6	2.6	7.2
Percentage of total	63.5	73.1	54.9	49.2	(1)	.8	53.1	52.7	30.0	85.1
Distant States—heavy trucking:										
Florida	7.2	7.4	14.8	15.1	4.5	34.5	11.6	3.7	1.2	.6
Louisiana	1.1	.7	2.8	2.5	3.0	65.7	.2	13.3	(1)	.2
Percentage of total	8.3	17.6	17.6	17.6	4.1	38.8	10.0	4.6	1.2	.8
Nearby States—heavy trucking:										
Illinois	.5	.2	8.0	5.6	91.1	95.5	33.0	11.3	.3	.4
Indiana	.8	(1)	1.5	1.5	70.9	93.5	2.6	5.9	(1)	(1)
Michigan	1.0	.7	6.0	9.0	77.0	87.8	.2	24.3	(1)	.3
Wisconsin	2.5	3.5	13.8	3.2	44.1	40.0	64.4	60.6	3.5	2.8
Percentage of total	4.8	4.4	29.3	19.3	72.4	81.0	47.0	53.6	3.8	3.5
All truck States	13.1	12.5	46.9	36.9	43.3	58.4	23.2	21.7	5.0	4.3

[1] Less than 1/10 of 1 percent.

Data from annual reports of Market News Service.

CARLOT DIVERSIONS OF SOME COMMODITIES ARRIVING LARGELY BY TRUCK AT THE CHICAGO MARKET, 1939, 1952

	Arrivals				
1939	*Rail*	*Truck*	*Total*	*Rail unloads*	*Percentage diverted*
Apples (excluding Washington)	1,349	1,297	2,646	1,012	25.0
Cabbage	2,585	729	3,314	1,317	49.1
Celery	2,523	780	3,303	1,392	44.8
Onions	3,987	361	4,348	2,446	38.7
Strawberries [1]	143	1,006	1,149	97	32.1
Tomatoes	5,486	732	6,218	4,015	26.8
Total	16,073	4,905	20,978	10,279	36.0
Percentage of total market	12.7	41.5	15.2	14.8	10.1
1952					
Apples (excluding Washington)	758	1,288	2,046	345	54.5
Cabbage	1,863	1,311	3,174	1,220	34.5
Celery	4,178	960	5,138	2,354	42.8
Grapefruit	1,429	732	2,161	1,275	10.8
Onions	5,209	846	6,055	2,532	51.9
Oranges (Florida)	1,451	981	2,432	1,323	8.8
Strawberries [1]	283	357	640	265	6.3
Tomatoes	5,223	1,311	6,534	3,216	39.6
Total	20,394	7,786	28,180	12,530	38.5
Percentage of total market	18.6	40.1	12.0	20.9	16.4

[1] Does not include express shipments.

Data from annual reports of Market News Service.

is a continuing one. Well-known brands are owned by the distributor, and packing and shipping in the country are under his direction. He determines to which market shipments will be made, seeks out buyers, and determines selling prices. He may also make cash advances to the packers before shipment is made. Distributors take a percentage of sales rather than a fixed fee as compensation for their services.

Comparable to the distributor is the selling agent. He represents a large growers' organization, like the California Fruit Growers Association. He does not, like the general distributor, sell commodities other than those of his employer, and his control over carlot movements and prices is more restricted.

Formally organized trading is found in the auction market, which is present in some of the large terminals. Well-graded, well-packed oranges, lemons, grapefruit, pears, apples, cherries, pineapples, and (in the New York market) some vegetables and nuts are sold. Cars consigned to the auction through brokers are unloaded into an auction warehouse. Sample boxes are opened, and sales are made at auction on the basis of inspection of the samples. The buyers are jobbers, truck-jobbers, institutions, small chains of retailers, and agents acting for retailers.

Future trading in white potatoes is conducted on the Chicago Mercantile Exchange.

A point that has been noted and is discussed more fully in the next two chapters is that forces making for change have been operating in the terminal markets. Improved grading

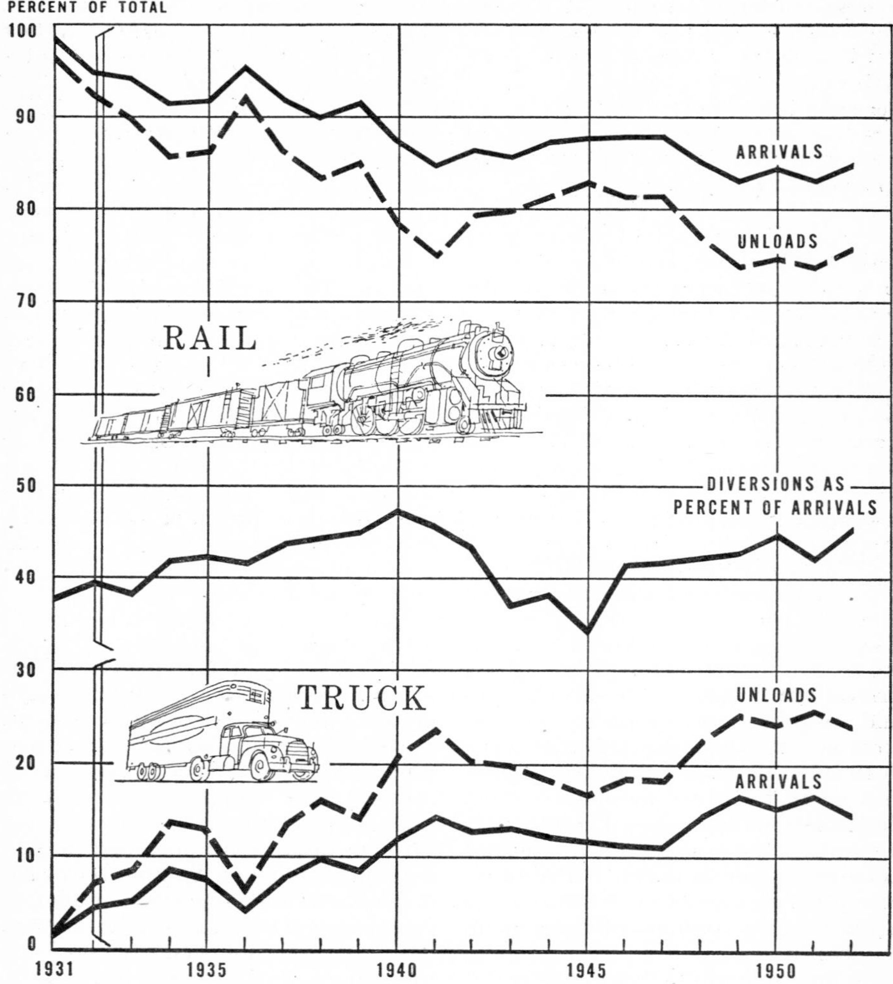

and packing, inspection at the shipping point, and improved communication have prepared the way for increased decentralization in the marketing of the perishable products. Special transportation rates and privileges, such as blanket rates and diversion of cars en route, and the increased use of motortrucks are additional factors.

Brokers and distributors (especially those integrated with growers' associations or chainstores) consequently have made it possible to give wide distribution without concentrating shipments to so great an extent in the large terminal markets. A smaller proportion of the cars that do arrive is unloaded into the jobbing market.

Responding to a rising demand, more fruits and vegetables have been going to market in frozen form or as juice or juice concentrates, which move through different trade channels. The volume of fresh produce coming on the market therefore is lower.

Supply and demand prices generally prevail in these markets. Most fruits and vegetables, being perishable and nonstorable, must be sold when they arrive in the market. Thus price is determined by the current and the immediately prospective supply and by current demand in a given market.

Exposure of the grower and country shipper to drastic price changes in the terminal markets resulted in various measures designed to give the shipper a greater measure of control. Members of growers' cooperative marketing associations may centralize control of the sale of their products in a marketing manager or selling agency, but this control may not be permitted to result in a monopoly control of the market supply. Centralized control of selling also assures a better distribution of the growers' produce among the several markets. A surplus of fresh products may be processed into juice or frozen form and sold and advertised under a brand name to achieve better control over price.

Under the Agricultural Marketing Agreement Act of 1937, producers, associations of producers, processors, and others engaged in handling an agricultural commodity have extensive marketing powers in the interest of giving greater stability to prices.

No clear-cut proof can be given to support the contention that terminal markets for fresh fruits and vegetables are less important as points of physical concentration and redistribution than they were in 1931 or earlier. Data of total shipments by rail and boat with which to compare market receipts (arrivals) or carlot unloads are inadequate because of the omission of important commodities from the list on which reports by the railroads are made. No data on motortruck arrivals and unloads are available before 1931 for most markets.

Rail and boat shipments for the commodities reported (fresh peppers, potatoes, spinach, sweetpotatoes, tomatoes, turnips and rutabagas, watermelons, the mixed vegetables, apples, citrus fruit, grapes, peaches, pears, apricots, cherries, cranberries, plums and prunes, strawberries, and mixed deciduous fruit) declined 29.6 percent from 1931 to 1951. Rail unloads of all commodities at Boston, New York, Philadelphia, Atlanta, Chicago, Los Angeles, and San Francisco were 76.4 percent of total unloads at those markets in 1931 and 51.9 percent in 1950. Truck unloads increased from 23.6 percent to 48.1 percent of the total in the same period. Total unloads were 2.4 percent lower. It would appear that the function of these markets as points of concentration by rail and boat had diminished along with declining rail shipments.

A shift in the channels of distribution for fruits and vegetables away from the wholesaler and jobber, located in the central market place, to the large-scale chainstore and supermarket helps to account for the decline in reported total unloads in these markets. Deliveries by truck from origin points direct to the warehouses of chainstores and supermarkets are not fully reported in the statistics compiled by the Market News Service. During the period under consideration those organizations greatly increased their share of the total business in perishable produce.

It may be concluded also that redistribution from those markets by truck and in mixed carloads by rail is now of considerably less importance than formerly when unloads were in a much higher ratio to population in those cities. Outlying cities and towns are now being served directly by rail and by truck from the producing areas.

For the central market, the function of area distribution outside of the metropolitan area has declined.

The fortunes of the terminal fruit and vegetable markets seem to be wedded to relatively long-haul rail transportation. As truck operation increases, the shipper is given a more flexible instrument in terms of routing and size of load. The decline of the rail terminals may well have begun in the depression years when rail freight costs were a heavy burden, because prices were low. Truck arrivals at the markets are equivalent to truck unloads, and the market to that extent becomes a dead-end consuming market. About 15 percent of total arrivals and one-fourth of unloads at Chicago were by truck in 1953.

In summary, it may be said that the terminal markets for fruits and vegetables as now organized serve principally as points of concentration and redistribution for products grown at a considerable distance from the market and moving principally by rail. They are also important for products of low value relative to bulk and weight, like potatoes, regardless of distance of the growing region from the market. As truck receipts increase, the markets will become less important as centers of redistribution.

The terminal markets of 1953 represented the culmination of a national marketing technique under which the bulk of consumption was at a maximum distance from specialized producing areas. Movement through the markets was facilitated by relatively cheap, long-haul rail transportation.

As population shifts to attain a more even regional distribution, we may (except for certain commodities which are subject to strict climatic controls) see a shift from this national pattern to a regional pattern of marketing under which the terminal or transfer markets will more and more take on the character of consuming markets. A continuing high level of freight rates would hasten the change. (*Edward A. Duddy.*)

The Essentials of Good Terminals

The essential core of the service of any terminal market is to provide a broad outlet for products and to establish the value of a commodity.

Unless meatpackers create a large demand for livestock, a successful terminal livestock market could not operate. The assembly of a large volume in turn draws buyers—and it takes buyers to make a market. It is also true that once a firm enters a business requiring farm products as raw materials it has an urgent need for those raw materials. The essential features of terminal markets—the economic assembling of large volumes of farm products and the satisfactory pricing of the products—suggest the answer to the question as to why some farmers under certain circumstances find it advantageous to use them. The same is true of the local shippers who buy farmers' products or handle them cooperatively.

Of the conditions that are essential to a terminal in providing a good market the first is that it must be a logical assembling point on the cheapest or most convenient route between producing and consuming areas. Grain moves from centers of production to centers of use. Wheat is grown in North Dakota and consumed as bread in Washington, D. C. The railroads that haul the grain run mainly through Minneapolis, Minn. There a terminal grain market has grown up to serve the big northwestern grain-producing area. From some parts of North Dakota the most economical route may lie through Duluth, Minn. If so, the grain may go to its terminal.

Second, it must be a convenient outlet for the farmers and dealers who use it. A large part of the livestock flows into each central stockyard from the area around it. Such areas vary with the size of the market and the degree of concentration of livestock production in the region. Farmers in such areas look upon the terminal market as their logical outlet. Further away, local markets, auctions, or local packing plants are closer to the farmers, and they sell more to them. A terminal market serving an area where the livestock population is too sparse to support such local markets will tend to draw from longer distances than one serving areas of more concentrated production. But other things being equal, the larger the market, the larger the area from which it draws. Some sort of principle of gravity seems to operate.

Third, the terminal market must accurately value products, including quality differences. The major interest of farmers in a market is: What prices does it return? One angle to correct pricing is accurate evaluation of commercial quality—the attributes of a commodity that may cause commercial differences in value—differences that consumers or processors or handlers deem important. That is especially important in fat cattle because different lots vary widely in value. To evaluate such differences, adequate numbers of trained and qualified specialists—both buyers and sellers—are needed. Their services can be utilized most economically if concentrated in a few places. So a large number of producers of high-quality cattle elect to sell at the central markets.

No similar emphasis on valuing quality has yet developed for hogs. Great attention has been put on weight as a value factor. Weight is, of course, a factor in commercial value of hogs because it causes differences in value. But it is not the only reason for differences in value. Guessing hog weights in arriving at the price per pound is apparently a much simpler and more widely spread skill than telling how much and what kind of beef lies under the hides of a lot of steers. The selling of hogs in central stockyards has not retained the same relative importance as it has for cattle.

Interest has increased in more discriminating systems for valuing hogs to encourage production of the meat rather than of the lard type. Hog buyers who represent packers requiring particular types of meat have found it more essential to discriminate than have the big-volume packers, who must absorb whatever kinds of hogs farmers in general send to market. The selective packers often are represented in the terminal markets by order buyers who often pay premiums to get the type of hogs wanted by their packer customers. To be a good order-buyer market, a large selection of livestock must be available so that such buyers can find an adequate number of the weight, grade, and class of animals needed to fill specialized orders. That means either large central markets or the larger local markets.

If the central markets would pay greater attention to valuing hogs for quality, more farmers might use the markets.

A fourth essential is that the terminal market provide a broad outlet. An effectively organized terminal market can find an outlet for whatever volume is offered.

Take the case of a buyer's market, in which the buyers are not hunting supplies but in which sellers are seeking the buyers. Such a market may develop in seasons of heavy production or when farmers may wish to increase marketings for one reason or another. The opposite is a seller's market, in which buyers are out hunting supplies and getting as close to producers as possible. In a buyer's market, products may flow into the terminals seeking buyers; then the importance of the terminal market is likely to increase. Buyers hunted out sources of feeder cattle for several years before 1952, but in 1952, with prospects for lower prices, cattle producers had to send more of their stock to the central markets in search of buyers.

It is often said that central markets are basic to price formation. The terminal market prices are certainly of great importance. They represent the values placed on rather large volumes. They are fully reported, and the prices and related information about receipts, shipments, and stocks on hand are widely disseminated.

In the grain trade the futures prices established in such terminal markets as Chicago, Kansas City, and Minneapolis are basic in buying and selling grain through the grain belts.

But the actual formation of prices involves wider areas of action than the central market. Grain moves from some producing areas in many directions and not always toward a central market. So the differences between terminal market prices and local prices may vary considerably according to the supply-and-demand conditions prevailing in particular areas.

Price formation is a matter of the balance of available supplies and effective demands within a general or a particular market area. Trading done at many points develops the price structure. Important centers of such trading for certain products are the central markets.

The widespread use of the grain futures has been noted. The basic values for quality cattle are established in central stockyards. For hogs pricing is more decentralized. The general structure is tied together by the packers' bids which may be for hogs at central markets, local markets, or auctions. Those bids are influenced mainly by estimated "cutout" values; that is, what the products are worth, and by individual packer's needs to maintain a desired level of operation. The actual prices are the result of trading in varying types of markets.

The terminal grain markets are used by dealers rather than by farmers because the standard unit of shipment for grain is the freight car. They also are on economic routes between producers and consumers of grain products, and large volumes of grain therefore can flow economically to and through them. They have developed facilities—processing plants, terminal elevators, and such—which can absorb large quantities of grain seasonally offered for sale. Storage is an important element in the business of a terminal market. Grading systems—a combination usually of State and Federal activity—provide official grades, which aid in the evaluation of quality.

Grain producers in some large areas do not make much use of terminal markets.

The soybean industry has developed largely on the basis of processing plants at interior nonterminal markets. Some important flour mills, corn-product plants, breakfast-food plants, and distilleries also are outside of the terminal markets. The commercial feed business—a large user of grain—is widely scattered. Rice milling also is largely done in the producing areas.

It may or may not be economical for mills to buy in terminal markets. The sole test is whether the cheapest transportation route lies through them. Where it does not, the mills tend to procure their grain in producing areas. That has given rise to the development of interior grain merchandisers at commercial centers in some producing areas. The firms buy in carlots from local elevators and sell to the processors.

Two things facilitate this nonterminal system. First, official grading of grain makes it possible to handle quality evaluation on the basis of these grades and the agreed-upon discount schedules for various quality factors. Second, the futures markets for grain provide a general indicator of the value of the different kinds of grain.

Certain large interior markets may be looked upon as terminal markets for cotton. Trading seems to center at them largely because of the necessity of evaluation of quality. Cotton is ginned at local points. There the farmer may sell or he may have it moved to a central warehouse for storage. Different bales of cotton vary in value according to quality. Both sellers and buyers find it desirable to have the value determined by experts. So the trade in spot cotton tends to center at a fairly limited number of interior markets where an adequate number of qualified people can locate to do this job economically. Among the largest of these markets are Memphis, Dallas, Houston, New Orleans, Atlanta, Lubbock, and Fresno.

Prices in them are tied together by the markets for cotton futures in New York and New Orleans. Sales at other points may be based on prices established in New York and New Orleans.

WHAT SITUATIONS will lead farmers to use the terminal markets for fruit and vegetables? Nearby growers may. They may have the choice between selling at a farmers' market, making direct sales to retailers, or using a commission merchant on the terminal market. The trend is away from selling at farmers' markets. Time has become too valuable to farmers to spend on sales in small lots. Trucks have widened the area within which the terminal market may be used.

More distant growers may sell to local dealers or through cooperatives as well as ship to distant markets, but there the risk of price change or deterioration of quality is very important. Most small growers in distant areas will shift the risks to a dealer or a cooperative.

What will decide the dealer as to sale on a terminal market? In most cases he can sell at his own packing shed or warehouse to a carlot or trucklot buyer. His decision will depend on various circumstances. It may pay him to consign to a terminal market products of particularly high quality or those that can be sold on a particularly high market. Produce that cannot be otherwise moved may have to be shipped to a terminal and sold for what it will bring. Various small-volume specialty items may have to be consigned. But with consignment the shipper must carry the risks of price declines and quality deterioration. However, a shipper who is continuously in the market and so may have many transactions spread out over time, reduces the risk on the season's operations by the averaging out of many individual returns.

The shippers who use the fruit auction companies at terminal markets have decided that it is worth while to assume the risks and costs involved in retaining ownership of their products until they can be sold to wholesale distributors in the terminal markets.

Only large producers located close to market so that economical transportation can be arranged can ordinarily sell eggs to terminal market dealers. Those who do so are usually located near one of the larger northeastern or Pacific coast cities. This method of sale rests clearly on getting fully paid for superior quality eggs. Over the country most farmers sell eggs to various types of dealers or cooperatives, which in turn have many choices of outlets, including sale to terminal markets. Certain types of terminal market operations tend to emphasize a standard quality of eggs accumulated by country dealers. Those eggs may be sold to local distributors, to retail stores, or to storage operators.

But the trend in egg marketing is toward emphasizing quality. The result is a movement toward integrated systems, in which milk distributors who also deliver eggs and large retailers or terminal dealers with quality-conscious trade develop country buying stations or make direct contacts with country assemblers. The effect is to go around the traditional terminal dealer. The latter is still an outlet for the eggs accumulated by country dealers who do not emphasize quality. Since there are many small producers to whom eggs are of little importance, this trade will likely continue in considerable volume. There are future and call markets for eggs in Chicago.

281437°—54——5

The farmer who produces eggs in volume will seek a buyer in position to pay premiums for quality.

The place of terminal markets for poultry is similar to that for horticultural products: To procure the poultry needed for consumption or processing in its consuming area. There still remains a market for live poultry in the large cities to supply various special groups. Farmers usually produce poultry in small lots, except for commercial broilers or other specialty poultry, and typically sell to local dealers. The latter use the terminal markets, for live or dressed birds, primarily because they constitute large outlets. Various trends in the poultry industry tend to reduce the importance of the poultry dealer at the terminal market. These include development of specialized areas of broiler and turkey production, which develop direct market arrangements; the decline in sales of farm-flock poultry, with increased egg production per hen; replacement of rail transportation by truck, which permits more direct movement to smaller consuming centers; increased dressing of poultry in producing areas with distribution of dressed poultry—either chilled or frozen—along lines used for fresh meat.

Boston has been the traditional terminal market for United States wool. The spinning mills were largely in its trade area and it is a port for unloading overseas supplies. Wool varies greatly as to commercial quality and requires expert graders to determine values. These facts led to a central market where qualified experts could assemble. Large wool producers may deal directly, but the large number of small producers must either sell to local wool buyers or turn their product over to a cooperative for sale.

Recent developments tend to reduce the relative importance of the central wool market. Cooperatives that grade and sell wool have grown, sometimes at interior grading and warehouse points, from which the wool is shipped directly to mills. Another is the decentralization of the wool-using industries and the decline in relative importance of the mills in the Boston area. But the necessity of expert grading and continued importance of the Northeast in wool use will cause Boston to continue of basic importance in the wool trade.

For a number of products terminal markets have not developed. Among them are fluid milk and cream; fruits and vegetables for canning and other forms of processing; tobacco, where local auctions are largely used; rice and peanuts, for which farmers deal directly with local mills or dealers; field peas and beans, which are sold largely to local dealers, who in turn sell to the wholesale grocery or processing trades; field and garden seeds, which seed dealers contract for or purchase direct.

All marketing arrangements have been developed by long evolutionary process. Their current form depends on the nature of the services required between producers and wholesale users. For some commodities sale in terminal markets has been economic; for others, it has not. This evolutionary process is still going on. (*L. J. Norton.*)

Changes in Structure

The structure of the agricultural marketing system has been changing rapidly. The general movement is in the direction of decentralization.

The system that originally developed as railroads opened up the West after 1850 was based on the methods of transportation and communication that existed then.

The team and wagon was an efficient unit for handling small loads for short distances over country roads, but it was too small and slow for long trips. The horse and wagon set the pattern of the country markets. They were local markets, small in size but large in number. Each served a territory with a radius of only a few miles.

The railroads were efficient for hauling large loads for long distances at high speeds. The markets that developed as a result were the central markets in the large cities and strategic transportation points.

The local markets and central markets complemented each other to form a fairly efficient system for getting farm products from producer to consumer. The markets in the country assembled small amounts into freight carload lots for shipment to the central markets. The central markets concentrated them into large quantities for milling, packing, and shipping to wholesale and retail markets in the consuming areas.

Prices in the central markets were loosely related, so that they could not fluctuate (except for short intervals) more than the additional cost of getting goods from one supply area to this or that other market. The central market system covered the globe for some commodities, such as wheat, that were durable, capable of standardization, and of high specific value so that transportation costs were low.

The central markets were usually hundreds of miles away from the local markets that fed them. The producer or local dealer seldom accompanied his goods to the central market. The great bulk of produce was consigned to commission men at the central markets. The commission men represented the seller. They made the best sale they could, deducted their commission from the proceeds of the sale, and remitted the remainder to the farmer or dealer who consigned the goods to them.

A shortcoming of the traditional local and central market system was the cost of the concentration of large quantities of livestock, grain, cotton, and such at the central markets. A typical central market for livestock might have half a square mile of pens, runways, railroad tracks, and other equipment, crowded with bawling and squealing livestock. The rent, depreciation, maintenance, wages and salaries, and livestock feed bill for running these hotels for livestock added up to a considerable sum. The concentration of physical products facilitated price making, but it was an expensive operation. It was a considerable item of cost, which showed up as a deduction from shippers' returns.

The cost of selling hogs at the Union Stockyards, deducted by the commission man from the buyers' check, was about 20 cents per 100 pounds before the Second World War and about 40 cents per 100 pounds in 1953. The cost of selling corn on the Chicago Board of Trade was 1 cent a bushel, or 1 percent if the price exceeded a dollar a bushel. Those amounts were only 1 or 2 percent of the purchase price, but they looked large to the farmer who had nearer home alternative markets where most of the central market costs were avoided and no costs at all were charged as such.

After the First World War, some new developments in transportation and in communication began to reduce the advantage of concentrating physical products at the central markets. The developments were the great improvement in motortrucks, the rapid extension of concrete highways over the countryside, and the radio.

Trucks and paved highways made decentralization of the handling of the product physically possible. The radio came along at the same time and made that decentralization economically coherent. In its field, communication, it was a perfect parallel to the other two inventions in their field, transportation, for the radio was the perfect instrument for disseminating market news to the decentralized market. The truck and the concrete highway scattered the market over the whole producing area; the radio scattered the market news over the whole area, right into the producers' homes.

They permitted easier assembly of livestock and livestock buyers from a wider area at country points. Numerous local auction markets appeared; by 1940, they accounted for nearly 10 percent of the livestock sold in the Corn Belt. The auction markets were like terminal markets in that they brought several buyers together in the same ring. They made a relatively good outlet for small lots and odd weights or grades of livestock.

The new intermediate markets, instead of being articulated vertically, as it were, with the central markets (both in flow of goods and prices) are articulated horizontally with each other. They are as likely to lead the central markets now as to follow them. The concentration, equalization, and dispersion of the physical goods that used to take place at the central markets is now spread all over the country—decentralized—and the price-determining and title-transferring process is spread along with it.

It used to be true that the great wholesale reservoirs performed an indispensable equalizing process. But nowadays the major part of the stream of agricultural commerce flows more directly from producer to consumer. Numerous smaller reservoirs upstream from the central reservoir now take care of most of the floods, and in so doing reduce the size of the job. Less concentration and less dispersion are needed, for much of the water is dispersed before it ever reaches the central reservoir; the traditional central market structure is giving way to the decentralized market structure of modern times.

In order to be concrete and specific, this general movement is discussed here in terms of two major farm products—butter and livestock.

Decentralization has been particularly evident in the marketing of butter. Most creameries in the United States sold their butter up to about 1900 through commission men in the wholesale market. Today the situation is reversed. Most of the butter bypasses the central markets entirely and moves instead directly from the creamery to the distributor.

Several reasons account for the decline in the volume of trading at the central markets after 1900. Quality of butter became more uniform. Storage facilities improved. Rail service became faster and more reliable. The danger of deterioration in transit lessened. Buyers began to make direct contacts with creameries in order to develop their own regular sources of supply. Many creameries made arrangements with them partly to avoid the brokerage and other charges at the central markets.

After the First World War, chainstores, butter-marketing cooperatives like Land O'Lakes, large dairy corporations, and meatpackers distributed larger amounts of butter directly from creameries to retail stores and institutions. Only about 17 percent of the butter produced in the United States was sold through the wholesalers located at the central markets in 1951. The rest moved directly.

Furthermore, less than 10 percent of the 17 percent that was sold on the central markets—that is, only about 1 percent of total butter production—was sold on the organized Mercantile Exchanges in Chicago and New York.

This bypassing of the central markets might mean nothing more than that most of the butter today moves by the most direct route from producer to consumer and avoids the charges (up to one-half cent a pound at New York) and the necessity for immediate or 24-hour delivery in New York or Chicago. But actually the reductions in cost are only one of the effects of direct movements of butter.

The most important other effect is the effect on butter prices. That effect is pronounced because of the method by which creameries sell their butter. Most creameries sell their butter on the basis of a sales agreement with a receiver of butter, which may run unchanged for months or years at a time.

This agreement generally provides that the creamery will be paid, not so many cents a pound, but such-and-such a premium over the price quotation on the Mercantile Exchange in Chicago or New York on the day of arrival. Thus the judgment of those who buy and sell the 1 percent of the butter sold on those exchanges establishes the price for the bulk of the butter that is sold direct without going through the exchanges.

It is paradoxical but true that the direct-sales-agreement system, which requires that there be a reliable central market price quotation on which to base the sales agreements, itself undermines the reliability of the central market quotation.

The reliability of the quotation has been questioned on two points:

First, the volume of trading and the number of traders is so small and the market is so thin that prices are unduly susceptible to manipulation by one or a few traders who deal in relatively small quantities.

Second, since the bulk of the sales agreements provide for premiums over the exchange quotation, either the exchange prices do not reflect supply and demand accurately (the prices are too low) or the price reports underquote the market.

Butter traders generally defend the market on the first score (thinness). They take the position that when butter is moving freely, with no surpluses or shortages, that is evidence that prices on the exchange are at the right level, in line with supply and demand. It is not necessary, at such times, for the volume of trading to be large. In principle, there is no need at such times for any trading at all to take place on the exchange. At other times, if butter is not moving freely and surpluses or shortages develop, traders will sell or buy on the exchange in an attempt to bring prices in line with supply and demand. It may not even be necessary, actually, to sell or buy at lower or higher prices, but only to offer to do so. A large volume of trading is not needed in any case.

Butter traders also defend the market on the second point (underquoting). Butter of known characteristics within the grade, bought direct, is worth a premium over butter on the exchanges that is not available for inspection before sale. Creamery managers know the situation and use the quotation as a basing price rather than an average.

A third feature of the decentralized marketing system is the extent to which it accurately reflects price differentials for quality.

On that score, the record is not so good. Upgrading, particularly in times of shortage, is widespread. The practice of paying for low-grade butter on the basis of a higher grade reduces the incentive to produce the higher grades and discourages quality programs. The differences in prices received by different Iowa creameries for the same grade of bulk butter have ranged up to 7 cents.

The average difference between the prices for Grade A and Grade B butter, however, was only one-half cent a pound in 1949 and 1950, when the difference in the New York quotation was 1.4 cents and in the Chicago quotation was 1.8 cents. The ranges of the Grade A and B prices received by the creameries overlapped widely. Since the prices received by creameries are not reported, the situation makes it hard for a creamery manager to tell whether he is getting the full market value for his butter.

An overall appraisal of the whole butter-marketing system and of the arguments pro and con may be put in the following terms:

The reductions in costs achieved under the decentralized butter-marketing system are such that traders are likely to continue to use it.

The effects on the level and stability of prices are controversial. An increase in the volume of trading on the exchange probably would be beneficial.

CATTLE, CALVES, HOGS, SHEEP AND LAMBS SOLD THROUGH CENTRAL MARKETS, 1923–51

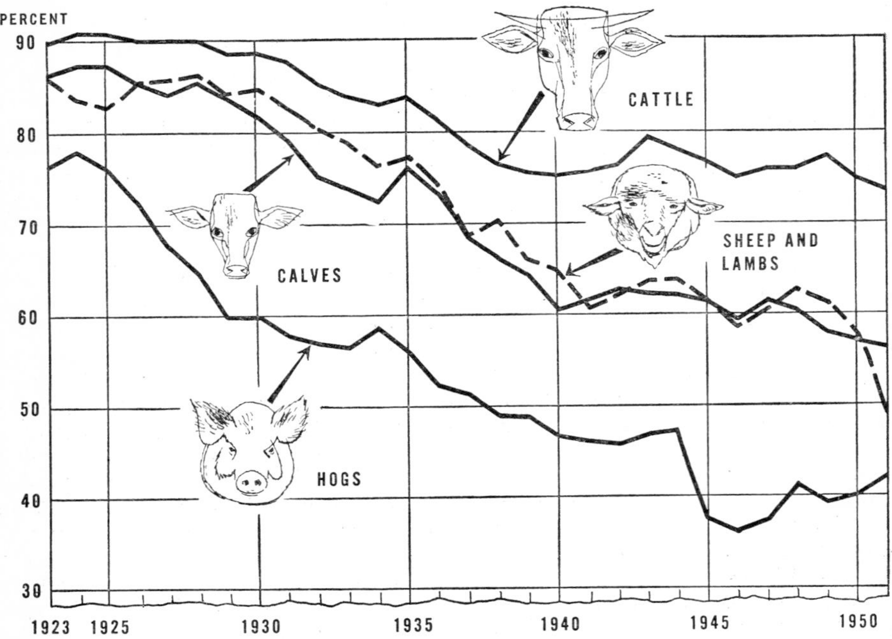

Certain changes in the rules of the Wisconsin Cheese Exchange in 1938 and later years were notably successful in increasing the volume of trading on that exchange. The following changes in the rules of the butter exchanges might be worth considering: Provide that the buyer pay assembly charges to the seller; provide for delivery at other points, such as Minneapolis-St. Paul, Mason City, and Kansas City; provide for fuller description of butter offered on the exchanges.

It would be helpful also if the central market reporting system of the Department of Agriculture (which covers several central markets, not merely the butter exchanges at Chicago and New York) were expanded to include bimonthly or quarterly reports on country creamery price differentials from the exchange quotations.

It has further been suggested that butter-market reporting might be decentralized, as it has been for hogs, in line with the decentralization that has taken place in the butter-marketing system. Prices received by creameries in the country could be reported daily by areas within States and by grades. This would give fuller coverage of the market, and could help individual creameries to know whether they were receiving prices corresponding to the grade of butter they produced.

In livestock marketing decentralization has also proceeded apace. The extent of the change is shown in the chart. Only 40 percent of the hogs in the United States, fewer than 60 percent of the calves and sheep and lambs, and about 75 percent of the cattle were sold through central markets in 1951.

Some observers believe that the central livestock markets are the most competitive markets. Where there are numerous buyers at one market, they say, there is active competition. But when livestock is sold direct, out in the country, there is usually only one buyer at each market point where the hogs are bought. There is "no competition." Prices are believed to suffer accordingly. Furthermore, some people believe that the growth of direct (i. e., decentralized) marketing reduces competition at the central markets, weakening the prices there and thus weakening the price structure over the whole market area.

We can appraise these arguments most clearly if we first get straight on what competition actually is, and what markets actually are, from an economic point of view.

The first argument, that there is no competition when hogs are bought direct, implies that competition exists only where several buyers are physically present. But competition—that is, offers to buy or sell—is not restricted only to those who are physically present. A buyer may come to my farm and offer 17 dollars per 100 pounds for my hogs. If I then pick up my telephone, and get a bid from another buyer, 50 or 100 miles or more away, of 50 cents more, or hear on my radio that prices are higher at other points, there is competition for my hogs right on my farm, just as if the buyers were physically present. In fact, I am in a stronger position with my hogs on my farm than if they were at a distant public market where they have to be sold within 1 or 2 days.

The second argument, that decentralized buying reduces competition, demand, and the prices at the central markets, and thereby reduces prices over the whole area, is similarly fallacious. If decentralized buying reduces the demand at the central markets, it reduces the supply correspondingly, so that the net effect on prices on this account would be nil. The market for livestock in which prices are determined is not simply a central market, but is the whole group of buyers and sellers, wherever they may be.

The group of buyers and sellers may be concentrated at one point, or at several points, or it may be widely scattered over the country. Prices are determined by the whole group in either case, and will be the same and determined by the same forces, in the one case as in the other, if the trading facilities are as good in the one case as in the other.

Looked at in this light, the arguments as to the effect of direct buying on the price of hogs are seen to miss the point. They assume that Chicago sets the price of hogs. That is not true. More hogs are bought in Iowa than in Chicago. It would be more accurate to say that Iowa sets the price of hogs than to say that Chicago sets it. Actually, neither one alone sets it. The price of hogs is set by the whole group of buyers and sellers all over the country, and for that matter, all over the world. In a centralized market it makes no difference to the level of prices whether the bulk of the trading is done on the east side of the pit in the case of wheat (or of the stockyards in the case of livestock) or whether it is done on the west side. And in a decentralized market it makes no difference whether most of the trading is done in the eastern part of the trading territory, or on the west side, or in a little knot in any one part, or all over the territory—if the facilities for trading are as good in the decentralized market as in the centralized market.

The danger from direct buying is not that it may substantially lower the price of hogs by undermining Chicago prices or some other assumed basic price. The danger lies in the extent to which the actual situation in hog marketing falls short of the proviso that "a scattered market is as good as a concentrated market, provided that the trading facilities are as good in the one case as in the other."

It is evident that if the trading facilities are not very good, individual sellers (or buyers) may suffer. If some seller who has not put himself in touch with the best bids available accepts $17.50 per 100 pounds for his hogs when he could have received $17.75 somewhere else, he loses 25 cents per 100 pounds. He would do better to pay a commission man to do his selling for him (if the price thus obtained were higher than the other by more than the commission and other charges). If market facilities are poor, direct buying may lose the seller more money than the commission charges he avoids by selling direct.

This puts the responsibility upon the packers and the farmers to provide first-class market facilities for direct buying, if farmers are to be protected from potential bad effects of the practice. The most important of these market facilities is a stream of current, accurate, and detailed market news as to livestock prices at all available points in the general market for livestock.

A second important need is for a uniform and relatively fine-grained system of grades, and an accurate way of determining where individual hogs or lots of hogs fall in that system of grades. It would do a farmer very little good to hear over the radio that hogs at a certain point were selling at from $16.00 to $18.00 per 100 pounds if he could not tell where his hogs would fall in the price range. The situation improves greatly if the market news is refined and standardized, so that a farmer can hear that Choice No. 2 hogs from 200 to 220 pounds are selling for $18.00 to $18.30 per 100 pounds. Even then the farmer may not get full value for high-quality hogs, for that grading system does not specifically include dressing percentage. That is left to the final bargaining between the seller and buyer, with the likelihood that both high- and low-quality hogs will be sold at prices closer to the average than their true cut-out value.

The live hog grades promulgated by the Department of Agriculture in September 1952 should help to bring about more uniform hog grading. But it is inherently difficult for even the most expert hog buyer to estimate the dressing percentage (yield of carcass) accurately, lot by lot, and still more difficult for farmers to do so. Farmers therefore cannot tell whether a buyer is knocking 25 cents off the price he will pay for a load because the hogs are filled and the yield will be low, or because he thinks he can take advantage of the buyer and get the hogs for 25 cents less than they are really worth.

I believe that the method of selling livestock by live weight, which grew up with the central markets, is not suited to decentralized markets. An alternative would be to sell by the carcass weight and grade, the method used for all slaughter hogs in Canada. Under this method, the hogs are identified by tattoo marks, the carcass weight is determined mechanically by electrical recording scales in the plant, and the carcass grade is determined at the same point by an impartial Government grader. The bargaining about the price is done by the farmer before his hogs leave the farm. The competition in this bargaining process is sharper and more accurate than the competition for live hogs can be, since prices can be quoted by sharply defined carcass grades and the weight and grade of the carcass can be accurately and impartially determined.

A third important need is a thorough study of packers' competitive practices in the decentralized markets, as compared with practices in the terminal markets. So little is known about either that all that can be done here is to raise one or two questions. Direct packer buying might lead to geographical division of market territory and thus to lower prices at the farm; this is unlikely in view of the heterogeneous nature of the competition in the area, but more needs to be known about the methods by which interior packers establish their prices from day to day. Direct packer buying might, alternatively, lead to more intensive competition among packers, and thus result in higher prices at the farm. Or it might intensify the duplication of packer buying and selling services, and thus widen middleman's costs; or it might enable buyers, sellers, and product to get together with less cost than those involved in using the central markets. Only a small beginning has been made with studies of this sort. Much more needs to be done.

The overall conclusion concerning the good or bad effects of decentralization in the marketing of farm products, then, can be put in these terms: Bypassing the central markets generally reduces marketing costs. The most controversial questions concern the effects on prices. In general, those effects on prices depend upon how accurate and timely the market news is, and how broadly it is disseminated to creamery managers in the case of butter, and to farmers in the case of livestock and most of the other farm products. In addition, the effects on prices depend upon how good the grading system is, and how fully competitive the buying system is.

A program of action to deal with decentralization in the marketing of farm products, therefore, calls for steps to bring market grades to the highest possible level of detail and accuracy, and disseminate market news on a decentralized basis comparable with the decentralization of the marketing of the physical product. (*Geoffrey Shepherd.*)

UNLOADS OF SELECTED FARM PRODUCTS, 1950
AT THIRTEEN IMPORTANT TERMINAL MARKETS

COMMODITY	UNIT	UNLOADS: RAIL	UNLOADS: TRUCK	PERCENTAGE RAIL	PERCENTAGE TRUCK
Fruits and vegetables	Carlots	342,073	314,496	52.1	47.9
Butter	1,000 lbs.	212,755	307,427	40.9	59.1
Frozen eggs	1,000 lbs.	7,021	42,786	14.1	85.9
Shell eggs	1,000 cases	1,003	17,558	5.4	94.6
Live poultry	1,000 lbs.	2,281	251,228	0.9	99.1
Dressed poultry	1,000 lbs.	154,868	498,610	23.7	76.3
Cheese	1,000 lbs.	185,545	99,010	65.2	34.8
Milk*	1,000 40-qt. unit equivalents	13,656	50,767	21.2	78.8
Cream	1,000 40-qt. unit equivalents	678	1,358	33.3	66.7

* Data from 3 markets only.

Food Retailers

The retail foodstore is the end of the marketing channel. In it the products of farm and factory in a multitude of forms are placed before the customers. Methods of retailing have changed greatly since 1900—and are still changing. On the whole, farmers as well as most segments of the consuming public have benefited. The corporate chainstores, which grew rapidly between 1900 and 1929, brought about many of the changes. Independent wholesalers and retailers set up voluntary chains to meet this competition. More recently, supermarkets and self-service stores have adapted food retailing to modern suburban living and automobile shopping. Food retailers have been adding nonfood items to their shelves. Families with larger incomes and homemakers with outside jobs have been willing to pay for more attractive stores and more service. The demand for services has been felt by restaurants, too, as more and more people eat out. Consumers spend some 3 billion dollars extra a year to have restaurants prepare and serve their meals.

Where the Customer Is King

Retailing is selling to the consumer. The retail foodstore is the end of the marketing channel. In it the products of farm and factory in a multitude of forms are placed before the customers.

The basic task of the food retailer is to provide service. He has to estimate his customers' wants and acquire and price at competitive levels the 3,000 to 6,000 items that one or more of the customers might want. He displays the items attractively, often in refrigerators or on suitable fixtures. His store must be convenient to his customers. Very likely he has to provide parking space, clerk service, self-service, delivery, and credit. He has to select, train, and supervise personnel to operate the store. Sometimes he processes food—grinds meat, prepares slaw, and prepackages meat, fresh fruit and vegetables, and cheese. Often he must advertise. One big job is to receive the merchandise into the store, prepare it for display, price it, place it on the shelves, and finally check it out—big because turnover in foodstores is fast. Finally, there is the major task of providing the capital, keeping records of transactions, and paying operating expenses. His efficiency in those tasks affects the prices the customers must pay for food.

Sales from grocery, combination, and specialty foodstores were 40 billion dollars in 1952. The 377,000 grocery and combination foodstores (with which we are primarily concerned here) had 33 billion dollars' worth of business.

Of the total grocery store sales in the United States in 1952, supermarkets (sales of more than 375,000 dollars a year) did 44 percent, superettes (75,000 to 375,000 dollars a year) did 35 percent, and small stores (sales under 75,000 dollars a year) 21 percent. Supermarkets and superettes, which were less than one-fourth of the total number of foodstores, had 78 percent of total sales in 1952.

In a representative group of supermarkets, 62 percent of the sales were of groceries and miscellaneous items, 26 percent were of meat, and 12 percent of produce.

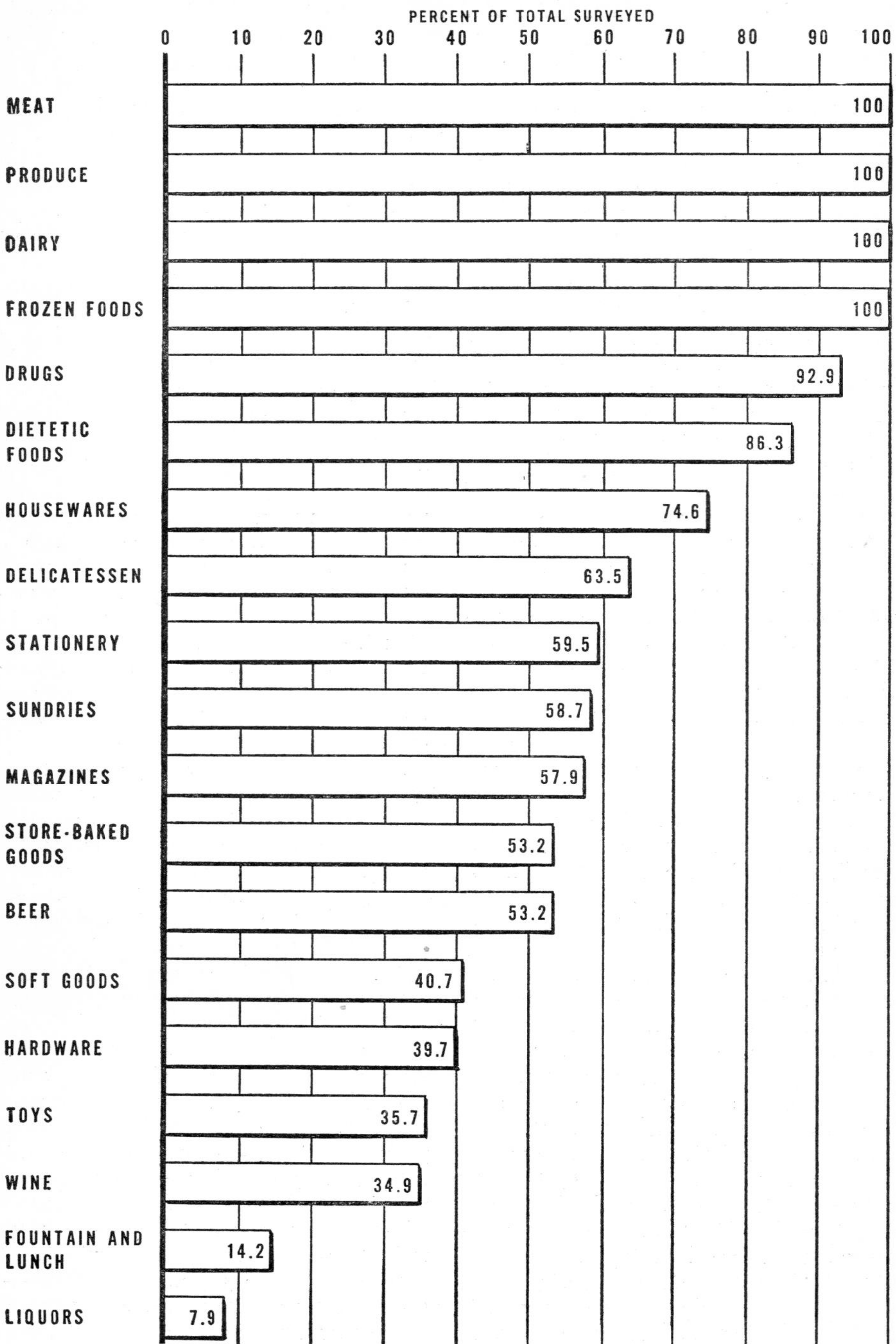
DEPARTMENTS INCLUDED IN SUPERMARKETS, 1952
PERCENT OF TOTAL SURVEYED
0
10
20
30
40
50
60
70
80
90
100
MEAT
100
PRODUCE
100
DAIRY
100
FROZEN FOODS
100
DRUGS
92.9
DIETETIC FOODS
86.3
HOUSEWARES
74.6
DELICATESSEN
63.5
STATIONERY
59.5
SUNDRIES
58.7
MAGAZINES
57.9
STORE-BAKED GOODS
53.2
BEER
53.2
SOFT GOODS
40.7
HARDWARE
39.7
TOYS
35.7
WINE
34.9
FOUNTAIN AND LUNCH
14.2
LIQUORS
7.9

Margins, which include operating expenses and the profit and vary by departments, are generally higher as perishability of the items increases. Typical gross margins of supermarkets in 1952 were: All departments, 16 percent; grocery, 14.2 percent; meat, 17.5 percent; produce, 24 percent.

Salaries and wages took more than one-half of the operating costs. Profits ranged from 1 to 2 percent of sales.

The independently owned and operated stores and the corporate chainstores are the two main types of retail foodstores. Approximately 355,000 independent stores made about 65 percent of the total foodstore sales in 1952; 22,000 chainstore outlets made the remaining 35 percent. The percentage of the total food sales made by chainstores has fluctuated between 30 and 40 percent since 1930.

A retail firm that has 1 to 10 units or stores is defined as an independent. In 1952 about 80 percent of the independent grocery and combination foodstores had annual sales of less than 75,000 dollars. These stores did only 33 percent of the business. The independent superettes and supermarkets (sales over 75,000 dollars) did 67 percent of the sales volume done by independents.

Independent operators have joined voluntary groups and formed cooperative chains to help them reduce costs and meet corporate competition from chains. About 37 percent of the 1952 estimated food-dollar volume was done by voluntary and cooperative group stores—a greater volume than that of corporate chains in the same period. The voluntary group or chain is composed of a group of independently owned retail stores associated with a wholesaler for buying, advertising, or other activities. The cooperative chain is composed of independent retailers organized to function cooperatively as a wholesaler or to perform the other merchandising functions.

A chainstore system is composed of 11 or more stores of similar type and centrally owned and managed. Among foodstores are national chains; regional chains, whose distribution is confined to one section of the country; and local chains, which most often operate in only one or two cities. Most of the chain outlets are of the superette or supermarket size.

The retail food industry is highly competitive. Each of its several types of retailers has competitive advantages that stem from its position as an independent or chain, small store or supermarket, and service or self-service store. Other competitive advantages reside in location, quality of management, and ability to buy favorably.

The personal nature of his enterprise and its flexibility sometimes give an independent retailer some advantages over the operators of chainstores. The independent retailer generally knows well his customers and employees in and out of his store. He knows what his customers want and can adapt his business to particular needs in food, prices, and services.

The trend of self-service in foodstores is both cause and effect of other trends. While self-service was becoming the predominant method of selling groceries, the size of the stores increased, wages of employees went up, workdays were shortened, the relative margins for handling food dropped, the amount of advertising increased, more items were stocked, and the importance of attractive displays, labels, packages, and promotional material grew.

It was estimated that 91 percent of the chain outlets and 73 percent of the independent retailers sold groceries completely self-service in 1952. The self-service sales of meats, dairy products, fresh fruit and vegetable items, and nonfood items have increased rapidly. With the help of self-service selling, average sales per employee have increased from 2,000 to 3,000 dollars a year in the old cracker-barrel days to more than 30,000 dollars a year in many modern supermarkets. The competitive advantage of selling self-service has been well established.

But many retailers have found it profitable or necessary as a competitive measure to offer their customers such services as delivery, telephone order, credit, check cashing, evening and Sunday openings, bundle pickup stations, distribution of recipes, cooking schools, air conditioning, and music for shopping pleasure. Delivery and credit are being discontinued but some of the services are being adopted by more and more retailers. Evening hours, especially, are fast becoming common.

The modern supermarket can offer customers more lines of merchandise attractively displayed at generally lower prices than the superette or corner grocery store. Supermarket numbers increased from practically none in 1930 to more than 16,500 in 1952. Most of the growth occurred during a period of generally rising prices when competition was not overly severe. As competition with other supermarkets becomes more severe and prices stop rising, the rate of expansion may slow down.

The small supermarket or superette has many of the advantages of a supermarket without some of its disadvantages. The superette often is a conveniently located neighborhood store, owner operated, with more flexibility than the supermarket. When served by a progressive, low-cost wholesaler, the superette can often buy and sell at as low a price as the supermarket. The superette may be able to adjust more successfully to falling prices than the supermarket, as it has smaller fixed costs and less outside labor.

As a result of the progress made in food retailing, some important changes are occurring in the retailer's job. His function as buyer has lost much of its significance because an increasing amount of standardization is removing differences between qualities and prices. An increasing amount of preselling by manufacturers, processors, and wholesalers requires less personal selling but increased display and promotional selling. For some nonfood articles, jobbers select the items, stock the shelves, maintain the displays, and do the re-ordering. All the retailer does is provide the selling space and check-out service.

The increasing standardization of food and the similarity of operation and practices are removing some differences between the chain and independent stores. Differences due to size are becoming greater than formerly, so that the supermarket has less and less in common with the small corner grocery. In place of traditional advantages, many retailers have substituted other than price incentives for customers to buy from their stores—more attractive and comfortable premises, more pleasant personnel, and a greater variety of items. (*R. W. Hoecker*.)

What the Chains Did

The corporate chain was an innovation in its emphasis on lower operating costs in relation to sales in fields of retailing where higher costs were common. How could that be done?

The chain got customers to trade in its stores despite a reduction in the number of its free services. Customers were asked to carry their own packages home, to wait upon themselves, and to pay cash.

The chain emphasized faster turnover of goods.

It made use of division of labor. Specialists could be used for all important aspects of the business and could be organized into regional groups. Thus the Great Atlantic and Pacific Tea Company has its executives and specialists in its headquarters and their counterparts in several regions.

Use was made of integration. The chain owned or leased its own motor-trucks for delivering goods from its warehouses to each unit store. It could set up wholly owned subsidiaries to buy meats, fruits, and vegetables at wholesale. It also could own its own factories.

And the chain could transfer goods, methods, and personnel between stores at different locations. Of incidental importance was the ability to get some income from the sale of waste materials, salvaged goods, and the like.

One of the chains' innovations was the clean, modern, well planned, well arranged store. Exteriors and interiors were painted regularly in bright colors. Stores were well lighted. The National Tea Company in 1920 had an average investment per store of 5,000 dollars; in 1953 it was more than 100,000 dollars.

The chain developed advanced techniques for selecting and training clerks and managers who could operate the units according to overall policies and with a degree of uniformity.

Another source of improvement was the skillful selection of store locations on the basis of careful study, analysis, and experimentation.

Corporate chains have been among the pioneers in the use of Government grades for labeling their own brands of goods and in the sale of unbranded goods, such as fresh meats. The chains also have experimented in carrying wider assortments of goods. Inventories of unit stores of the National Tea Company increased from 1,000 dollars in 1920 to 50,000 dollars in 1953.

The chain and many unit stores in one area could make more widespread use of semistandardized advertisements at lower expense. Only the independent retailers who sell shopping or speciality goods in the better shopping districts normally can afford to use much well-developed advertising. But the corporate chain by developing large total sales volume and volume per unit store, and because of wide geographical coverage, can afford to use advertising widely and effectively even for foods. In fact, the ability to use mass advertising media locally, regionally, and, in some cases, nationally is one of the greatest sources of strength in sales promotion. These advertisements can then be related to point-of-sale promotion and display.

As to market risks, the chains may secure a better distribution by diversifying locations and through the use of advanced forms of marketing research. They can often reduce their insurance burdens as well because they can combine unlike risks. This is true, for example, of such risks as burglary and fire. It is most unlikely that all unit stores will be burglarized or burned down during any fiscal period.

Experimentation with new marketing methods is another contribution to the improved marketing operations. The chain, because it has a large number of widely distributed stores, and because it has the specialists and financial strength, can experiment in pilot stores, in so-called representative or test areas, or in other ways.

The ability to enter into processing is a significant competitive influence regardless of whether it is used to secure the benefits of integration or to exert pressure on suppliers.

The chains' influence extended to various service industries—transportation, storage, finance, and the like. Through direct ownership of facilities or through the pressure of their accumulated demand for services, the chains upset existing relationships and caused new relationships to be formed. If costs in public warehouses were prohibitive, or if it appeared savings could be made, they could build their own facilities. If the common carriers' rates were high, they sometimes could provide alternative facilities.

The first supermarkets were the creations primarily of the independent retailer. The corporate chain, however, adapted this principle to the food field and to other lines of retailing. As a result, they have strengthened the basic qualities of the supermarket while permitting each chain to secure larger dollar volumes of business with far fewer stores.

The chains and other retailing units have been among the leaders in experimenting in the sale of lines of merchandise not usually associated with a given line of business. Drugs, socks, dresses, hardware items, and shirts are among the items stocked in foodstores. Others may carry magazines and books. In Logan's supermarkets in Nashville are branches of the public library. The widened lines add volume, attract more customers, and increase the average sale per customer.

The retail food industry is one of the most competitive in our country. Grocers realize about one cent profit on each dollar's sales. The food retailer's gross margin will average around 17 percent as compared to about 34 percent for department stores. The primary reason for this difference is the self-service feature of the supermarket. High volume and high turnover at a low profit is the principle upon which the supermarket industry has been built.

After the Second World War, when foodstuffs began again to become plentiful and competition began anew the squeeze on profits, food retailers began to look around for high-profit, high-turnover, nonfood items to add to their merchandise lines. It became apparent that drug, department, hardware, and variety stores were selling many nonfood items on a service basis that could be offered on a self-service basis advantageously to the heavy traffic of the supermarket. Gradually the grocer began adding to his shelves such items as cigarettes, candy, beauty and health aids, houseware items, stationery, magazines, clothing, and appliances. Thus began the second phase of the revolution in food retailing.

Almost one-half of all cigarettes sold are handled by retail foodstores. Beauty and health aids are carried by practically all supermarkets and their volume represents almost a half-billion dollars in sales annually. More dentifrices are sold in foodstores than in drugstores. The sale of kitchen utensils and other hardware items, plus nylon hose, men's socks, and other items of clothing fast became part of the supermarket operation.

The sale of nonfood items represents between 10 and 15 percent of the total sales of the supermarket. Of course, some operators have gone into certain nonfood lines more extensively than others. For example, J. Weingarten & Co., of Houston, Texas, has a complete ready-to-wear soft lines department in several stores. His nonfood lines represent about one-third of this total volume.

The expansion of the grocery store into nonfood lines has had a terrific impact on the retailers whose lines have been invaded. They have realized that the supermarkets' basic competitive advantage lies in the fact that food automatically produces more traffic than nonfood items. Several drug chains and department stores are installing food departments of their own. In addition, an increasingly large number of retailers who have been hurt by the supermarket on nonfood lines are fighting back with the same self-service techniques that hurt them.

Such a move to "scrambled marketing" tends to accentuate the intensity of competition between types of stores normally not competitive. It creates a basis for new types of wholesale middlemen, such as "rack jobbers." And, once again, it is forcing the older types of retailing to analyze their operations in order to squeeze out costly, inefficient methods of operating. Undoubtedly, as did the independent retailer in years gone by, these older types will develop new aspects in order to compete more effectively.

As the size of store and as the average sale per customer have increased, the corporate chain has had to experiment continually with new physical arrangements. Shelving had to be adapted to self-service. Store directories were introduced to facilitate locating needed items. Goods-carrying carts appeared. Facilities needed for preserving frozen and packaged foods were designed. Check-out stands were improved.

Chains, such as the Lucky Stores in California, have developed methods by means of which groceries can be placed on shelves in units sufficient to take care of several days' sales. This permits the use of semimechanical devices for moving goods. It means also that most of the stocking of shelves can be done during hours when there is little or no customer traffic.

Finally, the chains have been among the leaders in experimenting with new color schemes so far as interior decorating is concerned. Safeway has built a number of windowless stores in order to get more shelf space within the same area. (*E. T. Grether, David A. Revzan.*)

The Chains As a Lesson in Marketing

The Great Atlantic and Pacific Tea Company, the largest chain in the United States in 1954, started operations in 1859. The Jones Brothers Tea Company of Brooklyn, which became the Grand Union Company, was organized in 1872. F. W. Woolworth started in 1879.

They are mere newcomers, however, in the field of chainstores. A number of stores under one ownership was reported in China as early as 200 B. C. The Mitsui chain started in Japan in 1643. The Hudson Bay Company operated a number of stores on the North American continent as early as 1670. Andrew Jackson owned several retail stores in Tennessee. The Worthington Manufacturing Company of Ohio had nine stores by 1818.

The difficulties of management prevented any large growth before 1900. John Wanamaker at one time had stores in several cities, but it took so much of his time to supervise them that he sold all except the ones in Philadelphia and New York. Often a successful merchant would start additional stores in other cities, only to find that his managers were taking his profits.

The development of management principles and accounting practices was a factor in the large growth of chainstores after 1910. Better accounting techniques meant that goods could be charged to the stores at retail selling prices and the managers had to account for all merchandise received.

The chainstore illustrates the viewpoint that new marketing institutions start and grow on the basis of low prices. They try to find a way to enter a market profitably and use low prices, made possible by laborsaving methods, as one of the devices of entry. The new firm usually obtains a foothold and gradually comes to find a place in the market and is accepted.

The grocery chains in particular were able to undersell many of the independents because of the lower cost of goods, better management, limited stocks which were turned rapidly, more attractive stores, and limited services, especially the cash-carry method, which came in after 1910. Once the chains established a sufficient sales volume, they bought their goods directly from the manufacturers and performed their own wholesale functions.

George Francis Gilman, founder of the Great Atlantic and Pacific Tea Company, saw that there was a big difference between the price of tea at ship's side and the price of tea to the consumer. He saw a chance for profit while selling at lower prices than other retailers. In an early advertisement Gilman claimed the elimination of several middlemen, including the speculator, the wholesale tea dealer, and the wholesale grocer.

Between 1880 and 1910, staple goods commonly passed through three mid-

281437°—54——6

dlemen: A sales agent, broker, or wholesaler; a smaller wholesaler or a jobber; and a retailer. That was the heyday of drummers—traveling salesmen. They went everywhere and called often on all retailers, no matter how small or remote. They traveled by train, stage, hack, buggy, and horse. To them no road was impassable.

An established chain could buy from a manufacturer, operate its own wholesale warehouse, and supply the goods to its own retail stores. It needed no salesmen between wholesaler and retailer. It saved the time that retailers spent with the salesmen. The manager of a chainstore mailed his order to the warehouse.

As the chains grew, there also was a saving in selling between manufacturers and chain warehouses. Manufacturers needed fewer salesmen. A buyer for a large chain could buy for all the chain warehouses and might negotiate one contract covering requirements for several months. The manufacturers made savings also in fewer shipments, less credit risk, less expense in making collections, and more certainty of outlet for products they produced.

So, between 1900 and 1929, hundreds of new chains came into existence. In the 1920's the food chains claimed that they undersold the independent grocers by as much as 15 percent. By the 1930's, however, the difference had been reduced to 6 to 9 percent.

Chainstores by 1929 accounted for 10.8 percent of the total number of retail stores in the country and 22.2 percent of the total dollar volume of retail sales.

No wonder that the burgeoning of the chains became a topic of public discussion. At dinner tables and public forums, people were arguing about chainstores: Will the neighborhood merchant soon be a thing of the past? Do chainstores depress farm prices? How far will the trend go? What are the secrets of successful chainstore operation? Does the system result from unethical and unlawful practices? Are chainstores desirable from a social point of view? Is there danger that the chains will become a monopoly in the distribution of goods?

And, as often happens, the topic of public interest became a political topic.

A suggestion was made before the National Association of Retail Grocers at Los Angeles in 1922 that a law should be passed limiting the number of chainstores to be permitted in any community. The independent grocers of Missouri took the suggestion seriously and brought about the introduction in their legislature of the first tax bill aimed at the chains. The proposal was not enacted—Missouri is one of 20 States that have never passed any type of legislation against chains.

The legislatures of Georgia, Maryland, and North Carolina in 1927 passed the first chainstore tax laws. Between 1927 and 1941 more than 1,100 bills were introduced in State legislatures over the country. Sixty bills were enacted in 28 States. The cries of independents were strengthened by the need of legislatures for new sources of revenue during the depression years of the 1930's. The bills were contested bitterly by the chains.

In 1931 the United States Supreme Court handed down a decision that chainstores could lawfully be taxed in a different manner from independent stores and that the tax could be graduated according to the number of stores operated.

Books, pamphlets, Government documents, magazine and newspaper articles, radio addresses, and public speakers devoted a great amount of attention to the pros and cons of this subject.

"Trade-at-home" campaigns, "the future of our children" arguments, "keep Littletown's money in Littletown" slogans, and "absentee-ownership" themes were part of a widespread campaign by independent retailers and publicity experts. A Senate resolution of May 5, 1928, called for an inquiry into chainstore operations by the Federal Trade Commission. The assignment took the Commission 6 years to complete. Its final report was made to the Senate in 1934. It disclosed several competitive advantages gained by the chains through the receipt of brokerage payments, advertising and promotional allowances, and discriminatory prices from manufacturers. In an attempt to correct these "inequalities," the Robinson-Patman Act became law on June 19, 1936. The purpose of the act was to prevent discriminations in price and other practices that affect adversely free competitive enterprise.

Another major attempt to tax the chains out of existence came in February 1938, when a bill was introduced into the House of Representatives. It was aimed primarily at the chains that operated stores in a number of States. Under its provisions, the annual tax which could be imposed started at 50 dollars a store on the tenth to the fifteenth store and then increased to 1,000 dollars on each store in excess of 500. After the tax was computed on this basis, the resulting amount was then to be multiplied by the number of States in which the chain operated to get the total tax due the Federal Government. A & P would have had a tax of 471,620,000 dollars to pay on its 1938 earnings of 9,119,114 dollars.

Three national farm organizations—the American Farm Bureau Federation, the National Grange, and the National Council of Farmer Cooperatives—came out against the bill. That they should take such a stand is important because so many farmers believed that chainstores were harmful to them. The argument that the chains' low prices depressed the market and in turn left less for the producer carried a great deal of weight in the reasoning of many persons in the farming areas.

A main factor leading to a modification of such thinking was the success of the National Association of Food Chains in moving the 1936 California peach crop. A large carryover from 1935 and a bumper crop in 1936 put before the California growers the prospect of a selling price less than production costs. The 34,000 chainstores put on a successful nationwide campaign to move the surplus and so made friends in a time of need. Similar promotions for beef, dried fruits, turkeys, grapefruit, lamb, canned pears, cotton goods, and dairy products won many more supporters in farming areas.

Thus farmers were among the leaders in preventing passage of the bill, which would have abolished chains simply because they were chains and not because of any specific objectionable feature.

During those years of fighting against tax proposals and an adverse public opinion, the chains also were slowly increasing their share of total retail sales. In 1939 they had about 24 percent of the retail volume of business, although in the total number of stores they dropped from 10.8 percent in 1929 to 7.5 percent in 1939.

Why? Grocery stores and filling stations were mostly responsible for the decline in the number of chainstores. In the impoverished 1930's came the supermarkets, the first ones operated by independent retailers. An increase in the use of automobiles meant that cash-carry stores could be located farther from consumers. Consequently thousands of small neighborhood stores closed and much larger units opened.

Among the factors that spelled success for the supermarkets, the self-service method ranks high. Clarence Saunders had used it as early as 1916 in his Piggly Wiggly store in Memphis, and cafeterias had used it even earlier.

In time a new institution tends to lose its price advantage because of its own greater expenses and cuts in prices by established sellers. In their competitive struggle, the chainstores have lost much of their price advantage and have increased their stocks, acquired expensive buildings and fixtures, and added parking facilities. Although comparative figures are lacking, many independents were believed in 1954 to be fully competitive on prices.

Established independent retail men began years ago to seek the advantages that arose from a cooperation with fellow merchants. They had to get their goods on equally advantageous terms if they were to compete fully with the chains. There arose new types of organizations to that end.

Among them are wholesalers who reduce their expenses by drop-shipping, giving franchises to retailers, handling merchandise on a cost-plus basis, or getting retailers to concentrate their purchases with them. Most of them have a large number of retailer customers who operate as voluntary members. Some wholesalers join together for cooperative buying. Another group comprises retailers who buy cooperatively through buying clubs, retailer-owned wholesale houses, and cooperative buying offices.

The cooperative and voluntary organizations have had their largest growth among grocers. Many others sell hardware, drugs, variety goods, dry goods, and automobile accessories. The retailer-owned cooperatives and the voluntary groups were prompt in matching the chainstore advertising that their stores offer "more for your food dollar." They likewise have made extensive use of specials and loss-leaders and have given assistance to their retail members in devising and adopting pricing policies that permit long margins on some items and extremely low markups on other merchandise. They have made their stores attractive, have carried better assortments of merchandise, and have adopted cash-carry and self-service methods.

Today the chains have become a commonly accepted feature of our distribution system. The clamor of the 1920's and the 1930's appears to have died away. Census data in 1948 showed that the chains were doing a smaller share (22.8 percent) of the total retail business than they did in 1939. Only 6 percent of the total number of retail stores are part of chain organizations. Measures against the chains have been introduced into many State legislatures since 1940, but few have passed.

Through competition furnished by chains, independent merchants have been forced to adopt new techniques. The farmers, the other segments of the consuming public, and the independent merchants themselves have benefited. Through legislative enactments and public pressure, many of the chains have come to realize that they have an obligation to the communities in which they are located and have modified their policies to support various community activities and enterprises. In all, the consumer has reaped the benefits from the introduction of this system, which has been instrumental in bringing him better merchandise at lower prices. (*Paul D. Converse*, *Robert H. Cole.*)

The Role of the Wholesaler

The food wholesaler is the middle link in the food distribution chain. He assembles in relatively large quantities a vast variety of food produced and processed in all parts of the world and resells the food in relatively small quantities to retailers and institutions.

The wholesaler serves basically his retail, hotel, restaurant, and institutional customers. His major functions are assembling, warehousing, order taking and delivery, and furnishing his customers with such services as merchandising aids, credit, and help in store engineering.

Most wholesalers furnish a limited amount of warehousing, because one of the wholesaler's primary functions is to break up the large shipments of an item into smaller orders for delivery to customers. Because large volumes of merchandise are moved through the warehouse, it should be convenient to rail and truck traffic and constructed and organized so that handling costs can be kept low.

Except for the cash-and-carry operation and for some perishables, the wholesalers' customers do not buy directly at the warehouse. The wholesalers must provide for some means of taking and delivering orders. The high degree of standardization and quality control throughout the food industry makes it possible for the wholesaler to take orders over the telephone, through salesmen, or with printed order forms. After orders are received, the various items are assembled by the wholesaler, loaded on trucks, and delivered.

A problem of the wholesaler is to maintain the rapid flow of merchandise through his warehouse to his retail and institutional accounts. He attempts to do so by furnishing a wide selection of merchandise, competitively priced. He often furnishes advice to help the retailer sell more goods.

Food wholesalers are of two general groups. According to the 1948 Census of Business, there were 17,367 establishments, which handled more than 11 billion dollars' worth of groceries, confectionery, meat, and other food specialties a year. In the same year there were 13,560 establishments wholesaling more than 7.5 billion dollars' worth annually of perishable consumer goods, such as dairy and poultry products and fresh fruits and vegetables. Of the grocery wholesalers, there were 4,265 general and 13,102 specialty wholesalers. Of the wholesalers that handled perishables, about half specialized in handling dairy and poultry products and the others specialized in handling fresh fruits and vegetables. In the years from 1929 to 1948 the numbers of these establishments increased more than 50 percent; the largest increase occurred among dairy and poultry wholesalers.

Wholesalers in each of the groups differ in the amount of specialization, the kind of arrangements they have with their retail or institutional customers, and in number and kind of services. Some include such services as buying and assembling goods, maintaining salesmen and merchandising specialists, mailing or supplying price lists and catalogs to customers, supplying credit, warehousing, and delivery service. But other wholesalers furnish practically none of those services.

Wholesalers may have various types of organizations. In 1948, there were 2,963 wholesalers who did not sponsor voluntary groups of retailers, but operated on a full-service basis, with salesmen, delivery, and such, or on a limited-service basis. More than 600 wholesalers served retailers who had voluntarily affiliated themselves with the wholesaler; in return for special services or prices, the retailers belonging to those voluntary groups purchase most of their supplies from the sponsoring wholesaler. There were 211 retailer cooperative chains. There were 405 cash-and-carry wholesale depots, usually operated in conjunction with other wholesale establishments. The depots usually cater to the small retailer and furnish a minimum of service. There were 51 wholesalers who specialized in the sale of foods and related products to hotels, restaurants, public institutions, steamship lines, and other institutions. The chainstore organizations also did wholesale business for their retail outlets.

Two large groups primarily service wholesalers: Food manufacturers and food brokers or agents. In 1948 there were 4,276 sales branches and offices maintained by food manufacturers, who sold nearly 9 billion dollars' worth of processed food. More than 4,000 brokers and agents negotiated for their principals more than 7 billion dollars' worth of food sales.

A food broker is a resident sales agent who sells food and grocery products to wholesale buyers within a well defined area on behalf of his established principals—the manufacturers, processors, packers, refiners, and other producers. A food broker does not take title to the merchandise. Primarily he obtains orders for the seller, and the seller ships, invoices, and collects for the product directly from the buyer. The food broker usually charges the seller a fee of 1 to 5 percent of sales for his services.

Most common in the grocery industry is the general wholesale grocer, who does not sponsor a retail group of stores and sells annually 1 to 2 million dollars' worth of merchandise. They do business with 300 to 400 retailers, who have annual sales of 50,000 to 75,000 dollars each. The wholesaler commonly requires a gross margin of 8 to 11 percent; his retail customers require gross margins of 20 to 25 percent. Usually the grocery wholesaler is only one of a number of other grocery, meat, produce, frozen food, and specialty wholesalers who supply the retailer's needs.

An increasing number of general wholesalers (about 200 in 1930 and more than 600 in 1948) are building their annual sales volume to 10 million dollars or more by sponsoring voluntary chains of a relatively small number of retailers who have annual sales of at least 100,000 dollars each. They furnish the retailers many of the merchandising and supervisory services that chain organizations give their outlets. Through the modernization of their facilities and handling and selling practices, these wholesalers are reducing their operating costs to less than 7 percent. They are broadening the lines they carry so that a few are able to fill practically all the needs of their retail customers. Instead of 15 or more wholesalers of all kinds calling on a single retailer, only 2 or 3 now call on him, and substantial savings in retailers' time and costs result.

Food wholesaling is becoming closely integrated with food retailing. The corporate chains led the way in this field and are being followed by the independents through their service programs. The trend toward larger retail outlets is being followed by larger wholesale outlets and the expansion of the retail foodstore into nonfood items has caused the same kind of expansion by their wholesale suppliers. (*R. W. Hoecker.*)

When Meals Are Eaten Out

More and more of the Nation's food supply is reaching the ultimate consumer in the form of meals "eaten out" rather than as food bought at the grocery store or produced at home.

The upward trend is slow—14 percent in 1939 and 16 percent in 1948. Much of the increase is probably due to higher incomes. Greater urbanization and employment in large industrial and business establishments also have contributed to it.

What does this trend mean to farmers, food processors and distributors, and consumers?

The figure, 16 percent, indicates how big a share of the total demand for farm products comes from our eating places. It is the ratio of the value of food eaten out (in terms of retail store prices) to the total retail value of all food consumed in 1948. In terms of actual dollars, about 10.5 billions of dollars were spent for meals and related food items in 1948, about one-fourth of the market value of all food sold to consumers by farmers, wholesalers, retailers, and eating places that year.

To eat out, Americans spend about 3 billion dollars extra a year. Would they spend that sum to buy more food? No. Actually they might buy less food in terms of total farm value if there were no restaurants. Many people eat more when they eat a good restaurant meal and they often eat more expensive types of food than they ordinarily do at home. Not to be overlooked are between-meal snacks, which are readily available at moderate prices in restaurants and drugstores. The extra amounts of everyday foods and the emphasis on more costly foods mean greater demand for farm food products, particularly livestock products, and for better quality of most foods.

On the other hand, a substantial proportion of the meals eaten out probably represents only a shift in place from the family table to the restaurant, as school children and workers eat in the school and factory cafeterias, or lunchrooms, or at drugstore fountains, instead of going home for the midday meal. Such a shift probably has little effect on the total demand for farmers' food output.

From facts gathered from a pilot survey of selected eating places in Minneapolis by the University of Minnesota in cooperation with the United States Department of Agriculture some conclusions can be drawn about the kinds of food eaten away from home.

The rates of consumption of meat, poultry, and fish probably average higher when people eat out, and thus contribute to the relatively strong demand for these products since 1940.

The heavy use of fats and oils in deep-fat frying in restaurants seems to be a significant factor in the demand for cooking fats and oils, and therefore in the demand for lard, soybeans, and cottonseed.

The popularity of soft drinks, confectionery, ice cream, sweet baked goods, and coffee for between-meal snacks probably increases the demand for sugar, milk, flour, and coffee. A little extra money in pockets of school children and workers and rest periods during working hours permit people to buy a soft drink or sundae or cup of coffee and piece of pie much more often. Snacks away from home may sometimes reduce food consumption at home at meal time, but they probably are often just extra. Accordingly, we believe that greater eating away from home increases the demand for farm food products because of extra amounts of foods purchased and because of some shifts to higher priced foods.

There are perhaps 600,000 eating places, of which one-third are street restaurants. The others are commercial in-plant feeding establishments, hotel dining rooms, drugstore fountains, dining cars, hospitals, school lunchrooms, department and variety store restaurants, boardinghouses, and clubs.

The size of the industry makes its demand for food important to food processors and marketing agencies. Eating places often require and pay for special services from their suppliers. Such services depend on how big the eating places are and how much food preparation is done in their kitchens. Part of the extra cost for marketing services may be offset by less work and cost of meal preparation in the restaurants. On the other hand, some of the costs arising from small-scale operations may be reflected in slightly higher meal prices for a given quality of meal.

The Minnesota pilot study indicated that only a small proportion of meat supplies for eating places in Minneapolis is bought directly from packers or their branch houses. Most of the eating places seem to prefer to buy specially cut and prepared roasts, chops, and steaks. They prefer frequent and prompt delivery service, so they buy from restaurant and hotel meat purveyors who specialize in such services or from large meat markets doing partly wholesale and partly retail business. They pay prices 3 to 6 percent above those charged by packers' outlets. The small short-order establishments often buy at retail stores, but two-thirds of the places studied reported paying less than retail prices.

Although the preparation of poultry for cooking requires much work, only 15 percent of the firms covered in the Minneapolis survey in 1950 reported buying poultry cut up, 23 percent dressed but not drawn, and 62 percent dressed and drawn. Indications are that the purchases of cut-up poultry have been increasing rapidly in the past 2 or 3 years as more supplying firms are prepared to cut up the poultry in accordance with specifications or desires of eating places.

In view of rising wage rates for restaurant help and improvements in factory processing of so many foods, eating places have come to rely more and more on canned, frozen, or other types of preprocessed foods. The major exception to this trend appears to be freshly baked cakes and pies. About two-thirds of the Minneapolis restaurateurs surveyed believed that buying processed foods reduced total costs.

In several metropolitan areas, commercial processors are now delivering peeled and cut-up potatoes and apples to eating places. This represents another forward step in transferring food-processing labor from the institutional kitchen to the food factory.

Bulk milk dispensers, refrigerated and highly sanitary, have come into use in most States since 1949. Their use reduces both food and labor costs and substantially increases sales volume of fluid milk as a beverage. At the same time a marked increase in the use of spray-dried nonfat milk solids for kitchen work has taken place.

Standardized bakery product and dessert mixes are used more and more.

Besides food, eating places pay for labor, equipment, furnishings, utilities, repairs, and for the use of capital. How much they cost is indicated in data from 240 eating places in 1940. Food costs of individual establishments were related to their sales and ranked in order. The middle or median ratio was 47 percent; other costs and profit made up 53 percent. Costs other than food took 56 cents of the restaurant meal dollar in Minneapolis in 1949, but only 45 cents of each dollar spent for meals in Fairmont, Minn., a much smaller town, on the basis of case studies made there under the Minnesota survey. (*Marguerite C. Burk, Paul P. Logan.*)

MARKET VALUE AS PAID BY CONSUMERS AND ESTIMATED RETAIL VALUE OF CIVILIAN FOOD, BY CHANNEL OF DISTRIBUTION [1]

Channel of distribution	1939				1948			
	Market value		*Estimated retail value*		*Market value*		*Estimated retail value*	
	Food sold or supplied	*Food sold, supplied and furnished*	*Value*	*Percentage of total*	*Food sold or supplied*	*Food sold, supplied and furnished*	*Value*	*Percentage of total*
	Billion dollars	*Billion dollars*	*Billion dollars*	*Percent*	*Billion dollars*	*Billion dollars*	*Billion dollars*	*Percent*
On-premise consumption:								
Public eating places:								
Meals and fountain items sold	2.7	2.7	[2] 1.5	8.4	8.1	8.1	[3] 4.8	9.8
Food furnished civilian employees and withdrawn by proprietors	....	.3	.4	2.2	....	.5	.7	1.4
Total public eating places	2.7	3.0	1.9	10.6	8.1	8.6	5.5	11.2

Private eating places:								
Meals sold by clubs, institutions, schools	.2	.2	.2	1.1	.8	.8	.5	1.1
Food furnished employees by clubs, institutions, schools	....	(4)			....	.2	.3	.6
Meals sold by boarding houses	.3	.3	.2	1.1	.6	.6	.4	.8
Total private eating places	.5	.5	.4	2.2	1.4	1.6	1.2	2.5
Institutions and transportation agencies:								
Meals supplied to civilian patients or patrons	.2	.2	.2	1.1	1.0	1.0	1.1	2.2
Food furnished civilian employees	....	.1			....	.3		
Total institutions and transportation agencies	.2	.3	.2	1.1	1.0	1.3	1.1	2.2
Total on-premise consumption	3.4	3.8	2.5	13.9	10.5	11.5	7.8	15.9
Off-premise consumption—sales:								
By retail stores	10.7	10.7	10.7	59.5	32.0	32.0	32.0	65.3
By commissaries, service trades, other establishments not elsewhere classified	.2	.2	.2	1.1	.8	.8	.8	1.6
Directly to consumers by farmers, hucksters, manufacturers, wholesalers	1.2	1.2	2.0	11.1	2.3	2.3	4.0	8.2
Gross sales	12.1	12.1	12.9	71.7	35.1	35.1	36.8	75.1
Less retailers' sales to eating places [5]	.3	.3	.3	1.7	.9	.9	1.0	2.0
Net sales to consumers	11.8	11.8	12.6	70.0	34.2	34.2	35.8	73.1
Food consumed on farms where produced	....	1.1	[6] 2.9	16.1	....	2.8	[6] 5.4	11.0
Total	15.2	16.7	18.0	100.0	44.7	48.5	49.0	100.0

[1] For information on sources of data and methodology see "Distribution of the Food Supply of the United States" in *Agricultural Economics Research*, Vol. IV, No. 3, July 1952, and chapters 2 and 9 of *Eating Places as Marketers of Food Products*, Marketing Research Report No. 3, BAE, 1952.

[2] Food cost estimated at 47 percent of sales based on National Restaurant Association survey; markups of 20 percent used to retail.

[3] Food cost estimated at 50 percent of sales; markup of 19 percent used for cost to retail sales value.

[4] Included with public eating places. Probably less than $100 million.

[5] Rough approximations only.

[6] Estimated farm values of farm food products sold in 1939 and 1948 were 38 and 52 percent of estimated retail value, respectively.

Trade Abroad

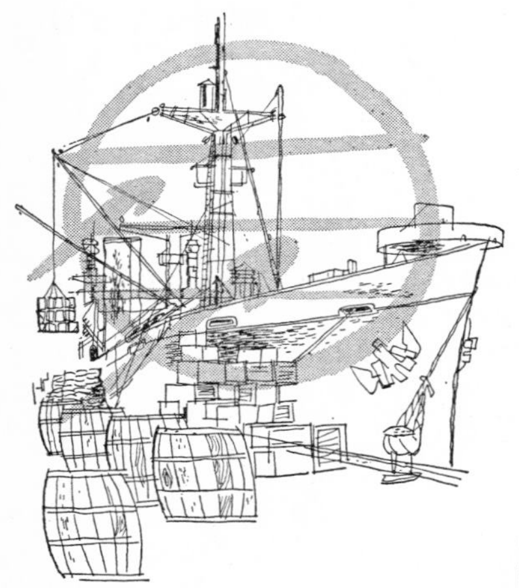

Sales of the American farm products in the world market since 1952 have been going down. Agricultural exports also have declined in relation to our total exports. In 1953 they made up 18 percent of the total. Desirable as the products of American farms and factories may be, most foreign customers have only a limited supply of dollars with which to buy them. Other barriers are likewise important in the restriction of United States foreign trade. The governments of many importing countries are committed to a policy of protecting their own farmers and those of their colonies or territories. They therefore use tariffs, the quota system, foreign-exchange controls, import licenses, and sometimes quarantine regulations to control the flow of imported agricultural products. Two-way trade seems to offer a sound and workable solution to the situation. American farmers need large foreign outlets for cotton, wheat, tobacco, and other products. To maintain and expand those outlets is one of the big challenges facing American agriculture.

Selling in Foreign Markets

United States farmers sold about 3 billion dollars' worth of agricultural products in the export market in 1952–1953, a year in which total cash farm receipts were 32 billion dollars. Over a period of years, American farmers have exported the equivalent of the production of one farm out of every ten. To put it differently, the annual share in that market, if it could be equally divided, would be just about 900 dollars for each one of our 3.7 million commercial farms.

Important as it may be, the American farmer's share in the world market has steadily declined since the early part of the twentieth century, just as has the volume of agricultural exports in relation to the total United States exports in the past 75 years. From about 1865 to 1880, agricultural products made up four-fifths of our total exports. Then, as population increased and the industrial production became relatively more important, the proportion of agricultural to total exports dropped steadily. It had fallen to about one-half in 1910, and thereafter declined so rapidly that by 1940–1941 agricultural exports made up only about 9 percent of total United States exports. The proportion has been much higher since the Second World War, partly because of lend-lease and foreign aid programs, and has averaged close to 30 percent. Agricultural exports in 1953, however, made up about 18 percent of total United States exports.

Cotton, grains, and tobacco, except for a brief period between the two wars, have usually accounted for two-thirds of our total agricultural exports. Fresh and dried fruit exports were impressive from the early 1920's to the end of the 1930's. They accounted for an average of 13 percent of the total of United States agricultural exports between 1934 and 1939. The percentage has been much lower since then. Both wars gave a tremendous impetus to exports of livestock products. Their volume has been reduced by import restrictions and payment difficulties since the Second World War.

Cotton alone accounted for one-half or more of our total agricultural exports before 1940. More recently it has made up about 30 percent of the total on a value basis and has been second only to grain. The importance of the export market to the cotton farmer is illustrated by the fact that during the 5 years before 1914 cotton producers sent to the export market more than two-thirds (8.8 million bales) of the crop. By the late 1930's it had dropped to 42 percent (5.3 million bales) of the crop. Since 1945 about one-third of the United States cotton crop has been exported as raw cotton and another 5 to 10 percent in the form of textiles.

Grain exports have almost always ranked first or second among United States agricultural exports despite droughts, depressions, wars, and efforts of other countries to develop their own sources of supply. Since the Second World War, one-third of our wheat has been exported. Rice exports, which began in a small way during the First World War, totaled more than one-half of the crop in 1951 and 1952.

Tobacco has ranked below cotton and grains in both tonnage and value of exports, but it has been a stable seller on the world market.

The most important export outlet for our farm products continues to be western Europe. In the postwar period the volume of its imports has declined, but nevertheless Europe still takes about 50 percent of the total United States agricultural exports compared with 60 percent between the wars and 80 percent before the first war. Our leading European customers are the British Isles, Western Germany, Italy, France, the Netherlands, and Belgium.

Western Europe is only 70 percent self-sufficient in food (caloric value) and almost wholly dependent on outside sources for its cotton and much of its tobacco. Western Europe must look to the world market for much of its food, fiber, and tobacco, but it does have exportable surpluses of some specialty crops and products which it

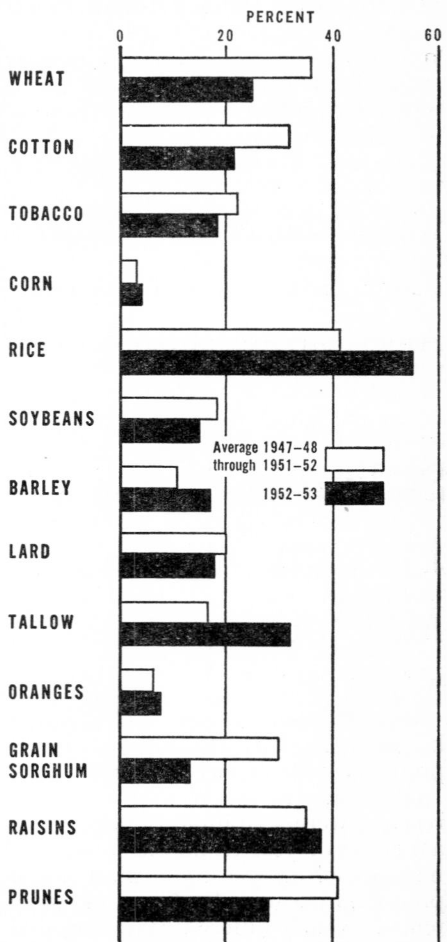

is anxious to sell in order to obtain the foreign exchange necessary to pay for imports. Outstanding among Western European agricultural exports are dairy products, hams and bacon, wines and spirits, nuts, bulbs and flowers, olive oil, flax, hemp, and hops. Some other products, among them fruits, vegetables, and eggs, are important only in intra-European trade.

Europe and the United States thus have products that they want to sell, but in recent years the process has not been simple. Selling in the foreign market is a specialized business that requires a knowledge of foreign languages, weights and measures, currencies and exchange, laws and regulations, customs procedures, transportation facilities and rates, insurance, trade terminology, and methods of financing and doing business.

The sources of foreign exchange have been a matter of concern to nearly all countries interested in sound international trading operations. Before the First World War, the United States, as a debtor nation, paid its obligations by selling much-needed raw materials to Europe. More recently, exports have consistently exceeded the imports, and European countries have been able to finance the resulting trade deficits only because the United States has provided funds through loans and grants. Since the situation pertaining to balance of payments has reversed itself, European countries now obtain United States dollar exchange with which to pay for American products from the following sources:

Sale and shipment of agricultural and industrial products, raw and manufactured, to the dollar area.

Dollar income from sales of transportation services and from American tourists and investments abroad.

Shipments of gold to the United States and the sale of United States stocks, bonds, and real estate.

Dollar earnings from United States troops stationed in Europe and from United States Offshore Procurement contracts.

Loans from private banks, the United States Government, or from such institutions as the Export-Import Bank and the International Monetary Fund.

Grants from the United States Government to other governments through military aid programs. Sale for local currencies of up to 250 million dollars of United States surplus agricultural products to friendly foreign countries was authorized for 1953–1954 under section 550 of the Mutual Security Act of 1953.

"Three-way" trades and compensation agreements, which may or may not involve several products and countries.

Barter deals in agricultural commodities, now widely used, are a means of doing business without the actual use of foreign exchange. Again, as a partial result of the United States agricultural export program, agricultural commodity and export subsidies available for use do have the effect internationally of providing an additional source of dollar exchange to the receiving country.

In addition to the dollar shortage, trade barriers of various kinds are also important in restricting United States foreign trade. The attitude of the governments of importing countries over a long period has had an important influence on foreign trade policies. The governments of most importing countries are committed to a policy of protecting their domestic producers and those of their colonies or dominions. As a result there are laws, regulations, and other measures designed to control the flow of imported agricultural products. Among the measures are tariffs, the quota system, foreign-exchange control, import licenses, and quarantine regulations.

Tariffs are actually taxes on products brought into a country. Tariffs add to the cost of the imported product. Consumers pay that cost in the final sales price. Tariffs restrict but do not necessarily prohibit imports unless they are unreasonably high. They may be administered arbitrarily, however, and customs regulations are sometimes so antiquated and complex that they discourage and often prevent imports.

Although tariff reduction has been the subject of numerous international conferences, rates on many products are still high enough to present a formidable barrier to trade.

The quota system, generally a necessary adjunct of the economic controls imposed by a country in balance of

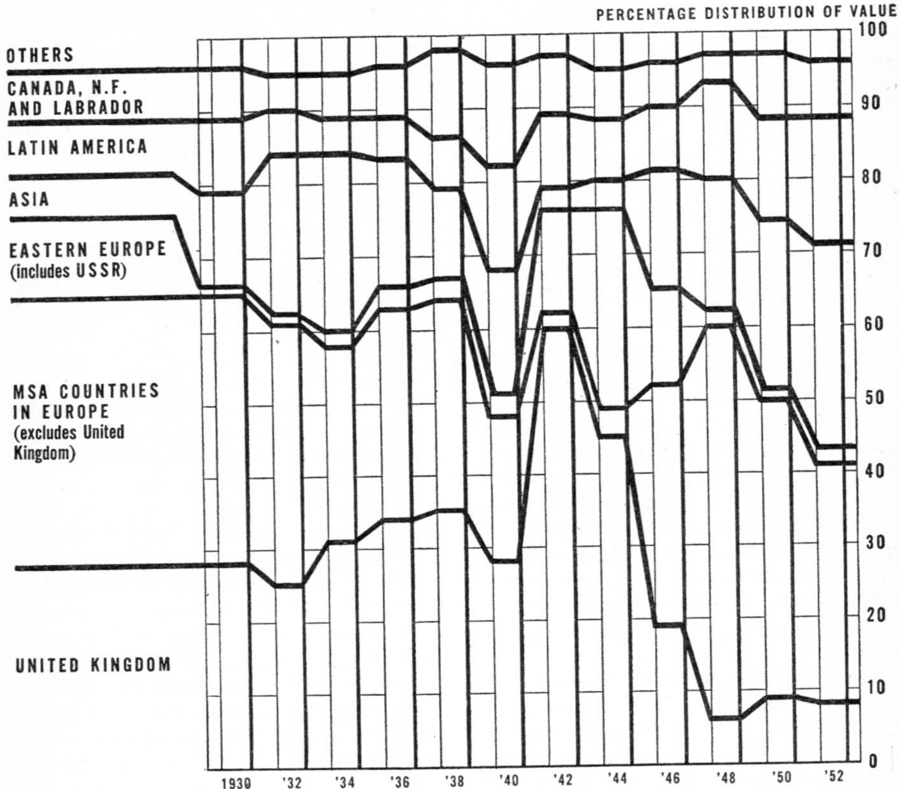

payment difficulties, has been used by many countries to restrict and control the flow of imports. The import quota assigned to a particular product or country may be so low as to constitute an embargo.

Import quotas may be allotted on a basis of first come, first served, or they may be divided by countries of origin or possibly on the basis of a past record of business by the importer of that product.

Foreign-exchange control is used by some countries to regulate imports and to protect their foreign-exchange position. Foreign governments often direct that purchases of their importers be made in countries other than the United States in order to conserve their limited supply of United States dollar exchange.

Foreign-exchange controls can be implemented in many ways. The following illustration in France shows the complexity of selling United States products in a foreign market. After the Second World War, French foreign exchange control regulations provided for a bonus dollar plan. The plan enabled the exporter of French products to the United States to use 3 percent of his total dollar income from those sales in any way he wished, free from all restrictions. Dollars in this category were referred to as free dollars. Rather than use the dollar income in his own business, the exporter might sell the dollars to a French importer who, in turn, might wish to use them in the purchase of United States goods or products for importation into France. Free dollars were so sought after in 1953 that they cost the importer 750 to 800 francs to the dollar, whereas the legal rate was 350 francs. This exchange-control procedure often more than doubled the cost of an imported product which could be purchased only with free dollars.

The remaining 97 percent of the exporter's dollar income was restricted. Twelve percent had to be used to purchase and import the items that the government considered essential to the economy of France. "Twelve percent" dollars sold for about 425 francs. The French controls required that the balance of 85 percent be sold to the government at the rate of about 350 francs to the dollar.

The elimination of the 3 percent or bonus dollar arrangement by the French Government in November 1953 is another evidence of the tightening of controls over dollar imports into French territory.

The absence of free convertibility of currency is another major deterrent to world trade. In the absence of major changes in the international economic policies of most of the countries of the free world and a better balance in the flow of trade, it is probable that the situation of inconvertibility of major currencies will persist.

Import licenses may be used to enforce quotas, control the limited supply of foreign exchange, and hold imports to the level desired by the importing government.

Quarantine regulations are of particular interest to exporters and importers of United States agricultural products. Sanitation and plant and animal quarantine regulations are designed to protect health and prevent plant or animal diseases or insect infestation from being carried from one country to another. The regulations perform a necessary function if they are objectively administered. They may be employed, however, to effect real restrictive barriers or actual embargos.

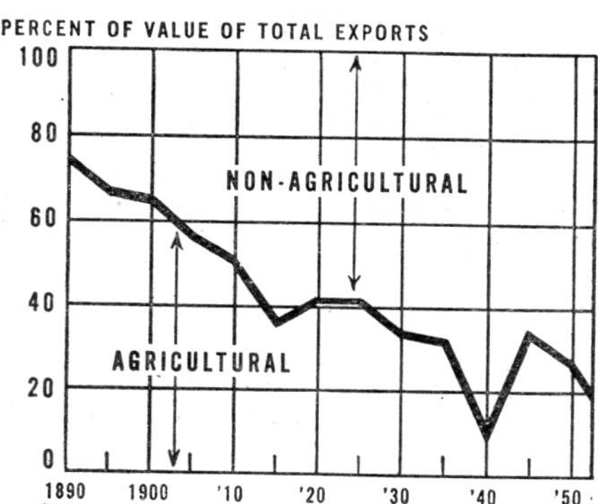

Moves toward lowering the barriers to the free flow of goods in foreign trade channels have been variously received. Some have been welcomed by certain groups and bitterly condemned by others. Often the moves to liberalize trade have been the concern of only two countries. Sometimes they have taken the form of worldwide efforts directed toward the solution of foreign trade problems on a broad front.

For many years the United States Government, backed by American farm organizations and other groups, has been a leader in the drive to increase world trade. In 1934 the Congress passed the Reciprocal Trade Agreements Act, which made it possible for the United States to enter into an agreement with another country for the reduction of tariffs in return for similar reductions by the other country. Since the passage of the act, agreements have been signed with more than 50 countries which, in total, carry on 80 percent of the world's trade.

The Reciprocal Trade Agreements Act has made it possible for the United States to participate actively in the General Agreement on Tariffs and Trade (G. A. T. T.), as concluded

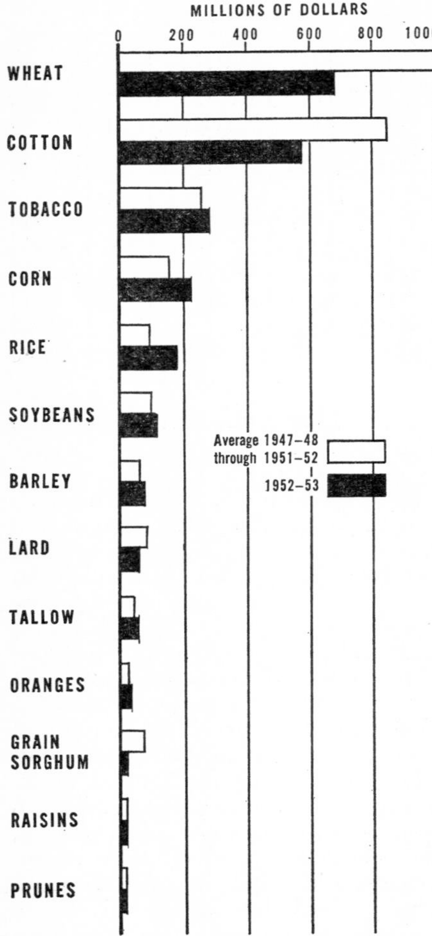

after the Second World War. The G. A. T. T. provides for a multilateral effort on the part of partners to the agreement to effect tariff reductions that apply to all partners alike. The agreement includes around 45,000 items or products and covers well over half of the import business of the 30 participating countries. Agricultural products make up a substantial proportion of the list of items covered by G. A. T. T.

Although both the Reciprocal Trade Agreements Act and G. A. T. T. have not been effective in all instances, tariff reductions since 1930 have been impressive. For example, immediately before the passage of the act, the average United States duty on items subject to tariff was just under 60 percent. In 1952 more than 58 percent of the items imported into the United States entered duty-free, and those subject to duty carried an average rate of about 13 percent.

In addition to the Reciprocal Trade Agreements Act and G. A. T. T., there have been other types of multilateral effort toward the solution of world trade problems. Among those of special interest to agriculture is the International Wheat Agreement, participated in by 49 countries. The present agreement covers 421 million bushels of wheat for a period of 3 years, beginning August 1, 1953. The previous agreement ran for 4 years.

Through the auspices of the Food and Agriculture Organization of the United Nations, there have been efforts to promote an International Commodity Clearing House, which would perform on a worldwide basis somewhat the same type of service now being performed by the Commodity Credit Corporation within the boundaries of the United States.

THE ROUTE TO THE FOREIGN MARKET is long and seemingly strange. In order to outline briefly some of the principal marketing steps involved in exporting agricultural products, it might be useful for us to follow one perishable product, apples, from a shipping point in the Pacific Northwest through the normal export market channels to a wholesale produce market in Europe.

When the importer and the exporter get together to take the first of the long series of steps that must be taken before the transaction can be completed, they have back of them an efficient international distributive system built up through many years of trial and error.

The procedures used by importers

VALUE OF TOTAL UNITED STATES AGRICULTURAL IMPORTS, 1952, In Millions of Dollars

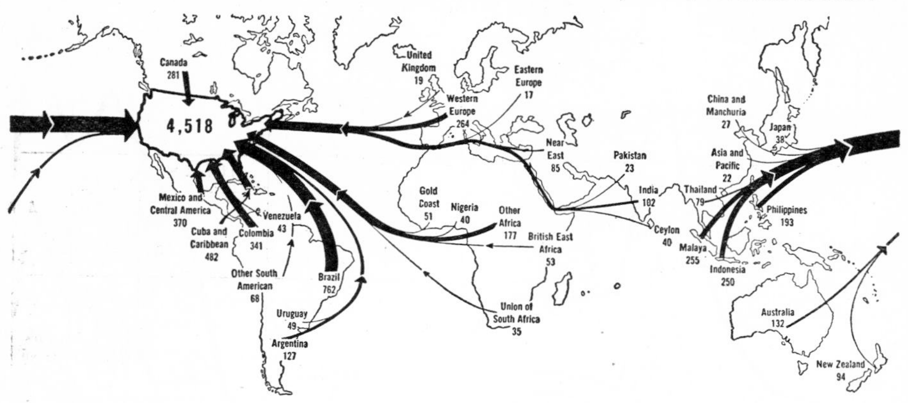

and exporters vary by commodities and by countries, but the whole process is a closely integrated team job in which each firm or agency plays its part. Even though the successful importer or exporter is not directly responsible for the performance of each of the long list of required marketing services, he must have an intimate knowledge of what happens to his commodity at each step of its long journey to the foreign market.

Several types of shippers are at the disposal of the fruit importer. The importer of apples may purchase from or through large growers, growers' cooperative sales organizations, fruit companies doing an export business, or export brokers, who may or may not have their own packing facilities.

The terms of sale under the exchange conditions in existence in 1953 were usually cash against documents, F.A.S., that is, delivered alongside the ship. If exchange and other conditions permit, the terms may be sale on open account, sale on a joint account, a guaranteed cash advance (usually early in the growing season). The shipper generally quotes prices on the basis of dollars per box rather than in metric tons and foreign currencies.

The F. A. S. sale (cash against documents) provides that the shipper be responsible for all operations, transactions, and expense up to the time the shipment arrives at the dock—shipside—and is ready to be loaded into the hold of the ship.

Under the provisions of that type of contract, the shipper selects the fruit at the local packing plant or the warehouse and makes certain that it is graded and is packed according to export specifications. When the ship's sailing schedule is known, he has the fruit loaded into a refrigerated railway car or truck and has it started on its way to the port so that it will arrive in time to be loaded aboard the ship. On arrival at the port, a forwarding agent usually takes over as representative for both the shipper and the foreign buyer. The forwarding agent receives the shipment at the docks, inspects its condition, and obtains from the rail or truck company the receipts and manifests which are evidence that the shipper has discharged his legal responsibility under the F. A. S. contract. When the documents have been turned over to the bank, the shipper can draw the cash set up to his account by the importer through the device of a letter of credit. It should be mentioned, in passing, that even though the shipper has discharged his legal responsibility at this point, he and the grower are vitally concerned with the quality and the condition of the fruit

281437°—54——7

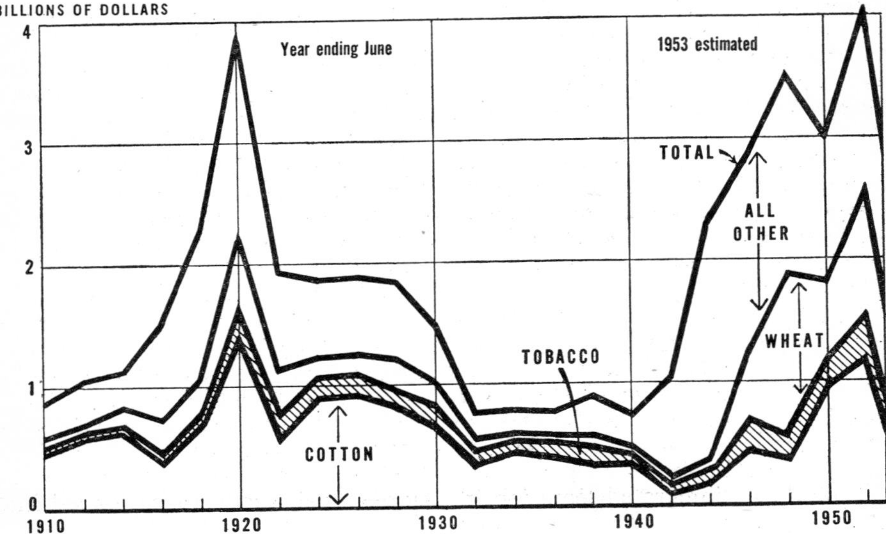

until it reaches the table of the foreign consumer.

Since the shipper's legal responsibility terminated upon delivery of the apples to the shipside, the forwarding agent for the importer takes over. He has previously scheduled ship space on the desired date and has arranged for insurance to cover the fruit while it is in transit. He supervises the loading into the hold of the ship and sees that the boxes are properly stacked and braced, after which he receives the ship's manifest, which is an inventory of the shipment and evidence that it is aboard. The steamship company is responsible for the proper ventilation, temperature control, and the general condition of the cargo while it is en route.

On arrival at the foreign port, the importer's agent is on hand for the unloading of the shipment. He inspects the cargo for possible damage in transit, pays customs duties, if any, and sees that the shipment is cleared through quarantine. With these out of the way, the agent schedules either rail or truck transportation to its final destination, which may be Paris. In Paris, the shipment is received by the importer and stored in his warehouse until it is sold. Since auction sales are prohibited in France, the importer must sell on the basis of private sale to the wholesaler, who in turn sells to the retailer. Through one of the many types of retailers, the fruit finds its way to the French table.

Two-way trade seems to offer a sound and workable solution to the situation that means less American apples and other fruit on European and world tables and less American wheat, cotton, tobacco, soybeans, and lard in world channels of trade.

Products that American agriculture and industry are producing have a worldwide sales appeal and a reputation for quality and dependability. Nevertheless, sales of American products in the world market have been declining and apparently will continue to decline until two-way trade—that is, United States imports and exports—can be brought into an approximate balance.

Desirable as the products of American farms and factories may be, most foreign customers have only a limited supply of dollars with which to buy them. If they cannot obtain dollar exchange by export sales, they must become selective in their purchases from us, and they are forced to conserve their dollar exchange by increasing production within their borders, raising barriers to keep out United States products, and buying in countries that are willing to enter into acceptable trade arrangements, which usually involve an exchange of goods for goods.

Increased American imports will not necessarily solve the entire United States foreign trade problem, but it will help. Unless the American farmer and industry are willing to increase imports to a level that will approximate exports, their stake in the world market might continue to decline. (*Omer W. Herrmann.*)

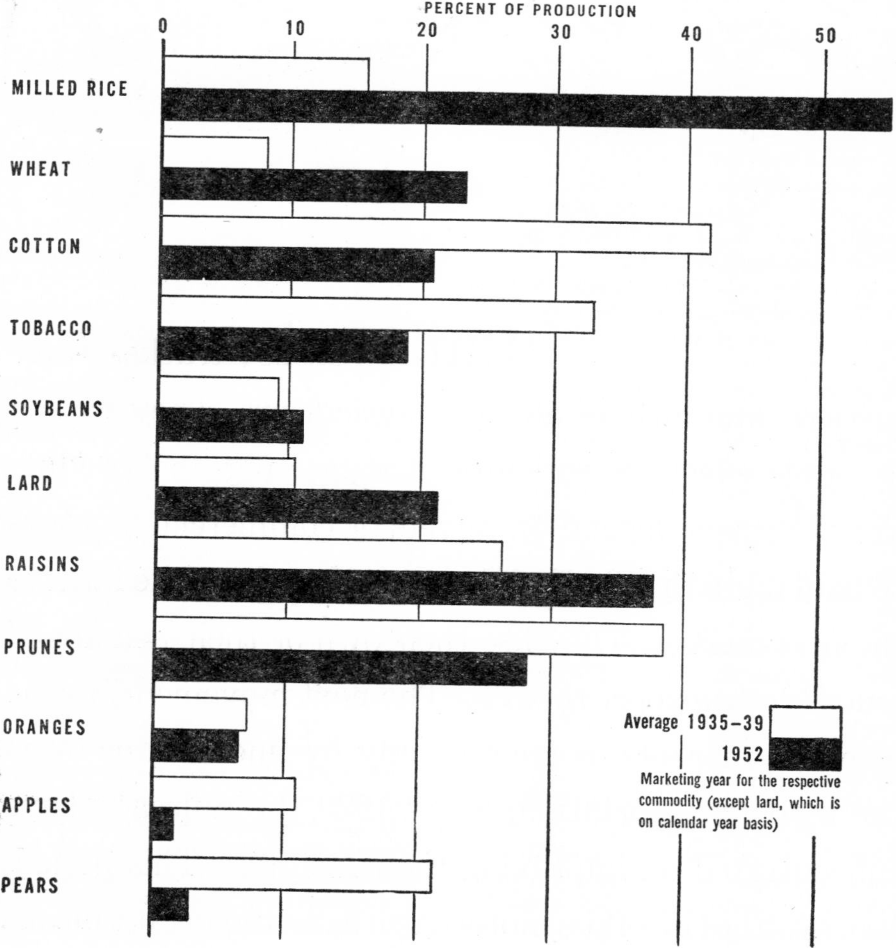

Transportation

Railroads, trucks, water carriers, and airlines all serve agriculture. They have a dynamic effect on agricultural marketing and production. Farmers depend on buyers or commercial truckers to haul more than half of their products from the farm to the first market. They use their own or their neighbors' trucks to transport the rest. The next movement, to the terminal markets, is done mainly by line-haul or over-the-road transportation. Since 1920 the railroads have concentrated on improving their facilities. This period, too, saw the rise of the motortruck as an important means of transporting farm goods. Many improvements have been made in refrigeration in transportation, the lifeline of marketing high-quality perishable foods. For a long time farmers have known the close relationship between effective regulation of transportation and satisfactory rates and services. They have been disturbed about the rising trend of freight rates since the war, which has contributed substantially to the increase in costs of marketing their products.

From Farms to the First Market

Farmers depend on buyers or commercial truckers to haul more than half of all their products from the farm to the first market—the relatively short hauls from the field to grading or packing sheds, cotton gins, country elevators, or to local livestock auction markets or the other collecting or shipping points.

Beyond that first step in the marketing process, at least one more haul by rail, truck, or other carrier usually is required, and nearly all those hauls are made in hired or buyers' trucks or by rail or other carriers.

Transportation service normally is measured in terms of the quantity hauled (tons, bags, boxes) and in terms of ton-miles—a combination of quantity and distance. Two tons of potatoes loaded on a truck and carried 3 miles, for example, would be expressed as 2 tons or as 6 ton-miles of transportation service. If the distance had been 10 miles, the measure would still be expressed as 2 tons hauled, but the ton-miles would be 20.

Similarly, if a single ton were hauled by truck 3 miles to a packing plant and then transported by rail to a wholesaler 97 miles away, the transportation service would be considered as 2 tons hauled—one loaded on a truck plus one loaded on a railroad car, even though in both instances it may have been the same ton. The service would also be expressed as 100 ton-miles, consisting of 3 ton-miles by truck and 97 ton-miles by railroad.

On the basis of tons hauled, farmers in 1948 used their own or their neighbors' trucks to transport to initial markets about 45 percent of all agricultural crops, livestock, and products that leave the farms. If only one additional haul were involved to reach the final market, the share of the total tons hauled in farm-owned vehicles would amount to about 22 percent. The total number of tons hauled would be doubled by the additional movement. Similarly, if two hauls, in addition to the initial haul from the farm, were involved, farm trucks would account for only about 15 percent of the total number of tons hauled. In terms of ton-miles, the share performed by farm trucks would be considerably lower than either 22 or 15 percent, mainly because initial hauls in growers' trucks are characteristically much shorter than the total length of the subsequent movements.

The use of farm trucks for the initial movement varies widely among the types of products. For example, growers themselves furnish about 80 percent of the transportation service needed to move cotton from the field to the gin. Only about 20 percent of the livestock is hauled off the farm in farm-owned equipment; most farmers haul an animal or two at a time to nearby local auctions in their own equipment, principally during slack seasons. About 60 percent of the livestock is hauled in trucks hired by farmers, and the rest goes in trucks supplied or hired by the buyers.

About 30 percent of all milk leaves the farms in farm-owned trucks. Tank truck service for collecting milk at farms has been started in a few areas, however. Glass-lined tank trucks are being used with increasing frequency for picking up fluid milk from farm storage tanks, mainly in the West, Northeast, and Midwest.

Market gardeners themselves haul about half the volume of fruits and vegetables that leave the farms. Sometimes the first hauls are to farmers' markets in town, but more likely they go to cooperative assembly points or to nearby commission houses. Southern growers particularly haul their fresh produce to small country auctions. In the South and Southwest, parts of the Midwest, and somewhat in the Northeast, itinerant truckers are active. They buy fruits and vegetables from the growers and sell them wherever they can find a market.

Although growers still supply transportation to move a little more than half of the grain from farms, deliveries can be made only for short distances if hauling is to keep up with harvesting. Hauls to terminal points are largely by for-hire truckers. Some grain is hauled to country elevators by combine crews who provide both harvesting and hauling services to growers.

Horses and wagons are still used in the South to transport about 20 percent of the cotton from fields to gins. Small quantities of grain and miscellaneous crops are hauled by wagon in other regions of the United States, especially the Midwest. Nevertheless, the overall importance of wagons is small. They account for the movement of less than 3 percent of the total tonnage leaving the farms. Nearly all the rest of the tonnage moves by truck. Trailing of livestock has all but been abandoned. Few farms or ranches have railroad sidings or facilities for loading on boats for movement by water.

Of a total of some 9.2 million trucks in the United States, about 2.5 million are owned by farmers. Why, one asks, don't farmers do more of their own transportation?

There are a number of reasons. First, only about 35 percent of all the farms in the country own even one truck. Ownership also varies considerably by size of farm. Among farms of fewer than 10 acres, about 1 in 6 has a truck, but about half of the farms of more than 99 acres have trucks.

A second reason is that most farm trucks are small. About 40 percent of the farm trucks have rated capacities of one-half ton or less. Small trucks are uneconomical for large-scale hauling. About half of the trucks on farms are rated as having a capacity of 1 or 1.5 tons. They are useful mostly for general hauling in local service and are too small for heavy or long-distance hauling. Fewer than 10 percent of the farm-owned trucks have a rated capacity of more than 1.5 tons.

Many farmers who do not own trucks can do light hauling for themselves by hitching small utility trailers to their automobiles, or by hauling heavier trailers (or wagons) behind farm tractors.

Farmers usually own only one truck.

AGRICULTURAL COMMODITIES MOVED FROM FARMS TO INITIAL MARKETS IN FARM-OWNED, HIRED, AND BUYERS' EQUIPMENT

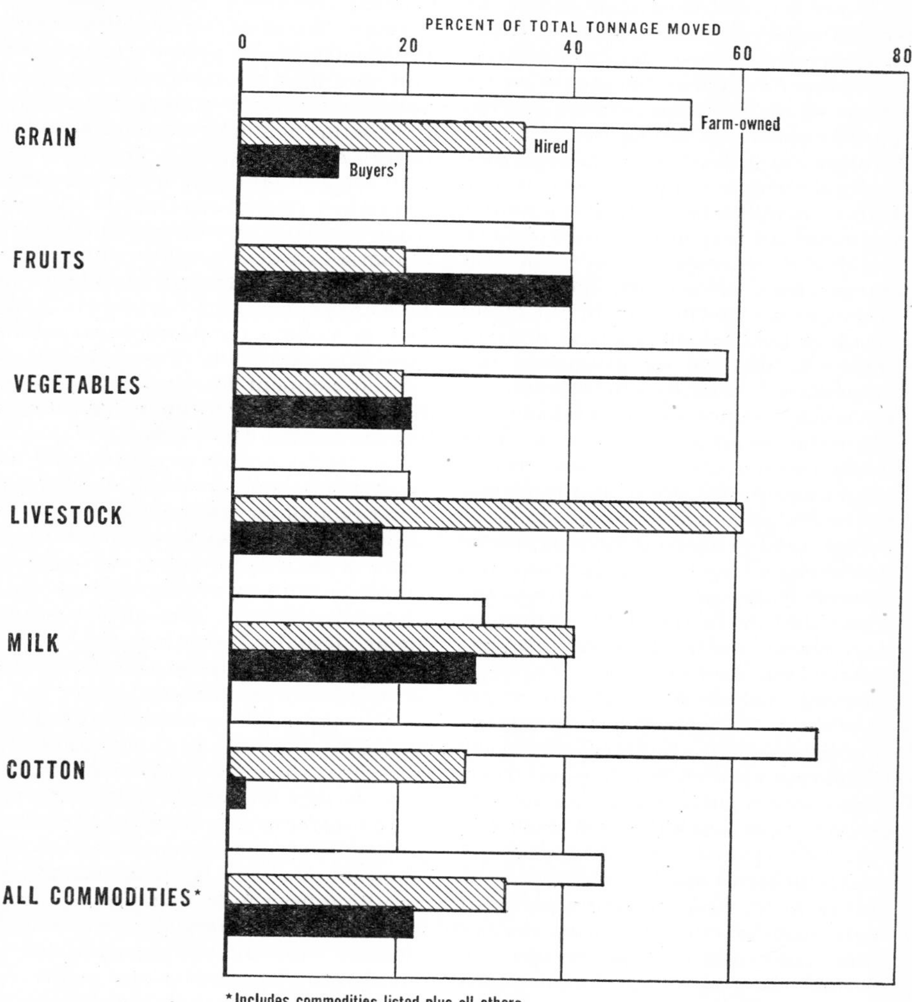

Among truck-owning farms, the average number of trucks owned was 1.2 per farm in 1950. In view of the seasonality of farm marketings, such a wide scattering of small-capacity equipment cannot meet peak transportation needs. Farmers therefore rely greatly on for-hire trucks, which can be marshaled for the specific kind of service needed at the time the commodities are ready for market.

Should not farmers supply a larger share of their transportation needs, either by increasing their ownership of hauling equipment or by buying specialized vehicles? The answer is not simple. A major factor is how much of the year an expensive truck would stand idle. If trucks were to be idle during long off-periods, the possible advantages of ownership might easily be offset by depreciation and obsolescence, as well as by insurance and other costs that are incurred even when the trucks are not used extensively.

Another point involves the desirability of owning special-purpose trucks. Heavy equipment, for example, should not be driven into lettuce fields to move the crop to the packing shed because of probable damage to soil and crop. But drivers' wages and other costs would make the use of the light equipment uneconomic for the longer hauls from the packing shed to market.

Many special types of equipment have been developed for transportation between fruit orchards and packinghouses. They include low-bed trucks with fork-lift attachments for loading boxes or lugs that have been stacked in the orchards by the picking crews. Such trucks are too specialized for general farm hauling. During a period of high utilization, economies derived from them may be a major factor in cutting costs, but most farmers have neither sufficient volume nor long enough seasons to justify owning them individually.

Still another factor that bears on the wisdom of supplying one's own transportation is the increased dependence on custom harvesting and hauling. It is becoming more common, for example, for farmers to contract for the harvesting of potatoes. Besides harvesting, the contracts usually cover hauling to the packing sheds, even though the hauling work is done by separate labor crews. In western areas where carrots, lettuce, and celery are grown, some growers are doing less of their own hauling. Cooperatives or shippers cut, trim, and box the produce in the field and haul it off the farm. The principal advantage of such contracts is gained largely through improved timing of the overall operations.

In some situations it is desirable that the farmer continue to supply his own transportation. A primary advantage of market gardeners near metropolitan areas, for example, is their ability to deliver prime produce to farmers' markets or nearby commission houses or even to households. Fast transportation at frequent intervals is desirable. Special trips at odd times to meet customers' convenience often are worth while, even though a loss may be incurred on the individual transaction. That type of service may sometimes be supplied more efficiently either by contract with a local truck operator or through ordinary commercial trucking channels than by farm-owned equipment. Usually, however, the grower finds it desirable to furnish the service with his own equipment.

A long marketing season with rather uniform quantities of produce leaving the farm during a large part of the year makes an almost ideal situation for a grower to supply his own trucking service. The marketing of poultry and eggs is an example. Here economies resulting from full utilization of equipment are augmented by the benefits derived from the producer's ability to control the movements and to oversee all contacts made with buyers.

Whether a farmer will do his own farm-to-market hauling or will hire it done often depends on the extent to which he needs a truck for other purposes. Fertilizer, tools and equipment, fencing materials, containers, and the

PERCENTAGE OF ALL FARMS REPORTING MOTORTRUCKS, BY SIZE OF FARM, 1950

Size of farm	*The United States*	*North-eastern region*	*North central region*	*Southern region*	*Western region*
	Percent	*Percent*	*Percent*	*Percent*	*Percent*
Less than 10 acres	17	25	16	13	29
10–99 acres	24	38	24	19	48
100 acres and over	49	57	45	45	76
All sizes	34	44	37	27	56

DISTRIBUTION OF FARM MOTORTRUCKS, BY RATED CAPACITY, 1948

Manufacturers' rated capacity	*United States*	*North-eastern region*	*North central region*	*Southern region*	*Western region*
	Percent	*Percent*	*Percent*	*Percent*	*Percent*
½ ton and under	41	36	37	51	33
More than ½ but less than 1½ tons	16	15	17	15	16
1½ tons	35	38	40	29	41
More than 1½ tons	8	11	6	5	10
All capacities	100	100	100	100	100

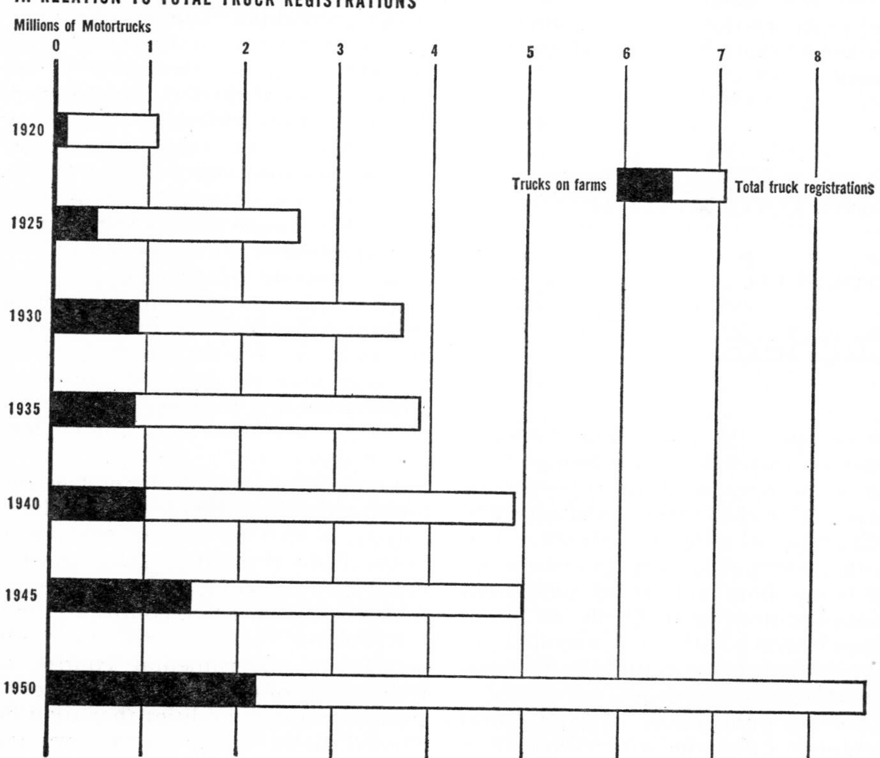

like can be moved about quickly to where they are needed on the farm when a truck is handy. If he has much of this on-farm hauling to do, a farmer is likely to own an all-purpose truck, which can be used to haul farm commodities to market. And many farmers prefer to pick up feed, seed, oil, coal, lumber, and other supplies for their own or their neighbors' use. With his own equipment, a farmer can pick up supplies in town after he has delivered his produce.

It appears likely that the transportation supplied by farmers will continue to be mainly in general-purpose small-capacity equipment and under circumstances in which convenience plays a large part. Often the farm truck is also the family passenger car, or "second car." Some farmers own heavy equipment and find it profitable to engage in long hauls, but it is unlikely that such farm-truck ownership or use will become a major factor in the transportation of farm products to market. (*Donald E. Church, Margaret R. Purcell.*)

The Kinds and Uses of Carriers

Basically the movement of farm products through the marketing channel is accomplished in three major steps—from the farm to local assembly points (nearly entirely by truck); then to the terminal markets in consuming areas by line-haul or over-the-road transportation; and finally to retail stores by truck within the metropolitan area and to other outlets in the surrounding trade territory.

The seasonal nature of agricultural production and the wide distribution required by many farm products call for the services of a number of different types of carriers. The railroads and trucks transport the bulk of the agricultural traffic, but both water carriers and airlines are used at times. They all serve agriculture. They also have a dynamic effect on the agricultural marketing and production.

The railroads are common carriers—they hold themselves out for hire to the general public and are regulated by the Federal Government (when State lines are crossed) and by State governments (when the transportation services are performed entirely within the States).

Sometimes railroad freight cars, such as refrigerator cars, are privately owned by shippers of agricultural commodities. When the cars are turned over to the railroads for hauling, however, the carriers control them in the same manner as they do their own cars.

Many types of motor carriers haul farm commodities. The trucking operation itself may be primarily the same in most cases, but the status of the various types of carriers in the eyes of the law is quite different.

The first broad classification is one between for-hire and private truckers.

The for-hire class of carriers hold themselves out to transport the property of others at some specified rate or charge. Private truckers, on the other hand, engage in the transportation of their own property. In the movement of agricultural commodities, private truckers may be farmers, groups of farmers banded together in some cooperative, and processors, wholesalers, or retailers.

Truckers who hold themselves out for hire are of two types: The regulated carrier, which is subject to control under Federal or State laws, and the unregulated carrier, which is exempt from Federal or State control.

Regulated carriers are generally subject to governmental control of rates, areas of operation, the routes of travel, and commodities that may be carried. In this group are the common carriers, which like the railroads hold themselves out to the public generally, and contract carriers, which provide service to shippers under contract.

Unregulated for-hire carriers are generally subject only to regulations concerned with the commodities that may be carried, safety, and qualifications and maximum-hour restrictions for drivers. They have complete freedom as to rates that may be charged and areas or routes of operations. Under Federal and State laws, trucks transporting exclusively unmanufactured agricultural goods are in this category and therefore have considerable flexibility and freedom in their operations. This exemption from regulation for the trucks engaged in the movement of agricultural traffic has been a tremendous aid in the marketing of farm products and has given rise to a distinct type of carrier known as the exempt trucker. The total movement of agricultural commodities from producing areas to terminal markets by unregulated trucks is considered to be much greater than the movement by regulated carriers.

A comparison by the Interstate Commerce Commission of the number of federally controlled carriers with the unregulated carriers revealed that in 1950 there were 20,042 authorized motor carriers under the Interstate Commerce Act, as compared with an estimated 40,000 unregulated carriers engaged principally in hauling farm commodities and fish. The figure given for regulated carriers includes those hauling all types of commodities, and only a small number of such carriers are exclusively agricultural haulers.

Private carriers include a large and diversified group of operators. There are about 4.5 million privately operated trucks, besides those on farms. Individuals or business concerns operate them to transport a wide variety of products in intercity and local services.

Some intercity movement of farm products is done by processors, wholesalers, and chain retailers, but the bulk of commodities is transported by independent merchant truckers, whose operations are not regulated. They transport sizable volumes of fresh fruits and vegetables from Florida to eastern and midwestern markets. Food processors, produce merchants, and packinghouses employ large numbers of their own trucks both for over-the-road transportation and local distribution.

The transportation of agricultural commodities by water and air carriers is only a small part of the total movement. The bulk of the water movement is of grain on the Great Lakes and inland waterways. The agricultural traffic by air consists mostly of high-valued commodities, such as cut flowers and nursery stock, which require speedy handling. Various types of livestock, poultry, and seeds are sometimes transported by air.

FRUITS AND VEGETABLES usually are transported considerable distances to important terminal markets. For example, of the total volume of important fruits and vegetables (22 varieties) received by rail and boat in the New York terminal market—the largest in the United States—about 40 percent is received from assembly points in California. Another 25 percent is received from Florida. Next are Maine, Arizona, Idaho, Texas, and Oregon.

Almost all the oranges received in the large eastern and midwestern markets come from California and Florida. Cantaloups, grapes, and lettuce are received almost entirely from the Western States.

Grain is transported shorter distances to terminal markets. The large wheat markets of Minneapolis and Duluth, for example, are supplied by the adjacent wheat areas of North Dakota, South Dakota, Montana, and Canada. Chicago, the principal corn market, obtains most of its corn receipts from Iowa, Illinois, Indiana, and Wisconsin. Grains transported to other major markets—Omaha, Kansas City, St. Louis, Milwaukee, Toledo—generally move from nearby areas.

Butter is produced principally in the

Midwest. To get it to the large markets of New York, Philadelphia, and Boston takes a relatively long haul. But the haul to Chicago, the largest butter market in the United States, is much shorter. The same is generally true of cheese, for regardless of the location of the market, a large part originates in Wisconsin.

Shell eggs are produced both in the vicinity of the important eastern terminal markets and at considerable distances from them. At the New York market, for example, New York, New Jersey, and Pennsylvania supply large volumes of eggs, and relatively short hauls are required. Iowa and Minnesota also ship large numbers of eggs to New York and other eastern markets, where relatively longer hauls are necessary. The distances that frozen eggs are transported in reaching terminal markets follow the same general pattern as shell eggs, but large volumes also are transported to the East from as far west as Missouri.

Most live poultry is transported relatively short distances to the important terminal markets. In the Chicago market, for example, almost all of the live-poultry receipts are registered from sources in Illinois, Indiana, Iowa, and Wisconsin. Small amounts of live poultry are obtained from Arkansas and from Tennessee. Other important markets on the east and west coasts show a similar pattern of relatively short hauls for receipts of live poultry. The large terminal market at San Francisco receives all of its live poultry from California.

Dressed poultry does not show as heavy a concentration of producing areas near the terminal markets. The important sources of supply in general are in areas adjacent to the important terminal markets, but a significant share of the shipment comes from more distant assembly points. Receipts are registered at the New York poultry market from practically every State, but the largest volumes are from nearby States, notably Delaware. Massachusetts is the main source of dressed poultry in the Boston market. Iowa supplies the principal volume for the Chicago market.

Milk is transported relatively short distances to terminal markets. New York receives most of its milk from New York State, Pennsylvania, and New Jersey. Philadelphia gets its milk mostly from Pennsylvania and Maryland; Boston, mainly from Vermont and Maine.

The distances that livestock is transported to terminal markets vary with different types. Most of the sheep and lambs, even when destined for eastern markets, originate in the Western States. Hogs are supplied in most markets from producers in nearby farm areas. Cattle and calves usually are shipped to nearest markets, but in the Southwest and West that may mean long distances. Livestock produced in Texas, for example, may be transported considerable distances in reaching Fort Worth, the principal local market, and even much farther to Kansas City, Omaha, or Chicago.

These examples of the distances between producing areas and terminal markets indicate a vital need of agriculture for a varied and flexible transportation system, in order that the many different farm products may reach both near and distant markets.

About 19.2 million tons of fresh vegetables were transported in 1951 from the producing areas to terminal markets in consuming areas. An estimated 8.7 million tons, or 45.3 percent, moved by railroad (including express) and 10.5 million tons, or 54.6 percent, by motortruck. An additional 8.4 million tons were shipped to processing plants, mostly by truck.

Transportation of grain from country assembly points to terminal elevators is one of the railroads' main sources of business. The moving of grain and grain products is about 55 percent of the yearly total agricultural tonnage of the railroads.

The amount of grain transported by truck to terminal markets has been relatively small, compared to the amount moved by the railroads. For example, at the Chicago grain market (of a total of 208 million bushels of all grains received) 7.7 million bushels were brought in by truck in 1951. The railroads carried 132 million bushels, about 65 percent of the total. The rest reached Chicago by water.

But an indication that trucks are competing with the railroads for grain traffic was given in a study, *The Transportation and Handling of Grain by Motor Truck in the Southwest*, by the Department of Agriculture in May 1952. Of the 117 firms surveyed (country elevators, terminal elevators, flour mills, feed mills) 90 reported the use of motortrucks along with railroad facilities for shipping and receiving grain. Of the total amount of grain shipped from the 49 country elevators that reported truck movements, about 35 percent was transported to terminal points by truck. Of the total grain received at the terminal elevators, flour mills, and feed mills, the amounts transported by truck were 32.5 percent, 25 percent, and 34.7 percent respectively. (The percentages relate only to establishments reporting truck and rail movements; consequently the percentage of grain moved by truck for all establishments would be somewhat smaller.)

The volume of grain moved by barge on inland waterways has increased, chiefly in response to favorable transportation rates. The tonnage of grain and mill products carried on the Mississippi River and its tributaries between 1940 and 1950 went from 441,075 to 2,422,000 tons, a gain of about 450 percent.

Trucks are used much more extensively than the railroads in transporting livestock to terminal markets. Of more than 76 million head of livestock that were brought to 65 public markets in 1952, trucks transported about 73 percent. Of the various types, the percentages transported by trucks were: Cattle, 75.7 percent; calves, 80.4; hogs, 81.3; and sheep and lambs, 48.8.

The influence of distances in the selection of carrier is indicated in the high percentage of sheep and lambs received at the public markets by railroads as compared to other kinds of livestock. Because most of the sheep and lambs require a long haul in reaching the terminal markets of the Middle West and East, the railroads receive a major share of that traffic.

THE PERISHABILITY of many agricultural products and the methods of marketing them have led to a high degree of specialization of transportation equipment and services.

Livestock is taken to market by rail in special stock cars and cattle trucks. Tank trucks carry milk in bulk from farms to processing plants. Vegetable oils are transported in special tank cars and trucks.

Many perishable crops move to market in refrigerator rail cars (most of which are owned by the shippers) and refrigerator trucks (which mostly are owned and operated by common- and contract-carrier trucking companies).

The carriers offer various auxiliary services, which are adapted to the marketing requirements of the product.

The three most generally used are transit privileges, reconsignment and diversion privileges, and protective freight services. The first two are provided almost exclusively by the railroads. Protective freight services are available from both the railroads and motor carriers. Without them the market for many farm products would be greatly restricted.

Reconsignment and diversion privileges give the shipper the right to change destination, routing, name of the consignor or consignee, or any other change that requires a change in billing or an additional movement of the car. They allow the shipper to move his products from point of origin to some intermediate point and to final destination at the through rate, which is generally lower than the combination of intermediate rates. Reconsignment and diversion privileges are set forth in the railroad tariffs with a clear statement of all the conditions under which they may be used and the charges that will be made for the particular service. Reconsignment charges are collected in addition to the freight rate.

Reconsignment is practiced widely in the rail shipment of grain, cotton, livestock, fruits, and vegetables. Fruits and vegetables sometimes are shipped from California, Arizona, Texas, and Florida before the shippers know the ultimate destination of the cars or the buyer. The cars are routed to a reconsignment point, from which shippers are able to take advantage of the most favorable market. The produce is sold en route to brokers and wholesalers after the train is on the way. The marketing of farm products is speeded up because shippers are not required to wait for a buyer before shipping their products. Many truck operations likewise are geared to redirect or divert loads en route to points of need.

The transit privilege, a characteristic of railroad transportation, is the right of a shipper to stop off his product at an intermediate or transit point for inspection, conditioning, storage, or processing with the privilege of reshipping it to the final destination under the original through-freight rate that applied from point of origin to final destination.

Transit privileges applicable to many kinds of commodities are published in the railroad tariffs. The milling in transit privilege, perhaps the most widely used, makes it possible to ship grain, particularly wheat, from point of origin to some intermediate point, there to be stored, marketed, or processed and later reshipped to the destination at the through rate. A major part of the grain assembled at many country elevators throughout the grain-producing areas thus can be funneled into a small number of terminal markets for inspection, grading, sale, storage, and processing by mills.

The same type of privilege has been extended to feed grains, such processed products as cottonseed and soybean meal, different grades of sirup and molasses, and other commodities. Sacking, barreling, and boxing in transit and cleaning, grading, and mixing in transit are other privileges important to the producer and shipper of farm products.

For shipments of livestock by railroad, there are tariff provisions for feeding and grazing in transit. Concentration in transit permits such commodities as cotton, eggs, dairy products, and dressed poultry to be concentrated at certain assembly points for subsequent shipment in carload lots without sacrificing the advantage of the through-freight rates. Storage in transit permits many commodities to come to rest at strategic terminal locations for later distribution or to await a favorable market. This privilege is particularly valuable to shippers of nonperishable commodities like grain, beans, sugar, tobacco, and meats.

The livestock industry has also been granted the privilege of stopping shipments at transit points to test the market. Various commodities have been granted a stoppage in transit privilege, under which carload shipments may be partly loaded or unloaded in transit without loss of through-freight rates.

The transit privilege introduces an element of flexibility into the railroad freight service by permitting the carrier to adapt the freight service as a whole to the varying needs of commerce and industry. Such privileges provide many advantages to the shipper of agricultural products, for they tend to equalize competitive conditions, facilitate the marketing of commodities, relieve congestion at terminal markets, and reduce shipping costs.

Many shipments of perishable freight require special protection against heat and cold on the way to market. Some vegetables require precooling services before shipment. Others require heating service. Shipments of potatoes, for example, must be ventilated during warm weather and protected against freezing during cold weather. The transportation of perishable fruits and vegetables and packinghouse products in refrigerator cars is a special freight service in the sense that it requires special equipment and fast or expedited freight-train services and also because the icing service performed in these cars is special in character. A separate charge is collected by the railroads to cover the cost of providing the refrigeration. The charge varies according to the type of refrigerant used or icing service performed.

Special charges may be assessed against shippers of livestock for bedding, car cleaning, and fumigation or disinfection of stock cars. Sometimes the railroads make a service charge for preparing cars to receive special shipments. The various charges are published in a general perishable protective tariff, in which nearly all railroads participate.

The special protective services provided by motor carriers are primarily the provision of refrigerator vans for perishable products. The movement of agricultural products to market by truck generally is faster than by railroad; the products need to be protected for a shorter time.

It has been the practice of railroads to impose a charge or penalty on shippers and consignees if they hold cars for loading, unloading, or for other purposes beyond a specified time. The Uniform National Car Demurrage Rules permit a "free time" of 48 hours for loading or unloading and 24 hours for reconsignment, diversion, and reshipment, or holding a car in transit on the order of the shipper, consignee, or owner, or holding a car for other purposes that are defined in the rules.

The average-agreement provision of the rules is especially important to large shippers or consignees who handle hundreds of cars. It permits a shipper or consignee to enter into an agreement with the carrier under which demurrage charges are computed on the basis of the average detention time during a calendar month instead of on the basis of straight demurrage. A system of debits and credits is used to arrive at a net figure. The demurrage charges thus may be reduced substantially under what they would have been had straight demurrage been assessed.

In many public yards in our larger cities where fresh produce is received, it is customary for the consignee to market the shipments directly from the cars. When cars are so used, the railroads may impose an added penalty, called track storage charges. They are usually equal to the demurrage charge but are in addition to it. Produce dealers often find it cheaper to market their goods from the cars than to pay rent for store space.

Before satisfactory transportation services can be performed, agricultural products must be properly prepared, packed, and loaded into freight cars or trucks. The relatively high rate of damage during the transportation of many products proves how important those operations are.

The average claim payment per carlot for all fruits, melons, and vegetables, as reported by the Association of American Railroads, has been as high as $21.33 (1949); the average claim for certain commodities (cantaloups) has gone as high as $41.45 (1951) a car. The claim payment for all fruits, melons, and vegetables in 1951 was $17.32 a car. The payment for loss and damage claims in 1951 on watermelons was $37.10 a car, oranges $18.10, apples $17.33, and honeydew melons $29.99.

Losses from decay or spoilage in transit are not generally allowable as a valid claim by transportation agencies, nor are the shipping charges for moving the spoiled products usually recoverable.

Proper packing and loading of rail cars or trucks is important in the interest of making delivery of commodities in salable condition and reducing loss and damage claims. It also is important because of the possibility of reducing transportation costs through more efficient utilization of shipping space.

A study by the Department of Agriculture in 1950 (*A Comparative Study of Packing, Transportation, and Refrigeration Costs of Bushel Baskets and Wirebound Boxes for Transportation of Peaches*) indicated that the substitution of a suitable wooden wirebound box for the commonly used bushel basket resulted in less shipping damage and considerable savings because the rectangular shape made more efficient use of refrigerator car space possible. It was pointed out that as long as the refrigeration charges are on a flat rate per car, shippers would make an immediate saving of 25 percent on refrigeration costs by heavier loading, where feasible.

Another study by the Department in 1951 (*Reduction of Cantaloup Loss and Damage in Rail Transportation Through Use of the Upright Loading Method*) showed that placing cantaloup crates on end rather than on side in loading rail cars made possible a load of 312 crates to the car, compared to 288 by the standard lengthwise loading method. Most of the damage sustained by agricultural commodities in transit can be traced to improper packing, loading, and bracing, or to rough handling by the carriers in the transportation process.

SPEED is probably the most important single service factor in determining the type of transportation shippers use. Agricultural goods are unlike most others in that the speed with which they are transported to market has a greater effect on their value. Spoilage and fluctuating prices are two ever-present elements of risk in the marketing of farm products.

With the great advance in good highways and modern equipment, trucks have made big strides in reducing transit time, particularly in over-the-road speeds. Fruits and vegetables grown in the South are commonly trucked 400 miles in one night in order to make early-morning delivery in New York, Philadelphia, and Baltimore. As the haul lengthens, however, the speed advantage of trucks over the railroads diminishes, and for hauls of more than 1,000 miles the railroads carry most of the traffic. As the organization and operating efficiency of motor carriers continues to improve and interstate operating rights are extended, it is possible that trucks will increase their share of the long-haul traffic.

For example, several motor carriers operate schedules that provide for third-morning delivery in Chicago for fruits and vegetables produced in the Central Valley of California.

Speed is also important in marketing some staple agricultural products, especially during the harvest season. Fast delivery of new grain to market substantially reduces the amount of loss and damage, particularly when it has a high moisture content. Moist grain sealed in a boxcar will deteriorate if the transit time is long and the financial loss to the owner may be considerable. The longer the transit time, the greater the opportunity for the grain to lose weight from shrinkage. Although most of the commercially sold grain moves by railroad, more and more shippers have been using trucks to speed up delivery of grain to market.

Motor carriers are sometimes preferred to the railroads because of convenience. When farm products are loaded into commercial trucks at the farm or are purchased by merchant truckers, the farmer is saved the time of hauling his products to market. Trucks are suited to the needs of small markets, because the less-than-carload shipments can be assembled into truck loads at assembly points and dropped off at markets en route as needed. It takes a town of 20,000 population to use a carload of citrus fruit. Small lots cannot be shipped economically for long distances by railroad but they can be handled by trucks.

Transportation cost always is an important consideration. As between types of carriers, the question of cost is more than simply a comparison of rates. Rate differentials, where they exist, are important to shippers, but where the railroads and trucklines actively compete for traffic, rates are generally adjusted accordingly.

One element in total transportation cost is the location of assembly points and terminal markets with reference to rail lines and truck routes. Location may be a controlling factor because trucks generally provide pickup and delivery service without additional charge whereas the railroads do not. For assembly points and markets removed from immediate rail service, the added cost of hauling commodities by truck to and from rail points may alone compel the use of through truck service.

The nature of the commodity and the size of shipments also affect cost. For relatively bulky commodities, which move in large quantities, like wheat, the railroads can offer special low carload rates, which motor carriers generally have not been able to meet. But for many commodities that are shipped in quantities of less than the usual rail carload minimums, the motor carriers are able to offer lower rates because of the smaller capacity of their trucks. A shipment which for the railroads may be less-than-carload can be full truckload for motor carriers, entitling the shipment to a truckload rate as compared to a less-than-carload rate by rail.

The costs of transportation have claimed an increasing share of the total cost of distributing farm products. Estimates prepared by the Department of Agriculture show that intercity transportation for farm products bought by civilian consumers increased from 9 percent to 13 percent of the total marketing bill between 1929 and 1949. For 1953 the percentage of total marketing cost chargeable to transportation was probably even greater because of the substantial increases in freight rates over the previous 4 years. The level of railroad freight rates in 1953 was about 79 percent higher than it was in 1938 and 1943. Rates on farm products, however, have increased somewhat less than have rates for all commodities because of holddowns, especially on the shipments over long distances.

For many shippers rate increases have created serious problems. High transportation rates tend to restrict the market for many farm products, particularly if they must be transported far. Both railroads and motor carriers recognize this condition and frequently make selective rate adjustments to equalize rate increases from competitive producing areas to a common market. Shippers also have sought to meet the problem of increased transportation costs through wider use of contract trucking arrangements and by operating their own trucking equipment.

Farmers and handlers of agricultural products pay about 4 billion dollars a year for the transportation of farm products. Agriculture is entitled to get its money's worth in rapid, reliable, and low-cost transportation.

Both producers and consumers will benefit through a diversified and flexible transportation system where all types of carriers are permitted to operate between producing areas and terminal markets in accordance with the needs of agriculture and the users of its products. (*William J. Hudson, Don C. Leavens.*)

A Century of Progress

A little more than a century ago the only means of moving goods from one place to another were the horse, the boat, and the canal barge. Now we see

281437°—54——8

the diesel locomotive and trailer truck so often that we scarcely stop to think what they mean to our well-being.

In most of our cities the current supply of food on hand is only enough to feed their people for a few days. New supplies must arrive each day. The process of developing the transportation systems that make that possible has been actually the process of building facilities to meet the needs of a growing country and economy.

By 1920 railroad mileage had grown to its peak of 250,000 miles of tracks, which reached all major agricultural areas. The abandonment of unprofitable lines had brought it down to 223,000 miles in 1953. During those 33 years the railroads concentrated on the improvement of their facilities.

A major advance during that time was the development of the diesel-electric locomotive, more powerful and more economical than the coal- and oil-burning steam locomotives; 65 percent of all freight service, 70 percent of all passenger service, and more than 75 percent of all yard service was rendered by the diesel by 1953.

The capacity of freight cars has been increased from an average of 42 tons in 1920 to 53 tons in 1953. Improved trucks and draft gears have provided a smoother ride and cushion the impacts resulting from taking up slack in trains or switching cars in yards.

Reduction of grades and curves, heavier rails and ballast, and elimination of the grade crossings have made trains safer and faster. Terminals have been improved. In a modern train classification yard, devices that utilize electronics, compressed air, and gravity have made it possible for one switch engine and a few men to do the work for which a fleet of engines and many men would have been required in 1920. Radio, loudspeakers, and two-way communication between the main office and key points in the yard speed the movement of cars. The schedule for perishable freight from California to Chicago was reduced in 1952 from 7 days to 6. In 1953 a new expedited service of 62 hours between those points was made available to shippers.

Centralized traffic control, in use on more than 20,000 miles of track in 1954, enables one man, sitting before an illuminated map on which moving trains automatically show their position, to set signals and throw switches over districts of 200 miles or more. Radio communication between station and train and between front end and rear end of trains has become available. Road installation of wayside-to-train communication increased from 17,000 miles of road covered in 1949 to 47,000 in 1953, and installations in yards increased from 84 to 220.

But a good transportation service means more than adequate equipment. It is important to have enough cars, or motortrucks, or river barges, but it is just as important to have them available where and when they are needed. If a grower in California has 10 carloads of lettuce ready for shipment to eastern markets today, he needs 10 cars on track at his packing plant into which to load the lettuce today; tomorrow is not good enough. Barring unusual circumstances, a highly organized system of refrigerator-car distribution maintained by the railroads and the car lines sees to it that he has the cars today.

Speed of movement and dependability of service have become increasingly important, with smaller inventories and faster turnover of food supplies.

Transportation systems must be able to adapt to new or changed transportation requirements—as when new areas are brought into production by reclamation of land; or new products, such as frozen foods, must be handled in a special way; or a shift in population makes necessary the movement of milk for long distances. Above all, the costs of transportation must be kept at a reasonable level.

The development of new methods and facilities for transportation often may open up additional outlets for the farmer's products and give him a greater choice of potential sales opportunities, as illustrated in the marketing of livestock.

Up to about 1920 the movement of livestock in the Midwest was by railroad to such markets as Chicago, St. Louis, Kansas City, Omaha, Minneapolis, and Sioux City. Unless one farmer was feeding enough cattle or hogs to have enough ready for market at one time to make up a carload shipment, other cattle or hogs had to be assembled from a number of farmers by livestock shipping associations or local buyers.

Then came the motortruck. A local trucker, picking up stock from a number of farmers in the afternoon, could deliver them to a market for sale the following morning. The movement of livestock was no longer tied to railroads and their schedules. Local concentration markets and auctions and a tremendous growth of meatpacking at interior points, such as Albert Lea, Minn., and Mason City, Ottumwa, and Waterloo, Iowa, and other points, followed.

A concurrent development was an increase in the sale and direct movement of livestock from the farmer to the packing company—and the bypassing of intermediate handlers and the lessening of the numbers and cost of such services.

Livestock trucks of the early 1920's had simple stake and rack bodies without tops. They could carry only a few animals at one time. Modern semitrailers, up to 35 feet long, have strong steel frames, aluminum roofs, an enclosed nose, sliding doors for proper ventilation, and partitions that protect animals against injury on their way to market.

Special trailers for hauling grain have capacities of 600 bushels and more. Some have hopper bottoms or hydraulic lifts for quick unloading. Trailers not equipped with hopper bottoms usually are unloaded at terminal elevators by hydraulic lifts, which raise the front of the trailer so that the grain runs out into the elevator pit.

Trucks and trailers with van bodies haul many different kinds of farm and food products—flour, feed, rice, sugar. Insulated and refrigerated, they transport dairy and poultry products, meats, fruits and vegetables, and frozen foods. Tank trucks deliver bulk milk to distant cities. Other types of tank trucks haul bulk molasses and liquid sugar from refineries to canneries and beverage plants. Special covered hopper trailers transport granulated sugar, flour, malt, and other bulk commodities that are susceptible to contamination. Deliveries of bulk feed are made directly to farms and ranches.

For the delivery of highly perishable foods, such as milk and ice cream, directly from the processing plant to the consumer, trucks are designed to give full protection to the product and to permit drivers to make door-to-door deliveries with a minimum of time and effort.

Some railroads use motortrucks to deliver less-than-carload merchandise on lines where greater speed of delivery can be obtained at lower cost. Under present laws, a railroad may use motortrucks only as a substitute for rail service which it formerly provided, and only with the permission of the Interstate Commerce Commission. A few railroads have set up a special service for motortrucks between large cities where highway traffic is heavy. One or two loaded truck trailers are put on a flatcar equipped with means to anchor the trailers in place. The trailers are delivered overnight to their destinations several hundred miles away. The next morning the trailers are removed from the cars, and trucking-company tractors hook on and haul them away to make deliveries to its customers. The railroad charges a flat fee for each loaded trailer, with a smaller charge for any trailers returned empty. The trucking company profits by the saving in the wages of drivers and wear and tear on its equipment; sometimes it avoids the payment of taxes for using the highways of intermediate States. The public benefits from the lessening of congestion on the heavily traveled roads.

Some use has been made of freight boxes or vans of one-fourth to one-half the capacity of a railroad boxcar. The vans can be moved readily from the bed of a specially equipped motortruck trailer to a railroad flatcar, or the reverse. In order to make the shift, however, the floor of the flatcar and the bed of the trailer must be at approximately the same level. Such vans have also been used for truck-water service from ports on the Pacific coast to Alaska; the vans are lifted from the truck bed to the deck of the ship by the ship's tackle, which also is used to transfer the vans from the ship to flatbed truck trailers or flatcars on arrival in Alaska.

A coordinated rail-water ferry service has been available between certain Gulf and Atlantic ports. The railroad cars are transferred to shipboard; the rails, laid on the decks, have a capacity of about 100 cars.

Possibilities of coordination of the different types of carriers have been widely discussed. The declaration of national transportation policy in the Interstate Commerce Act refers to ". . . developing, coordinating, and preserving a national transportation system by water, highway, and rail, as well as other means, adequate to meet the needs of the commerce of the United States. . . ." Nevertheless, there has been a great deal of competition but little actual coordination of services among the different carriers.

Railroads, with long trains, low unit costs over long distances, and private rights-of-way, are better fitted to handle some traffic than are trucks or inland water lines. On other traffic the speed and flexibility of the trucklines and their comparatively low costs for hauling relatively short distances give them an advantage. For some movements, particularly of commodities in bulk where the path of the waterways they follow is not too circuitous, the barge or boat lines are the most economical.

Yet the carriers, particularly the trucklines and railroads, compete for the same traffic, even though some of it may not actually produce enough revenue to cover all elements of the costs of hauling it. In such situations it might be that a coordinated rail-truck service would mean a profit for both and better service to the public, as in the case of the truck trailer flatcar service. More of this kind of cooperation would be of benefit to the economy of the country.

Few strictly cargo planes were in operation commercially in 1954. Most of them were rebuilt passenger planes not designed specifically for hauling freight.

Whether air transport becomes a significant factor in the volume movement of agricultural products will depend on whether builders can produce planes with operating costs sufficiently low to be competitive with the surface carriers, service considered, and also whether air terminals with capacity adequate to handle volume tonnage may be developed.

Transportation costs are not limited to the number of cents per 100 pounds, or bushel, or ton the shipper has to pay the carrier to get his product from one place to another. Quite as important are the cost of the containers that protect the commodity in transit and during subsequent handling, the cost of labor for loading and unloading, the shrinkage in weight that might occur in transit, and the losses and damage that result from rough handling of cars in trains or terminal switching and through failure of refrigeration in transit.

The relative inflexibility of freight-rate levels, which have become higher and higher, has led shippers to seek ways to cut the auxiliary costs—toward better methods of loading to reduce transit damage to the commodity;

cheaper containers better adapted to efficient methods of handling into and out of cars and trucks; the use of labor-saving materials-handling equipment; the possibilities of savings through the use of shipping pallets; more efficient and less costly protective services, such as refrigeration; and improvements in cars and motortrucks. The shippers look, too, to the possibilities of eliminating traditional intermediate marketing services that may be avoided and marketing in bulk some commodities that have been moved in containers.

Progress has been made along many of those lines. Research and experimentation with refrigerator cars and motortrucks have brought about many changes in the equipment and in methods of refrigeration. The improvements have saved shippers millions of dollars annually. But more work in those and other fields remains to be done. (*John C. Winter.*)

Iceboxes on Wheels

Refrigeration in transportation has been the lifeline of marketing high-quality perishable foods.

Since 1900 the railroad car companies have constructed an immense fleet of refrigerator cars for hauling foods to terminal markets. Refrigerated trailer trucks came later.

Some of the improvements in refrigerator cars are insulated bulkheads, to keep the product loaded at the bunkers from freezing; basket bunkers, to increase the refrigerating efficiency; the increased thickness of insulation and provision for more complete air circulation. Refrigerator cars for transportation of nonfrozen foods have 4 to 4.5 inches of insulation. Superinsulated cars for frozen foods have 6 to 8 inches. A construction feature that gives better air circulation is the space—3.5 to 7 inches—between the floor racks and the car floor. An inch of space is provided behind wall racks in some cars built to transport frozen foods.

Refrigeration in rail cars is obtained primarily by the use of iced bunkers. Most cars have bunkers at both ends, but some have overhead bunkers instead. Some refrigerator cars are equipped with fans to circulate air through the iced bunkers and around and through the load. The fans are operated by a belt connected to a rubber-covered drive wheel which rests on the wheel of the car and operate only when the car is in motion. The forced air circulation accelerates cooling of the commodity and reduces the usually wide spread of temperature between the top and bottom layers of the load. Approximately 45,000 cars, or 43 percent of all refrigerator cars, were equipped with fans in 1953.

Ordinary water ice is most commonly used for cooling refrigerator cars. For hauling frozen foods, however, refrigerants capable of holding the temperature down to 0° F. are needed. And the cars, being insulated, are also used for keeping products warm that would be damaged from freezing or overcooling. Tropical fruits, for example, may need to be kept as high as 65° F. For such service heaters are installed in the cars in winter. Cars in standard refrigeration service are initially iced to capacity, sometimes re-iced before starting, and re-iced to capacity at all regular icing stations, which generally are located along the railroad right-of-way about 24 hours' running time apart.

Modified refrigeration service consists of variations from the standard service, such as initial icing only, re-icing only at selected points, or icing in the upper half of the bunkers only.

Leafy vegetables and some other high-moisture produce, such as cauliflower and corn, require body icing.

Crushed or snow ice is placed in and between the packages and over the load. Melting of the crushed ice tends to keep the vegetables fresh and moist. When a product is body iced, it usually is not necessary to ice the bunkers except in the summer on transcontinental runs.

Heavily insulated cars are required for shipping frozen foods by rail. Refrigeration is obtained by the use of a mixture of water ice with 30 percent salt added, or by mechanical units installed in the cars. In some instances dry ice (solid carbon dioxide) is used in bunkers alone, or in conjunction with some secondary refrigerant. The number of refrigerator cars suitable for holding 0° temperature cannot accommodate all of the frozen-food traffic.

The key to suitable long hauls of frozen foods by rail seems to be more and mechanically better refrigerator cars. The best temperatures to be obtained from water ice and salt are often too high for ample protection of frozen foods, and the cost of dry ice seems to stand in the way of rapid development of its use. There were 396 mechanical refrigerator cars operating over the railroads in 1953; 301 additional cars of various types were on order.

Experiments in truck refrigeration have progressed along with the development of motortruck transportation. First attempts to refrigerate trucks consisted of the use of water ice and salt in barrels or boxes. The method did not chill all parts of the load uniformly. Then bunkers were installed in trailers and air was circulated over the water ice and throughout the load by means of a fan over the bunker. The fans are belt driven by small gasoline engines on the outside of the trailers. Water ice in bunkers has proved to be satisfactory for truck shipments of fresh fruits and vegetables. Dry ice in bunkers is satisfactory for some fresh products and for frozen foods if fans are used for air circulation. Sometimes dry ice is used with a secondary refrigerant.

Mechanical refrigeration in motortrucks has been developed so that it is a popular and reliable system. Units are available in several types and models. Some can maintain temperatures as low as −20° to −25°; others may be capable of only 0° to −5°. Manufacturers of all systems claim that their installations will maintain constant temperature control within a few degrees of the thermostatic setting. In a test conducted in 1952 by the Department of Agriculture on a newly developed system of mechanical refrigeration with a truckload of frozen turkeys from California to Massachusetts, the refrigeration unit held product temperature to −13° for 11 days. (*James A. Mixon, Harold D. Johnson.*)

Regulations and Policies

For a long time farmers have known the close relationship between effective regulation of transportation and satisfactory rates and services. They have had a decisive role in the development of Government regulation of railroad rates and services, beginning with the Granger movement of the 1870's and extending to Federal control with the passage of the Act to Regulate Commerce in 1887, which created the Interstate Commerce Commission.

Ever since that time, agricultural groups have been keenly interested in the question of transport regulation. They supported many amendments to strengthen Federal control of railroads between 1887 and 1920. They sponsored the Hoch-Smith Resolution in 1925, by which they hoped to get adjustments in rail rates in order to relieve the agricultural distress of the 1920's. During the depression of the 1930's farmers tried to have reduced the high freight rates then in effect as one means of relieving their distress.

Failing to do that and faced with a proposed 15 percent increase in rail rates in 1937, farm groups secured the adoption of section 201 of the Agricultural Adjustment Act of 1938. It authorized the Secretary of Agriculture to present economic data on the agricultural situation to the Interstate Commerce Commission and to file complaints against rates and charges on farm products. The Department of Agriculture has been active in cases covered by that legislation.

All the major forms of domestic carriers—railroads, pipelines, water lines, motor carriers, and air carriers—are regulated. All but the air carriers and the natural gas pipelines are subject to the jurisdiction of the Interstate Commerce Commission, under the provisions of the Interstate Commerce Act, as amended.

The air carriers are regulated by the Civil Aeronautics Board, which was created with the passage of the Civil Aeronautics Act of 1938.

The natural gas pipelines have been regulated by the Federal Power Commission since 1938.

Railroads are more completely regulated and have been regulated longer than the other types of transportation. The scheme of regulation developed for railroads has generally been applied to the other systems, but with many modifications, especially with respect to contract and specialized or bulk carriers.

Haulers of farm products by truck, for example, are exempt from the economic regulatory provision of the Motor Carrier Act of 1935 (part II of the Interstate Commerce Act). Bulk carriers of grain by water are also exempt from the economic regulatory provisions of the Transportation Act of 1940 (part III of the Interstate Commerce Act).

Common carriers are closely regulated. They must have a certificate of public convenience and necessity in order to operate. They must charge reasonable and fair rates. Strict control is exercised over their security issues, accounts, reports, pools and combinations, and discriminations. Their minimum and maximum rates are regulated.

Contract carriers are less completely regulated than common carriers, as they are not subject to the same legal requirements. Contract carriers must secure a permit to operate and file their contracts with the regulatory agency. They must observe minimum rates, keep accounts, and submit reports.

Private or noncommercial carriers are not regulated, except with respect to safety and sizes and weights of vehicles.

Transport regulation, by no means a static matter, has been modified in scope, form, and purpose since the Act to Regulate Commerce was adopted in 1887.

The railroads until 1920 were generally regulated as a monopoly, although attempts were made to enforce competition among the carriers. The many regulatory amendments adopted between 1887 and 1920 increased the duties and powers of the Interstate Commerce Commission with respect to certain practices considered inimical to the public interest. The railroads encountered financial and service difficulties during the First World War and were taken over for Federal operation.

When they were returned to their owners in 1920, the Congress decided to change regulatory policy in several important respects. In the Transportation Act of 1920 the major permanent provisions were designed to create and maintain an economical and efficient system of railroad transportation. The Interstate Commerce Commission was instructed, so to speak, to become a friendly but firm elder brother to the railroads, rather than a stern and perhaps hostile critic and disciplinarian.

But the depression in agriculture

that began in the 1920's, the rise of competition by the motor, water, and finally air carriers, and also the general business depression of the thirties changed the situation in a way that could not have been foreseen in 1920.

Rail revenues declined 50 percent between 1929 and 1933. Rail credit was in a sad state in the 1930's. Rail insolvencies were at a record high level in 1938.

A large diversion of traffic to the competing modes of transportation occurred and changes in the location of industrial and agricultural production probably took place in order to avoid high railroad rates.

Other forms of transportaion had financial difficulties after 1929. Heavy subsidies from the Federal Government probably kept the water and air carriers from going under. Oil pipelines and motor carriers fared somewhat better, but many companies, especially those that ran trucks and buses, failed.

The Congress soon after 1930 consequently adopted a series of laws that had the effect of broadening greatly the scope of the Interstate Commerce Act, enlarging the powers and duties of the Interstate Commerce Commission, and otherwise increasing Federal control of the means of transportation.

The first significant depression measure was the Emergency Transportation Act of 1933. Among other things, it established the Office of Federal Coordinator of Transportation to study ways to improve conditions in all forms of transportation, to effect economies and eliminate waste in railroad operation, and to promote the financial reorganization of railroads. The Federal Coordinator was authorized to issue orders if necessary to accomplish the purpose of the act.

The act did not work out as expected because of the opposition of railroads, organized labor, and communities likely to be affected adversely by a reform of railroad operations. The Federal Coordinator could make proposals but hesitated to issue orders that would be binding on the carriers. His office during its 3-year life became essentially a research organization for the investigation and report of ways and means of improving transportation conditions. The reports were of two types. One type dealt with questions of regulation and legislation, and four reports were issued. Some of the legislative recommendations of the Federal Coordinator were adopted by the Congress, particularly the recommendation that Government regulation should be extended to motor and water carriers. The other type of report was concerned with specific methods of improving the services and operations of the railroads. These suggestions were not received favorably by the industry.

The Congress passed the Motor Carrier Act in 1935 as part II of the Interstate Commerce Act; the former Interstate Commerce Act became part I of the enlarged act. It grew out of a combination of circumstances: Refusal of the United States Supreme Court in the Duke case in 1925 to permit a State to regulate the affairs of interstate motor carriers within the State; and support of Federal legislation by railroads and railroad unions, by the Interstate Commerce Commission, and by the older concerns who wished protection against "fly-by-night" operators.

The chief opposition to the new statute was voiced by farm organizations, who feared that regulation would hamper trucking operations for the benefit of the railroads. Consumer, shipper, and the traveler groups also refused to support the legislation. Some truckers, chiefly contract carriers, were skeptical. But the opposition was not powerful enough to overcome the forces that favored the act.

While, in the main, the interstate motor carriers are regulated on the railroad pattern by the 1935 law, there is a fair number of significant differences. Many motor carriers, including haulers of farm products, are exempt from economic regulation, and small motor operators are not regulated so completely as are the large operators. Motor carriers, unlike railroads, also are not subject to the long-and-short-haul clause (which prohibits higher rates for shorter than for longer hauls of the same class of traffic over the same line in the same direction, the shorter haul being included within the longer), and their intrastate rates cannot be controlled by the Interstate Commerce Commission.

The domestic water carriers were placed under the Commission's jurisdiction with the passage of the Transportation Act of 1940 (part III of the Interstate Commerce Act). As in the case of motor-carrier regulation a few years earlier, this legislation was supported chiefly by groups within the industry, by the railroads, and by the Commission. It was not the result of complaints by shippers using the water carriers. Farm groups voiced opposition to the proposed law, fearing that the regulation might be in the interest of the carriers and not the public.

The Transportation Act of 1940 transferred to the Interstate Commerce Commission the jurisdiction over the water carriers engaged in domestic commerce previously placed in the hands of the Maritime Commission. It also brought additional domestic water carriers under regulation, and greatly enlarged the Interstate Commerce Commission's power over all the water carriers covered by the act. Common carriers are more completely regulated than contract carriers. Certain bulk carriers of commodities such as grain, iron ore, and coal, as well as tankers and the private carriers, are exempt from regulation. Those exemptions are of sufficient importance to cause the Commission to complain that its jurisdiction "is limited to a small proportion of the total transportation by water performed in the United States." It is true that probably not more than 10 percent of the domestic water tonnage is subject to the act.

One other piece of depression regulatory legislation worthy of note here is the Civil Aeronautics Act of 1938. It followed, in the main, the model established in the Interstate Commerce Act, but the Congress created a new body, the Civil Aeronautics Board, to exercise the regulatory powers, rather than placing them with the Interstate Commerce Commission. The act was of no direct interest to farmers, who made little use of air service at that time.

The only important regulatory innovation since 1940 was the establishment of freight-forwarder regulation in 1942, with enactment of part IV of the Interstate Commerce Act. It gave the Interstate Commerce Commission authority over freight forwarders, except by air, much like its authority over rail, motor, and water carriers. Freight forwarders are car-loading and truck-loading companies that act as middlemen between shippers and carriers in the movement of merchandise and other high-rated freight.

IT MIGHT APPEAR that the era of experimentation with national regulatory policy has come to an end and that no further major changes will be required. The country had a long period of sustained prosperity during and after the Second World War. All forms of transportation experienced substantial increases in traffic and revenues after 1940.

Prices and costs rose sharply since 1940, but freight and passenger rates also advanced substantially. The rail freight-rate level in 1953 averaged about 80 percent above the level at the end of the war. Rail freight rates were increased 11 times between July 1946 and May 1952.

Other modes of transportation have also had important increases in their rates and charges, particularly since 1946. It would be natural to assume that carriers, shippers, and travelers should all be prosperous and, therefore, content with the existing system of regulation.

A deeper look into the situation, however, is needed.

Many carriers were in a weak financial condition in 1954, despite the high rates and the generally heavy traffic. Without large Government subsidies, numerous water and air carriers would face disaster. A slackening of general economic activity would affect all the carriers seriously and many could not survive even a moderate recession without help.

And, while farmers and other users of transport service show greatest concern over rates in periods of depression and low commodity prices, they have been disturbed about the rising trend of freight rates since the war, and they wonder whether regulatory policy may not be at least partly responsible for the situation.

Evidence of the widespread dissatisfaction with regulatory policy is found in proposals for reorganizing national transportation activities, including subsidy and promotion as well as regulation, and in the many studies of specific aspects of transportation, such as the rail passenger deficit, subsidies, relative economy and efficiency, taxes, and competition. The studies have been conducted under governmental and private auspices.

Critics of regulatory policy divide over the question of what changes in policy should be made. Some believe that, in view of effective competition among the carriers, public regulation or at least thoroughgoing regulation is unnecessary or harmful.

Other critics think that some regulation should be retained, primarily to control the monopolistic practices of carriers. These groups think that the competitive modes, such as highway and water carriers, should not be regulated. A modification of this view is that regulation should be confined to the prevention or elimination of specific abuses, like extortionate rates and unjust discriminations, and the safeguarding of safety and public investment in transport facilities.

A few authorities suggest that more regulation is needed to improve the situation.

Before deciding whether any of these suggestions has merit, it is necessary to set forth standards by which to evaluate them and the present system of regulation. The statement of national transportation policy incorporated into the Transportation Act of 1940 serves this purpose well. According to this statement, the intent of the Congress is to develop, coordinate, and preserve a national transportation system adequate to meet the commercial, postal, and military needs of the country. The several modes of transportation are to be fairly and impartially regulated, with the inherent advantages of each preserved. None is to be artificially restricted in favor of a competitor. All are to be coordinated in the economic sense that each carrier is serving the traffic it is best fitted to carry. All of the regulatory statutes contain prohibitions against unreasonable rates and discriminatory rates and service, and all reject the monopolistic organization of transportation. Implicit in this ideal of fair and impartial regulation is free user choice, which would presumably act intelligently on the basis of rate and service competition to allocate the available traffic economically among the several modes of transportation and among the individual carriers.

Assessed in these terms, public policy falls somewhat short of assuring "fair and impartial" regulation that will preserve the "inherent advantages" of each mode. The ideal can be realized only if the rates and services offered shippers and travelers reflect appropriate economic costs. But preferential subsidies nullify to a great extent the regulatory policy of recognizing and preserving the inherent advantages of each mode. The "costs" confronting the regulatory bodies are not strictly comparable, and the rates established do not express the true economic realities. Subsidies to transportation agencies have led to misapplication of resources and made the task of regulation a difficult one.

As for the relative merits of the

proposed alternative regulatory policies, mentioned above, it would appear that a more flexible scheme of control would assist in establishing the kind of optimum transport system visualized in the statement of national transportation policy. Large-scale carriers tending to be monopolies should be regulated to prevent excessive earnings and to secure the benefits of scientific and technological progress for the public. The railroads and pipelines continue to be carriers of this type. The truly competitive, small-scale carriers should be regulated only as to abuses that cannot be corrected through free competition. Motor, water, and air carriers tend to be enterprises of this character.

The point to be emphasized is that the amount and kind of regulation should be adjusted and applied according to the economic characteristics and behavior of each mode of transportation.

Regardless of the Federal agency or agencies that perform the promotional function, Government will no doubt continue to provide some kinds of basic transportation facilities.

To date, no feasible alternative has commended itself to the public for the construction and management of an improved system of highways, waterways, and airways. The practical problem is how to coordinate these programs with one another and with regulatory policy, to the end that the public may enjoy the services of a truly modern, efficient, and economical system of transportation. Farmers, no less than the public generally, have a vital interest in the solution of this problem. (*Ralph L. Dewey.*)

COMPARISON OF FEDERAL CONTROL OF MOTOR CARRIERS BY TYPE OF CARRIER

BASED ON THE INTERSTATE COMMERCE ACT, AS AMENDED

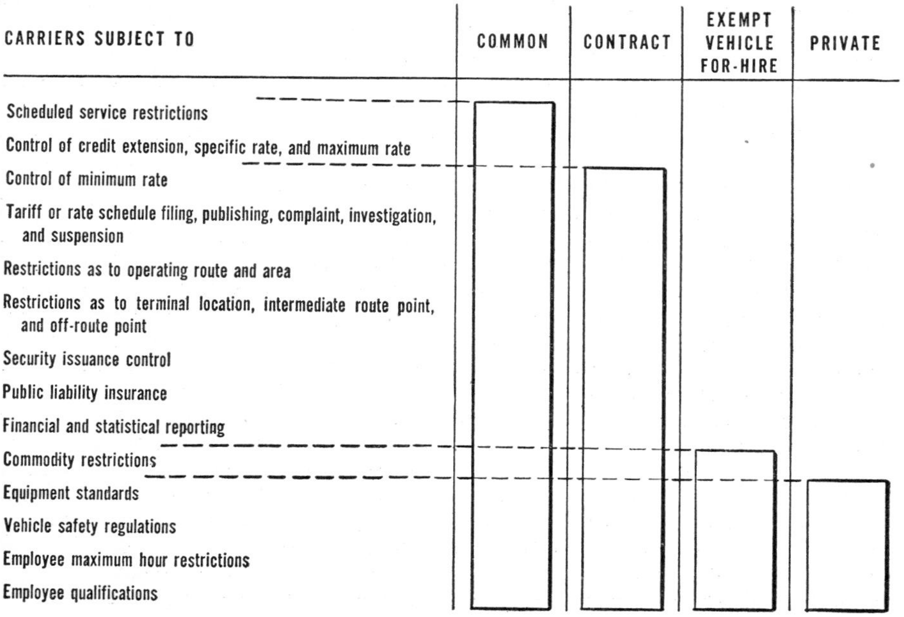

CARRIERS SUBJECT TO | COMMON | CONTRACT | EXEMPT VEHICLE FOR-HIRE | PRIVATE

Scheduled service restrictions

Control of credit extension, specific rate, and maximum rate

Control of minimum rate

Tariff or rate schedule filing, publishing, complaint, investigation, and suspension

Restrictions as to operating route and area

Restrictions as to terminal location, intermediate route point, and off-route point

Security issuance control

Public liability insurance

Financial and statistical reporting

Commodity restrictions

Equipment standards

Vehicle safety regulations

Employee maximum hour restrictions

Employee qualifications

Storage

Farm products are stored to make them available the year around, to balance periods of plenty and periods of scarcity, and sometimes to make them more used. Each class of farm products has its own particular conditions under which it can be stored without much, if any, loss in quality. The requirements range from the one extreme of no structural facility to large cold-storage houses with elaborate equipment. The average farmer does not give enough thought when he stores his products with a public warehouseman. Many times he does not know what will, or will not, happen to his products in storage. Public warehouses are similar to banks in many ways. Products are stored in warehouses; money is placed in banks; in both, the depositor has a legal right to get back in kind and value the thing he deposited. Protection of depositors in public warehouses, however, has not kept pace with the protection given depositors in banks. Here we offer farmers some advice about assuring themselves that their products are safely and properly stored.

Ways and Means of Storage

All products are technically in storage during the interval between harvest and consumption. During that time they may be moved from one place to another; be processed by canning, curing, freezing; or subjected to various treatments such as grading, sorting, and packing, any of which may change their form, shape, and taste so that a different product results.

Our major grain crops average about 6 billion bushels a year, which move into storage at harvesttime to be utilized later. In recent years more than 1.5 billion bushels have been carried over from one year to the next.

Our cotton crop may be as much as 15 million bales, with a yearly carryover of at least 2 million bales, all of which must be stored. A crop of 15 million bales yields about 5 million tons of cottonseed, which also must be stored until it is used.

We usually keep in storage more than a year's supply of tobacco at all times. As the new crop is harvested, stocks in storage may exceed 3 billion pounds, out of which moves cured tobacco for domestic manufacture and export.

We can store only a few of our fruits and vegetables in the fresh state for any length of time, although apples, potatoes, onions, and a few others are stored for several months in the fresh form before being eaten. Many fruits and vegetables are preserved by canning, pickling, freezing, and drying. Some 70 billion pounds of vegetables are consumed annually in the United States. Roughly 80 percent of this volume is consumed fresh, 17 percent canned, and 3 percent frozen. About 30 billion pounds of fruits are included in the diets of our people each year. About 17 billion pounds are consumed fresh, 7.5 billion canned, 3 billion frozen, and 2.5 billion pounds consumed in the dried form.

We tend to consume meats at the rate the live animals are marketed from farms. Reported storage stocks of fresh and cured meats at times reach a total of about 750 million pounds, but probably a larger volume is involved in the normal movement in marketing channels from slaughter through retail stores.

We may have on hand as much as 125 million pounds of butter, 250 million pounds of cheese, and also large amounts of canned and dried milk products in any year. Cold-storage holdings of shell eggs sometimes reach a peak of more than 5 million cases in July. Additional quantities of eggs are stored after drying or freezing.

EACH CLASS of farm product has its own particular conditions under which it can be stored without much, if any, loss in quality.

Some products, like tobacco and cheese, go through a storage period—curing—to improve quality. Some crops, such as hay, can be stored in stacks in the field without great loss in quality. Cotton can be stored without serious damage with little protection.

But products like whole milk, meats, green vegetables, and fresh fruits require exacting temperatures, humidities, and ventilation. Even then they may spoil so rapidly that they must be canned, frozen, or otherwise processed if their edible qualities are preserved.

Because of these variations, storage requirements range from the one extreme of no structural facility to large cold-storage houses with elaborate equipment.

IT IS ESTIMATED that at least 10,000 cotton storage houses in the country have a capacity of 20 million bales. Since cotton bales can be stored almost any place, the volume of suitable cotton storage space can be considered quite variable.

Grains are more exacting. The moisture content of grain must be suitable for storage and must be kept at that level while the grain is in storage. Most of our facilities for storing grain are on farms in the form of corncribs, bins of wood and metal, and other containers into which bulk grains are stored after harvest. Farm structures and facilities were used to store about 6 billion bushels of harvested grain in 1953. Off-farm storage space in more than 20,000 grain elevators at country and terminal points is estimated to be sufficient to store about 2 billion bushels of bulk grain.

Much of the storage space in grain elevators is used primarily to assist in the market movement of grains, with one lot of grain remaining in such space for only a short period. Therefore, although enough off-farm grain storage space is in existence in the country to store about all the grain which so far has needed to be stored off the farm, much of such space is apparently needed in the market movement of grain and is not available for longtime storage.

THE TOTAL AMOUNT of refrigerated storage space reported in public, private, and semiprivate warehouses in 1953 was 711 million cubic feet. It was used mainly to store fruits and vegetables, meat products, poultry products, and fish. An enormous amount of storage space for canned and packaged foods and other dry groceries and provisions is maintained by manufacturers and processors, by wholesalers and retailers, and in pantries and kitchens in households.

Most types of tobacco are stored 1 to 3 years. Space in tobacco warehouses is estimated to be enough to store more than 3 billion pounds of tobacco. Numerous tobacco houses on farms and auction warehouses, where the product is sold, provide additional storage space.

The amount of space in barns and other storage structures on 5 million farms, in the structures at processing plants, in wholesale warehouses and stores, in 375,000 retail foodstores, and in some 50 million dwelling units probably exceeds the known space enumerated in the foregoing.

Surplus or reserve stocks generally should be stored close to the area of production. Transportation costs for getting them into storage are thereby kept down and storage facilities and operations are usually less expensive.

As the storage period progresses, therefore, if prices fall (instead of going up enough to cover the additional costs of storage) chances are much better of holding down economic losses. Also, if the product is somewhat perishable and is stored for an indefinite period and sorting, grading, and packaging are performed before marketing, or the product is changed in form and stored for an indefinite period before movement into distribution channels, storage facilities close to production areas will aid in preventing undue waste of labor and capital.

Considerable amounts of wheat and cotton can be stored some distance from the point of production along the principal channels of domestic and export movement. Railroads encourage the practice by granting transit privileges, which permit storage at points along the major routes under through rates. For example, one large grain elevator at Enid, Okla., draws its supplies mainly from the Winter Wheat Belt. Grain is moved from farms to country elevators at harvest so that sufficient quantities can be assembled to permit carlot shipments by rail. A number of country elevators in turn feed large subterminal elevators, where the product is stored until its final destination becomes known.

Substantial quantities of wheat are also stored in large terminal elevators in ports like Galveston, New Orleans, and Baltimore in order to expedite export operations. Only sufficient volumes to permit shipload quantities reasonably sure to move through the particular terminal are stored there at any one time.

Substantial volumes of wheat also are stored at points of processing in large cities near or in the general areas of production or along the major flow route. Minneapolis, Kansas City, and Buffalo are examples. The purpose is to assure necessary supplies—working stocks—for stable blends and efficient operations.

Corn, primarily a feed crop, generally is stored on the farm in the area where it is used. Exports and domestic nonfeed uses seldom take more than 10 percent of an average corn crop.

Facilities necessary to protect the stored corn in most places are relatively inexpensive.

Storage of apples in cold-storage plants at or near the orchard has become important because of the time, labor, and facilities required for proper sorting and packing. Refrigeration near the orchard relieves packers and shippers from having to pack and ship the fruit immediately after picking. The orchardist can protect his fruit while it awaits packing and he can employ a crew of skilled sorters and packers for longer periods instead of having to mobilize large crews of inexperienced workers for a short time. Some varieties of apples can be stored 5 to 7 months. Orchardists who grow varieties that ripen at different periods can utilize storage houses efficiently for a large part of the year. However, quantities of apples are stored in public cold storages in large cities and in wholesale produce warehouses for the purpose of providing pipeline stocks in the distribution system and evening out fluctuations in supply and demand.

Late-crop potatoes are stored in relatively inexpensive "common" or air-cooled warehouses or underground pits and cellars. In Maine, New York, Idaho, and the Red River Valley, where most late potatoes are grown commercially, outside temperatures during harvesting and storing alike are such that permit natural storage. Therefore, because of the climate in the area, the relatively long distances to markets, and low value per pound, it is more economical to store most late-crop potatoes on farms or in potato storage houses in the area of production until they are marketed.

The more complex the marketing system for a particular commodity and the greater the distance between the production and consumption areas, the

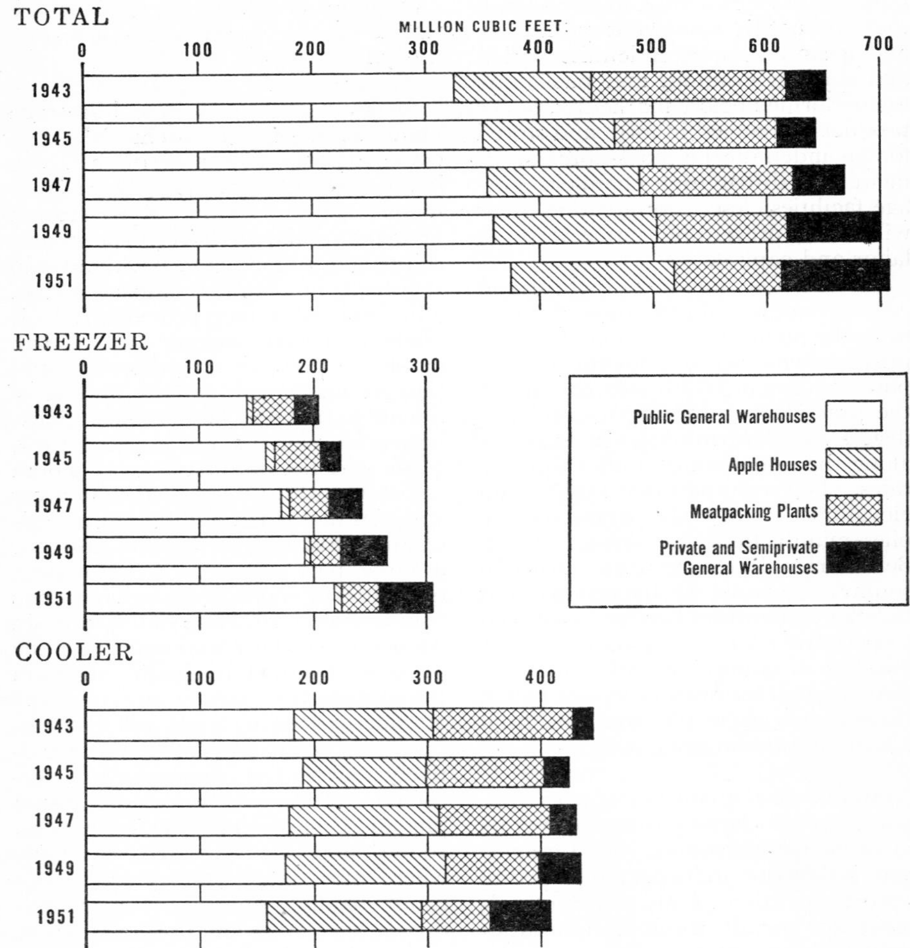

greater is the need for quantities of the product to be stored at various points in the marketing channels. For example, large amounts of butter are stored in cities close to the area of production and in large consuming cities great distances from where the butter is produced.

Many products that require expensive storage facilities are stored for relatively short periods. Those facilities may be utilized more efficiently if they are located so as to permit other surplus products to be stored in the same space at other periods of the year.

Butter, frozen cream, shell eggs, and

similar commodities therefore are stored in public cold storages in cities near the producing areas, in transit at points along major flow routes from producing areas to consumption areas, and in large consuming centers.

Many products must be properly matured before they are put into storage. The length of storage life of most perishable commodities depends not only on how nearly proper temperature and humidity conditions are maintained in storage, but also on how promptly heat is removed from them immediately after harvest. With many perishable products, precooling—the prompt application of refrigeration prior to normal storage or transportation—is the key to successful storage.

Fresh fruits and vegetables, living organisms, continuously generate heat and evolve carbon dioxide during storage. As each commodity has its own peculiar requirements, best storage temperatures and humidities are determined by experimentation and study.

A summary of effects on fruits, vegetables, and some other perishable products of storage conditions is given in Circular 278, *Storage of Fruits, Vegetables, and Cut Flowers*, of the Department of Agriculture. Similar information is given for other food products in *Safe Storage of Food*, published by the Department of Agriculture in 1945.

Some products require controlled atmospheric conditions. For example, apples as they ripen in storage give off ethylene gas, which stimulates the ripening of other apples in the room, and other gases, which (if allowed to accumulate around the fruit) cause apple scald. By purifying the air with activated coconut-shell carbon (charcoal) one can remove naturally evolved ethylene and scald gases and keep the fruit firmer and better.

Protection also must be provided against fire, theft, wind, vermin, and other types of possible losses. Proper sanitation must be maintained. (*Russell L. Childress, Thew D. Johnson.*)

281437°—54——9

Safe and Unsafe Storage

To the farmer who stores his products on his farm, safe storage generally means getting them out of the weather. He knows that rain, wind, and sunshine lower their quality, but he may not reckon with the dangers of loss from fire. He may think little of the harm excess moisture and heat may do to grains, beans, and nuts or the tremendous losses rodents and insects can cause.

Nor does the average farmer give enough thought when he stores his products with public warehousemen. Again his first idea is to place them under shelter. Many times he lets some itinerant trucker take his grain to a elevator without knowing what kind of protection the elevator affords or what equipment it may have. He may know little about the financial responsibility of the elevatorman or whether qualified persons will properly inspect, grade, and weigh the grain. He often does not know whether the grain will be sold or shipped somewhere else for storage.

Frequently he is not offered a warehouse receipt. Even when he does ask for one he sometimes does not get it until months after he has deposited the grain with the warehouseman. Some farmers do not think about a receipt unless they want to borrow on the product. Some refuse a receipt, fearing they might lose it. Some do not read the terms of their receipts.

Failure to get the receipt may mean that the farmer has not stored his product but has actually sold it to the warehouseman at the market price on the day of deposit. Such a transaction may come about through the tariff of the warehouseman. Sometimes the first item in the warehouseman's tariff reads: "Unless arrangements are made for storage before grain is received, grain will be purchased by us at market price on the date received." The tariff is posted at the warehouse. It is supposed to give notice to all depositors of the conditions on which their grain is received. Perhaps several months afterward, when the grower comes for his grain, he is told (particularly if the price has gone up) that the grain was bought by the warehouseman on the date the farmer deposited it with the warehouseman. Settlement is made as of that date. If the market went down in the meantime, settlement may be made on the basis of market on the day the farmer called for his grain. If no question is raised, the farmer may be charged storage from the date the grain entered the warehouse until the date he calls for delivery, even though the grain was sold the same day or a few days after it was deposited.

Or the tariff might specify that grain is deposited on the basis that the warehouseman may dispose of it when he wishes and that settlement will be made according to the price in that market when the depositor demands the grain. That results in several situations, none good. It permits the warehouseman to use the grain of depositors as his working capital. If the market should fall between the time the warehouseman sells the grain and the time the depositor calls for it, the warehouseman has been in position to make a profit out of the depositor's grain though he had not invested a cent in it. If the warehouseman failed since the date of deposit, the farmer would not be able to get the grain; instead, he would have to participate with all creditors in a distribution of any assets the warehouseman might have.

Storage under such conditions cannot be termed safe storage. It has too many unknowns.

Safe storage to a miller has a different meaning. He wants a reasonable quantity of the product stored at or near his mill where it will be kept in good condition and available for use any day. If he is a prudent businessman, he will keep it fully insured, at least against losses by fire. He will examine his product frequently to see that it is not deteriorating. He will take measures to guard against infestation.

To the merchandiser of commodities who buys from the farmer or from other merchants and accumulates his purchases at concentration points, safe storage usually means a facility that he owns or controls and is equipped to keep spoilage and loss at a minimum. Some merchandisers place their products with warehousemen who serve the public for a fee and who are held responsible for the safekeeping of the products entrusted to them by the public.

The banker who makes loans on stored products generally has the best idea of what is safe storage. The product is his security. He investigates the warehouseman's financial responsibility, the storage place and its equipment, the kinds of insurance carried, and the protection given by law. In short, the banker wants to know what he may expect to get if the loan is not repaid.

In marketing, safe storage should mean a system of storage facilities available to the public in which producers or any others may store their products with assurance that when the products are desired the lawful owner can obtain the same product he placed in storage or one of like quantity and grade.

Safe public storage should exist in producing, concentration, and distributing points.

Not always have farm products been stored safely in public warehousing.

Maybe a roof leaked and water dripped on the products. Maybe pilferage took place.

Maybe careless warehousemen did

not check the products to make sure that they were in good condition. Maybe if losses occurred, they denied liability, leaving two courses to the depositor—make the best settlement he could or resort to the courts.

Such conditions used to exist so often that special laws had to be passed in some of the grain-producing States. Troubles continued, nevertheless. There was no effective control over receipts, and warehousemen were charged with manipulating prices of grain in the Chicago market. They were charged with spreading false reports as to the condition of grain in storage, thereby destroying confidence in warehouse receipts and forcing down the market price.

Control of nine-tenths of the elevator space in Chicago by a few railroads and warehousemen led to excessive charges and discrimination among patrons. Those conditions and falling prices of wheat led Illinois to amend its constitution in 1870 in an attempt to control warehousing.

Other states passed special laws on warehousing. Some were repealed. Some of the laws are weak, and seem to guard warehousemen's interests more than the depositors'. A lack of uniformity in the laws removes negotiability of receipts beyond the boundaries of the State in which the warehouse is located. Most laws do not provide sufficient protection. One State requires a bond of only 1,500 dollars. Some States permit nominal personal bonds, the value of which is not determined carefully.

In a number of States no investigation is made of the financial responsibility of the warehouseman. His facilities are not examined and no investigation is made to determine his competency. No provision is made for adequate supervisory service. In a State that has more than 700 warehouses under license, there are but 4 inspectors, yet each house is supposed to be inspected every 60 days.

The uniform warehouse receipts act has been passed in all the States. It relates almost entirely to the form of warehouse receipt that a warehouseman should issue and rights and obligations under warehouse receipts. It has no provision for inspection or supervision. It requires no financial responsibility. It provides for no bond to protect depositors. The care that a warehouseman must take of products entrusted to him is only that of "a reasonably careful owner." The receipt does not show whether the commodity is insured.

The Congress passed the United States Warehouse Act in 1916. It applies only to staple and unprocessed agricultural commodities, not to semimanufactured and manufactured goods derived from agricultural products.

It authorizes the Secretary of Agriculture to set up standards for the inspecting and grading of farm commodities and to issue licenses to warehousemen. But it is not mandatory; warehousemen decide for themselves whether to apply for licenses and place their operations under the supervision of the Department. The Secretary is not required to license any warehouseman unless he finds that the warehouseman can comply with the regulations. He is authorized to examine the operations of the warehouseman after licensing as often as he deems necessary; if it is found that a warehouseman is not complying with the law and regulations, he can suspend or revoke the license.

Amendments in 1931 gave the Secretary exclusive jurisdiction over all licensees with respect to all matters regulated under the United States Warehouse Act and strengthened the penalty section of the law.

As a result, bankers have come to recognize and accept Federal warehouse receipts as prime warehouse collateral.

In the segments in which the law applies, particularly cotton and grain, the largest warehouse operators in the country are licensed under the law.

Since 1940 the value of commodities stored and handled through federally licensed warehouses has ranged from 2 billion to 4 billion dollars a year. As far as known, holders of federally licensed receipts who have presented legitimate claims to the Department have suffered no loss since adoption of the law. The amount the bonding companies have paid has been small.

The Congress in 1933 wrote into the Agricultural Adjustment Act this clause: "No person engaged in the storage in any public warehouse of any basic agricultural commodity in the current of interstate or foreign commerce shall deliver any such commodity upon which a warehouse receipt has been issued and is outstanding without prior surrender and cancellation of such warehouse receipt. Any person violating any of the provisions of this subsection shall, upon conviction, be punished by a fine of not more than $5,000 or by imprisonment of not more than two years, or both."

Many country grain warehousemen complained after a few years that because of their limited capacity they would have to forward their grain to terminal facilities. Because the receipts they had issued were negotiable, however, they could not get back the receipts. To ship such grain placed them in violation of this law. The law was amended in 1940 to permit operators of country public grain warehouses who lacked sufficient space to accommodate all depositors to move stored grain under such regulations as the Secretary of Agriculture might prescribe. No regulations have been issued. This section of the act has not been further amended or repealed.

Public warehouses are similar to commercial banks in many ways. Products are stored in warehouses; money is placed in banks; in both, the depositor has a legal right to get back in kind and value the thing he deposited. If a product is stored and its identity preserved, the depositor is entitled to get back the identical product he stored.

Protection of depositors in public warehouses, however, has not kept pace with the protection given depositors in banks—maybe because bankers deal with a much larger segment of the public than do warehousemen and bank deposits in the aggregate are much greater than the money value of agricultural products stored in public warehouses. Nevertheless, losses caused by warehouse shortages are just as painful to the victims as any other losses, and products worth several billions of dollars are frequently on deposit in public warehouses.

Except for warehouses licensed under the United States Warehouse Act, public warehouses generally receive little Government supervision. Individual depositors must rely almost entirely upon the integrity of the warehouseman. It is practically impossible for a depositor to examine a warehouse and assure himself that the products he stored are on hand and in good condition. That is especially true where products of different depositors are commingled, as they are in most grain, rice, and bean warehouses. Under those conditions, a depositor would have the same difficulty in examining a warehouse as he would have examining a bank because the deposits of all depositors are commingled. The entire operation of a warehouse or bank must be analyzed. Examination of a portion with a view to determining that the interest of a single depositor is protected proves nothing.

Although the Federal Government supervises all warehousemen who voluntarily apply for and obtain a license under the Warehouse Act, the number of such warehousemen constitutes a relatively small percentage of the total number of warehousemen.

Since the law is not mandatory, only warehousemen who are willing to submit to the jurisdiction of the Secretary apply for licenses. That would suggest that those who apply are the ones who would be least likely to go wrong. A warehouseman whose license is suspended or revoked by the Secretary very likely can get a license from a State authority and in some States may be required to obtain such license.

Such a case came up in 1952. The warehouseman's license was suspended for conversion of grain and issuance of false receipts. Within less than a week, he had a State license. The case was prosecuted by the Department of Justice. The warehouseman did plead guilty to conversion and was fined, but all the time the case was pending, he continued to operate under the State license.

Pending better legal safeguards, and better enforcement of laws, this advice is given:

Farmers should demand receipts that give protection, that show the kind of product they deposit and its class, grade, and weight or quantity, and that state definitely what will be delivered.

Farmers should always demand that they be given a warehouse receipt immediately upon deposit of the products with the warehouseman. Under no circumstances should a farmer permit a warehouseman to ship his products to some other warehouse or to another warehouseman without the farmer's permission and without adequate protection. Such permission should be in the form of a written contract, which definitely states the basis on which permission was granted, how the product is to be handled, and what the costs will be. Anything short of this may result in misunderstanding and disappointment to the producer. He should insist, when the product arrives at the other warehouse, that the receiving warehouseman should promptly issue a receipt in the farmer's own name for the products received and mail it to the farmer. The insistence by farmers that the warehouseman hold their products in store in his own warehouse may bring more adequate warehouse facilities in the production areas.

Farmers should not permit a warehouseman to treat the grain as sold to him when they deliver it unless they intend to sell it then and there. A public warehouseman's first duty is to store for the public and not to buy for himself.

If the farmers sell their products to the warehouseman, they should insist upon prompt settlement and not be put off to some indefinite future date and at an unknown price. Farmers should insist on having a copy of the warehouse tariff.

Farmers, furthermore, should answer to their own satisfaction these questions: Why am I placing my products in storage? What do I expect to get back? What assurance have I that I will get back my product in good condition? Is the warehouseman financially responsible? Does he have adequate storage and handling facilities and competent assistants to care for products while in store? Will the warehouseman properly and honestly inspect, grade, and weigh my products? Will I get a warehouse receipt, and, if so, what will be its terms? Will it show the correct weight and grade of my products? Will the warehouse receipt constitute a definite enforcible contract? If the warehouseman does not want to give me a receipt, should I entrust him with my products? How much will it cost me to store? Have I studied the warehouseman's tariff? Is the warehouseman bonded, by whom, for the benefit of whom, in what amount, and with whom is the bond filed? Is the warehouseman subject to supervision and the warehouse and contents subject to inspection by a competent Government agency? Of what does this supervision consist?

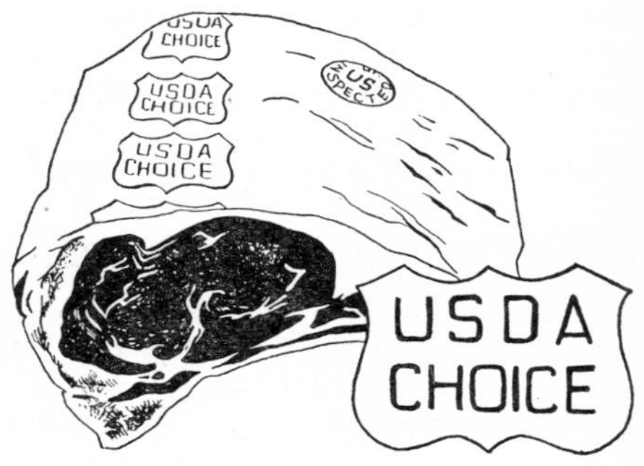

Processing

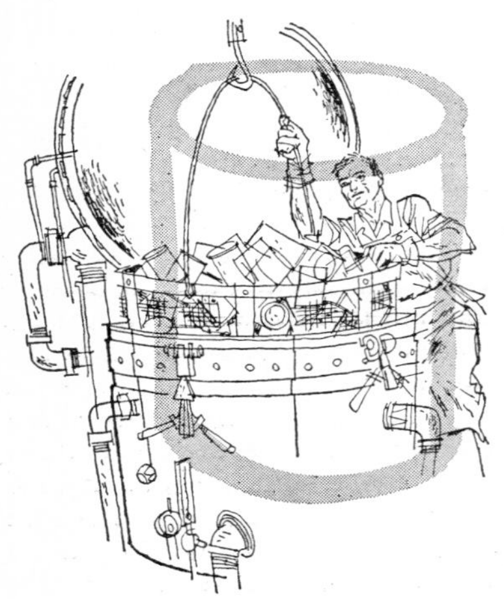

Almost everything that a generation ago was made in the home or on the farm now can be bought ready made. Many new and improved products, such as frozen foods, also can be bought. The great increase in food manufacturing has required farmers to make many adjustments in production. To many farmers it has provided outlets for products that they could not otherwise grow profitably. It has also added to marketing costs, for the additional services performed have to be paid for. A way to reduce the cost of processing is to increase the efficiency of processing methods. Automatic instruments, improved machinery and equipment, methods of handling goods in bulk lots, continuous operations are some of the improvements already made. Better packages and packaging also have helped. The modern package makes possible self-service retailing, facilitates the use of trade-marked brands, and increases sanitation, buying convenience, and efficiency in handling—developments that most of us, farmers and consumers, cannot now get along without.

What Our Grandparents Did Not Have

Almost everything that a generation ago was made in the home or on the farm now can be bought ready made.

Our grandparents used for baking about four-fifths of the flour milled in this country. They churned almost all the butter Americans ate. They killed and prepared much of the meat eaten. They made their own soups, sausage, salad dressings, clothing, and countless other items. Such tasks, which a generation ago were a part of farm and home life, have been taken over by commercial factories, 85,000 of them.

The 1947 census listed 40,000 food plants, 31,000 apparel plants, 8,000 textile plants, 5,000 leather plants, and 1,000 tobacco plants.

But beyond merely shouldering former activities of home and farm, the specialized factory produces new and improved products.

Frozen foods are an outstanding example. The production of frozen fruit, vegetables, poultry, meats, seafoods, fruit juices, and specialties increased twelvefold between 1938 and 1953. In 1953 the entire output of frozen foods was about 5 billion pounds, 3.4 billion pounds of it produced by 1,400 commercial packers and more than 1.5 billion pounds in 11,000 frozen-food locker plants.

The older canning industry produced more than 20 billion pounds in 1953, nearly double the production in 1938.

New forms of dried food are becoming established more slowly. Dried fruits have been marketed for years. Dried eggs and dried milk products are finding expanding uses in prepared ice cream mixes and flour mixes.

Forms of dried milk are also going into homes in increasing amounts, particularly in the high-priced fresh milk sections of the South, in new, small packages.

Rather spectacular expansion has occurred in producing the table-ready meats, processed cheeses, canned citrus juices, frozen concentrate juices, prepared cake mixes, baby foods, and precooked frozen and canned specialties. Factory production of canned fruit and vegetable juices has more than trebled since 1938. Canned and ready-to-serve meat products have been rapidly expanding. Half of the orange crop and nearly one-fourth of the commercial meat production in the United States in 1952 were processed in the form of ready-to-serve canned, and cooked, cured, dried, or frozen products.

The factory prepares an almost complete menu of food for children. More than 50 pounds for every child under 3 years of age was produced in 1952, compared with 2 pounds in 1935 and practically none in 1930.

OTHER FORMS of food that have become widely used as a result of factory specialization are all-purpose vegetable shortening and the special bakers' shortenings, margarine, potato chips, soft drinks, malt drinks, new flavorings, seasonings, and candies. Newer products on store shelves include exotic salad dressings, canned shelled nuts, cheesed popcorn, fried onion rings, and fried bacon rind.

Old-line products have also been increasingly improved in sanitation, uniformity, nutritional value, shelf life, quality, and appearance.

Examples include the more sanitary handling and pasteurizing of milk and other dairy products; mechanical grading and standardization of fruits, vegetables, and other food products as to size, weight, and color; improved sterilization of canned food; addition of antioxidants to lard to reduce rancidity; use of ultraviolet radiation to slow down bacterial growth in fresh and cured meats, bread, and other products; retention of nutrients, mainly vitamins, in processed rice and other foods; and adding vitamins and other nutrients to fluid milk, canned evaporated milk, margarine, flour, bread, fruit juices, and numerous other foods.

The development of "artery and stitch" pumping of hams and bacon and controlled temperatures and humidity in smoking greatly reduces time in curing and smoking pork and produces higher quality, milder cured, tenderized, and ready-to-eat cured meats.

The consequences of modern food processing to every household have become so commonplace that their revolutionary nature may be forgot.

The farmer as a businessman is affected in several ways by developments in commercial processing. An outstanding example of the effect of improved factory processing upon producers is shown by what has happened to the citrus industry. Since 1930 the production of citrus fruits has more than doubled. Yet, by reason of improved canning and freezing methods, demand has been so stimulated that this greatly increased production has been marketed at substantially higher prices than growers would have received for equal volumes of the fresh fruit.

Another illustration of what factory technology can do to the profitability of farm enterprises is indicated by the substantial displacement of butter by margarine in one decade and of lard by vegetable shortenings in a somewhat longer period. Some farm enterprises are hurt. Others become more profitable.

Producers of strawberries who formerly had to sell their berries sometimes at relatively low prices because they had to be marketed quickly now can have them frozen or sell them to freezers who freeze them and sell them in distant markets, as well as hold them for sale during seasons of the year when berries are not available. Farmers producing early out-of-season fruit and vegetable crops in such regions as Florida and California are confronted with competition from processed frozen foods produced and stored in midwestern or eastern areas closer to heavy consuming centers.

The milksheds that once were isolated are becoming increasingly vulnerable to supplies shipped in from distant sources because of improvements in processing, packaging, and transporting fresh and dried milk. Consider, as a possible future change, the potential impact of in-shipment of fresh, dried, or frozen milk from distant sources to the Los Angeles area. Milk is now produced there under high-cost conditions; cows, hay, and feed must be brought in.

Increasingly the farmer must adjust volume, variety, and quality of commodities produced to the requirements of modern processing.

Newly developed nonfarm products compete with farm products in industrial uses. Synthetic fibers, leather substitutes, synthetic detergents, and rubber-base paints compete with wool, cotton, leather, fats, oils, and such. The impact on prices of hides, tallow, and grease has been particularly severe. The effects also permeate the entire market for livestock, oilseeds, dairy products, cotton, and wool.

A more general consequence of the increase in food manufacturing to the farmers is its effect on the price spreads between the farmer and consumer. For example, when the farmer sold his butter, he got paid for the churning. When he sells the cream or whole milk, someone else collects the churning cost. All manufacturing services must be paid for if they are to continue. From two-thirds to three-fourths of the food and nearly all the farm fiber and tobacco now move through commercial factories.

Broadly speaking, both the farm and factory are food processors in the sense that they are engaged in conversionary operations: The farm plant is the open field and the feed lot working in close harmony with nature to provide the basic foods and fiber, whereas the commercial factory refines, separates, and converts the products to more useful forms.

Since 1915 the services of the factory have come into relatively greater demand. As a result of their great expansion, the processors' share of the retail dollar has steadily increased. Before the First World War, the factory took a little more than 10 cents of each dollar spent for food. In recent years it has taken about 20 cents—primarily a result of services rendered. The increased share does not invariably reduce the profitability of farming, nor does it invariably increase the profitability of food processing. But it does increase the inflexible cost factors in providing food. Consequently farm prices are more vulnerable to changing supply and demand conditions, which greatly affect farm profits.

According to the 1951 survey of manufacturers, more than one-fourth of the people employed in commercial manufacturing work on products originating on the farm. Most of them carry on activities once done on the farm itself or in the home kitchen. Two-thirds of those employed in the agricultural industries are engaged in textile, apparel, and leather production, in which hand labor is relatively more important.

As for foods, by far the greatest concentration of manufacturing activity centers on grain products—in milling, baking, brewing, distilling, alimentary paste products, breakfast cereals, and so forth. Less than half as much is given over to each of the next two largest categories—the manufacture of sweet goods (sugar, chocolate, candy, soft drinks, and flavorings) and the manufacture of meat products (fresh meat, ready-prepared meats, and poultry). Those groups together accounted for roughly 70 percent of the value added by food-manufacturing plants in 1951. Of the remaining 30 percent, about a third was concentrated in processing fruits and vegetables (canning, freezing, drying, and fermenting) and about as much in dairy manufactures and oilseed milling.

No one factory that processes farm products can be called a typical one. The factories differ in size, equipment, layout, use of labor, location, and ownership. But the processing of farm products does differ significantly from other processing with respect to its economic environment.

Because farm products tend to be bulky, perishable, and relatively costly to move, the problems of where to locate plants and how to organize processing turn appreciably on reducing the total freight cost in bringing raw materials in and shipping products out and in maintaining quality. The solutions must take into account the tendencies for supplies to be unstable in volume and quality, for shifts to occur in regions of farm production, for transportation rates to change, and for consumers to migrate. The result is that frequently there are no permanent solutions to organizing for most economical processing operations.

Individual food lines do have more or less characteristic ways of organizing to meet the relatively stable features of their economic environment. For example, the corn-refining industry typically operates with plants several hundred times larger than the natural-cheese plants. Efficient processes in corn refining require large-scale equipment for steaming, grinding, floating, extracting, transforming, and drying to obtain starch, sirup, sugar, oil, and feed from the corn kernel. The typical natural-cheese factory can get along with little more than vats. The principal limitation on how far a natural-cheese factory can make economies with larger volume, however, depends on added unit costs of reaching out for more milk. Indeed, the size of cheese plants has increased several fold largely because of improvements in transportation. Yet the transportation of milk and corn are essentially different, and it is doubtful whether the making of natural cheese will ever be carried on in huge plants.

Factories making shortening, margarine, refined cane sugar, chocolate and cocoa, soap, and textiles usually are large, because unit transportation costs increase slowly relative to the increased economies of the large-scale processing. But factories making butter, ice cream, cottonseed products, canned vegetables, dressed poultry, bread, soft drinks, and ginned cotton tend to be fairly small because their transportation costs increase more rapidly—because of bulk and perishability—than processing economies emerge as larger volumes are put through the plant.

Economic environment determines plant location. Plants locate close to sources of raw materials if weight loss during processing is appreciable as in the case of condensed milk, cheese, butter, beet and cane sugar, cottonseed, and similar products; if raw materials are quite perishable, such as in processing raw fruit and vegetables; or if the customers for its products are more widely dispersed than suppliers of its raw materials, as in soybean milling and corn refining.

On the other hand, plants manufacturing relatively bulky or perishable finished products—such as bread, cake, ice cream, soft drinks, and beer—usually locate close to their consumption outlets.

Between these extremes in location, the pattern is blurred. Sometimes the most strategic location furnishes good transshipment facilities—for example flour milling at Buffalo, where inbound grain moves by water transport and outbound flour moves by rail and truck. In other cases the quality and cost of labor is an important determinant as in textile mills. And in others the only rationale seems to be tradition and a lack of compelling reasons for moving elsewhere.

DRASTIC CHANGES in the numbers and size of plants have occurred since 1940. This is to be considered against a background of a great market growth—the physical volume of manufactured foods, textiles, apparel, and leather each increased more than 50 percent.

In foods, 1 out of every 10 plants dropped out of the business, and the surviving plants shouldered the added volumes. On an average, operations of food factories increased some 60 percent, reflecting the triumph of larger operations. Some plants have simply been too small to compete successfully. The greatest reductions in food plants occurred in the manufacture of bread, cake, butter, flour, natural cheese, ice

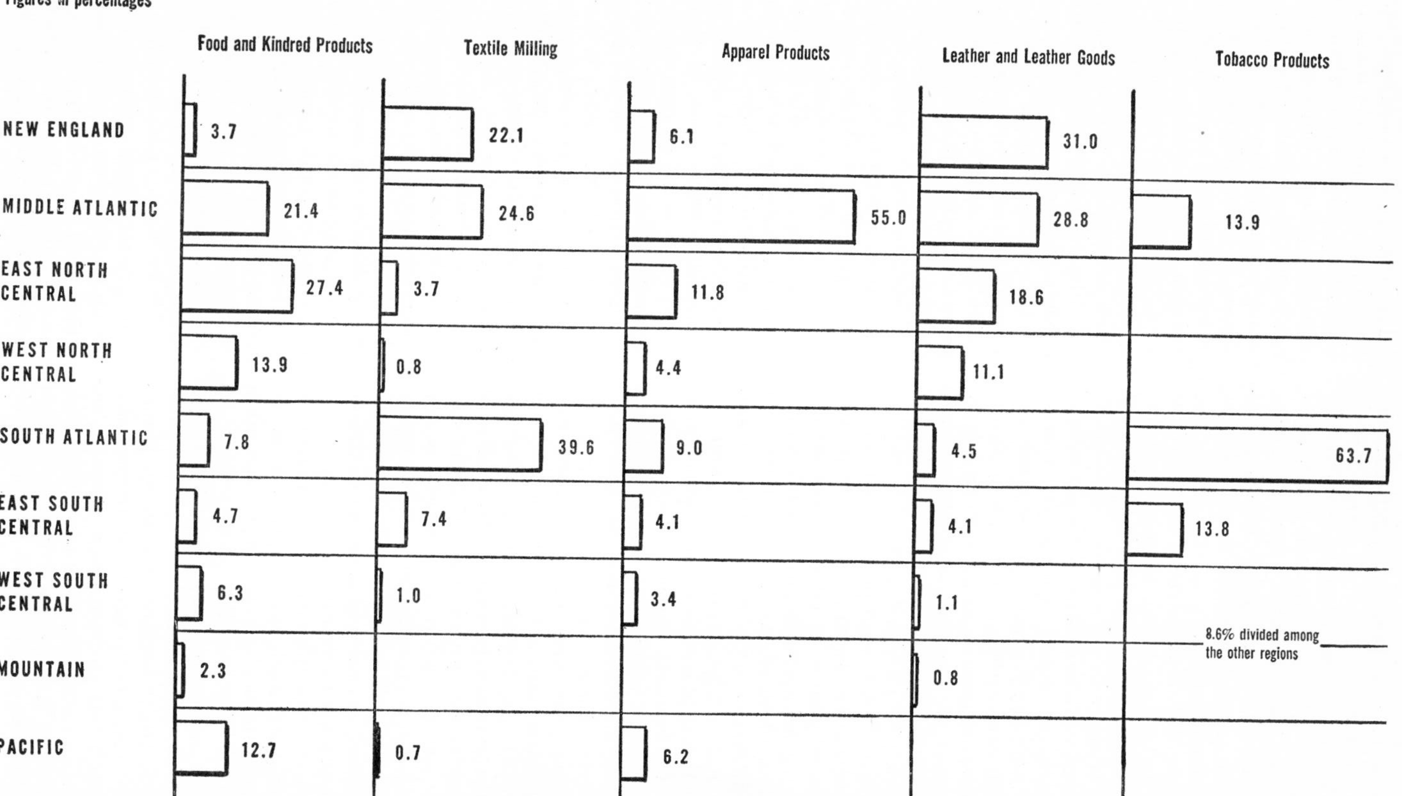
ESTIMATED DISTRIBUTION OF PROCESSING ACTIVITY, 1951, VALUE ADDED BASIS
Figures in percentages
Food and Kindred Products
Textile Milling
Apparel Products
Leather and Leather Goods
Tobacco Products
NEW ENGLAND
3.7
22.1
6.1
31.0
MIDDLE ATLANTIC
21.4
24.6
55.0
28.8
13.9
EAST NORTH CENTRAL
27.4
3.7
11.8
18.6
WEST NORTH CENTRAL
13.9
0.8
4.4
11.1
SOUTH ATLANTIC
7.8
39.6
9.0
4.5
63.7
EAST SOUTH CENTRAL
4.7
7.4
4.1
4.1
13.8
WEST SOUTH CENTRAL
6.3
1.0
3.4
1.1
8.6% divided among the other regions
MOUNTAIN
2.3
0.8
PACIFIC
12.7
0.7
6.2

cream, dressed poultry, spaghetti, and macaroni.

Yet an increase of plants occurred in some lines of food manufacture, such as processed cheese, meat, candy, canned fruits and vegetables, pickled fruits and vegetables, frozen foods, and flavorings.

Why did not existing plants take on the added volume, as the markets expanded, in view of the potential advantages of large-scale operations?

Some of the answers are apparent. The entry of new firms in the manufacture of processed cheese is traceable to an expiration of basic patent rights. Meatpacking plants multiplied partly because of the opportunities created by the wartime control program for meat.

But a greatly improved system for transporting livestock and meat also allowed plants to locate closer to the centers of livestock production.

The large expansion in numbers of soybean mills is due partly to the favoring of medium and small mills in wartime; partly to change to solvent extraction, which requires an entirely new plant; and partly to the advantages of locating close to new production areas.

The processing of fresh fruits and vegetables shows the compelling advantage of locating plants close to farm production rather than hauling commodities greater distances to existing plants. In the very nature of the business, it is generally prudent for the large canner or freezer to add plants at other locations instead of expanding operations at existing locations.

As facts stand, the larger plants do dominate agricultural processing. If, for example, two-thirds of the food plants—the smaller ones—were to cease operating, the total output would decline only about one-fifth in most lines. In consequence, there would probably be less variety in the remaining output and we might have to do without our favorite brand of bread, wine, or ham. In any case we might not be very happy with the results.

The essential advantages of large-scale operations include fuller use and better combinations of existing equipment; continuous processes instead of batch processes; bulk handling equipment; electronic instruments for automatically controlling temperatures, pressure, humidity, and rate of flow; in-plant laboratories for quality control; and utilizing the byproducts and wastes to better advantage.

But firms with small plants still compete alongside the firms with the large plants. Their staying power is due in part to transportation advantages, as well as to closer management supervision. The little feed mill, packing plant, and brewery cannot be easily displaced as long as they deal with the neighboring communities and tailor their plant investment and operations accordingly. An increase in the freight rates (75 to 80 percent since 1946) probably has worked in favor of many smaller plants that sell their products close to home.

Because the small plant has less specialized equipment, it can switch more easily to more profitable lines of business when the market conditions change. Having fewer persons to discharge or reemploy, it may shut down and start up more readily in response to an adverse market movement than a large plant with hundreds of employees.

Further, some small firms make specialty products and thus are not in direct competition with larger firms. The large-volume firm cannot exploit every market opportunity; most often it must limit itself to the popular sizes and forms of the product—the ones that lend themselves best to continuous large-scale operations.

The existence of genuine economic bases for small operations has enabled small business enterprises to get started in processing. These include individuals, partnerships, corporations, and farmers' cooperatives. Some ultimately grow into large enterprises as they successfully exploit opportunities.

Farmers have made substantial progress through their cooperatives in the processing of a number of commodities. For example two-fifths of the butter, one-sixth of the natural cheese, and one-half of the nonfat dry milk solids are produced by some 1,800 dairy cooperatives. About one-eighth of the canned fruits, one-seventh of the frozen fruits, and about one-third of the dried fruits are produced by 130 fruit and vegetable cooperatives. Cooperative wineries in California process about one-third of the bottled wine. Six rice cooperatives mill nearly one-third of the rice. Cooperatives are also fairly important in cane sugar milling, soybean and cottonseed milling, honey production, and many other activities.

Changing conditions continue to pose problems for individual processing firms. Their solution requires a careful analysis of specific factors in each situation.

Solvent-extraction methods for cottonseed and soybean milling increase the rate of oil recovery and the gross returns. But a solvent system requires making a new investment and a fairly large volume of output must be maintained. Should a small or medium-size mill therefore convert to the solvent methods?

For years meatpacking has been migrating into the interior. Chicago plants do less and less of the slaughtering. Presumably they may retain the market of the immediate metropolitan and a limited surrounding area, but they are losing their grip on more distant markets that they used to serve. What changes should a Chicago packer with excess capacity make to meet such emerging situations? Another trend under way in the meat industry is that of putting up meat in frozen and packaged forms. How should the packer adjust his plant and branch-house operations to this impending change?

Should a poultry dresser eviscerate and cut up poultry, or should the retail stores continue to do it? Should a textile mill install new equipment that operates more efficiently but requires a careful selection of cotton, or should it continue with less efficient, more versatile equipment? It helps to know economic processes in settling on a course of action. The final decision is a private one, and the market will inform the firm in its own convincing way whether the decision was correct.

From the public standpoint it is important to recognize that even when a firm does know the direction of the most profitable adjustment it often is hindered by defects and artificial barriers in marketing arrangements.

Thus, the textile miller may balk at installing more efficient machinery simply because he has no confidence he will be able to locate the exact quality of wool required, even though such wool does exist.

Locally imposed barriers may arbitrarily prevent milk from going to plants which could make most economical use of it.

Narrow group interests may unreasonably prevent new technological changes in factories and retail stores.

Government price-support programs may seriously interfere with the efficiency of processing operations in some commodities.

A better knowledge of and a constructive program for strengthening the weak points and minimizing the drawback of current market arrangements would be a major contribution to efficiency and progress in commercial processing.

These are all continuing problems of a changing economy. One of the most significant of these changes has been the rapid growth of the processing industries. There are strong foundations for their continued expansion. One has only to project the major forces underlying the growth of the past 25 years to the next quarter century to visualize the large potential generated by continuing population growth, rising incomes, changing ways of living, and advances in food and fiber technology. (*Allen B. Paul, Lorenzo B. Mann.*)

Better Ways of Handling Food

Despite a great increase in mechanization, an estimated 30 percent of the labor cost in food processing in 1954 went into the handling of materials.

Since 1940 or so a trend has grown toward bulk handling, particularly in receiving incoming raw materials and moving them through the different processing operations. The delivery of liquid and raw sugar, chocolate liquor, and fluid milk in tank trucks, for example, cuts handling costs and improves sanitation in factories. Some perishables, such as eggs, peaches, and apricots, probably never can be handled in bulk.

Semibulk systems of handling flour have been tried by several baking concerns. They use tote containers, which are bins (usually of aluminum) that hold about 3,500 pounds of flour. The flour is placed in the bin at the mill, sealed, and shipped to the bakery. There the bin is connected with a conveying and measuring mechanism so that the flour can be removed automatically from the bins and in controlled quantity. The empty tote bins are returned to the flour mill for reuse. Sometimes flour is delivered directly from the mill to bakery by pneumatic conveyors. It has been estimated that for each 100 tons moved in a given time, the conveyors save the work of 13 men.

Water conveying (sometimes called hydroconveying) is used as a means of moving green peas, lima beans, cut corn, string beans, and citrus fruits along a horizontal path and even from a lower point to a higher one. To do that a pump that will not mash the commodity has been developed. The method saves time, but under some conditions may cause deterioration, notably the leaching of nutrients.

In the bulk handling of such commodities as wheat, corn, oats, peanuts, and soybeans, unloaders have been devised that give trailers and large trucks the laborsaving advantage associated with dump trucks. A loaded truck or tractor trailer is driven onto a ground-level unloading platform. After the brakes are set, the front end of the platform is raised. The tailgate of the truck is then opened, and the load flows into a bin or conveying system.

The same principle is used in the handling of citrus fruit and grapes for juicing. The economies of transporting grapes in bulk and unloading them at the processing plant seem to offset the disadvantages of greater crushing, molding, and souring. Man-hour requirements for unloading have been reduced about 90 percent.

Automatic instruments were unknown in the earliest days of food processing. Instruments such as thermometers were used merely as indicators, and the operator manipulated valves to get the desired temperature. If he forgot to open the proper valve, the product spoiled.

Among the accurate and efficient control devices now in use are proportioning pumps, indicators of acidity (pH), flow meters, level indicators, and all sorts of instruments to record and control temperature, humidities, and pressures. They have lowered labor costs, reduced human errors, and made for more uniform quality in a product.

Other developments involve centralized control panels and electronic applications. An observation station at a central control panel indicates existing operating conditions in the plant at the moment and provides a continuous record for future reference.

Leaders among purely technological developments that have raised the level of productivity in food processing are those that have made possible the shift from batch operations to continuous operation. Continuous methods have tended to reduce costs through replacement of hand labor or the less efficient machines and to improve the quality of the product by reducing the time during which it is exposed to contamination or the deteriorating effects of air and heat.

The retort, or pressure cooker, was invented in 1874. Patents for continuous cookers were granted in 1902; they were in general use in 1935. In the old batch method, which used the horizontal or vertical retort, cans of food were loaded into iron crates. The crates were placed in the retort, which was closed by hand. Care had to be taken that the retort was properly vented during the preheating so that all air was eliminated. After processing, the retort was unloaded. In continuous cookers, the canned product is continually conveyed in and out of the retort and the operation goes forward without interruption.

Fruit juices used to be pasteurized by batch methods in kettles or by heating in the final container. Such methods impaired quality. In flash pasteurization, which came into use for fruit juices about 1935, the juice is heated to a high temperature for a few seconds, cooled slightly, and then filled into containers, which are cooled immediately.

An improvement on that method is short-time, high-temperature pasteurization, which is followed by rapid cooling and filling under aseptic conditions into sterile containers. In some instances this method produces finished products of better flavor and color than the equivalent lower temperature, hot-filling method. There is also economy in fuel and cooling water.

Sugar is extracted from sugar beets by a diffusion process invented more than a century ago. The sliced beets, called cossettes, are loaded by hand into diffusers, each of which holds about 4 tons. Through the diffusers, which are arranged in batteries of 8 to 12, warm water circulates in such a way that the freshest water enters the diffuser that contains cossettes from which most of the sugar has been extracted. If 12 diffusers are used, 1 is being filled, 1 is being emptied, and 10 are in circulation.

Processes have come into use which end the laborious loading and unloading. In one continuous process, cossettes are fed onto a special carrier, which transports them through a series of narrow tanks against the reverse flow of warm water. Besides saving labor, the continuous process is said to extract the sugar more completely from the cossettes, the diffusion juice is more concentrated, and the spent pulp is better drained and ready for processing for cattle feed. More than 25 percent of American beet sugar factories had continuous diffusers in 1954.

Continuous solvent extraction of oil from soybeans, cottonseed, and other oil-bearing materials has made for greater yields of oil. The increase has more than offset the additional installation and operating costs required, if enough oilseeds are available to justify large-scale operations for all or most of the year.

Besides the higher extraction efficiency than by expeller or hydraulic pressing, solvent extraction can be operated, when desired, to produce a meal in which denaturization of the protein has been held to a minimum. Such a meal is better suited for industrial uses. For feed purposes, however, the meal is improved by moderate heating.

Odorless and tasteless oils are in demand for margarine, shortenings, and salad oils. Older methods of deodorizing were batch operations, the oil being heated in a tank under a vacuum. It was found that savings of steam, as well as of time, were possible by bringing the oil and steam into contact in countercurrent streams, as part of a continuous deodorizing process. In such a process, introduced into the United States in the late 1930's, less steam is required to remove the volatile substances from the oil. Some saving of heat is effected by using the hot oil leaving the deodorizer to heat the raw incoming oil. A semicontinuous deodorizing process was introduced in 1948. It combines flexibility of the batch deodorizer and the economies of continuous countercurrent operations.

Macaroni products used to be made by the batch process, and driers were loaded and unloaded by hand. Continuous macaroni presses, in use in the United States by 1940, made obsolete the mixer, kneader, and older style press. Operations previously performed by individual machines are handled by a single unit comprising a continuous feeding system for semolina and water, a continuous mixer, and continuous kneading and extruding devices. Continuous driers are replacing the small drying chambers that have been standard since 1912 for the drying of macaroni.

The use of continuous ice cream freezers since 1930 has brought some economies, especially in large-scale manufacture. It brought also an increase of the proportion of ice cream marketed in prepackaged containers. Continuous freezing makes possible a more precise control of overrun than is possible by batch freezing.

Continuous buttermaking is being carried out on a limited scale in the United States, but is rather widespread in Europe. Because the texture of this butter is somewhat different from that of regular butter, it may not appeal to those accustomed to regular butter.

The common method of preparing pickles requires more than 9 months, because it involves a long brining step to obtain "salt stock." Around the middle of the 1930's, a method was developed for preparing "fresh-pack pickles," which eliminated the long and tricky brining step. The product thus obtained is not exactly the same as the brined product, but the taste is much the same and it has been well accepted by the consumer. The new method does not require large amounts of storage space for the same output level, and is well adapted to an assembly-type, straight-line operation.

New machines have made possible cheaper production of more and better food products. The outstanding example is canned, single-strength and frozen concentrated citrus juices, which were made possible by automatic juice extractors. Practically all orange and grapefruit juice was extracted by hand in the early 1930's. One man could extract 10 gallons of orange juice or 25 gallons of grapefruit juice an hour; on that basis about 2,500 workers would be needed to extract enough juice to keep one modern citrus processing plant running for 1 day. One automatic extractor produces as much orange juice in 1 minute as one man could extract by hand in 1 hour.

Improvement in designs of vacuum evaporators has made possible concentrated fruit juices of high quality. Pans and circulating evaporators employing steam at relatively high pressures were used about 1930. Several new types of evaporators, developed about 1940, permitted heating the juice in thin films. They used the heat of compression of ammonia or heat from recompression of the vapors evolved during concentration, both of which could be controlled better.

The commercial utilization of molecular distillation took place about 1935. The material is distilled from a very thin heated layer to a nearby condenser, the operation being conducted under a very high vacuum (of the order of about one-millionth of an atmosphere), so that the molecules being distilled can make the jump between the distilling surface and the condenser without bumping into one another. The design of molecular stills capable of fulfilling those conditions and having large evaporating and condensing surfaces within a compact apparatus presented considerable difficulties. The difficulties were overcome by ingenious engineering design, and molecular stills are used for handling materials unstable to heat, such as vitamin A concentrates and vitamin E (used as antioxidants), and for preparing monoglycerides (useful as emulsifiers) from vegetable oils.

Significant advances have been made in the design and manufacture of machinery and equipment for the baking industry. Vibrating sifters take up less floor space than older sifters. Tunnel and tray ovens are equipped with automatic loading devices to assure a complete and uniform load. Newly designed slicers will cut 50 to 60 loaves of bread a minute with a minimum of crumbs. Other improved machines are automatic pan washers, more efficient rack washers, the electronic control devices, and more sanitary conveyors.

Attempts to recover the volatile flavoring constituents of fruit have been numerous since 1930. In 1944 it was found possible to strip and concentrate the aroma of apple juice at atmospheric pressure without damage to flavor. Continuing improvements in devices for rapidly stripping the aroma from the juice have made the process applicable to the juices of grapes, cherry, and other fruits. The restoration of these natural flavor concentrates to concentrated fruit juices has made possible the production of quality fruit concentrates, hitherto impossible. Volatile fruit concentrates are also used to flavor confections, frozen desserts, beverages, and other food products, replacing to some extent synthetic flavors. Volatile flavor applied to condensates obtained from making preserves under vacuum has yielded essences which, like the aroma concentrates obtained from fresh juices, can be used to contribute natural fruit aroma to other food products.

New machines have speeded up the slaughtering and dressing of poultry. An electric knife stuns and relaxes the bird, makes killing and packing easier, and reduces bruising caused by thrashing. Specialized machines, such as a gizzard cleaner, increase the speed of cleaning and eviscerating. Mechanical pickers with longer and more flexible fingers have been developed. Mechanical washers (actually pickers) finish picking under a water spray. Used at the end of the eviscerating line, they can reduce bacterial contamination by 85 percent.

Developments in the food-packing equipment have brought increased speed and greater flexibility for handling packages of different sizes at variable operating speeds. Automatic or semiautomatic machines have been designed to wrap and package a wide variety of food products from pretzels to turkeys.

Some machines combine weighing and filling operations in one unit. Machines have been designed that can close 300 to 400 cans a minute, more than twice as fast as the best machines in 1925.

Sanitation measures affect both the quality of the end product and the cost of producing it. With increasing responsibility and public interest, processors now give more thought to sanitation—to the products themselves, the purity of the water used, the personal hygiene of workers, and proper waste disposal.

Improved sanitation in food processing has been brought about by better materials for building, better plant and machine design, and new techniques.

In-plant chlorination is now recognized as a distinct advance in sanitation procedure for canning plants, although it cannot be used to replace good housekeeping. In-plant chlorination reduces bacterial population, reduces time spent in cleaning up, and makes it possible to carry on continuous processing operations for longer periods.

Cleaning in processing plants was accomplished before 1930 chiefly by using soap powders, mild alkalies, and scouring powders, materials that leave a film on the surface that in time forms a dirt-holding coating. Synthetic detergents are particularly suitable for degreasing dirty surfaces.

281437°—54——10

Modern food plants are constructed for better sanitation. In many of them have been used glass brick for better lighting; special window glass that lowers transmission of infrared rays, thus reducing heat; fluorescent lighting to reduce shadows; rubber-base and fungicidal paints; air conditioning; synthetic resins and plastics; stainless-steel tanks to replace wooden tubs; tanks mounted for easier cleaning; and glass and stainless steel piping in place of copper, which often was a source of deteriorative changes in food conducted through such pipes. Centralized operation means better sanitation, less exposure to outside contamination, and less wall space to keep clean.

Waste disposal and byproduct utilization have grown in importance since 1930 because of increased food processing. Solid wastes from the fruit and vegetable processing industries alone probably amount to some 7 million tons annually. The tremendous amounts of liquid effluents from processing plants must also be disposed of without creating health nuisances.

Since about 1930 considerable progress has been made in the disposition of both solid and liquid wastes. More efficient trickling filters and chemical treatment have reduced nuisances from liquid effluents. Some have been concentrated for the recovery of usable products; for instance, corn steep water used for culture media in antibiotic production, Steffens waste for monosodium glutamate, and preparation of citrus and pear molasses from effluent of citrus feed and canning plants, respectively.

Solid wastes have been dried for feed. Of particular significance in this field is the use of citrus and apple wastes for cattle feed and pectin manufacture; tomato waste for food for dogs and fur-bearing animals; pea vines and pods for feed admixtures; leafy vegetable wastes for the preparation of chlorophylls and carotenes and for feed; waste brewers' yeast for food and feed; pear waste for edible sirups and feed; beef blood for industrial and pharmaceutical uses; and animal glands for medicinals. (*G. E. Hilbert.*)

Whys and Hows of Modern Packaging

Modern packages are designed to contain and protect the form and quality of a product and to facilitate its timely and efficient movement through trade channels.

And, let it be added in the same breath, to attract and please customers. To utility have been added color, art, design, imagination, and convenience. Plain bottles have become attractive decanters. Boxes that contain pancake and biscuit flour carry recipes. Cheese comes in gay tumblers. Bags that protect carrots can be put to a dozen uses in a kitchen. Tins for cake and candy are almost like jewel boxes. But with all that, the packages have to be cheap enough to permit a commercially feasible method of distribution, and they have to provide some benefits to growers, distributors, and users of food.

Many materials are used—sawed wood, veneer, paper, paperboard, burlap, cotton, steel, glass, packaging films, and aluminum foil. The nailed wooden boxes and crates used for some farm products require more than 1.5 billion board feet of lumber, or substantially more lumber than the annual production in the New England States. Food packages alone use about 2.6 million tons of steel and more than 4 million tons of paperboard. Hundreds of thousands of bales of cotton are used annually in the manufacture of cotton bags, most of which are used for packaging farm products. The sturdy burlap bag, commonly used for packaging bulky farm products and supplies, is made from jute or jute fabrics imported from Pakistan and India. Sharp curtailment of imports of jute during the Second World War created special problems in the packaging of such products as grains, sugar beets, and potatoes. Kenaf, a substitute for jute, is being produced on an experimental basis in Florida and in some Caribbean countries.

Many purposes and reasons underlie the development of modern packages.

Prompt packaging and proper and speedy handling of perishable products into cold rooms or cars at the point of production minimize damage from physical handling, delay deterioration from aging or from destructive organisms, and so prolong the marketing life. Breaking the mass into small lots makes possible the rapid reduction of temperature. The type and size of package largely determine the time required in precooling and its effectiveness.

Modern packaging makes possible self-service retailing, facilitates the use of trade-marked brands, and increases sanitation, buying convenience, and efficiency in handling.

An example: Not long ago all red meats were packaged for the customer after she had made her selection from the meat counter. But in order to adapt red meats to self-service merchandising, the meat had to be cut, weighed, and wrapped in some type of package before being placed on retail display—a development commonly referred to as prepackaging. We like to see the particular cut of meat that we buy, so the prepackaging of meats was not generally feasible until the development of satisfactory transparent films. Visibility was important, but other packaging problems also arose because of the characteristics of red meat. It generally is dark red immediately upon being cut and becomes bright red soon after being exposed to the oxygen in the air. The extent of the oxidation process and subsequent darkening of the meat, after a longer period of exposure to the air, is related to the amount of oxygen to which the meat is exposed.

Cellophane, one of the first packaging materials developed that provided sufficient visibility to the product, was tried for prepackaging meats. A special type of cellophane had to be developed which would permit enough—but not too much—oxygen to penetrate the package. Other types of films, among them a rubber hydrochloride film, also met the requirements of red meats.

The increasing use of trade-marked brands has been facilitated by packaging. A distinctive package and a distinctive brand name create in the customer's mind the impression that the product within is also distinctive. Advertising and sales campaigns generally can be made more effective when they can be tied to a packaged product.

Examples of the convenience in using kitchen-serviced foods are vegetable salads, peeled potatoes, soup mixes, coleslaw, potato salad, macaroni salad, and deviled eggs. Some of them are prepared in a central processing plant or chainstore warehouse. Many of the prepared prepackaged vegetables, such as coleslaw and salad mixes, may be packaged in specialized packing plants.

Green and leafy vegetables, such as lettuce, may be prepackaged in transparent films, which prevent loss of moisture and reduce wilting and reduce the cost of marketing by reducing waste and spoilage losses.

Sanitation is another reason for modern packaging. When products like lettuce and other leafy vegetables, which are not cooked, are properly packaged, the chances of contamination are lessened. Many fruits sometimes attract gnats or fruit flies while they are on display in retail stores under conventional conditions, and packaging them in transparent containers makes a more sanitary method of merchandising.

Customers seem to like the extra convenience of the prepackaged vegetables. Housewives find it more convenient to pick up a package of carrots than to select a bunch of carrots, which often is wet, and then wait for a clerk to remove the tops. Many—but not all—customers prefer to pick up a clean package of potatoes rather than select them from a loose or bulk display. Processed cheese is now molded in the proper form and cut in individual slices and packaged in consumer-size containers almost entirely automatically in manufacturing plants. Natural cheese is also prepackaged in retail stores. The efficiency in handling cheese, particularly the retailing operation, thus is greatly increased.

Many retailers have limited space for storing perishables. Some who are not well trained in the techniques of displaying and preserving the perishables usually prefer deliveries in quantities that can be disposed of in a day or two, and the trend is toward smaller wholesale shipping packages. An example is the half-size boxes for California lemons and western iceberg lettuce, which eliminate the need to repack the products at terminal markets to satisfy retailers' requirements.

Shipping containers may be designed to promote sales to the ultimate consumer in the original package. The lug boxes used for apricots and the half-bushel basket for eastern peaches and Idaho prunes reflect attempts to satisfy the housewife's demand for a quantity of fruit for home canning that can be conveniently handled in a limited working and storage space.

Although the size and shape of packages most acceptable to consumers often are matters of trial and error, research by Government and industry is being applied to the question. For instance, in a test period of 3 weeks, consumers in three cities showed a preference for apples in 3- or 4-pound bags over similar apples in 5-pound bags.

Small families like fractional packages—such as two kinds of cake that are wrapped as one. The design of the package is important as well—square milk bottles require one-third less space than round bottles. Short ketchup bottles tip over less easily than tall ketchup bottles. A package should not fall apart on the way home. It has to be easy to open. Potato packagers have found out that the customer does not want to get out a pair of pliers to unfasten the wire tie of a paper bag. Consumers complain when they cannot close a cellophane bag after using part of the contents.

Improved packaging materials, containers, and methods are being developed. Dried fruits used to be packed and shipped in 25-pound wooden boxes. Now dried prunes are packaged at the point of production in a variety of packages, the most common of which are paperboard boxes laminated with aluminum foil and transparent film bags. In a modern plant, processed prunes travel by conveyor belts into a hopper, where they are preweighed into 1- or 2-pound lots. A machine makes the film bag and fills it with the prunes. Propylene oxide (or ethylene oxide) is automatically injected into the package at the time of filling to prevent development of mold on the prunes. The packages are automatically sealed and packed by hand in fiberboard shipping cases.

The average buyer may not be greatly interested in the fact that the prunes are packaged in Saran, a polyvinylidene chloride, or in a film known as K–202, which is a cellophane with a coating of a modified vinylidene polymer. But the buyer considers it important that the right properties are provided in the packaging material to maintain the quality of the product placed in it: The housewife finds, when she opens the package, that the prunes are soft and not dried out, as they often were in the old wooden cases.

A vast array of chemicals is used in manufacturing packaging materials. More than 60 different types and thicknesses of cellophane are manufactured to meet specific uses.

Cellulose acetate, another common flexible transparent film, is clear and crinkles less quickly than cellophane. It is often used as a window in cartons, such as those used for cakes or other pastry products. It is also commonly used for packaging tomatoes and cut flowers. Because it is highly permeable to water vapor transmission, however, some products packed in it wilt rapidly.

Pliofilm, which is a rubber hydrochloride film, is transparent, durable, and moisture-vaporproof. It is used on such items as beef rib roasts because it is less likely to be punctured by sharp bones than is cellophane. Since it is impervious to moisture, it is a good film for packaging such items as dill pickles or sauerkraut.

Polyethylene, one of the newer packaging films, has a rather milky appearance. It is vaporproof and durable. Carrots will keep crisp and turgid in a polyethylene bag for a long time.

Many perishable products need some kind of inner packing. A mere paper or cotton wrap may serve the purpose by preserving cleanliness, as when used on meat cuts shipped in veneer boxes or on fruits to prevent the spread of decays, which may develop in transit. Still other moisture-resistant wraps are used in the common crates to contain the snow ice with which some vegetables are packed for cross-country shipment. Chipboard or corrugated liners and cover pads protect fruits from the rough inner surfaces and cutting edges of wooden shipping containers. Shell eggs withstand the normal hazards of handling only when isolated one from another in the shipping package, usually by means of vertical and horizontal chipboard dividers, or the cell-type package. For berries and other small fruits, the inner packing is itself a container.

Because the disposition to be made of perishable products usually depends on their quality and condition, such products must be accessible to inspection by all who follow the original receiver in the chain of distribution—wholesaler, jobber, retailer, consumer. Consequently an essential of a shipping package is that it lends itself readily to opening and closing with a minimum of damage to the container or disarrangement of the contents. That is also an important requirement for the export packages, which often are subject to several customs inspections.

Some products are packed and repacked in different forms before reaching the consumer. Very little wheat in the natural state reaches the consumer. After leaving the country elevator, it becomes stock feed, breakfast cereal, flour for household or industrial use, bread, other baked goods, pie and cake mixes, or foods prepared in various forms.

A processor considers a number of factors in selecting materials and types of containers. Generally he tries to select a package that most economically meets such basic requirements as protection and preservation of quality, convenience, preferred sizes, and attractiveness.

Often the most important factors are technical. The common tin can, for instance, is made from cold-rolled steel sheets covered with a thin coating of tin. The thickness of the steel varies with the size of the can. The thickness of the tin coating varies with the corrosive nature of the product to be packed. For certain classes of foods, a coating of enamel is applied to the inner surface of the can. The enamel varies with the character of the product. One kind of enamel prevents the fading of highly colored products like berries and beets. Another prevents the formation of iron sulfide and the resulting discoloration in sulfur-bearing products, such as cream corn. Some meat products require enamels that are resistant to fats. Fruit juices require special enamels.

Some cans hold one serving, some two, others three or more, up to sizes for use in restaurants and institutions. For fruits and vegetables alone, 32 sizes of cans are commonly used in efforts to satisfy consumers' preferences. The sizes were developed over a period of years, largely by trial and error.

The problem of selection may be even more complex if paper, metal foil, packaging films, and similar flexible materials are used. They must be odorless, tasteless, and nontoxic when they are used to package food. Also to be considered are cost, general attractiveness, resistance to moisture, greaseproofness, strength, stretch or shrink, and gas and odor impermeability or (sometimes) permeability, transparency, resistance to light, chemical inertness, and printability. Because foods are subject to various types of breakdown or contamination, many packages embody combinations of several properties.

Because most foods tend either to pick up or lose moisture in storage or on the shelves, the problem of moisture control probably is encountered most often. If the moisture content becomes too high, prepared cake mixes may lose their leavening property and powdered milk will become lumpy and difficult to reconstitute. Cereals require packages that are moisture-resistant but at the same time can allow the escape of odors that may build up in the package.

A major problem in packaging many foods is to prevent insect infestation and, in frozen foods, to prevent access of outside air so as to minimize enzymic and chemical changes. Hence the proper sealing of packages is essential.

Greaseproofness is important. Seepage from products like baked goods, cake and pie mixes, and nuts is likely to stain the package and make it unsightly and unsalable. Absorption of oil or grease from without may induce rancidity. Packages for butter and other fatty products, susceptible to odor contamination, must be impermeable to gases and greaseproof.

Glass containers also present some problems. For some unexplained reason, grapefruit products do not stand up well in them. Apple juice appears to keep best in bottles of brown glass. Easy opening features, reclosing devices, pour spouts, and possible reuse value are other factors.

THE COST of packaging a farm product seldom remains constant. Even if all other elements of cost in a particular plant remained essentially unchanged, the cost per unit probably would vary seasonally because of changes in quantities handled. And, at a specific time, costs among packers would vary because of differences in equipment, in efficiency of labor and operations, and in quantities of product packed. An average cost figure, therefore, generally has a wide range of scatter about it and may quickly become obsolete.

Nevertheless the results of a few studies are cited, mainly to point out that packaging costs represent a significant segment of the consumer's dollar and that an increase or decrease in costs is likely to have a corresponding effect upon the part of the consumer's dollar that the farmer gets.

In a week of heavy receipts in 1951, among seven cooperatives the costs of packing materials for a 30-dozen case of consumer-grade eggs in cartons varied from about 73 cents to 99 cents. The direct labor costs for cartoning and packing a case of eggs at one of the plants was about 64 cents. The cost of packaging material and packing labor, therefore, averaged about 5 cents a dozen.

A study by the Department of Agriculture indicated that in 1950 for every dollar's worth of canned fruits and vegetables bought by the housewife an average of 10 to 15 cents represented the cost of the cans and about 2 cents the cost of the shipping case. If she bought frozen fruits and vegetables, 4 to 9 cents out of the dollar represented the cost of containers and wrappers and about 1 cent the cost of the shipping case.

Other estimates indicated that in 1952 the cost of container and shipping case, per pound of nonfat dry milk solids, was about 1.2 cents for barrels or drums weighing 200 to 225 pounds, about 3 cents for 25-pound tins packed 2 in a wire-bound box, and approximately 3.5 cents to more than 4 cents for consumer packages. In some multiple-pack consumer packages are packets, each of which holds the right amount of powder to make a quart of reconstituted skim milk. The more elaborate the package the higher its cost. Such a package, however, may be economically sound if it helps to expand sales materially.

Indeed, the story of nonfat dry milk solids illustrates how improvements in assembling, processing, and packaging can lead to a substantial expansion of the market for a farm product. The production of nonfat dry milk solids increased from 565 million pounds in 1942 to 842 million pounds in 1952. It takes about 11.7 pounds of skim milk to make 1 pound of dried product, so that about 3.2 billion more pounds of skim milk were utilized for nonfat dry milk solids in 1952 than in 1942. Without that expansion, the skim milk probably would have been fed to livestock or wasted. Although the expansion was induced by wartime requirements for overseas uses, packaging advances enabled the industry to divert much of the product to domestic consumer sales afterward. Packaging costs therefore should not only be evaluated in relation to the physical functions which the package performs, but also in relation to the effectiveness of the package in promoting sales.

Mass-production or assembly-line methods, in many instances employing highly specialized machines and equipment, are used in the packaging of some farm goods.

A machine can count such products as lemons and tomatoes. Another sorts dry beans, lemons, and tomatoes, by the amount of color showing on them. Machinery is used to package such items as rice and nuts and put the packages into shipping containers. Bakeries use machines to form a loaf of bread, turn it over, convey it through the baking ovens, slice it, and wrap it.

Still, a lot of hand labor is used in packaging many common products. Spinach is an example. Growers take great care to cut the leaves by hand and pack them into paper-lined baskets. Some spinach is field-packed. Some is trucked from the field to the nearby packing sheds, where it is graded and then repacked into baskets. Crushed ice is put in the baskets, and the spinach usually is under refrigeration until it reaches the terminal markets.

At the terminal prepackaging plant the spinach may be placed into refrigerated storage until it is ready for sorting and grading by operators who remove bruised and inferior leaves. It is then automatically transferred to huge washing tanks to remove any sand still on the leaves. Then the leaves move on a chain conveyor under sprayers that remove any other foreign material. Most packaging plants use a series of water sprayers. In some an antiseptic solution is added to the water to kill bacteria on the leaves. The thoroughly washed leaves are placed in centrifugal machines that remove excess water. The dried leaves travel down a conveyor belt to be bagged by hand in transparent film bags. The filled bags are sealed, packed into shipping containers, and placed under refrigeration to await shipment. Often the spinach is transported to retail stores in refrigerated trucks and is displayed in refrigerated produce cases in the store.

Such a complicated series of operations accounts for the big difference in the price received by the grower of the spinach in Eagle Pass, Tex., for example, and the price the customer pays for spinach some 2,000 miles away in Boston in winter.

Because of their varying characteristics of conformation, quality, and condition, most of the unprocessed farm products do not lend themselves readily to mechanized packaging other than possibly the overwrapping and sealing of containers previously filled by hand.

The packaging of some fresh products at the shipping point was largely in the experimental stage in 1954.

A great deal of research has been started in the Department of Agriculture to determine the economic feasibility of prepackaging fresh fruits and vegetables at the shipping point and at the wholesale and retail levels in the receiving markets. Meanwhile, most consumer packaging of those products was done by the wholesaler or by the retailer with limited use of machines.

Fully automatic packaging is feasible only with products that are uniform enough in physical properties to insure a uniform flow through the operation and that are handled in large enough volume to warrant the relatively high initial outlays. Fluid milk, canned goods, and cereals, sugar, and butter typify products that are adaptable to rather complete automatic packaging.

Machines for filling, packaging, and closing ice cream containers were introduced in 1947. They eliminate hand labor, increase output, save floor space, and improve sanitation—advantages that offset initial costs of the machines.

The packaging technique often is complex. Flexible or semiflexible containers for packaging dry materials, for example, usually are fed into the machine in the flat. The machine opens and sets them up on the conveyor belt, shakes them during the filling operation to induce uniform filling, weighs each package and rejects any that are improperly filled, seals the acceptable ones, and finally places them in the shipping container.

Sometimes the containers are actually made at the time of packaging from tubular material fed into the machine from rolls. Machines that form flat material into packets and automatically fill, wrap, close, and perhaps hermetically seal them are common.

Products that arrive at the destination in damaged condition usually are discounted in the market. Too often packers sacrifice the factor of safety to that of cost, and find themselves unable to recover in-transit damage attributable to inadequate packaging.

To insure full pack at destination and prevent damage from movement within the package, it is customary to pack certain fresh fruits and vegetables with a crown or bulge at the top of the container—a desirable and justifiable practice when the amount of bulge is not too great. But often bulge packing has been carried to extreme lengths, so that there is damage in transit. The carriers point out that excessive bulge and pressure packing prevents the covers from being securely fastened and otherwise weakens the containers through undue stresses and strains. Therefore some tariff provisions limit the amount of bulge permitted on containers when shipped by rail.

Throughout distribution, packaged products may be handled and rehandled many times, loaded, unloaded and reloaded, or stacked in storage, one upon another, several layers deep. Each package has to withstand the tremendous vertical pressures to which it may be subjected, the wracking motion of moving vehicles, and the impacts of sudden stops and starts.

The kind and amount of packing required to insure safe delivery vary with the product. Shipping containers include nonrigid textile or paper bags or wraps for the hard products, the fiberboard and veneer packages, and the sturdier nailed wooden box or barrel for the more delicate and fragile products. Whether a material is adequate and suitable may depend on the character of the material and also on how well the container is put together, how wisely it is packed, and how expertly it is loaded into the transporting vehicle.

Wood is often selected for shipping containers that need a high degree of sturdiness and rigidity. They include boxes made with sawn lumber, wirebound boxes, boxes made of plywood or other wood products, and baskets and hampers. Packaging experts generally use the lightest wood that will do the job so as to reduce the effort of handling and the cost of transportation. But the native species of wood may dictate the type of container selected. In the soft pine regions of New England and the Pacific Northwest, the nailed wooden box, constructed of sawn lumber, has been preeminent; baskets, barrels, and wirebound boxes, usually made of rotary-cut veneer, are likely to predominate in areas where the local species do not lend themselves readily to nailing.

The tremendous increase (estimated at 400 percent since 1925) in the use of fiberboard shipping boxes attests their general suitability for many products. Among their attributes are lightness in weight and resulting low transportation costs; economy of storage space, because they may be stored empty in the flat; ease of setting up for packing and closing after being packed; freedom from rough surfaces, inside and out; and relatively low cost. Advertising and other material can be printed on them.

Fiberboard containers that are not specially treated, however, are not moistureproof and sooner or later lose much of their strength and rigidity under normal atmospheric conditions.

The customary single-wall boxes, while quite adequate for canned and other packaged goods capable of supporting their own weight, are usually not considered suitable as bulk shipping containers for some products. The cost of treating fiberboard to overcome this weakness is virtually prohibitive for ordinary usage. Multiwall construction, of untreated material, tends to correct the defect. Thus where extended cold storage is not contemplated, egg cases and fruit boxes, so built, have proved to be quite adequate. The multiwall principle also is applied to paper shipping bags (notably for potatoes) and makes them quite suitable for many dry, bulky products.

Folding or setup cardboard boxes have been used for many years. The production of boxboard containers for all uses approximated 1.6 million tons in 1925; by 1951 the production was approximately 5.6 million tons. Some of the increase was due to the development of paper milk bottles and containers for other liquid and semiliquid products and a host of frozen foods. A new style of spout, which pours like a pitcher, has been perfected for gable-style milk cartons.

The size and shape of shipping containers are important. Heavy, cumbersome packages get more abuse through dropping than those that one man can conveniently handle. Packages may be handled with reasonable care on the farm, but later handlings may be rough. Particularly at terminal markets where solid loads are broken for city distribution, handlers must quickly load many packages. The clumsy, awkward package usually suffers most in the process. A package is in good proportion if the width and depth (cross section) are about equal, and the length is about twice as great as the depth.

The Association of American Railroads recommends that the familiar legend "This side up" be replaced or supplemented by large red arrows pointing up on all four sides of the container. The arrows are understood by everyone and they help a foreman check quickly whether containers are properly placed in a warehouse or on a truck.

High labor costs are forcing consideration of improved methods of handling packaged products.

In collaboration with the Department of Agriculture, the Washington State Apple Commission has designed, constructed, and placed in experimental use a portable mechanical lift for high-piling and breaking out high-piled boxes. Clamps are used for gripping the lower boxes in stacks to be moved. Costs are more than cut in half.

Packages are selected that are best suited to being transported and stored intact in large units on pallets (movable platforms), as a means of eliminating or lowering the cost of repeated handling of individual packages. Because the pallet itself may serve as a "package," palletizing often results in a saving of packaging materials. It also reduces damage and simplifies warehouse and inventory procedure. One requirement of successful palletizing is that packages be of such sizes and shapes that they stack securely and economically on standard pallets.

The canning industry in a booklet, *Simplified Practice Recommendations*, published by the Department of Commerce, has directed attention to the problem. Some progress has been made in simplifying the containers. In general, rectilinear containers are found to be most efficient and best suited to stowing on pallets or in storage. Round types, such as barrels and tubs, are least economical of space.

Too many sizes and shapes of packages put a burden on producers and consumers—greater costs of manufacturing and carrying in stock a large number of different kinds of containers; handling odd-size containers in transportation, storage, and the distributive system; and merchandising confusing amounts of a product, with the result that sales are made at a disadvantage for lack of a definite basis of sale and of accurate market information.

To facilitate trading and to prevent misrepresentation, the Congress passed the Standard Containers Acts of 1916 and 1928, which fixed the standard sizes of baskets and hampers for fresh fruits and vegetables. They do not apply to other types of containers commonly used for such products. During the Second World War, however, shortages of wood and metals did lead to compulsory simplification in that the manufacture of wooden containers for fresh fruits and vegetables and of tin and glass containers for processed foods was limited to a relatively few practical sizes. Much strategic material was conserved and an effective salvage and reuse program was carried out. But to a large extent those programs of simplification did not long survive the lifting of controls.

For years the Department of Agriculture and various groups in industry have been working together to develop uniform national standards for containers of certain agricultural products.

Since 1921, the chief function of the division of simplified practices of the Department of Commerce has been to centralize and coordinate the efforts of producers, distributors, and consumers in developing and applying simplified practices that will reduce the waste and inefficiencies resulting from excessive and unnecessary varieties of products and containers. The Department supports all simplifications of practice that have the backing of at least 80 percent of the industry.

Experience has proved that a successful program depends on five steps: A careful survey to determine existing sizes and varieties and the demand for each; the elimination of the sizes and varieties for which there exists only a small or irregular demand; the retention of any package for which a necessity exists; periodic resurveys as a basis for revisions and improvements; the unabated interest and active support of producers, distributors, and consumers.

The work in connection with those fundamental steps is spearheaded by a standing committee selected by the industry. Simplified recommendations have been advanced for nearly 30 categories of containers, most of which are used for agricultural products in one form or another.

Research in the field of packaging was expanded during the Second World War. Activities were centered at the United States Forest Products Laboratory in Madison, Wis., where extra-durable containers were designed to withstand the hazards of sea water, extremes in temperature and humidity, decay, corrosion, and very rough handling. Because the shipping space was at a premium and lumber and other packaging materials were scarce, compactness and economical use of materials also were paramount considerations. Crates and boxes were designed to eliminate useless air space, and the minimum weight of lumber needed to protect an article was determined.

Improvements in the durability and compactness of containers and more economical use of materials and labor remain fundamental objectives of research by Government and industry. To these are added scores of diverse problems that relate to packaging and containers, indicating that it takes continuous research, experimentation, and testing to develop better and more efficient containers for marketing agricultural products. (*L. C. Carey, Gertrude G. Foelsch, Donald R. Stokes.*)

FLOW OF FOODS IN THE UNITED STATES

1935–39 AVERAGE TONNAGE, IN MILLIONS OF TONS

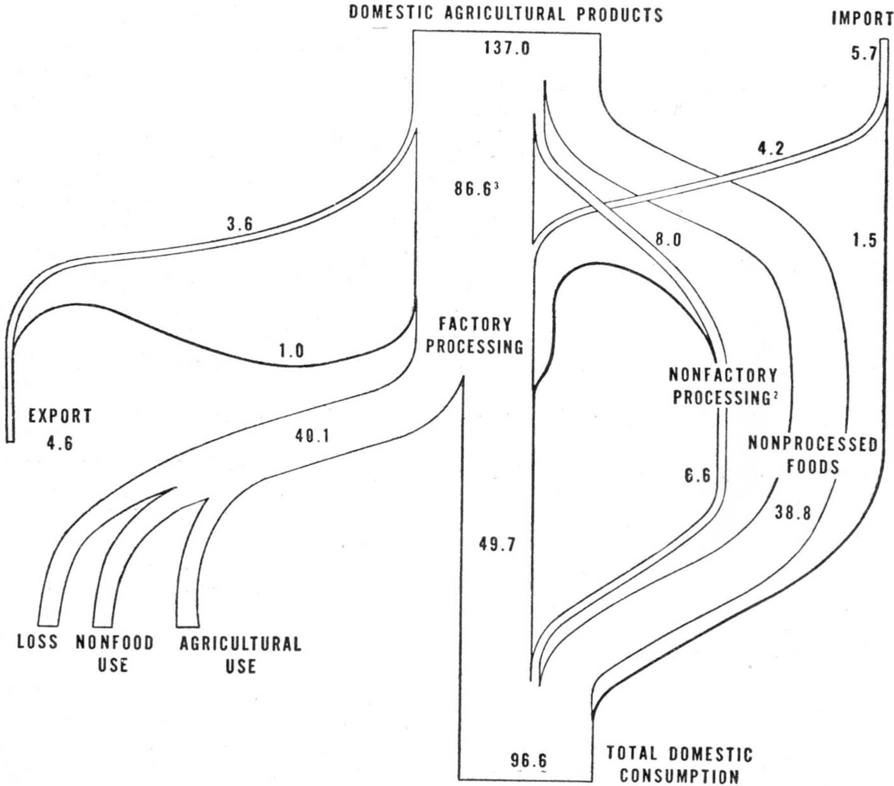

1. Includes eggs, nuts, fresh fruit and vegetables, dry peas and beans, and milk and poultry used in producers' households.
2. Includes butter and livestock used in producers' households; home canned fruit and vegetables, and poultry dressed in nonfactory establishments.

Excludes 2.3 million tons of grain used in making alcoholic beverages.

Grades, Standards

In any exchange of goods the buyer and seller must agree on how much of a commodity is to be delivered. As soon as trade gets beyond simple barter, it has to depend therefore on weights and measures. Likewise, all trading, except simple barter, involves price. Price in practically all markets is a common denominator by which are expressed unlike details of size, amount, weight, and quality of products being traded. Besides weights and measures, therefore, standards for other attributes of goods have been developed. Grading is a basic function in practically all transactions.

The purpose is to establish a common language understood by buyers and sellers as a basis of judging the quality of a product in relation to its sales price. Grades are useful to all persons who engage in trade. They are also useful in describing the quality of many consumers' retail goods. Controversy over compulsory grade labeling of consumer goods has waxed strong, however. Much of the argument has been concerned with the system of grading to use.

Units and Standards of Measurement

In any exchange of goods the seller and buyer must agree on how much of a commodity is to be delivered. As soon as any trade gets beyond simple barter, it has to depend therefore on weights and measures of some kind.

In early days each locality or each social and political unit developed its own measures. The result was a vast diversity of units and methods of measurement and with it misunderstanding and the possibility of fraud.

The processes of trade are eased if the weights and measures to be used are prescribed by some authority and are not left as a subject for argument between buyer and seller. So regulation of weights and measures by law has been undertaken in all civilizations of which we have record.

But customs so closely related to our everyday life are slow to change. Even in countries that long ago adopted new systems of units the old names often remain in use. In Paris, after 100 years of compulsory use of the metric system, hucksters still cry the price of fruit per livre (pound), just as the Berliner talks of the Pfund, even though the weight of each is actually a half kilogram.

Our own customs are equally hard to change even when they cause some real trouble: We still give statistics on grains in bushels, although by law deliveries must be by weight and although farmers in some sections prefer to talk of barrels or of hundredweights.

In relatively recent times marketing areas have grown to the extent that local and even national customs and regulations regarding weights and measures have had to be adjusted and—as far as practicable—unified and simplified.

When uniform practices are not attainable, it is necessary at least to know the units in which major producing areas measure a commodity. The price the Kansas farmer gets for his wheat depends upon the size of the crops in Canada, and Argentina, and Australia. To collect and distribute information on crops one must know about the units and money used in each country.

In manufactured products the need

for uniformity of measurements is still more obvious. A replacement bolt that does not fit may put a tractor out of business, whether it be in Illinois, Brazil, or Africa.

The world has made much progress toward such uniformity. Considerable diversity exists in details of each system, but two general systems now dominate trade throughout the civilized world—the metric, based upon the meter and the kilogram, and the English or "Imperial," which has as its basic units the yard and the pound.

The metric system was primarily a result of the French Revolution. It was itself a revolutionary development. A reform of weights and measures was urgently needed because France was a composite of kingdoms and principalities, and large differences existed between the units used in different parts of the country. Instead of trying to adjust and reconcile the diverse units, the scientists to whom the problem was assigned devised an entirely new system. The two chief characteristics of the system were that its units should be derived from unchanging natural standards and that units of various sizes should all be related by factors of 10 or its multiples, so that calculations could be made simply by pointing off decimals or adding ciphers.

As an unchanging natural standard of length, the committee chose a quarter of the circumference of the earth to be measured along a meridian passing through France. The practical unit, the meter, was to be one ten-millionth part of that quadrant. After extensive surveys by competent geodesists to determine the length of the quadrant, a platinum bar was made as a standard to represent the meter in a usable form. The unit of weight, the kilogram, was to be derived from the meter by making the kilogram the weight of 1 cubic decimeter (that is, a cube one-tenth of a meter on a side) of pure water at the temperature at which the water is most dense (about 37° F.). As had been done for the meter, however, the scientists made a standard of platinum to represent the kilogram in usable form.

As usually happens in such difficult measurements, the length of the meter bar and the weight of the kilogram cylinder were later found not to correspond exactly to the natural standards from which they were derived. Also on account of the departure of the kilogram standard from the intended weight, the liter (unit of capacity), defined as the volume of 1 kilogram of water, is slightly larger than the cubic decimeter which it was intended to equal.

The French Government decided to adopt the units as preserved by the platinum standards and thus in effect discarded the first principle on which the system was based. The simplicity of the decimal system, however, and the urgent need for uniformity in weights and measures led to the widespread adoption of the new system.

Its use was made mandatory in France in 1840, and gradually spread to other European countries.

An act of the United States Congress in 1866 provided: "It shall be lawful throughout the United States of America to employ the weights and measures of the metric system; and no contract or dealing, or pleading in any court, shall be deemed invalid or liable to objection because the weights and measures expressed or referred to therein are weights and measures of the metric system."

Formal international acceptance of the metric system was brought about by meetings in 1870, 1872, and 1875, which resulted in a treaty that set up a permanent organization to maintain and perfect the system. The organization included a laboratory (the International Bureau of Weights and Measures), to be placed on neutral international territory given by the French Government, and an International Committee on Weights and Measures to direct the work of that bureau.

The first duty of the new organization was to provide standard meter bars and standard kilograms for the International Bureau and for the countries that were members of the organization. As material to make the standards, the Committee chose platinum alloyed with 10 percent of iridium.

The making of the standards and their calibration took many years. In 1889 they were completed and distributed to the various countries to serve as national standards. One particular meter bar and one kilogram were selected as the prototypes, or basic standards, and deposited in a subterranean vault at the International Bureau. At intervals since then the meters and kilograms of the several countries have been taken back to the International Bureau for comparison with its standards.

The metric system therefore has the advantages of being founded upon well-established standards of the highest attainable accuracy and of having a competent organization to make sure that worldwide uniformity is maintained over long periods. Also in the everyday use of the system, as well as in learning it, the making of all calculations by multiplying or dividing by tens is a great saver of labor.

A minor advantage is that names for all multiples of the basic units are formed in a systematic way by prefixes, as follows:

milli=one thousandth
centi=one hundredth
deci=one tenth
deka=ten
hecto=one hundred
kilo=one thousand

So, for example, 1,000 grams make 1 kilogram; one thousandth of a gram is 1 milligram. There is, however, a special name for 1,000 kilograms, 1 metric ton, or tonneau, which happens to be only 1.5 percent smaller than a British or long ton.

Originally 17 countries signed the metric treaty of 1875. The number belonging to the weights and measures organization has since increased to 33. The metric system is used exclusively in all continental European countries. It is the legal system in all of Latin America and in several Asiatic countries, although older units still remain in use in many countries. China, India, and Indonesia have planned to introduce it gradually to replace the many local units still in use. Thus the whole world uses or expects to use the metric system, except the English-speaking countries, and in them the metric system is used in nearly all work in science.

ALTHOUGH THE METRIC STANDARDS made of platinum-iridium have served their purpose very well, many scientists have cherished the belief that the system should eventually be based upon natural standards of even greater permanence. In particular, certain wavelengths of light have long been considered as possible substitutes for the metal bar as the ultimate reference standard of length. The natural materials, such as cadmium, mercury, and krypton, which might be used to produce light for this purpose, however, are really mixtures of "isotopes," that is, each of them includes atoms that have diverse atomic weights although they are designated by the same name and atomic number and are so similar in structure that they cannot be separated by ordinary chemical procedures. The various isotopes of a given element produce wavelengths slightly different, so that the waves given off by a natural element are complex in form. This complexity limits the accuracy of measurements made by using such light waves.

Research on atomic structure has provided methods for producing materials containing only one isotope of an element. Such material gives off waves simple in form; they produce fine, sharp lines in a spectrum. With them measurements of length can be made much more precise than is possible with lines ruled on metal bars. Consequently in 1953 an Advisory Committee of the International Committee on Weights and Measures, including members from 11 countries, recommended that wavelengths produced by some isotope be adopted to supersede the bar as the basis for the definition of the meter. This recommendation would become effective upon approval by a General Conference on Weights and Measures. The conferences convene at 6-year intervals, and one is scheduled for 1960.

THE UNITED STATES was a party to the treaty of 1875 and received two meter bars and two kilograms in 1889. Meter No. 27 and kilogram No. 20 were accepted formally by President Harrison on January 2, 1890. Since then they have been considered as the primary standards of the United States. From them are derived the precise values for units in the "English" system as well as those of the metric system.

Following the example of the 1866 act of the Congress, several States have recognized the legality of using metric units—Idaho, Kansas, Massachusetts, Nebraska, Ohio, South Dakota, and Tennessee. California law permits use of the metric system in contracts and in the marking of goods to show weight or measure. In Nevada designations of weight or volume may be in metric units in lieu of the customary units.

Nevertheless every one of the States named has some requirement as to commodities or containers that must conform to the customary units. For example, bread must be in 1-pound loaves and milk bottles must hold 1 quart or the usual fractions of a quart. Although stated to be legally permissible, then, the metric units are practically not used at all in trade in the United States.

Our customary, or "English," units are the result of gradual evolution of customs among the people, rather than of logical or scientific planning. Varieties of the units are universally used in trade in all the English-speaking countries, but they can hardly be called a system.

They include, in fact, several systems, a conglomeration of discordant series with no simple relation either between the different sets of units or between units of different size in a given series. For example, we use, for different purposes, three series of weights (avoirdupois, troy, and apothecaries') and the only unit common to all three is the grain.

The irregularity of steps between units is well illustrated by measures of length. We divide a yard into 3 feet, and a foot into 12 inches; 5.5 yards make a rod, 40 rods make a furlong, and 8 furlongs make a mile.

In the United States we have dry as well as liquid quarts and pints, the difference being more than 16 percent.

In actual trade, confusion between these two kinds of units has been largely removed by requiring most dry commodities to be sold by weight instead of by dry measure, but in liquid measures we still divide a pint into gills for some things and into fluid ounces for others.

The diverse units we use were inherited from colonial days when the English settlers along the Atlantic seaboard naturally brought with them the customs, including the weights and measures, of the mother country.

The history of the various units in England can be traced back to medieval times. The actual origin of some of the units is doubtful. Somewhat different units were used in different sections of England and for trade in different kinds of goods. As trade developed, royal decrees from time to time prescribed standards of measurement. The decrees in general simply confirmed units already established by custom of the people or of the guilds that controlled the trade in various commodities, but they brought about a fair degree of uniformity in the country. The American colonies, although acting separately, consequently obtained from England weights and measures that were substantially of the same kind although they were not in exact agreement with each other.

The foundation of present United

States units is itself complex. The need for uniform weights and measures was fully recognized when the Colonies united, and power to establish them was given to the Federal Government.

The Articles of Confederation provided, "The United States in Congress assembled shall also have the sole and exclusive right and power of . . . fixing the standard of weights and measures throughout the United States." The Constitution, effective in 1789, likewise included the provision that "the Congress shall have Power to . . . fix the Standard of Weights and Measures."

President Washington's first annual message to the Congress in 1790, and later messages by him and his successors emphasized the need for action to assure uniformity of weights and measures, but to this day there is no legislation defining the basic units of our common system, the yard and the pound. The uniformity of practice which we have was brought about by other means.

The first act of Congress establishing a definite standard was a law of 1828, providing that a brass weight obtained by the minister of the United States at London in 1827 should "be the standard troy pound of the Mint of the United States, conformably to which the coinage thereof shall be regulated." That weight was supposed to be an exact copy of the standard troy pound of Great Britain. While the act of Congress quoted made this troy pound only the standard for coinage, it practically became the basic standard from which the avoirdupois pound was derived.

The next step was taken to meet needs of the customs service. In 1830–1832 the Treasury Department, in response to a resolution of the Senate, made a survey of weights and measures then in use at customhouses in various American ports. The survey showed that serious differences existed between ports. The Treasury Department proceeded to furnish uniform standards. As a basis, the Department adopted a standard avoirdupois pound and a yard. The pound was derived from the troy pound of the mint by taking the ratio for the two accepted in England, that is, 7,000 to 5,760. The yard was the 36-inch interval between two specified inch marks on an 82-inch brass bar made in London 20 years before for the Coast Survey. A gallon of 231 cubic inches and a bushel of 2,150.42 cubic inches were adopted. They were old English units, the wine gallon of Queen Anne and the Winchester bushel, and were believed to represent more closely than any other English units the average values of the measures in use in the United States, although both of them had been abolished in England in 1824.

The action taken by the Treasury Department to unify the weights and measures of the customs service was viewed with such favor that the Congress decided to give it wider effect. A resolution of June 14, 1836, directed the Secretary of the Treasury "to cause a complete set of all weights and measures adopted as standards and now either made or in progress of manufacture for the use of the several customhouses, and for other purposes, to be delivered to the governor of each State in the Union, or such person as he may appoint, for the use of the States, respectively, to the end that a uniform standard of weights and measures may be established throughout the United States."

The concluding clause of the resolution appears to be the expression of a wish rather than the exercise of the constitutional power to fix the standard of weights and measures. Nevertheless, the effect has been practically to establish uniform standards, because the States have used the standards supplied and nearly all States have adopted them by law.

The Act of July 28, 1866, which legalized the use of metric units, included tables of conversion factors which "may be lawfully used for computing, determining, and expressing in customary weights and measures the weights and measures of the metric system." Recognizing the superior quality and probable permanence of the metric standards, the Office of Weights and Measures, then a part of the United States Coast and Geodetic Survey, announced on April 5, 1893, that thereafter the customary units, the yard and the pound, would be derived from the metric standards "in accordance with the Act of July 28, 1866."

The act of 1866 gave 39.37 inches as the practical equivalent of 1 meter. Turning this about, the 1893 announcement defined the yard as being exactly 3600/3937 meter, and that definition is still used in the United States. The equivalent for the kilogram was stated in the law as 2.2046 pounds, but in defining the United States pound several digits have been added. In accordance with a comparison of the British pound with the kilogram reported in 1883, the pound has been defined as equal to 0.4535924277 kilogram.

The adoption of those definitions did not make any appreciable change in the ordinary units, because the values adopted were those already in use as nearly as they could be determined. Exact and permanent standards had never been made to represent the customary units. Deriving them from the metric standards had the double advantage of providing the best basic standards known and of tying together the units of the two systems so that their relative value remains permanently fixed.

The custody of the standards was transferred from the Coast and Geodetic Survey to the National Bureau of Standards in 1901, when the latter Bureau was established, but the units as set up by the Survey have been maintained. The primary metric standards are therefore the basis for precise calibration of other standards representing the customary, or English, units as well as the metric ones.

Uniformity among the States in basic standards was attained largely by the general acceptance of the sets of standards distributed in accordance with the congressional resolution of 1836. In other respects, however, there was wide diversity of practice—in sizes of packages or containers, other customs of the market, and the enforcement, or lack of enforcement, of regulations designed to assure the use of correct weights and measures in trade.

The Constitution gives the Federal Government full power to regulate trade between States and with foreign countries, but there might be argument as to whether its power "to fix the standard of weights and measures" covers regulation of market practices within a State.

At any rate, the control of local use of weights and measures has been largely left to State and local authorities. Such a condition might naturally lead to the perpetuation of local or regional practices, but in fact various influences have worked toward national uniformity. One is the rapid growth of interstate trade. For example, the nationwide distribution of fresh fruit and vegetables from concentrated sources of supply makes it advantageous for both producer and consumer to have uniform practices so that special packing or handling for different markets will not be necessary. In turn, the progress made toward uniformity of requirements has assisted greatly in the development of interstate trade.

Such desirable uniformity of practice in methods of sale of products has been promoted by voluntary cooperative action of State, city, and county officials in National Conferences on Weights and Measures. The conferences, begun under the leadership of the National Bureau of Standards in 1905, have been held every year since then except when wartime conditions prevented. Officials of almost every State have taken part. Agreement has been obtained to take uniform action on many regulations. One of the early projects was the drafting of a model law to provide for inspection of weights and measures. It has been amended and extended from time to time to include many specific requirements on which general agreement has been reached. Most of its provisions have been enacted into law in a majority of the States.

The net result of cooperative action by State authorities, combined with Federal requirements covering forms and sizes of certain containers, such as barrels and baskets, has been to establish a large degree of uniformity in the marketing of farm products. This uniformity is based upon our customary units of weight and measure.

The adoption of a more simple system, easier to learn and to use in records and calculations, might be economically justified by the net savings of time and trouble over a long period of years. Any radical change from the customary units, however, would involve vast expense and cause much misunderstanding and confusion during a period of transition. Such a change would be politically possible only if desired by a majority of our people throughout the country. No such desire apparently exists, and it is safe to assume that there will be no change in our practical weights and measures in any foreseeable time.

Foreign trade must continue to involve dealing with units different from ours, and to a considerable extent each segment of commerce has its own peculiar customs with regard to measurement of commodities. With regard to general systems, we are out of step with the rest of the world. All of the more important countries outside the English-speaking world differ from us in using the metric system. Furthermore, while our customary units are called "English," none of those in use in the United States is precisely the same as the one called by the same name in the countries of the British Commonwealth. In the basic units, yard and pound, the differences are very small, and we may eventually get rid of them by a little change on each side. The British gallon, however, as tourists who visit Canada may have learned, is one-fifth larger than ours (277.42 cubic inches instead of 231); while the British bushel is about 3 percent larger than ours (2219.36 cubic inches instead of 2150.42). The British bushel is exactly equal to 8 gallons, so that quarts and pints are exactly the same for liquid and for dry measure.

Units of additional kinds become necessary as more and more technical developments play a part in everyday life and business. Electrical units especially concern the farmer as well as the city dweller, whose bills depend upon the number of kilowatt-hours used. To set up these units originally requires elaborate apparatus, but the basic ideas are simple.

The amount of electric current (amperes) flowing in a conductor can be measured by the push or pull that coils carrying that current exert upon each other. The "pressure" making the current flow is measured in volts. The product of the numbers of amperes and of volts is the power (the rate at which work is done) in watts. The number of watts multiplied by the number of hours of work gives the energy supplied in watt-hours. The watt-hour is a rather small unit; 1,000 watt-hours, or one *kilo*watt-hour, is a more convenient magnitude for accounting.

Energy supplied by electricity is regularly measured in kilowatt-hours, and electrical generators are commonly rated on the basis of their output in kilowatts. However, the power of the machines that drive the generators, such as waterwheels or steam engines, is usually stated in horsepower, one horsepower being about three-quarters of a kilowatt (746 watts). Electric motors likewise are generally rated in horsepower, although the power used by other electrical appliances is indicated in watts or kilowatts.

Lamps also are marked to show the number of watts, that is, the amount of power they use, although the user is generally interested in the amount of light that comes out of the lamp rather than the electrical power that goes into it. The amount of light is stated in lumens. Small sizes of ordinary filament lamps give about 10 lumens for each watt used. Larger sizes produce up to 20 lumens per watt.

Practical grading in the market is commonly done by eye, usually by comparing the product with standard samples, but the establishment of the standards and the checking of their constancy from year to year are based upon specifications and methods of measuring colors which have taken many years to develop. So in this field, as in many others, experimental work goes on to extend our systems of measurement. While the basic principles and the fundamental units are well established, new uses for measurement develop and greater convenience and certainty are demanded so that the work of the measurement laboratory is never done. (*E. C. Crittenden.*)

Price Is a Nexus and a Symbol

Price offers the nexus through which quantities, qualities, or other attributes of goods are finally measured when they are bought or sold.

Price is also a symbol of a standard. Goods or services that are being exchanged are measured in terms of some medium of exchange. It may be based on gold, or on silver, or (as in some past or more primitive societies) on shells, on certain types of stones, or on cattle, or wives, or tobacco (as in the American Colonies), or on whatever offers a basis for calculating exchange of values.

Although gold is never seen in ordinary trade because law prohibits its circulation in our domestic markets, prices used in everyday transactions in 1954 tie back to the basic standard of 35 dollars for every troy ounce of gold. But the value is also measured in terms of dollars for a given weight of the product, the troy ounce.

Gold against which the dollar is evaluated must be free of impurities and of a certain degree of fineness. Thus, money, which is the standard for price and which is one of the simplest of all standards, gets its measure of value in our economy from the number of dollars which our Federal Government will offer for a given weight of a particular quality of the metal.

Price in practically all markets is related to some usual, accepted common denominators relating to size, amount, weight, and quality of products being traded.

For instance, prices on corn relate to bushels of 56 pounds and to grade; on cotton to pounds and to staple; on cattle to hundredweight and to grade; on butter to pounds and to score; on eggs to dozens and to grade and to weight per dozen; on most feedstuffs to hundredweight or tons and to percentages of carbohydrates, protein, fiber, and, in more recent years, often to vitamin content; on fertilizer to tons and to formulas expressed in percentage of active ingredients; on lumber to thousands of board-feet and to grade; on barbed wire to spools of 80 rods each and the number of points on the barb; on roofing to 100 square feet of specified weight; on electricity to kilowatt-hours, and so on to the myriad other items which make up a farmer's, or any other person's, purchases and sales.

Great numbers of other standards also are back of the finished products. The feed manufacturer buys various grains, such as No. 2 yellow corn, or No. 3 barley, and oilseed meal or meat scraps on the basis of their protein content, then mixes them with alfalfa meal or other commodities to make a new product. Similarly, the manufacturer of barbed wire buys wire, as well as barbs, having specific types of steel. The fertilizer manufacturer buys on the basis of active ingredients, then mixes his raw material to get another combination, which accords with standard formulas that sell at premiums or discounts from other mixtures.

THESE MEASURES of products, their components, and value are used widely. They serve a useful purpose, or they would be discarded. What are they and where did they come from?

Weights and measures were important enough to get some mention in 1215, when English barons at Runnymede wrested the Magna Carta from King John.

Kingly grants alone apparently were insufficient to insure either accuracy and precision in weights and measures or their wide acceptance and use during those early times or since. The principles of the Great Charter, reaffirmed by Edward I in 1297, stated, among other things: ". . . One measure of wine shall be through our Realm, and one measure of Ale, and one measure of Corn, that is to say, the Quarter of London. . . ."

Shortly (in 1303) the same king approved the Assize of Weights and Measures, which stated: ". . . By consent of the whole Realm the Kings measure was made, so that an English Penny, which is called the Sterling, round without clipping, shall weigh Thirty-two Grains of Wheat dry in the midst of the Ear; Twenty pence make an Ounce; and Twelve Ounces make a Pound, and Eight pounds make a Bushel of London; which is the Eighth part of a Quarter." Later, in 1593 during Queen Elizabeth's reign, parliament decreed ". . . that a Mile shalbe reckoned and taken in this manner and no otherwise, That is to saye, a Myle to conteyne Eight Furlongs, and Every Furlonge to conteyne Fortie Luggs or Poles, and every Lugg or Pole to conteyne Sixteen Foote and Halfe."

The best measures then known—the foot, the hand, grains of wheat—were used to establish exactness and, it was then believed, objective means for calculating mass, weight, and distance in a uniform way.

Authoritative decree even at those early dates affirmed usage and directed that objective means of measurement should take the place of an experienced eye or a practiced hand. But the problem was not settled at any fell stroke. Time and again from the thirteenth century through the eighteenth century, governing bodies, especially the Crown, Parliament, and the London city council, tried to establish the right prototypes for weights and measures and to distribute to cities, towns, and markets throughout the kingdom and to the Colonies models with which local vessels and measures could be compared.

The models were few and far between in the Colonies. Also, for strictly local trading, the exact standard which should be used was not so important as that the standard should remain constant. But there was considerable trade among the Colonies as well as with Europe—enough so that the need for standard weights and measures was recognized in the Articles of Confederation. When they were supplanted by the Constitution, Congress was given authority in Article I, Section 8, to fix the standard of weights and measures. But again it took more than constitutional authority to bring about precise objective measurements as a basis for standards and to have them widely adopted and used. We did inherit, or brought with us, however, a system of weights and measures which, with modifications, established the basis for so much of what we take for granted today. The system for the early land surveys in the Colonies ultimately was extended across the continent and remains with us.

One significant break from colonial custom was made by the new States in the system of coinage. Thomas Jefferson, who previously sponsored the decimal system of coinage, later, as Secretary of State and in response to a request from the first session of the first Congress for a proper plan for uniformity of weights and measures, proposed two plans. The first was to ". . . define and render uniform and stable the existing system . . . and to reduce the dry and liquid measures to corresponding capacities by establishing a single gallon of 270 cubic inches. . . ." The second plan was ". . . to reduce every branch to the same decimal ratio already established for coin, and thus bring the calculations of the principal affairs of life within the arithmetic of every man who can multiply and divide plain numbers."

Standards were not limited to just weights and measures in the Colonies. There were, as in England, many others. Laws applied to inspection of flour, beef, pork, pickled fish, and tobacco, to the dimension of shingles, staves, boards, and hoops, to the size of barrels for liquor, beef, pork, fish, pitch, tar, and turpentine. In the legislation of the Province and State of Maryland, in reference to tobacco, the dimensions or gage of tobacco hogsheads were fixed by 14 acts between 1658 and 1789.

The assize of bread, of English pattern, was enacted at various times by colonial or town assemblies. This was an ordinance or regulation bringing this important staple under public control. A Massachusetts act of 1646 fixed the standards for bread upon the basis of the penny loaf. The price did not vary. The weight of the penny loaf of three different types of bread—white, wheaten, and household—was set according to variations in the price of wheat. Supplementary enactments are recorded in 1681, 1685, 1696, and 1720–1721, with repeal of all of them in 1801 by an act of the State legislature, which retained the provision that bread be sold by weight and marked with the weight and the baker's name.

Some similar enactments prevailed throughout most of the Colonies in an age when many forms of food were difficult to come by and short weighing was common and easy. Mills were presumed to have a public interest. Millers ranked by law in many places with State officials, college professors, ministers, and physicians in exemption from jury duty or military training. The mill was given public privileges because of the importance of its functions, which made it an institution of first necessity to every community. On the same account it was subject to public control as a local monopoly and it must accord with the prescribed rates and standards of conduct.

The open sway of economic individualism reached its zenith in the United States in the second quarter of the nineteenth century. The market excesses of the period may be neatly epitomized in the compact legal expression *caveat emptor*. Buyers dared not trust unknown sellers. Warranties depended entirely upon the integrity of the warrantor. Measures of quantity and quality were so lacking or inexact as to make it difficult to arrive at a meeting of minds, the essential element for each exchange of goods in the market. The pendulum had swung from a close regulation of markets, which hindered marketing in earlier centuries to a marketing welter that recognized and conformed to but few standards. Trade was hampered by lack of solid foundations for appraising and calculating values. Merchants and their customers who wanted to carry on honest, straightforward business were often impeded by the reputation for sharp and spurious dealings of others in the same markets. In addition, these same persons often had to deal with the sharpsters and in doing so they had to try to provide for sufficient margin to cover their additional risks.

Congress, recognizing the national character of the standards problem, in 1901 created the National Bureau of

Standards out of the Office of Weights and Measures. The Public Health Service in 1902 was given supervisory control, through licensing, of the manufacture, sale, and the distribution of biological and like products used in the treatment of diseases of man.

The Meat Inspection Act and the Food and Drugs Act were both passed on the same day, June 30, 1906. The Department of Agriculture in 1907 was granted appropriations to study Federal standardization. The Virus-Serum-Toxin Act of 1913 gave to the Bureau of Animal Industry, through licensing, supervision and control over viruses, serums, toxins, vaccines, and analogous products for use in the treatment of domestic animals. The Cotton Futures Act of 1914 established the Department in standardization work, and the use of official cotton standards was made compulsory on the New York and the New Orleans Cotton Exchanges in 1915.

The Standard Barrel Act of 1915, passed under the weights and measures clause of the Constitution, fixed the cubic contents of the standard barrel at 7,056 cubic inches. The Standard Containers Act of 1916, with 1934 amendments, fixed standards of dimension for the 2-quart, 4-quart, and 12-quart Climax baskets and set up the dry pint basket, the dry quart, and multiples thereof as the standard basket for small fruits, berries, and vegetables.

The Standard Containers Act of 1928 fixed standards for hampers, round stave baskets, and splint baskets for fruits and vegetables and for other purposes. The Grain Standards Act of 1916 required the use of Federal standards when grain is sold by grade in interstate commerce.

The Food Production Act of 1917 provided authority for establishment of standards and for permissive inspection services on fruits and vegetables as well as on other products. The Tobacco Stocks and Standards Act of 1929 authorized the Secretary of Agriculture to establish standards for the classification of tobacco stocks. The Tobacco Inspection Act of 1935 provided for tobacco standards and for mandatory and free inspection at designated auction markets.

The Agricultural Marketing Act of 1946 gave the Secretary broad powers to develop and establish standards for most of the farm products. These powers, supplemented by annual appropriations, provide the basis for development and administration of standards.

The Bureau of Internal Revenue establishes standards for packaging, branding, and labeling, and size and fill of containers of alcoholic beverages. Consumers must be provided with adequate information as to the quantity, quality, and identity of products. The Federal Trade Commission has defined certain methods and acts and practices as unfair, although standards of fair competition are not defined.

Federal specifications have been developed, in addition to the foregoing, to cover thousands of items that the Federal Government purchases in the open market or on direct order. The specifications provide standards for guidance of Government purchasing agents, for inspectors, and for any party who may wish to use them.

The work of the National Bureau of Standards has been extensive and outstanding in developing basic research as a foundation for standards and in helping other agencies, associations, and business enterprises to develop standards. Although the Bureau does not issue standards as such, much of its work is done to help others develop standards. The Bureau works with the Federal Specifications Board, the American Society for Testing Materials, the American Standards Association, and others to develop and promote precision, accuracy, simplification, and unification of standards in materials, parts, and products. In addition to the Bureau's research in the basic sciences to establish accuracy of measurements, it also assists in applied research. One of the Bureau's early projects in applied research was the development of specifications for electric lamps. Tests are carried on to find the answers to many questions, such as how long certain types of soles of shoes will wear, the effect of outdoor exposure on plastics, and thousands of other experiments which help to develop standards by which the value of commodities may be judged.

The need for a unifying force in the development of national standards has meant that the Federal Government has been invited (or, at times, forced) to take a leading part in the work. Many of the problems are similar to the one that plagued farmers, merchants, and the country in general on trying to get uniform weights and measures. The needs of trade are such that standards must be just as good in California or Texas as in New England.

Measurement is the basis of all science and the application of science to the field of market standards requires a knowledge of the products and the transactions to which it is to be applied. The development of market standards for grain, or cotton, or tobacco, or potatoes requires the application of scientific techniques, such as weight, size, color, moisture content, nutritional units, and similar measures, to the product and the evaluation of such factors in the minds of buyers and sellers. When combinations of factors are summed up for usual trading purposes, they can then be considered as a standard. If the trade in general, or the general buying public, considers these combinations of factors as a common pattern, standards or grades may be set forth for such products and trading on the basis of such standards is facilitated.

Farmers buying feed for some purposes may want particular vitamin content. The feed mixer in purchasing dehydrated alfalfa meal finds prices per ton varying in accordance with the units per pound of pro-vitamin A or carotene, because those units are important nutritionally to the feeder.

Tomato canners long have paid premium prices for bright color in the raw product. The problem was a direct monetary concern to the tomato grower, because he should be paid premiums for the better colors; to the canner because he wanted the better colors and would pay premiums for them but he did not want to pay any premiums for mistaken judgments on color; and to the inspector because he wanted to ascribe the proper color rating to the raw product so that both parties, the farmer and canner, would be treated fairly and justly.

Proper color was determined by the practical eye of the canner's agent or by an official inspector. The color determination, even with color charts, involved judgments based on sensory perception. Our scientists have been able for a long time to establish color quite objectively on the basis of light refractions.

However, tomato buyers, inspectors, and farmers were faced with the problem of applying known scientific techniques for color determination under operating field conditions. This meant that apparatus must be developed whereby persons with the usual ability and experience of a buyer or an inspector could determine quickly and accurately the proper color rating of the raw product.

A research team was organized in 1949. Growers, canners, manufacturers of scientific instruments, and State agricultural experiment station personnel, inspectors, and other department experts cooperated. The first year the results were promising but not entirely conclusive. Analysis of later research showed that not only was the team on the right track but workable solutions were in sight. Continuation of the work in 1952 showed some apparatus proved up quite well and that inspectors could expect in time to have equipment for a scientific measurement of color in tomatoes so that an objective determination of this important factor could be made quickly under field conditions.

Here we see the significance of precise, accurate measurements. Canners and growers long were aware of the importance of color in tomatoes. Color affected their pocketbooks. But what the eye of the canner saw, the grower did not always see, and vice versa. And sometimes neither grower nor canner fully agreed with the inspector. The new devices provide an improved scientific approach to measurement of an important factor affecting the value of a farm product. The importance of color in tomatoes has not changed by this development; only an objective means for applying accurate measurements in a uniform manner throughout the country has been devised.

STANDARDS are often first introduced through law to prevent or eliminate abuses in the market. The Meat Inspection Act and the original Food and Drugs Act are examples. They prohibit the movement in interstate commerce of substandard meats, foods, and drugs. Items were substandard because they were injurious to users, or they were offensive to buyers, usually for sanitary reasons. The effectiveness of these public regulations and the standards they enforce is best attested by the fact that no reputable business organization would wish to return to the days of such vicious competition and no consumer would wish to be the potential victim of a marketing system which provided so little protection against so many possible abuses. Minimum standards have been established by these acts below which meats, foods, and drugs should not fall. Buyers are thereby protected both physically and economically from potentially injurious products.

The Cotton Standards Act and the Grain Standards Act legally established the principle in our marketing system that when these farm products are compared with standards the varying qualities may be grouped into grades. Inspectors can determine and can officially certify the particular grade or grades of a product offered for sale. Certificates are determined by law to be prima facie evidence of the product's quality as shown on the certificate. Grades in those products were not new, but again, as in the early history of weights and measures, legal enactment solidified and assisted custom in facilitating the carrying out of the better interests of trade. Buyers and sellers are assisted by the use of grade standards in evaluating the products. A miller who wants a particular quality of wheat, or a textile manufacturer who wants a particular color and staple of cotton, can buy the grade needed from wholesalers, brokers, or through the respective commodity exchange and rest assured that the product received will accord with the terms of the sales contract.

The Standard Barrel Act and the Standard Containers Acts established measures of capacity. Under the container acts the customhouse bushel is officially approved as a basic measure and round stave baskets may be manufactured only in specified fractions or multiples of the bushel. Also, the standard basket or other container for small fruits, berries, and vegetables shall be fractions or multiples of the dry quart.

Standards for fruits and vegetables and other products were authorized as a war measure in 1917. The many fruit and vegetable standards which have since developed provide stratification of quality or grades for each product on which standards have been issued. The grades established a minimum quality below which no official grades apply and any portion of the product falling below this line is referred to officially as unclassified and in trade parlance as culls. That portion of the product which is as good as or better than the minimum quality may fall within the grades established for it. United States Standards for Potatoes, which are commonly used for farm and wholesale trading, establish the following grades: U. S. Fancy; U. S. Extra No. 1; U. S. No. 1; U. S. Commercial; and U. S. No. 2. In addition, size classifications are estab-

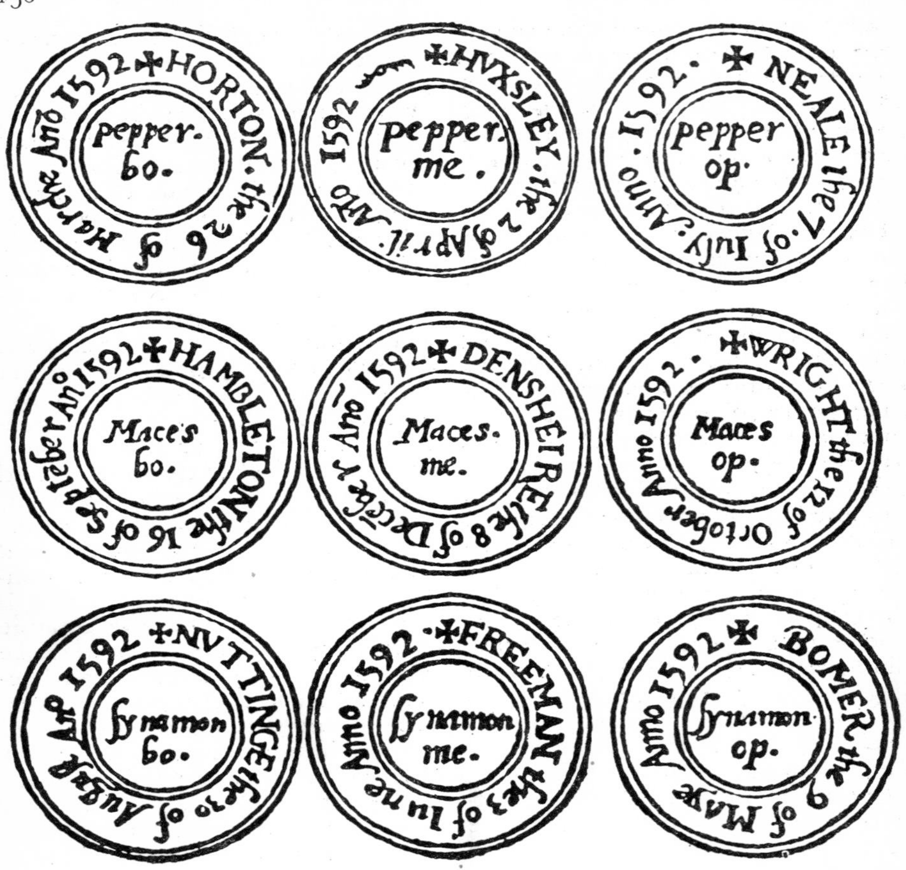

MARKS USED BY SIXTEENTH CENTURY GROCERS IN LONDON FOR SPICES

lished based upon the diameter or weight of tubers, with Size A referring to larger potatoes and Size B to small; i. e. 1½ to 2 inches in diameter.

U. S. Consumer Standards have also been issued for potatoes. They embody much the same quality characteristics as the wholesale potato grades, but the quality stratification differs somewhat from the other. Potatoes are separated under this system into U. S. Grade A small, medium, medium to large, and large, and into U. S. Grade B small, medium, medium to large, and large. The consumer standards attempt to simplify the system of quality distinctions by reducing the number of classifications which the consumer must keep in mind.

Federal or Federal-State inspectors, by sampling or through a continuous inspection, determine the grade or grades of fruits and vegetables when they are called upon for their services.

Any attempt to project an outlook for market standards finds the answer partly reflected in the past. Market standards, as so many other human institutions, move slowly, but they do move. The time seems long and far distant since the English knights at Runnymede got an unwilling King John to agree to one measure of weight, and one measure of breadth, and one measure of length throughout the land.

Very many of the relationships upon

which our measures were founded have been lost. For example, when starting the second half of the twentieth century, the human foot from which our basic measure of length originated is used in name only to measure length. Even last century's basic yard as preserved in a well-protected platinum bar is giving way to the modern and more accurate spectroscopic lamp containing a single pure isotope of mercury. Atomic clocks, we are told, offer measures of time more precisely than the rotations of the earth. Chemists and nutritionists also tell us of the importance of vitamins and give us measures for determining where and to what extent they exist. Physicists adopt refractions of light to devices for quickly and accurately measuring colors affecting quality of foods. Means of measurements have advanced as science and invention have helped to serve man through the many institutions, such as markets, which also serve his needs. (*Edward E. Gallahue.*)

Grades and Grading

The purpose of grading is to establish a common language understood and used by buyers and sellers as a basis of judging the quality of a product in relation to its sales price.

Grading practices and grades must recognize the changes that may occur under varying conditions and in the commodities covered. The grade is the established measure of quality that is applied during the grading of the commodity in question. An inspector may do the grading, or the product may be graded and the inspector requested to inspect it and certify the accuracy of the grade. Not all inspection, of course, is related to grading.

Grading is a basic function in practically all transactions. Sometimes, as at tobacco auctions, buyers have their own private standards based on the use they have in mind. The standards may or may not be related to the 7 classes of 25 types of tobacco which are covered in the Federal grades and are used by the producer as a guide to the market value of his product.

The quality of grain, cotton, eggs, butter, potatoes, onions, and practically all other items bought and sold on the various commodity exchanges is designated in the terms of Federal grades. The transactions generally are based on certificates of grade issued under Federal or Federal-State authority, which are evidence in all Federal courts and most State courts as to the facts contained therein.

The price received for a given commodity at a given time does not always reflect its grade. Demand, available supply, and general market conditions are important factors.

Under certain conditions a commodity may have excellent flavor and food value but be downgraded because of poor appearance. One of indifferent flavor and food value may be placed in a higher grade because it looks good.

Some markets have definite preferences, such as a premium price for brown eggs, while other markets may discount them even though they are just as fresh and big as white eggs.

Some markets pay a premium for certain varieties of apples or potatoes because of size, shape, or color, without seriously considering flavor or general edibility.

But all factors of condition, such as decay and maturity, must be recognized in grading perishable items, regardless of any other qualities they might have. A shipment of Delicious apples, perfect in shape and color, would be sharply discounted in price if they were overmature even if they met U. S. Fancy requirements in all other respects.

Grading and grades do not necessarily refer in all instances to Federal grading and grades. When the terms are applied to agricultural products, however, Federal or State grades and Federal or Federal-State grading and inspection services are implied. Some private inspection agencies confine their operations largely to the needs of certain organizations or companies that desire special information closely related to their own business. Even the findings of those agencies are based primarily on Federal and State grades.

INSPECTION AND CERTIFICATION of farm products based upon established grades have become a fixed part of our agricultural economy over the years.

Many States adopted their own grading and inspection procedures, and the difficulty of correlating the various terms in both domestic and foreign commerce became more pronounced and complex. In 1917 Congress passed Public Law No. 40: The Food Production Act to Provide Further for the National Security and Defense by Stimulating Agriculture and Facilitating the Distribution of Agricultural Products. It authorized the Secretary of Agriculture to investigate and certify to shippers the condition as to soundness of fruits and vegetables and other foods. After the passage of the act a broad national policy began to take shape, and the confusion caused by conflicting trade terms and practices abated rapidly.

Any grading and inspection service, whether governmental or private, to be effective must apply uniformly the standards upon which its operations are based. An outline of some of the general procedures followed in the development of grades and the grading, inspection, and certification of some of the major agricultural commodities explains some of the problems in this important field.

THE AMOUNT AND QUALITY of yarn and cloth that can be made from a bale of cotton vary directly with the amount and kind of trash in the cotton. The color of the cotton fibers affects the usefulness in the bleached goods and its adaptability to dyes and other finishes. Smoothness of ginning and the extent of fiber imperfections affect the quantity of manufacturing waste and the smoothness and uniformity of yarn produced. Length of staple affects the fineness and strength of yarn. The various procedures required in the grading and classing of cotton require particular care and discrimination.

In classing cotton, samples are taken from individual bales and sent to one of the Department's boards of cotton examiners. The Department maintains more than 30 such boards besides the appeal board of review examiners. The classification or the determination of the grade and staple length of cotton is done manually by comparison of samples with the official cotton standards, which are used throughout the world where our American cotton is bought and sold.

Approximately two-thirds of the cotton crop is classed for farmers under the Smith-Doxey Act. The Department also classes all of the cotton tendered on futures and maintains a classing service for the general public.

VOLUNTARY INSPECTION of rosin and turpentine under the Naval Stores Act takes into consideration such factors in rosin as the color (hue, purity, and brightness), cleanliness, brightness, and freedom from foreign matter.

Turpentine specifications delimit the physical and chemical properties, including color, specific gravity, refractive index, initial boiling point, percentage distilling within established temperature ranges, distillation, polymerization, evaporation, residue, and acidity.

INSPECTION OF TOBACCO under the Tobacco Inspection Act is available on auction markets if growers vote for it. If two-thirds of the votes favor inspection, the Secretary of Agriculture designates a market or a group of markets for inspection.

The act also provides for permissive inspection, which is reimbursable, and for market news and demonstration. The service thus can certify to the seller the grade, furnish the current price for each grade, inform the farmer as to the best methods of preparation for market, and thereby aid the producer in securing the maximum return for his commodity.

Grades are established by division and subdivision of a given type or class of tobacco until a point is reached at which further subdivision is neither essential nor desirable. Each subdivision is called a grade.

The first division of the tobacco is made on the basis of its distinct characteristics caused by varieties of seed, soils, climate, and the methods of cultivation, harvesting, and curing. This division is called a class. There are seven classes: Class 1, Flue-Cured; class 2, Fire-Cured; class 3, Air-Cured; class 4, Cigar Filler; class 5, Cigar Binder; class 6, Cigar Wrapper; and class 7, Miscellaneous Domestic Tobaccos.

A type is a division of a class having common characteristics, which permit its division into a number of closely related grades. Tobacco that has the same characteristics and corresponding qualities, colors, and lengths is treated as one type. There are 25 types. Types 11, 12, 13, and 14 apply to Flue-Cured; 21, 22, and 23 to Fire-Cured; 31, 32, 35, 36, and 37 to Air-Cured; 41, 42, 43, 44, and 46 to Cigar Filler; 51, 52, 53, 54, and 55 to Cigar Binder; 61 and 62 to Cigar Wrapper; and 70 to Miscellaneous Types of Domestic tobacco.

The next subdivision divides each type into a grade, based on group, quality, and color. Group is determined by the shape of leaf, body, percentage of injury, and other common characteristics. Quality has six degrees: Choice, Fine, Good, Fair, Low, and Common; each is based on a combination of elements of smoothness, oil, maturity, body, width, porosity, color, color shade, finish, and uniformity. The third factor is color, under which each quality of the several groups is divided into colors as required.

The group, quality, and color are combined to form the grade, which describes any specific lot.

Official grain standards are in effect covering wheat, corn, barley, rye, oats, feed oats, mixed feed oats, grain sorghums, flaxseed, soybeans, and mixed grain.

Each kind of grain, except rye and flaxseed, is divided into two or more classes, which may be further divided into two or more subclasses. From two to five numerical grades are provided for each class or subclass. The quality of the grain for the respective numerical grades is measured by its relative freedom from moisture, damaged kernels, split or broken kernels, foreign material, and mixtures of other classes, and by its test weight per bushel. Grain is graded Sample grade if it contains those factors in excess of those permitted, or is below the required test weight in the lowest numerical grade, or is sour, musty, heating, has a commercially objectionable odor, or is otherwise of distinctly low quality.

Among the special grades are Weevily, Garlicky, Smutty, Bright, Heavy, and Plump. Those terms may be used in connection with numerical grade designations to reflect more adequately the quality and condition of the grain; for example, No. 3 Yellow Corn *Weevily*, No. 1 *Heavy* White Oats.

Amount of moisture is one grading factor for corn, grain sorghums, and soybeans, in which a maximum percentage is provided for each grade. For all other grains, the same maximum moisture percentage is provided for all numerical grades of each grain, and (except for mixed feed oats and flaxseed) a special grade, Tough, is provided for grains containing more than that percentage.

Under the U. S. Grain Standards Act, original inspections are made by inspectors employed by the grain inspection departments of the State or the grain exchange or by inspectors who operate independently on a fee basis. All inspectors must be licensed by the Secretary of Agriculture. They are not allowed to trade in grain or be employed by grain merchants.

Federal grain inspection supervisors at the various markets work with the licensed inspectors to keep them informed as to inspection methods and the correct interpretation and application of grading factors. Federal supervisors also take samples of a cross section of grain tendered for inspection under the act to determine whether the inspections by licensees are made properly. Anyone who is dissatisfied with an original inspection may request an appeal inspection of the Federal grain inspection supervisor in the district where the inspection is made.

The system has enabled the Federal Government to furnish an unbiased inspection service, based on uniform standards, to all segments of the grain industry.

GRADING AND INSPECTION services cover the grading of live poultry and shell eggs, the certification of dressed poultry produced under Department of Agriculture sanitary standards, inspection for wholesomeness of dressed poultry and dressed domestic rabbits, the grading of dressed poultry and ready-to-cook poultry, inspection of poultry for canning, and the inspection of frozen and dried eggs as to sanitary regulations.

Grading generally involves sorting as to quality and size and determining the class and condition of the products at the time of grading. Grading may be for class, quality, quantity, or condition.

The grade of shell eggs is determined by candling—placing the egg before a light, which shines through the shell. Candling shows the extent of moisture loss (shrinkage), the appearance and position of the yolk, and any foreign particles, such as small specks of blood, and enables the inspector to determine the quality of each egg. Classes of quality range from AA, the finest, to C, the lowest edible quality; A and B are intermediate.

Inspection, as used in the poultry regulations, refers to any inspection of poultry during operations involving the removal of the viscera to determine the condition of the poultry and its healthfulness and fitness for human food. In the preparation and processing of frozen eggs, inspection means the continuous supervision and certification that the product is sound and sanitary.

The service is elective and is supported by fees. It is conducted on the basis of cooperative agreements between the Department of Agriculture and State agencies.

All persons employed in the Poultry and Poultry Products Grading and Inspection Service who are authorized to issue certificates must be licensed by the Secretary. Only veterinarians can be full-fledged inspectors, but other inspectors may be employed under the supervision of a veterinary inspector.

Federal supervision is maintained on a national, regional circuit, and State basis in order to effect uniform application and interpretation of policies and grade standards.

FEDERAL GRADES form the basis for the efficient modern marketing of livestock and meats, although only part of the meat and none of the livestock is officially graded by the Department of Agriculture.

(Meat grading should not be confused with the inspection for sanitation and freedom from disease, also carried on by employees of the Department of Agriculture under the Meat Inspection Act of 1906, discussed on page 220.)

The official United States standards for market classes and grades of carcass beef were set in 1926. Grade standards have been extended since then to include the feeder and slaughter classes

USDA Classification and grading schedule for slaughter livestock and their carcasses

Class or kind	Subclass	Grades
Beef	Steer, heifer, cow[1]	Prime, Choice, Good, Commercial, Utility, Cutter, Canner.
	Bull and stag	Choice, Good, Commercial, Utility, Cutter, Canner.
Calf		Prime, Choice, Good, Commercial, Utility, Cull.
Veal		Same as calf.
Lamb		Prime, Choice, Good, Utility, Cull.
Yearling mutton		Same as lamb.
Mutton		Choice, Good, Utility, Cull.
Pork	Barrows and gilts	Choice No. 1, Choice No. 2, Choice No. 3, Medium, and Cull.

[1] Cows are not eligible for the Prime grade.

of most species of market livestock and meat derived therefrom. All the grade standards have remained practically unchanged since their origin, except for two changes.

The beef standards, which previously had provided for grading each class of beef (steer, heifer, cow, stag, and bull) on a separate standard, were modified in 1939 to provide for the grading of all steer, heifer, and cow beef on a single standard.

The beef standards were again modified in 1950, when the Prime and Choice grades were combined as a single grade Prime, the Good grade became Choice, and the beef from the younger animals in the upper part of the Commercial grade was designated Good. Corresponding changes were made at the same time in the standards for slaughter cattle. In 1951 similar changes were made in both the carcass and slaughter standards for veal and calf and for lamb and mutton. Standards were set in 1952 for slaughter barrows and gilts and their carcasses.

The system of U. S. grade standards for livestock and meat has been prepared so that the standards for slaughter animals coincide with the standards for their carcasses and the same grade name applies to both. Since it is possible to appraise more accurately the grade-determining factors in carcasses than it is in live animals, carcass grades are always considered as a reference for the grades of slaughter animals.

The only official use made of the standards for grades of live animals is the Market News Service in reporting sales of livestock, but the standards are used by all who trade in livestock.

The meat grading and stamping service, inaugurated in 1927, has expanded in volume until a large percentage of the higher grades of beef, veal, calf, lamb, and mutton are federally graded.

Except for two periods when price controls on meat were in force and when Federal meat grading was made compulsory by Government order, or when required by State or municipal regulations, the grading service has been strictly voluntary and performed only on request.

It has always operated on a fee basis. The fees are used to defray the costs of the service. The grading is done only by experienced Federal employees. Their work is reviewed constantly by local and traveling supervisors, whose responsibility it is to maintain a uniform application of the grade standards over the entire country.

The grade name and the letters USDA in a shield are stamped on meat. Except for beef and lamb, the class or kind of meat is also indicated in the stamp. The grade name is applied in such a manner that at least one imprint of the grade name appears on most retail cuts.

To insure that all meat which is federally graded is also wholesome, the grading service is restricted to meat that has been federally inspected or inspected by some Government agency whose inspection service has been approved by the Department.

The Meat Grading Service also conducts a rather extensive acceptance service for large-scale users of meat. This service consists of accepting carcasses, cuts, and other meat items, many of them processed or fabricated, according to definite purchase specifications furnished by the purchaser. Such purchases are usually made on contract and the grading service acts as the agent of the purchaser in certifying that the meats offered by the successful bidder comply with the contract specifications. This service is used by most Federal agencies and many State, county, and city institutions, as well as many private agencies, such as steamship lines, hotels, and restaurants.

THE DAIRY PRODUCTS grading service of the Department of Agriculture, authorized by an act of Congress, was inaugurated in 1919. At the inception of the grading service, the Department of Agriculture in cooperation with representatives of the dairy industry developed and promulgated U. S. standards for grades of creamery butter and Cheddar cheese. More recently U. S. standards have been developed and promulgated for swiss cheese, nonfat dry milk solids, and dry whole milk. Other miscellaneous dairy products, including process cheese, evaporated and sweetened condensed milk, canned whole milk, ice cream, and cottage cheese are usually graded and inspected in accordance with Federal specifications, Department of Agriculture purchase announcements, or other applicable contract specifications.

The service provides for grading at terminal markets and shipping points; resident grading at assembling and packaging plants, manufacturing, or processing plants; the sampling of the product for laboratory analysis; and surveys of manufacturing or processing plants to determine quality of raw material supply, condition of facilities and equipment, methods employed, and sanitation.

The actual grading and inspection are performed by Federal employees except in States where the cooperating State agency provides from its staff qualified employees, who are licensed by the Secretary of Agriculture.

To assure uniform grade interpretation and policy procedure, inspectors and graders work under the supervision of area supervisors, who report to the Washington office. This impartial quality evaluation of dairy products is recognized and accepted by producers, processors, assemblers, and distributors as an important procedure in the orderly marketing of dairy products.

FOR FRESH AND PROCESSED fruit and vegetables Federal grades were authorized under the Food Production Act of 1917.

Approximately 140 grades for fresh fruits and vegetables and more than 100 grades for processed fruits and vegetables and their allied products have been developed and promulgated. The volume, number, and variations of the commodities create complex problems that require constant study. Technicians are continuously engaged in amending existing grades, developing new ones, and devising better procedures for applying them.

Artists are employed to make models that show exactly the various fruits and vegetables and depict shape and limitations permitted in the various grades.

Grades for processed fruits and vegetables must take into consideration the manner in which the products are processed, any mold and foreign materials, and their general characteristics, as well as the factors of greatest importance to consumers.

All inspection and certification work is based upon those grades. Inspectors are subject to constant training and are closely supervised. Except where

State regulations or Federal marketing agreements and orders make it mandatory, the service is elective.

Continuous inspection service is furnished upon request to plants that process and pack fruits and vegetables.

All products then are packed under the constant supervision of Federal inspectors, and the packer may mark his products thus packed with the shield of the United States and the specific grade of the commodity. Such inspection is mostly of processed products, but some prepacking operators have utilized it for the packing of fresh fruits and vegetables on the basis of consumer grades.

Operations are conducted on both a Federal and cooperative Federal-State basis. Fees are set at a level that makes the service as nearly self-sustaining as possible. Practically all wholesale trading in the commodities depends directly or indirectly on the grades, grading, and inspection work conducted by this service.

A GRADING AND INSPECTION PROGRAM covering commodities so diverse and produced and marketed over such wide areas must necessarily vary in accordance with the nature and utilization of the commodities.

Nearly all the activities are conducted on a Federal basis or through cooperative Federal-State agreements.

Most of the Federal-State work is confined to points of origin. A major part of the work in destination markets is conducted by the Federal department alone. Because of the differences between the commodities and the various regulations pertaining to them, however, variation between the procedures of the various commodity branches of the Department of Agriculture is to be expected.

Except for the work performed by the Food and Drug Administration, all Federal and Federal-State grading and inspection of agricultural products, regardless of their many variations, have one thing in common in that the authority for their supervision and general direction rests in the Secretary of Agriculture. This responsibility is delegated, with varying modifications, down to the operating levels.

That procedure establishes a direct line of authority extending from the office of the Secretary into every important shipping-point area and terminal market in the country.

For most commodities the operations under cooperative agreements with States constitute an important part of the grading service.

Under these agreements, Federal, area, and State supervisors train, license, and supervise local inspectors who, in general, are employed by the respective States under the terms of cooperative agreements developed by such States and the United States Department of Agriculture. The agreements vary in accordance with different State laws and regulations. However, the basic Federal policies must be complied with to the extent that the various grades used are interpreted and enforced in a uniform manner, and that properly qualified individuals are selected to act as Federal licensees.

Federal or Federal-State certificates issued by the grading and inspection services are subject to appeal and can be reversed or sustained upon approval of the Washington office or delegated field office in accordance with facts established after review and analysis of the original inspection.

Because of the wide variety of agricultural commodities for which grades and grading services have been developed and the variations of handling and trading, it has never been feasible to establish uniform grade terminology or grading procedures. Commodities like grain, tobacco, cotton, and naval stores by their very nature must be handled and graded or classed in a much different manner from fruits, vegetables, meats, poultry, eggs, milk, butter, and cheese.

Producers, distributors, and consumers are concerned with certain factors relating to each commodity that are seldom common to all. The

281437°—54——12

terms U. S. No. 1, or U. S. Grade A, Prime, or 90 Score mean certain, definite things to the major perishable and semiperishable food industry, while Strict Low Middling, Nancy, Mary, Kate, Class 1 Flue-Cured, and No. 1 Heavy White Oats are well-known terms to those concerned with cotton, naval stores, tobacco, and grain.

Criticisms have been voiced that the multiplicity of terms was confusing to consumers. In some of the food items, such as eggs and processed fruit and vegetables, it has been possible to adopt the terms U. S. Grade A, B, and C, and have such terms carry through all wholesale trading channels direct to the retail level.

Consumer standards carrying the alphabetical nomenclature have been developed for some fresh vegetables, such as potatoes and tomatoes. Only a comparatively limited use has been made of grades developed entirely for consumer utilization. Future expansion of work in the strictly consumer field will doubtless depend upon the demand made for this type of service and the developments that may occur in the prepackaging industry. (*Merritt W. Baker.*)

Compulsory Grade Labeling

Interest in grade labeling of consumers' goods in the United States began in the 1920's, when many people felt dissatisfaction with the amount and kind of information given them about foods they bought.

Grades and grading were coming then to be generally accepted, especially in agricultural marketing, as devices for describing quality of goods. Grades were found to be useful to growers, processors, and market agencies. It appeared that they would also be useful to describe the quality of many consumers' retail goods.

Compulsory—or mandatory—grade labeling is generally accepted as the legal requirement that one of two or more generally recognized and accepted grades be used on the label of a product to denote its quality or size.

The compulsory labeling of milk with the grade was one of the first ventures in compulsory grade labeling of consumers' goods. Another was embodied in the McNary-Mapes amendment of 1930 to the Federal Food and Drugs Act, which provided that canned foods (except meat, meat products, and milk) below the standard of quality, condition, and fill of container promulgated by the Secretary of Agriculture shall be labeled "Below U. S. Standard—Low Quality but not Illegal" or "Slack Fill," as the case may be.

The law was sponsored by the canning industry. It gave consumers some measure of protection against paying a high price for low-quality products.

Interest in grade labeling grew in the early 1930's when incomes of many consumers fell to a low level. By then, however, opposition to it had risen, and controversy developed.

Controversy over grade labeling has waxed strongest during three different periods—when the proposal was made that compulsory grade labeling be written into the codes of fair competition of the National Recovery Administration; when efforts were made to pass a federal food and drug law containing provisions for quality standards for food; and when the Office of Price Administration issued regulations during the Second World War making compulsory the grade labeling of specific consumers' goods as part of its wartime program to establish and enforce maximum prices.

The Consumers' Counsel of the Agricultural Adjustment Administration in

1933 advocated compulsory grade labeling of certain agricultural products according to the grades already established by the Department of Agriculture.

The Consumers Advisory Board of the National Recovery Administration recommended that a uniform provision be inserted in all the codes requiring that a committee be appointed to develop a series of suitable standards for grades of commodities concerned and to develop accurate labeling which would be readily usable by consumers.

Efforts of the consumers' agencies to make grade labeling compulsory were on the whole unsuccessful. The absence of organized groups of consumers, the failure of some officials of the Administration to understand the consumers' position, and the urgency to get the codes into operation were largely responsible for their failure.

The greatest controversy developed over some efforts of the consumers' agencies to make the use of the grades for canned fruits and vegetables, as set up by the Department of Agriculture, compulsory in the code covering the canning industry.

The opposition of the canning industry was so great that the canners' code was put into operation in May 1934 without any provisions for grade labeling. The President, after signing the code, issued an executive order requiring the appointment of a committee by the canning industry to formulate standards of quality for the products of the industry and to make recommendations regarding the standards and labeling requirements within 90 days.

The report submitted by the committee was considered inadequate by the NRA Administrator in charge of the canning code. The matter hung fire, and the code, without the grade-labeling requirements, continued in force until the National Industrial Recovery Act was invalidated in May of 1935.

The National Canners Association took a leading part in the controversy. They maintained that compulsory grade labeling was impractical and undesirable and that it would be disastrous to the industry and to consumers. They disapproved the so-called ABC system, such as is used in the grades for canned fruits and vegetables set up by the Department of Agriculture. The system provides that a single letter, number, or term be used to designate each grade, with A, No. 1, or Fancy designating the top grade.

The major objections the canners raised rested upon the inclusion or omission of the factor of flavor in the grades. They argued that if flavor were included the grades would be unenforceable, because flavor was not susceptible to objective measurement and the quality grades without the flavor factor would be misleading. They maintained that an unenforceable or misleading system would be an incentive to misbranding. The idea of "descriptive labeling" was introduced as a counterproposal to grade labeling, which they feared would be forced on them.

The Consumers Advisory Board of the NRA considered feasible the use of the grades set up by the Department of Agriculture for canned fruits and vegetables as a basis for labeling products for over-the-counter buyers. Canners were then packing and selling their products according to those quality grades and on that basis were borrowing money from the banks. The Government purchased only products graded according to these standards.

The use of similar grade labeling on canned products was compulsory in Canada and their use seemed to be satisfactory. American canners who shipped goods into Canada and those who had set up plants in Canada were able to comply with these requirements without any apparent hardship.

The Consumers Advisory Board was supported in its stand by a few canners who were already using grade labels, a number of women's organizations, some Government officials, and labor organizations. Among those testifying at hearings in favor of the use of grade labels were representatives of the American Federation of Labor, Tri-State Packers Association, General Federation of Women's Clubs, National League of Women Voters, American Association of University Women, and the American Home Economics Association.

Compulsory grade labeling also became a matter of controversy in 1933 when a movement was started to replace the somewhat outmoded Food and Drugs Act of 1906.

One of the first bills introduced into the Congress to provide a new law contained a provision authorizing the Secretary of Agriculture to establish "standards of quality and fill of container for any food." It also contained provisions for labeling foods in terms of standards of quality and for the establishment of a voluntary inspection service for producers.

"Standards of quality" were generally understood to be for the purpose of grading goods. Such standards go beyond the standard of identity or the minimum standard below which no product may fall and still be allowed on the market. They go beyond the single standard of quality and the provision, such as the one in the McNary-Mapes amendment of 1930, that canned fruits and vegetables falling below the standard must be labeled. If more than one such standard is set up, three or more grades result.

Discussion inside and outside legislative halls waxed hot—producers against the standards and consumers and officials of the Food and Drug Administration for them. The pressure against standards and grade labels was so great that other bills were introduced more in line with the producers' views.

The new Food, Drug, and Cosmetic Act, finally passed in 1938, gave the Administrator the power to establish with certain exceptions a "reasonable standard of quality" for foods. The new act, by limiting the establishment of standards to "a standard" instead of "standards," precluded the establishment of any standards that provide three or more grades.

The controversy over compulsory grade labeling developed again in 1943. The Office of Price Administration was then faced with the problem of preventing hidden inflation through deliberate depreciation of quality.

As the authority to control this type of inflation was given to the Administration in the Price Control Act, officials of OPA turned to the use of standards in establishing ceiling prices. They also turned to the use of labels showing quality of goods because they could not enforce ceiling prices unless consumers knew the quality they received at the established prices.

Grade labels for consumers' use were required for women's rayon hosiery, beef, veal, lamb, mutton, butter, eggs, peanuts, rubber heels, and antifreeze. Labels for sheets and pillowcases showing type and size were required for retailers' use but not for consumers' although most retailers carried the labels through to consumers.

Producers raised few objections to the mandatory use of grade labels. Objections to the grade labeling of hosiery, however, were raised by the makers and distributors of the widely advertised products which were not given a price differential over unadvertised products in the same grade.

All went reasonably well until the OPA issued an order in January 1943 stating that ceiling prices of the 1943 pack of canned fruits and vegetables would be based on the grades set up by the Department of Agriculture and that those products must be labeled with the grade.

Canners protested this order. Their views regarding the compulsory grade labeling of their products had not changed since the NRA controversy. They joined with the opponents of the grade labeling of hosiery and attempted to get the OPA to rescind the order. Failing in that, they took the matter to the Congress.

Grade labeling was investigated by

the Congress in 1943. At least five congressional committees took a hand in the matter. The Boren Committee, a subcommittee of the Committee on Interstate and Foreign Commerce of the House of Representatives, held hearings, at which testimony was taken from manufacturers and distributors of canned foods, groceries, hosiery, knitted underwear, work clothing, and tool steel, all of whom opposed grade labeling. No statement was taken from consumers' agencies.

Legislation in June 1943, which appropriated funds for the war agencies for the following year, provided that no funds were to be used for promulgating or enforcing grade labeling of food products, wearing apparel, or other processed or manufactured products. The next month the Taft amendment to the Emergency Price Control Act repealed those provisions and denied OPA the authority to require the grade labeling of any commodity or to restrict the use of trade and brand names.

The Taft amendment also provided that OPA could not issue orders establishing prices based on specifications and standards unless they were in general use in the trade before the order; unless grades had been promulgated and required by another Government agency; or unless no other practicable method existed for effecting price control.

Grade labeling was again debated in 1944 before the passage of the act to extend price controls, but no changes were made in the Taft amendment when it was incorporated into the act.

Although grade labeling of other products was abandoned by OPA, that for specified meats continued through the war. The order for grade labeling of those products was issued by the Office of Economic Stabilization. The office received its authority from the President. It was made on the basis that grade labels were essential to the enforcement of ceiling prices. The grade labeling of meat had been satisfactory during its previous existence and its continuance was recommended by the industry.

The canners of processed fruits and vegetables sparked the opposition to grade labeling during the wartime controversy. They objected to both compulsory grade labeling and to the pricing of their products on the basis of grades. This resulted in an amendment to the Appropriation Act of 1944 which prohibited the payment of salaries of employees of OPA who used standards or specifications for processed fruits and vegetables other than those already in general use.

At the request of the Boren Committee, the OPA had canceled the order to price the 1943 pack of canned fruits and vegetables on the basis of grades. It was announced in July 1944 that the 1944 pack would be priced on the basis of grades.

The justification of the 1944 order was based on the fact that the Government grades were in general use in the canning industry and that therefore their use was justified under the amendment to the Appropriation Act of 1944. Some canners, naturally, objected to that order. The Comptroller General, who had the final word, said he could not approve funds for such a method of pricing because it was Congress' intent to prevent the use of grades.

Efforts were made early in 1943 by a number of organizations representing household buyers to obtain protection for consumers against rising prices and falling quality. Members of 28 national organizations requested the OPA to use informative labeling on clothing and other products.

Such organizations as the American Home Economics Association, the Congress of Industrial Organizations, the National Farmers Union, and the Brotherhood of Railroad Trainmen urged that because 55 percent to 60 percent of the country's pack of canned fruits and vegetables were bought and sold on the basis of Government grades, the grades should be used in pricing the products.

When trouble started in Korea and controls over prices were again instituted, the possibility of compulsory grade labeling was in large measure forestalled by those framing the Defense Production Act of 1950. Practically the same wording that was used in the Taft amendment in 1943 was incorporated in the act prohibiting the use of grade labeling and limiting the establishment of prices on the basis of grades.

Grade labeling of consumers' goods was instituted only for certain meats.

The Office of Price Stabilization required that each carcass and wholesale cut of beef, veal, calf, lamb, and yearling mutton must be graded and grade-marked according to the official standards for grades of the respective products as set up by the Department of Agriculture. The requirements were authorized on the basis that no practical alternative existed for securing effective price control of the products. They were accepted without any great protest and undoubtedly provided protection to consumers during the time they were effective.

Descriptive labeling was brought to the fore again during the wartime controversy over grade labeling as a counterproposal to the grade labeling. According to the canners' concept, decriptive labeling means: "The adequate descriptive label for canned foods states separately, in specific, uniformly used terms, readily understood by the ordinary person, and in legible type so arranged as to be easily seen and read, every fact about the product which is genuinely useful to the consumer and which can be stated. For the sake of uniform use and of equitable and ready enforcement, each term is either self-defined or is based upon an objective test."

A check list of 15 points to be covered in descriptive labeling of canned fruits and vegetables was published in 1942. The points included the name and variety name of product, type of pack, description of product and method of processing, seasoning, density of sirup, degree of maturity, five methods of describing quantity, and four points covering use. Those points provide little information about a product beyond that required under the Food, Drug, and Cosmetic Act. They emphasize quantity and use and provide practically no information about quality. The canners' association has been attempting to standardize such terms as "very young," "young," and "nearly mature" to describe certain vegetables and other similar terms for the other vegetables and for fruits.

The National Canners Association has been supported in its promotion of descriptive labeling by the National Wholesale Grocers Association, National Food Brokers Association, United States Wholesale Grocers Association, and the National Association of Retail Grocers.

Descriptive labeling of canned fruits and vegetables was not accepted by the NRA Administrator of the canners' code as an adequate method of describing quality of those products. Neither has it been accepted by consumers' representatives. It should be pointed out that use of a grade label does not preclude the use of descriptive labeling on a product. Some producers use both.

THE FOREGOING SKETCH of the controversy over compulsory grade labeling brings out many of the issues involved.

Practically all, if not all, manufacturers, processors, and distributors are opposed to compulsory grade labeling. Farmers now sell much of their products on the basis of wholesale grades and therefore are less seriously concerned.

Many arguments have been advanced against compulsory grade labeling. Some declare it is impracticable and costly. Producers of well-known brands fear that if they are required to use grade labels describing quality they will lose the competitive advantage they have built up about their brands through advertising, satisfied customers, and the like. Others who use grade labels on a voluntary basis do not want it made compulsory lest they lose their competitive advantage over those who do not use grade labels.

Compulsory grade labeling does mean a certain amount of regimentation of processors and distributors, but advocates declare the burden of such regimentation may be overemphasized; they point out that some States require grade labeling of such products as eggs and butter and that compliance has not overburdened any of the producers.

The administrative machinery necessary to enforce mandatory grade labeling is considered a disadvantage by some, but others point out that the Federal and State Governments now spend a tiny part of their efforts protecting consumers, especially consumers' pocketbooks.

Some opponents of grade labeling declare the cost would be prohibitive. The advocates challenge that contention and say it is not necessarily true for all products, and that the cost of administering compulsory grade labeling for many products would be small, especially in relation to the savings made by consumers.

Obstacles to grade labeling include the technical problems of measuring and testing qualities to determine conformity to grade. Another obstacle is that if grades are to be satisfactory they must be based on the qualities that consumers look for in goods. The information is not always available without considerable investigation. Also, consumers' wants change from time to time.

Even its most ardent proponents do not suggest that grade labeling be made compulsory for all goods. It is not necessary for some, and it may not be practical for others.

Compulsory grade labeling may be desirable for some goods even when no emergency, such as war or depression, exists—goods for which consumers have no way of identifying and comparing quality other than brand names. Two circumstances may bring compulsory grade labeling about. One is if producers cannot police the market through their own efforts and ask the Government for grade labeling to protect them against each other. Such circumstances arose when the canners instigated the McNary-Mapes amendment to the Food and Drugs Act. Again, if in the eyes of the general public the need for consumers' protection becomes serious and if producers are unwilling to take action, mandatory grade labeling might gain control. That happened when steps were taken to protect consumers of foods and drugs through the passage of the original Food and Drugs Act. (*Jessie V. Coles.*)

PERSONAL INCOME IN THE UNITED STATES, 1940-52

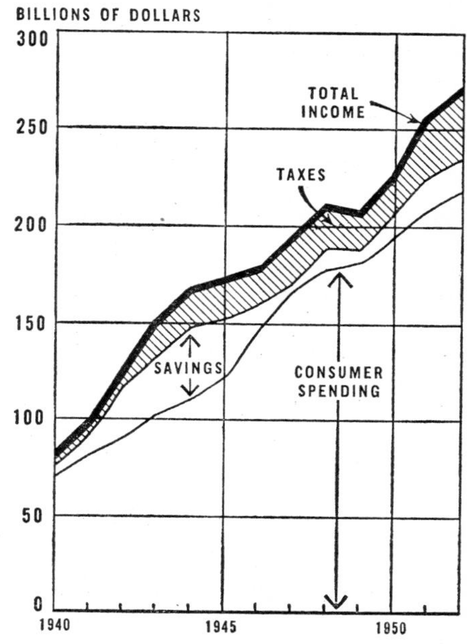

Facts—fast

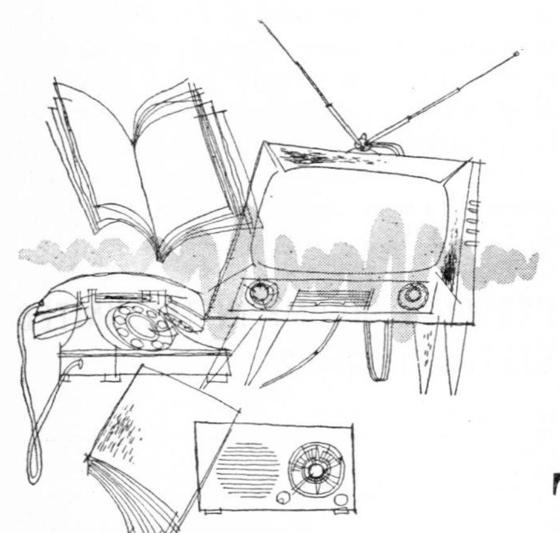

The network of telephone, telegraph, and teletype communications gets California lettuce and citrus, Louisiana strawberries, and Florida truck crops on their way at the best moment for shipment and makes certain their proper distribution to hundreds of wholesale buyers in just the amounts they stand ready to handle. Each person in the market needs information on some questions if he is to make orderly marketing plans. To the extent that the information is available and systems of communications are properly used to get the information where and when it is needed, the flow of supplies from farm to distant market can be made efficient. To the extent that we do not get the reliable information, or do not make the best use of instruments of communications to distribute it, we risk delay, waste, and other inefficiencies. The Department of Agriculture compiles hundreds of statistical reports on all phases of marketing and operates 11,000 miles of leased wire to all principal markets of the country. People also are informed through advertising and extension.

The Market's Nervous System

Out of half a dozen small shipping points in the Salinas Valley of California the refrigerator cars and reefer trucks roll every day in season to furnish millions of dinner tables with fresh lettuce.

The transportation is fast and dependable, but it alone cannot guarantee that the Nation's appetite for lettuce will be satisfied—that no place will get none while others have more than they can use. Within the brief period between certainty of harvest and shipment, shippers and wholesale buyers 3,000 miles apart must decide which markets get how much. They must also agree on prices. The long-distance telephone makes that possible.

The exact size of the lettuce crop is unknown almost up to the moment of harvest. A few days of the wrong kind of weather mean there is no crop.

Once ready, lettuce must be cut and on its way. It is a busy time for the shipper's telephone. Most of the crop is sold by the time cars and trucks are loaded.

But not all produce is sold before it is shipped, even with the telephone. By the time of shipment, however, the shipper has a good idea of where he expects to sell and sends all loads on their way. Unsold rail shipments are waybilled to the established "billing points"—convenient junction points from which they can be rerouted to a wide choice of terminals. Loads are sold before the cars reach the billing points, and diversion orders sent over the railroad's telegraph system keep them moving to their final destinations, where the buyers are prepared to receive them.

Unsold truckloads are simply started on their way to a tentative destination, with instructions to the driver to check at the usual routine stops for further instructions. The stops are usually combination service stations and restaurants, which specialize in serving the long-distance trucker. At one of them the driver will find a telephone or teletype message awaiting him that reroutes him to one buyer or perhaps two or more buyers of part loads. The only written record of the sale comes to the shipper days later in the form of a confirmation letter.

Thus does the well-knit network of telephone, telegraph, and teletype communications get California lettuce and citrus, Louisiana strawberries, and Florida truck crops on their way at the best moment for shipment and make certain their proper distribution to hundreds of wholesale buyers in just the amounts they stand ready to handle, without the gluts, scarcities, and other uncertainties that plagued produce distribution before we learned how to use modern communications to avoid consignment selling.

Advance knowledge of supply and prices is just as important to the wholesaler and retailer as to the shipper. In close touch with customer stores by phone, the wholesaler is then in position to get shipments out to the retail counter with little delay. Foreknowledge of supplies helps newspapers get the word to the housewife that now is the time, for example, to buy strawberries. Knowing both prices and supplies, the retailer can plan advertising promotions ahead of printing deadlines and get his floor displays ready.

Thus a housewife reads in the evening paper that "strawberry supplies are good this week, and quality is at a peak." Perhaps she finds a new recipe for shortcake in a nearby column. Or she may find strawberries mentioned prominently in the advertisements of supermarkets. Or, reading neither, she may simply go shopping, notice a featured display of strawberries, perhaps with a biscuit-mix tie-in and recipes. Whether editorial matter, advertising, or the point-of-sale display brings strawberries to her attention, the result is likely to be a sharpened interest in strawberries, and shortcake for supper some evening. Stimulation of demand is also a job for communications.

THE MARKETING ROLE of communications is most dramatic in the almost frenzied movement of delicate perishables, but no less important to the orderly, efficient marketing of storable staples like wool, grain, and cotton, or, indeed, any crop of value.

The organized markets that allow for the smooth operation of supply and demand depend for their existence on the quick availability to buyers and sellers of every kind of information that affects supply and demand. The information needs are much the same for all products. Only the means of communication differs.

The broiler plant in the Delmarva area keeps in hourly contact with its New York agents through shortwave radio in order to tailor its slaughter operations closely to market demand. Its field buyers' automobiles may be equipped with radio telephones to keep them constantly informed as to the changing needs of the plant.

The packer of canned goods may find the press news and mails adequate.

Whether the crop is lettuce, tobacco, wheat, hogs, or wool, whether communication is by newspaper, a farm magazine, telephone, or mail, each person in the market needs information on some questions if he is to make orderly marketing plans. To the extent that the information is available and communications systems are properly used to get the information where and when it is needed, the flow of supplies from farm to distant market can be made efficient. To the extent that we do not get the information, or do not make the best use of instruments of communication to distribute it, we risk delay, waste, and other inefficiencies.

Let us consider what these information needs are, and how they are met today in the marketing of one farm crop, beef cattle.

Our information needs might be considered reasonably well met if the various groups in the market could get these questions answered:

The farmer: What can I expect the supplies and the market situation to be like when the production I am now planning is ready for sale? What is likely to happen to my production costs while this crop is maturing? What is the best time to be ready to sell? For the crop now going to market, what does each market open to me offer?

The processor and the wholesaler: How much can be expected to come to market and what will its quality be? When can I expect it to arrive? What is consumer demand likely to be at that time? What are the prices of the raw material and finished product likely to be at that time?

The retailer: What is available, in what qualities, and at what prices? Which items would make attractive current promotions?

The housewife: What is available, in what qualities, and at what prices? Which offer the best current values? How can I use them?

The cattle farmer's first market decision comes with the decision of when to breed, for that determines within narrow limits when he will be ready to sell. Farm papers, newsletters, and outlook reports tell him what to expect in trends of prices and production costs and offer advice on timing. Thus a May issue of one farm publication advises southern farmers: "Breed beef cows this month to top feeder-calf market next October year. . . ."

After the cows are bred and the calves are born, farm publications, the radio, and the cattleman's local newspaper transmit revised information on trends of supplies and prices, the outlook for feed supplies and costs, and further advice on when to be prepared to market and in what condition. Daily radio and newspaper reports on the stockyards markets receive increasing attention as the time approaches to sell: News of prices paid, volume of receipts, and quality of cattle coming to market. The cattleman compares the different available markets and makes a decision to ship. If the calves are in good condition, the slaughter market may be more attractive than the feeder market. A telephone call to the local trucker, and the calves are on their way to dinner tables.

Months before the truck was loaded, the meatpacker had become actively interested in the calves of this crop. His staff had been watching official crop estimates, as reported in the daily financial and trade press, reports of the cattle population, feed supplies, and feed-price relationships. He obtained private reports from his surrounding area on probable supplies. He planned advertising copy for consumer magazines and got it off in time to meet acceptance deadlines, copy designed to stimulate demand for the plentiful products.

The packer's staff also had been busy studying the published reports on industrial production, industrial plans, and other information to help him forecast probable consumer demand when those calves have become steaks on the meat counter.

While those calves still had several months left at the feed box, the home economists on the staffs of women's magazines, the State colleges, and the Department of Agriculture had become interested. Those tempting beef recipes in the housewife's home magazine had been prepared 4 months or so before, and they had been planned to appear just when beef was a good buy on the market. They had to be planned also around the grades and types that were going to be in best supply, so the housewife would get the information about the cuts most available.

The day before the calves were shipped, the packer got all the information he could on probable supplies the next day and made any last-minute revisions necessary in his operations plans for the next day. When the calves arrived, he had to have just enough men on hand to handle them. He looked at the market news reports on expected rail arrivals and added in the not-too-accurate estimates on expected truck arrivals obtained from country contacts. On the morning of arrival, he scanned the teletyped market news on receipts at the other principal markets before buying. All the while his country buyers kept in close touch with the plant to be certain of its needs, prices, and supplies.

The meatpacker is in constant touch with the retailer through the local warehouses. Then as the beef becomes plentiful, previously prepared display materials and recipes are made available to help stimulate consumer interest. The market manager, kept informed by the warehouse on supplies and prices, is in a position to feature the attractive buys in his advertising.

From farm plan to the supper menu, communications facilities stand ready to transmit the information necessary for the efficient and orderly planning of the market process. The combination of all of our modern media of communication makes possible smooth operation of the intricacies of a nationwide marketing system, provided the right kind of information is made available in the right time and place through skillfully planned use of our communications instruments. Necessary information is not always as available as it could be, unfortunately, and planning for its collection and use has sometimes lagged.

A GOOD CASE in point is "en route" information on truck shipments. On April 13, 1953, without prior warning, the Chicago livestock market was deluged with 29,000 head of cattle, a run greater than on any other one day in 26 years, and only exceeded twice before in the history of the Union Stockyards. On April 14, only 4,000 head came to market, and on April 15, only 7,000 head. This unexpectedly large run made trouble and expense for everyone involved. The farmer undoubtedly lost out in price, which fell $1.50 per hundred on the 13th. The market was already declining, it is true, but the unexpected size of the run was certainly a factor in the size of the drop. The packer's operations plans were upset—he did not expect such large receipts. The hauler lost—his trucks and drivers were tied up longer than he had planned, waiting to unload. An accurate estimate of the total losses involved would be impossible, but a guess of 100,000 dollars for this one incident might not be too high. Yet only a few hours' advance notice of shipping intentions could have avoided the mess. An easily arranged delay in the shipping plans of nearby producers could have kept receipts within reason, to everyone's advantage.

Twenty-five years ago, when most livestock went by rail to central markets, a situation like this could not have arisen without advance warning. Rail shipments have to be planned some days ahead, and the rail organizations keep central records of rail movements and destinations. That information was, and is, made available to the trade through the Market News Service of the Department of Agriculture. But although the truck has been the dominant method of livestock transport since 1935, the only organized and accurate information on expected arrivals has been that of rail shipments.

Collecting data on truck shipments probably will never be as easy and cheap as getting information on rail shipments, but with today's flexible means of communication it is hard to believe a way cannot be found to do the job. Farmers, consumers, and everyone in between have been paying, because we do not have the information on expected shipments of livestock, of tree fruits, and many other crops for which lack of adequate preparation to handle the receipts can be critical.

Even for the types of information now made available in reasonably adequate amount, we do not always make use of the fullest potentials of modern devices. Livestock market reports reach the farm home today by radio almost as soon as the reporter gets them back to his field office. But in these days of good walkie-talkies, the reporter may have to spend as much as a half hour or more getting them back to his office by shank's mare.

"One picture is worth a thousand words" is nowhere truer than in the description of the grade of cattle sold at the quoted price. It is no secret that the buyer is much less choosy in what he describes as "good-to-choice" steers when cattle on the market are scarce than when the runs are heavy. But the use of televised market news is still confined to isolated local experiments.

A market organization that works even more smoothly than today's is possible with better information for planning. We have the instruments to get more and better information, to more people, more quickly, if we are willing to put a modest amount of energy, imagination, and funds into finding out how. (*Chester R. Wasson.*)

Reporting Supplies and Markets

Market information is much more than the condensed summaries of the receipts and prices at one place given on the financial pages of daily papers or by radio. Generally such reports are a synthesis of a host of factors that have culminated in action, or an exchange of commodities, at one point in the marketing system. For example, the report that No. 2 yellow corn at Chicago is $1.56 a bushel means that buyers and sellers have met on the trading floor and have agreed on a price after each has weighed his knowledge of many factors of supply and demand. The fairness of that agreement or price depends on things too numerous to list here. But it seems evident that if competition and pricing are to be effective and fair all buyers and sellers must have equal access to full information about the factors that influence the market.

In an earlier day the producer of livestock, grain, and the more perishable commodities could know fairly well the situation at his local market, where he sold his goods. But even then controversies developed. Some traders used all sorts of means (including carrier pigeons) to get the information about the crop and market conditions ahead of their competitors. Travelers from distant areas were questioned extensively. News of all kinds was highly valued and obtainable by the few who were in position to make the necessary contacts.

The areas of competition broadened as transportation developed, industry grew, the population increased around centers of manufacturing, and food supplies had to be drawn from greater distances. The local market became less of a factor in the pricing scheme; the market for agricultural products became national and international. The producer of winter wheat in Kansas became concerned with the production in all other winter wheat producing areas, including the Argentine and the Ukraine. He became concerned with the prices of wheat at Kansas City, Chicago, Buffalo, and New York.

THE DEVELOPMENT of market information services in the Department of Agriculture followed closely the pattern of the development of agricultural production. As areas of production spread out, the first thing needed was reliable information on total production. The institution of a crop and livestock reporting service was one of the first activities of the Department of Agriculture when it was established in 1862. As a matter of fact, demand was great for such a service nearly 25 years before there was a Department.

Now, the Agricultural Estimates Division, operating through the United States Crop Reporting Board, provides throughout the year statistical reports for more than 150 farm products. The reports include estimates of the acreages of the crops farmers intend to plant, acres planted for harvest, and harvested acreages. During the growing season monthly estimates of production are made on the basis of crop conditions or probable yield per acre as they are reported to the Department on the first of the month. Reports on the condition of pastures and ranges are issued monthly by States. Production estimates for 136 crops, including fruits, nuts, vegetables, and field crops are published regularly.

Statistics concerning livestock and poultry production include annual estimates of numbers and classes of livestock and poultry on farms January 1, and annual estimates of calf and lamb crops and chickens and turkeys raised.

Estimates of the pig crop are made twice a year. The report in June covers the spring pig crop and intentions for the fall. The report in December relates to the fall pig crop and intentions for the following spring.

The volume of milk and eggs produced is estimated monthly, and that of wool and mohair annually. The number of chicks and turkey poults hatched in commercial hatcheries is estimated monthly, and weekly reports are made for areas in which broilers are important.

A complete enumeration is made every year of the factory output of about 45 kinds of dairy products. Monthly and weekly estimates are made currently for the more important dairy products. Dairy plants keep comparatively accurate records of production, and in many States collection of data is facilitated by State laws requiring the firms to report the quantities manufactured. In 36 States the Department of Agriculture has entered into cooperative agreements with State agencies, usually the State Department of Agriculture, to provide for the joint collection of information and issuance of State and National reports. This Federal-State cooperative program was started about 36 years ago. It has not only prevented duplication of effort between the Federal and State agencies, but has enabled the two agencies working together to provide greatly increased services to farmers.

The larger part of all information obtained comes from individual farmers and businessmen, who cooperate with their fellows and with the Department to pool their information for the common good. The Department is largely dependent upon the willing cooperation of hundreds of thousands of voluntary reporters who complete and return questionnaires, with no reward other than the informational service they get and the knowledge that they are performing a public service and that the official reports are more accurate because of their help.

THE MARKET NEWS SERVICE came into being about 50 years after the crop and livestock reporting work—after many changes had occurred in industrial development, the growth of cities, and the expansion of railroads and communication facilities.

Production estimates and reports of crop conditions had been refined, but still it was apparent that the immediate supplies at one single market point strongly influenced the prices at that point; lack of accurate information on supplies and prices led to simultaneous gluts and scarcities in markets throughout the country. Farmers, dealers, handlers, and processors were trying to operate in the dark. More than ever they needed information about conditions in all markets.

The Department of Agriculture received many requests for help. A study was made, and in January 1913 the Secretary of Agriculture issued a report that recommended that a division of markets be established. It opposed the establishment of a market news service. The cost of a telegraphic service seemed prohibitive and the fear that farmers would be misled by the market reports seemed to be the main obstacle.

The Office of Markets was established in 1913. Work on market reporting began in 1915. The pioneer work was successful and mushroomed when the First World War placed heavy burdens on marketing systems.

The service has expanded steadily, until in 1953 most of the major markets were covered.

Information about one market is collected by a reporter who makes personal contact with the dealers, handlers, and others to get records or reports of sales. He observes the commodities at first hand and appraises them as to conditions and quality. The information so gathered is given to the press and radio stations and sent out through processed reports, telegraph, telephone, and personal contact. At the same time, through the facilities of about 11,000 miles of teletype circuits, the market reporters in each market interchange information several times during the market session. This information is posted or otherwise disseminated in the particular market so that as trading proceeds all parties have access to knowledge of what is happening in other markets.

A particularly significant feature of the fruit and vegetable market news service is the information obtained from reports of car loadings on all rail lines and reports of passing at railroad gateways. The information is telegraphed each midnight to the central market news office in Washington, D. C., where it is compiled and placed on the teletype circuit early the next morning. Another part of the information is obtained from the seasonal market news offices at the shipping points and through reports from the grading and inspection forces, growers, and shippers in the producing areas. For shipments by motortruck, receipts are obtained from 15 or 20 terminal markets, but information about movement by motortruck is incomplete.

Through these facilities traders on any market served will know what the supplies are on his particular market, what the supplies are on other markets, the conditions in the important shipping points, and the volume of loadings and passings, by which he may judge what may be expected in the immediate future.

For many livestock markets the local market news service provides the same type of service on advance receipts, which are based on reports from the railroads, shippers, and buyers, marketings on corresponding days for recent weeks, current demand and price trends, weather and road conditions, and other factors. On that basis the market reporter estimates the probable receipts of livestock on his market during the next 24-hour period. The estimates are posted on the exchange bulletin, given the press, and sent by teletype to other offices.

Market news also is provided on dairy and poultry products, grain, feed, tobacco, naval stores, molasses, and cotton.

Each service is adapted to the conditions under which the particular commodity is marketed. For example, in the marketing of eggs the service has followed the market trend and has based an increasing amount of its information on transactions at the country buying points. For some areas the livestock market news service covers the interior markets for hogs and sheep. Data as to grain and feed are gathered at strategic points and issued weekly on a national basis.

Trading in cotton is highly organized. The price quotation on the 10 spot markets, designated by the Secretary of Agriculture, are reported by the quotations committee on each market. The committees are under the supervision of the Cotton Division of the Department of Agriculture.

About 300 different qualities of upland cotton are reported. Prices are quoted as premiums and discounts off or on the base quality, middling 1⁵⁄₁₆-inch staple. The quotations are wired the Cotton Division office in Memphis, Tenn., where daily quotations are released to the wire services, newspapers, and radio.

Prices at other than the 10 spot markets are collected by employees of the Cotton Division by personal interview with buyers and sellers. About 10 additional markets are covered by this means.

Cotton prices delivered or landed at the mill points are also obtained from mills, merchants, and shippers. The prices are designed to provide quick and reliable information on average prices for various grades and staples most in demand by mills as well as the spreads between the spot prices and the landed mill prices in the various sections of the Cotton Belt and the New England States.

Estimates of grade and staple, important features of the cotton market information service, supplement the estimates of production by further defining the production into its component parts. Samples of cotton are obtained from cooperating gins and sent to the classing offices of the Cotton Division. The samples are stapled and classed by experts, and the results are forwarded to the Washington office, where a report is issued to show the quality of the crop being marketed. The report enables a producer or handler to determine about what portion of the crop will probably be of a particular grade—an important pricing factor.

For tobacco also the market information is a little more specific than for other commodities. Under the Tobacco Standards Act the Secretary of Agriculture is directed to provide a grading and market news service on any market where two-thirds of the growers utilizing that market vote in favor of the service, which is conducted by the Tobacco Division.

On the sales floor each pile is graded officially by a trained grader, and a ticket is marked to show the official grade. After the sale the market news man notes the prices and compiles a report. Each grower, buyer, or other interested person is provided a copy of the report for the previous day at the beginning of each sale. The report enables the grower to compare the bid price for each grade which he has to sell with the previous day's prices and decide whether he should accept or reject the bid price.

An important item in appraising the total market situation is the storage holding, which can have both a long- or short-time influence in the market because the commodity stored can be moved quickly into the channels of trade or held for varying periods.

Storage supply also can have a variable effect on transactions on individual markets, depending on the location of the supply in relation to the market. A given amount of wheat held in terminal elevators would cause a different market reaction than the same amount held at country elevators or on the farm. It is also important to know the grade or kinds of the commodity held, because there are different markets for parts of a crop having different characteristics. For example, it might be that the total amount of cotton held in storage was large, but if the stocks were mostly of short staple or low quality, the market for them might be depressed; but the effect would be the reverse in the market for cotton of long staple and high quality.

The Department of Agriculture provides a great deal of information on the storage holdings. The Agricultural Estimates Division collects information on farm stocks of many of the important grains and issues reports four times a year on stocks of grains in all positions. The Grain Division issues each week information on commercial stocks of grains at 45 points in the United States and Canada. Bulletins on tobacco stocks are issued quarterly; the reports show the storage supply by groups of grades so that the user can determine the supply of tobacco available for the several types of uses.

Cotton carryover stocks are reported shortly after August 1 each year. These statistics show the quantity by grade, staple length, and durability of upland cotton as well as the staple length of foreign cotton carried in the stocks as of August 1.

Monthly reports of a large number of perishable fruits and vegetables, dairy and poultry products, meats, and fish in cold storage also are issued by the Agricultural Estimates Division.

ORDERLY MARKETING requires more than just a group of reports on the more important factors of production, supplies, stocks, and prices, however. Reports and data on population, the level of employment, wages, average production costs (including wages of farm labor and costs of fertilizer and machinery) and such must be analyzed.

To fill this need the Department provides a number of services. Studies of marketing methods and costs point the way for greater efficiency in marketing and long-range production plans. Of major importance is the information on farm management and costs. This material is essential in the development of the outlook services provided by the Department and its cooperating agencies.

This continuous service brings together and analyzes information from many sources. The crop and livestock estimates, market news, information based on farm management work, and the marketing research studies all contribute basic information on agriculture. Related data on business conditions, the industrial employment and wages, and international developments are brought together also periodically in the form of comprehensive situation reports, which help farmers, processors, and handlers in making decisions.

The situation reports are preceded by an annual outlook report, issued each fall. It is designed primarily to meet the need for an analysis that looks ahead a year or two. To prepare the annual outlook report, all interested agencies in the Department and representatives of the extension services of the States participate in a thorough analysis of the farm situation.

The marketing services of the Department are careful that all parts of the market system have equal access to the reports.

An example is the releases of the Crop Reporting Board, which meets behind locked doors and sealed windows in a carefully guarded wing of one Department of Agriculture building in Washington. No one can enter or leave the wing during the time the board is at work. The release is controlled by law and strict regulation. The day and hour of the release of each report is scheduled a year in advance, and is made through special facilities. The precautions are taken because anyone who could get even an hour's advance notice of the content of the crop report would hold tremendous advantage in the market.

The release of outlook and situation reports and other reports from the Department are all scheduled well in advance and care is taken to give wide distribution to all of them.

More than 1,500 radio stations and 70 television stations cooperated in 1953 in the rapid distribution of information without cost to the Department.

Market reports reach uncounted numbers of readers of the market and financial pages of 1,100 newspapers. (*Sterling R. Newell.*)

To Sell Goods and Services

Today farmers are again phrasing a major marketing problem in their own language: "We can produce it, but can we sell it?" One of the answers in the affirmative lies in the better use of advertising and promotion by farmers, their organizations, and the industries allied with agriculture.

A well-known businessman, William Wrigley, Jr., once said, "I went broke

281437°—54——13

three times before I learned how to use advertising, but when I did learn how, it made me rich. There's nothing magical about advertising. Obey its principles and it will deliver."

Another famous American, Mark Twain, also commented many years ago on the value of advertising. He told about a reader who reported he had found a spider in his paper. This reader wanted to know if that was an omen of good or bad luck. Mark Twain answered: "Finding a spider in your newspaper is neither good nor bad luck. The spider was merely looking over our paper to see which merchant was not advertising so he could go to that store, spin his web across the door and lead a life of undisturbed peace ever afterward."

Advertising, and particularly agricultural advertising, has come a long way since those days. Its art and science have undergone great development, as can be readily seen by studying the advertisements of that time and those of today. The principal purpose of advertising, however, remains the same—to sell goods and services.

The Secretary of Agriculture has pointed out: "Our agricultural history plainly shows the value of (proper) selling. Without aggressive campaigning on the part of industry, it might have taken several decades to get hybrid corn adopted on the Nation's farms. Actually, it took only 10 years for industry and agriculture, working together, to put hybrid corn on virtually 100 percent of the Corn Belt acreage. Similarly, it took only 10 years for industry and agriculture, working together, to double the use of fertilizer. And it took only a little longer—about 15 years—for industry and agriculture, working together, to accomplish the present miracle of farm power mechanization."

What does the farmer think? In an extensive survey in 166 areas through the Nation 3 out of 5 farmers said they believed that the companies buying their products would sell less if they didn't advertise.

THERE'S NO QUESTION that well-planned advertising of high-quality products has been successful, in large part, from the point of view of the farmer who put an ad in the classified section of the local paper and of the million-dollar advertiser. Otherwise, more than 7 billion dollars would not have been spent in 1953 for advertising—140 times more than all advertising expenditures less than a century ago.

Many in the field of agriculture are well represented in that 7-billion-dollar figure. Many others, however, are not or they are poorly represented both in terms of the volume and the quality of the advertising.

The dairy industry, however, stands as an example of an agricultural business that is beginning to make greater progress in its advertising and promotion methods aimed at selling more milk and other dairy products. And high time, for that not-so-simple equation has been growing larger: Milk production up plus milk consumption down equals surplus and lower prices for dairymen. (Not to mention a multitude of other headaches.) When other businesses have the same problem, they step up their advertising and promotion campaigns to sell more products to more people.

Actually, advertising and promotion are vital parts of the marketing operation. Marketing, of course, is bigger than both of these parts, and bigger than sales alone, distribution, research, packaging, quality, or price, and each has to be satisfactory before advertising can do its best work. Marketing is a composite of all, and advertising and promotion should fit in with the other phases of a marketing program.

But in many instances they don't. Not so long ago (in 1950) a large dairymen's association made a quick survey of advertising in New York City "devoted to the Nation's No. 1 beverage." Its conclusion: "Nowhere does milk advertising hit the consumers in the eyes as forcibly as competing beverages." In fact, milk advertising was conspicuously absent in restaurants, drugstore and sandwich shop counters, grocery stores, and other points of sale. A look through five large newspapers in the world's largest milk market left the same impression.

Now this situation has changed somewhat, but still more of the dairy industry needs to get behind a continuous, hard-selling program with new approaches that appeal to more people—young and old. If it could recapture the market for the 129 pounds of milk per person which has been lost since 1939 (from 824 to 695 pounds), the surplus could be turned into a scarcity.

And many farmers firmly believe that this "lost" market can be recaptured. Furthermore, they are willing to put up money to help do the job. Here's just one example from a resolution passed by the New York State Farm Bureau Federation at its 1953 annual meeting:

"There is increasing demand from dairymen that the present 'Milk For Health' contribution of one cent per hundredweight be increased to provide for an expanded advertising and promotion program. Many of the other dairy states are already well ahead of New York in this field. Any such program, if it is to be successful, should have full support of a substantial majority of dairymen.

"*Be it resolved*, That we recommend that the dairy organizations and the 'Milk For Health' board consider plans for collecting additional funds for their effective use in promoting the use of milk.

"*Be it further resolved*, That we emphasize the value of self-help programs on the part of dairymen in marketing their product."

Add to this similar efforts by fruit and vegetable growers and other groups in various sections of the country. They don't want to fall behind in the competition for markets, and in the food business they realize they have more than 160,000,000 opportunities repeated three times every day to do a selling job for better foods, better diets, better health.

NOW LET'S CONSIDER those principles of advertising that Mr. Wrigley said would deliver results if they were obeyed. There are four:

1. Good advertising aims to inform the consumer and help him to buy more intelligently.

2. Good advertising tells the truth, avoiding misstatement of facts as well as possible deception through implication or omission. It makes no claims which cannot be met in full and without further qualification. It uses only testimonials of competent witnesses.

3. Good advertising conforms to the generally accepted standards of good taste. It seeks public acceptance on the basis of the merits of the product or service advertised rather than by the disparagement of competing goods. It tries to avoid practices that are offensive or annoying.

4. Good advertising recognizes both its economic responsibility to help reduce distribution costs and its social responsibility in serving the public.

To be more specific, just what makes a good advertisement? Getting an advertisement noticed is easy—as easy as getting attention by whistling at a farm meeting. But to get people to trust, believe, and act upon an ad in the newspaper or farm magazine, and to get a radio and television commercial listened to, respected, and responded to is a different matter.

The best advice is forget the flossy phrases and get down to facts. People want to know price, size, quality, performance, and other important facts about a product. They may not know anything about preparing advertising, but they can quickly spot a "hokum hawker" on the air and a phony ad in the press. Windy generalities start them yawning. Ditto for involved analogies, unsupported claims, irrelevant pictures, and the worn-out phrase. They want facts—specifically, the kind that show what's in it for them.

This last point shows up a common pattern which can be taken apart, identified, and profitably used in writing advertisements. These are the four basic parts:

1. Start with the right raw material—get all the facts. It's not enough to know all about the product to be sold. The advertisers should also find out all they can about the prospective customers they're trying to sell it to and about the media that will most likely be successful—newspapers, magazines, radio, television, outdoor advertising, direct mail.

2. Set up a valid and adequate objective for each advertisement. Often it requires as much creative ingenuity to establish the objective as it does to produce the ads. The best objectives are derived from customers' or prospective customers' wants, likes, or dislikes. Professionals get these answers through what they call market research.

3. Tell all that may be required to support the objective. This applies to pictures as well as to copy, and even to color when it can be used functionally. Advertisers should not shortchange an interested reader by leaving out details that may be vital to their message. Readers and listeners usually aren't concerned about "long" copy—only about dull or vague copy, which is never short enough.

This question often arises: If an advertiser has a certain amount of money to spend for advertising, is it better to spend it on large or small advertisements? The answer primarily depends on the type of product to be advertised or on what the advertiser is trying to accomplish. Sometimes a large ad is the best buy and sometimes a series of small ads will produce more results per dollar spent. Often a combination of both does the best job for the advertiser.

4. Appeal to the self-interest of readers. Any boastfulness, or unsupported claims, and vacant generalities create the embarrassing impression of a company or organization talking to itself in public. How much more effective it is to present the product story from the potential buyer's point of view—specifically, to show what's in it for him.

These four basic steps, advanced by Associated Business Publications, grew out of the experiences of hundreds of successful advertisers. Technically, the difference between a good advertisement and a very much better one is often so slight that it escapes recognition, unless there is a yardstick like this. It won't create any miracle ads, but it will certainly make it easier to turn out good ones.

PROMOTION also should be integrated into a marketing program. The possibilities for proper promotion with schools are virtually unlimited and the results achieved are relatively inexpensive. Some companies and organizations have rather extensive school services. Others are beginning on a small scale by scheduling speakers at schools on a variety of subjects, holding open houses, and supplying free teaching aids—leaflets, posters, booklets, and exhibits without advertising matter. Later they may produce a few movies. These aids tell the story of agriculture, a product, an idea, or an organization.

To accomplish worthwhile results, persons responsible for these promotional activities should know how individual schools and teaching systems operate, their problems, and needs.

Effective publicity as another part of a promotion program has to be intelligently planned. It will follow, of course, that the effective employment of publicity does not consist of scattering half-baked releases anywhere and everywhere in the hope that gullible editors and radio and TV commentators will "peddle apples" for a company or organization.

Newspaper and magazine space and radio and television time are worth money. They are the media's "products." Accordingly, no enterprise has the right to expect newspapers or magazines or radio or television stations to devote any part of their "product" to puffery of another's product. If a company wants puffery of either itself or its product—and that, of course, is a legitimate objective—then the company should take advertising space and pay for it. But if it expects free publicity, as part of a promotion program, that publicity should be honest and newsworthy and made up of timely, worthwhile facts, interestingly interpreted.

Sometimes, to be sure, a company or organization may "create" news by creating interesting situations—for example, anniversary celebrations, open houses in food plants, fairs, field days, contests, and the like. But still it must be news. That, in the modern view, is publicity. It is only one of the "tools" of a marketing program—not the be-all and end-all. (*William B. Ward.*)

Advertising: Another Viewpoint

Advertising must be viewed in the light of the competitive economy in which we live. Buyer and seller have to be brought together. Under conditions of normal abundance of commodities and products, the seller calls attention to what he has to sell. Buyers are not likely to beat a path to his door to buy his product. Advertising, then, is one of the aids in marketing, and that is why most advertising is tied in directly with identification of individual brands or with the products from specific areas.

There has been considerable controversy over advertising. United States businessmen and others spend more than 7 billion dollars a year for advertising. They think it works and are willing to foot the bill. On the other hand, some economists have contended that it is a waste; they hold that advertising raises the costs of doing business and interferes with free competition. Some nutritionists hold that advertising is not always a dependable guide for meeting consumers' need for information. Other critics condemn advertising because there have been abuses by some unscrupulous persons.

Some critics have argued that advertising tends to develop monopoly or concentration and that prices of some advertised products are more rigid than some other prices. The evidence does not point toward advertising as an outstanding factor in bringing about concentration, however. And advertisers who do not adjust prices often find themselves losing business to others who are willing to make such adjustments.

Advocates of advertising hold that it contributes to a high standard of living. They contend that it aids in putting new products on the market; that it is an economical way of doing an essential part of the merchandising job, namely, providing information needed in exchanging products; that it helps (through increased volume of business) to lower costs in many businesses; and that it is an important element in the encouraging of investment, whereby the gross product of the economy is raised to higher levels.

UNDER FAVORABLE CONDITIONS, advertising may accelerate demand, or it may hold back a declining demand for a product subject to adverse conditions of demand. The demand for lettuce has grown through favorable basic trends with little advertising. But substantial advertising expenditures have not prevented contraction of the demands for cigars, smoking tobacco, or wheat flour.

Advertising is also used as a means of increasing the selective demand for specific brands or products of individual businesses. Study has brought out several considerations that contribute to the successful use of advertising in increasing demand for individual business enterprises. They include a favorable primary trend in the demand for the products of the enterprise and an opportunity for effective differentiation of product. Advertising is certainly most effective when good advertising claims can be made.

Another factor is the extent to which the product has hidden qualities, or whether inspection by a buyer at the time of purchase reveals all external qualities that concern him.

Again, when some strong emotional appeals can be employed, advertising is likely to influence demand.

Another consideration is whether a large enough sales volume exists or is likely to be created to permit an advertising program large enough to influence the market at a reasonable cost per unit.

Also, the quality of a product must be maintained, consistent with advertising claims. Selective demand based on maintained quality calls for brands as means of identification to guide consumers.

Meeting the conditions that have been listed does not necessarily mean that all advertising programs will be successful. There are variations in conditions and skill in their evaluation and use. Some businesses choose to rely less on advertising, even when the factors are favorable, and use personal selling and sales promotion. Price reductions, especially, are also often tied in with advertising and other promotional work.

Another economic factor is whether advertising through increased volumes of business tends to affect favorably (from the consumer's viewpoint) the total costs of distribution and production. In some instances, evidence points to a reduction of overall costs through advertising; in other instances to an increase in costs. The social contribution of advertising rests primarily on its effects in a dynamic economy in aiding in the introduction of new products and the increase of investments required in their production and distribution.

In the case of new products, advertising aids in increasing demand. In the food field, the prepared breakfast foods are illustrative of new products whose consumer acceptance has been developed through advertising and aggressive selling activities.

Consumers are in search of revealing information regarding the multitude of items they have the choice of buying. Our markets normally afford the consumer a variety of products from which he can make a final choice. In our free economy, he exercises his freedom of choice in an atmosphere of influence through various types of aggressive selling, including advertising. The role of advertising in this environment is to act as a source of information justifying confidence on the part of those to whom the advertisements are directed.

Not only is it now generally accepted that good advertising should give the consumer the essential facts about the products. It is also generally agreed that advertising, as an effective selling tool, must be accompanied by a constant effort to maintain or improve the quality of the product offered.

Brand identification by consumers resulting from advertising has been an important factor in the development of many of the self-service features of present-day distribution practices in retailing. To the extent that it helps further self-service, advertising may be regarded as a laborsaving device in that it tends to replace personal selling at the point of sale.

Estimates of the advertising expenditures for farm products and foods are not available, but the volume is substantial. It includes payments by producers, manufacturers, and processors of agricultural products, including foods, and by retail establishments. Packaged grocery specialties are one of the largest classes of national advertising, while a glance at any leading newspaper, especially on a Thursday or Friday, will be sufficient to indicate the emphasis our leading grocery stores place on advertising.

If farm products in their original form are to be advertised, who should bear primary responsibility for furthering any advertising program? Should it be done by the producer or by handlers of the product after it has left the producer's hands? What should be done about quality control of the product during the production period, preparation for market, and within the actual time required for selling?

Considerations relating to each commodity will necessarily control the decision as to whether advertising is to be done and, if so, who is to carry the responsibility. Tobacco and citrus fruit are examples of two very different situations in this respect, although both have been well advertised. Tobacco before it is ready for market is subject to numerous processes, over which the producer has no control. He has no interest in brand ownership. As a result, advertising has been developed wholly at the manufacturers' level.

CITRUS FRUITS are different from the standpoint of producers' responsibility and opportunity. The experience of citrus growers of California and Arizona have been frequently cited because of the well-rounded program of quality control, product handling, research, advertising, and sales promotion. A summary of the scope and objectives of the program of Sunkist Growers, Inc. (formerly California Fruit Growers Exchange) will be of value.

For many years the organization, which in 1954 represented about 15,000 citrus growers in California and Arizona, has engaged in advertising activities. The primary objectives have been to increase the total consumption of oranges, lemons, and grapefruit; to stimulate consumer and trade preference for California and Arizona citrus fruits, and more particularly those labeled under the Sunkist brand; to increase the efficiency of merchandising through better display and faster turnover; and to encourage reasonable price margins. Those connected with the campaign have recognized the basic importance of standard grades, maintenance of grading standards, quality pack, careful harvesting, good packing and efficient transportation to insure arrival of the fruit in good condition at terminal markets, use of identifying brands, readily available supplies for customers whose interest has been stimulated by advertising. It is important that the basis of advertising is recognized as requiring maintenance of quality clear through to the consumer. "Sunkist" was adopted as a trade-mark in 1908.

Their advertising embraces the use of all the chief kinds of media (magazines, newspapers, posters, radio, television) directed to consumers and to trade and professional groups. It includes also service work with retailers, educational material for food teachers and students, doctors, dentists, dieticians, nurses, and public health workers, and public relations. Dealer service work, including sales-promotion activities, takes up about 22 percent of the advertising budget.

The program is based on research on cultural practices in fruit production, packaging, transportation, and so on, and in nutritional properties of citrus fruits. Research in the advertising department deals with trade and consumer studies on uses of citrus fruits and the accompanying trends and with nutritional research in medical schools, et cetera. Any proposed basis for influencing consumer purchases is carefully studied. More than 1 percent of the annual advertising budget is expended on the latter two types of research. Advertising appeals have been based primarily on taste and health.

In 46 years, the program has cost about 1.3 percent of the delivered value (the price upon arrival in terminal markets but not wholesale, jobbing, retail, and any other margins added at terminal markets) of citrus fruit marketed by the organization.

During the years the program has been in effect per capita consumption of citrus fruits in fresh and processed forms has increased from about 17 pounds to 87 pounds, or almost five times. Several factors were responsible, not the least of which were advertising and its related activities. Citrus growers have had the advantage of a favorable trend; their advertising rode with the tide to speed up consumer acceptance of a product favored by dietary trends.

THE IMPORTANCE of these broad dietary and taste trends is well illustrated by the lettuce situation. In 1953, United States commercial production of lettuce was slightly more than ten times what it was in 1918. Direct advertising by lettuce producers and marketers had no part in this expansion, but it is likely that they benefited by the efforts conducted by others to encourage the greater use of leafy vegetables as a way to improve the general dietary. Advertising by manufacturers of mayonnaise and the other producers of the ingredients of salads has aided lettuce growers.

The basic factors back of this trend, however, were the increasing emphasis upon the newer nutritional elements, vitamins, and the shift of American eating habits toward salads both because of the new nutritional discoveries and our rising standard of living, including the decrease in heavy physical labor on the part of many of us.

Joint action through cooperative organizations or through commissions or other bodies set up by action of State legislatures are two ways to increase the use of farm products. Such commissions have been set up for potatoes, prunes, onions, apples, citrus fruits, and other products. An example is the Florida Citrus Commission, set up by Florida in 1935. The law provided for assessments of 3 cents for oranges, 4 cents for grapefruit, 5 cents for tangerines, and 4 cents for limes on a basis of a standard packed box of 1⅗ bushels. The larger part of the funds is devoted to consumer advertising. Recognition has been given to a number of activities directed toward improving the marketing of Florida citrus fruit, among them the investigation and approval of license applications from shippers, canners, truckers, and express shippers; working toward improving the quality of fruit shipped under various grades; efforts to obtain a better identification of Florida citrus products for marketing purposes; and consumer advertising, primarily through newspapers, magazines, and television. Some advertising in professional publications of medical, dental, dietetic, and nursing groups stresses the nutritional and therapeutic values of citrus products. Merchandising representatives call on larger retail food outlets to assist with demonstrations and displays. The Commission also supports some research, primarily into the processing of citrus fruits and problems related to decay of fruit.

The Washington State Apple Commission, established by statute in 1937, is financed by an assessment of about 3 cents the packed box of fruit. Advertising is directed to consumers and distributors. The newspapers are used most. Through efforts of a field staff, the Commission tries to encourage the stores to adopt new merchandising ideas and otherwise to promote sales. Work with jobbers and wholesalers is undertaken. Studies are made of containers and packing and other handling methods.

THESE CITRUS AND APPLE examples clearly emphasize that advertising does not stand alone, but needs a well-organized program of quality control and improvement, and research and personal work in the markets to work toward the goal of creating effective interest in a product.

The various methods need to be tailored to the job at hand. A continuing evaluation of their effectiveness is a first requirement. If advertising and related activities appear to have reasonable possibilities of assisting in doing a good sales job, competitive conditions may well dictate that it be used. Each product constitutes an individual case and requires individual study and decision as to whether advertising can be helpful. (*Kelsey B. Gardner, Neil H. Borden.*)

Ways in Which Technicians Help

Of the many types of technical assistance needed in farm marketing, one of the most important is in preparing products for market. Inefficient ways of doing that reduce the returns to the producers and increase the cost to the buyer.

Long before the marketing man takes over, many hands have guided the sales destiny of a commodity.

Even before a seed is planted or a hatching egg is set, technical assistance has played the important part of advising on specifications for marketability which, if met in the final product, will assure that it will enjoy greater acceptability and be sold to the advantage of the grower.

Breeders of plants and animals work toward the traditional goals of higher production and ultimate salability.

A CIGAR furnishes an example. To appeal to the smoker, the wrapper tobacco must be finely veined and have a pleasing luster. The filler and binder tobaccos must burn well and have pleasant aroma and taste. Each of these three component types of tobacco is essential to make a cigar brand successful. Each type has been selectively bred with an eye toward its special use and marketability.

The commercial success of a brand of cigar is further influenced by the quality and appearance of the ash. That, in turn, is affected by fertilization—too much or too little of a single nutrient can be detrimental to the color of the ash and the flavor of the smoke. Technical assistance enters here, too, after analyzing smokers' demands, by passing along information helpful in formulating the plant fertilizers that have a part in producing the best possible cigar.

Pulling tobacco too green, letting it get overripe, or rough handling in the field are careless harvesting practices that technical assistance has done much to overcome.

Losses have also been cut down through the application of proper methods of curing tobacco. Among the difficulties involved are barn designs, types of curers, heat control, fire prevention, and efficient use of labor.

The cured tobacco must be handled several times before it is ready for market. It must be transported to the packhouse, "cribbed" or piled in lots, recribbed from time to time to insure proper aging, placed in a conditioning room to bring it into "order," sorted into grades, stacked under weights to prevent deterioration and to improve its appearance, and loaded and carried to market. The manner in which each process is done largely determines the market quality of tobacco.

THE GREAT expansion of poultry production was paced by development of marketing facilities. In some of today's great poultry centers there was originally only a nucleus of producers to justify central marketing facilities; the existence of a satisfactory market stimulated the growth of production plants. The effects of distance, time, and temperature on perishability had to be overcome. How does one set down one case of eggs in a distant city with quality equal to another case produced 50 miles from the market?

Or, how place in a distant city's stores a package of poultry, ready to cook, as fresh as the locally produced and dressed birds?

Within the walls of a modern egg plant there must be an artificial climate to safeguard quality. Architects and air-conditioning contractors must be instructed in the specifications to achieve that end by men who know what an egg can stand. Manufacturers of cartons are called in to design packages that will help to sell eggs as well as carry them safely to market. They also install handling equipment to save manpower. Management sends grading and inspection personnel to schools conducted jointly by industry service organizations and the technical men of farm schools and agricultural departments. These trained graders and inspectors carry back to producers information and practices which help to assure delivery of better eggs.

Good egg-marketing practices include frequency of collection, climate-controlled egg rooms, sanitary cleaning, and uniform sizing and packing. To deliver a dozen good eggs into a consumer's hands in 1925 required the production of 16 eggs; only 14 eggs at the farm level did the same job in 1954.

Technological progress is revolutionizing the marketing of dressed poultry. The market-preparatory functions have been removed from cities to country points, where sanitary and efficient buildings and equipment and the latest methods of processing and merchandising enable operators to do a better, cleaner, and cheaper job.

Poultry dressing moved forward as management applied the advices of technical specialists in grading, inspection, packaging, sanitation, quality control, refrigeration, mechanics, transportation, and sales promotion.

So confident of quality has the trade become that a chainstore company has offered for sale "unconditionally guaranteed ready-to-cook chicken," country dressed.

Even the variety of chick is predetermined because its feathering characters are related to efficient dressing, and skin color is a scientifically decided sales point. The retailing organization wrote the specifications: Uniform size, semiscald dressing, official inspection, immediate evisceration and refrigeration, and fast delivery to retail point. Technical assistance has shown grower and dresser just how these requirements can be met and how a market can be assured.

Proper layout and planned facilities in the larger wholesale market places are major prerequisites for efficiency. Even when design and equipment are good, poor management will further reduce efficiency. In many markets, especially the older ones, lack of proper equipment or use of outmoded equipment has greatly handicapped economical and efficient marketing.

Few city markets are built or renovated as often as once in a generation. Local people usually therefore lack the knowledge to develop new market facilities or to bring established markets up-to-date.

Here is a great opportunity for technical assistance. An impetus to progress has been the work of the Department of Agriculture and State departments of agriculture in guiding the development of terminal markets in large cities and in many secondary markets.

Examples of successful wholesale market development are those in Boston, Hartford, Conn., Columbia, S. C., and Atlanta. A good example of a retail farmers' market is the farmer-owned market at Trenton, N. J. It was built in 1948 following studies made by men of the Department of Agriculture and the New Jersey Division of Markets and the Extension Service. Its builders followed technical advice from producers, dealers, experienced farmer marketeers, and Federal and State agencies.

The help, available to any area, consisted of determining the amount of land required, the proper location for the facilities, the most convenient layout, the amount of the parking space needed, proper design and location of market sheds, protection from the weather in winter and summer, and proper display facilities for sellers.

Technical assistance has been used for expanding outlets and moving surpluses. An example is the extension food marketing program in the Northeast. It is a joint program of the extension services of State colleges of agriculture and home economics of New York, New Jersey, and Connecticut. Cooperating agencies include the State departments of agriculture in the three States, the New York City Department of Markets, and the United States Department of Agriculture. The information is developed in the metropolitan area office and disseminated through a weekly news letter to the trade, releases to food editors, scripts prepared for radio and television programs, and material for home demonstration agents. The material deals with the foods that are in plentiful supply.

The State Department of Agriculture of New Jersey publishes a weekly bulletin, called Auction News. It contains facts on vegetable supplies and prices at the shipping-point auction markets, and features the supplies in the immediate future. The mailing list is made up almost exclusively of wholesale buyers in the Northeast.

An outstanding contribution to the retailer of fresh foods has been the development of refrigerated showcases. Much of the research was carried on by makers of refrigeration equipment. Help has been given by representatives of departments of agriculture, who conducted tests of food conservation in stores and gave assistance to correct existing conditions by the installation of proper equipment. Employees of the Department of Agriculture have helped plan new types of checkout counters, wheel-type gravity conveyors, hand trucks, better methods of price marking, and display shelves of improved design.

In conducting special work with the ginning industry, cotton-marketing specialists of the North Carolina Department of Agriculture made hundreds of visits each year to more than 400 cooperating gins. They organized county groups of ginners, worked with cotton committees of farmers' organizations, and cooperated with the Extension Service and other agencies and individuals in carrying out a statewide program of improvement of the gins. They made many visits to cotton mills and members of the cotton trade to assist them in obtaining the particular qualities of cotton desired. Evidence of accomplishment in the work is shown in figures of the trend in North Carolina in the rough preparation of cotton, which amounted to 16.4 percent in 1946. The percentage dropped to 5.8 percent in 1949 and 3.6 percent in 1950. During the period the grade index of cotton produced in North Carolina rose from 89.3 to 93.7.

A fiber-testing laboratory was established in North Carolina in 1951. Its special activities include using laboratory test results in initial marketing and segregation of cottons for specific end uses; interpreting trade and mill terminology for producers, ginners, and initial buyers; interpreting and evaluating mill requirements; assembling and tabulating data with respect to production factors in the areas selected for fiber studies; and establishing correlation between production factors, gin processing, and fiber properties.

The application of technical assistance in a special program for safeguarding or improving dairy products in Wisconsin resulted in worthwhile accomplishments for both producers and consumers. Studies were first made of all factors that affect the quality of milk. The findings were used for the guidance of milk producers and plant operators.

Technical aid was aimed at correcting some of the difficulties in making cheese. Quality checks were made of the milk delivered to the plants to determine the causes of low quality, whether from indifferent handling on the farm and in hauling, or from more fundamental factors relating to dairy herds or feeding. Advice also was given on various phases of manufacturing, materials used, control conditions exercised, and quality characteristics at different stages. The output of one cooperating factory rose from a low percentage of highest quality to 71 percent of highest quality.

Worthwhile results also were realized in dairy improvement work begun in 1949 in Crawford County, Wis. Technical aid to milk producers and plant operators brought about some significant changes in practices used in this county. By testing the milk delivered to the plants it was possible to show quality problems resulting from improper handling.

Before the work began, there were no covered milk trucks or enclosed vans in Crawford County. Two were put into use in 1949, and 26 in 1950. By 1951 all milk trucks in the area were enclosed. Many milk houses and new or improved barns were built. The significance of these evidences of improvement in handling methods is verified by the trend in milk rejections, which were 8.2 percent in 1949, 6.4 percent in 1950, and 3.9 percent in 1951. (*Warren W. Oley, John A. Winfield.*)

Improvements Through Education

The Cooperative Extension Service at the colleges of agriculture and home economics in early 1954 had about 300 marketing specialists. Some were trained in the marketing of particular commodities. Others were trained in the construction and operation of market facilities and services. A few worked intensively on problems of retailing. Others worked on informational programs aimed to help consumers buy wisely. Some 5,600 county extension agents help specialists to disseminate knowledge to producers, shippers, processors, wholesalers, retailers, and homemakers.

Resident teachers in colleges and universities provide instruction in marketing. The courses have become more specific and more practical as the results of research have become available. Helpful also are teachers in vocational schools and technologists, economists, and the teachers in trade organizations, who work with both their own members and their clients.

More and more educational work in marketing is accomplished through discussion groups and forums in many communities and through the contributions of local discussion leaders. Educational programs initiated by extension workers are developed with the aid and advice of farmers, their cooperative associations, representatives of the trade, and homemakers. A few examples are given.

When research demonstrated the suitable size and kind of package for selling apples at retail, marketing specialists in New York saw the need to get the information to producers, packers, the manufacturers, inspection services, retailers, and consumers. Producers and packers needed to know the size and quality of apples most suitable to this method of merchandising, the kind and size of container, and what equipment and organization in the packinghouse would be most efficient. Retailers needed to be shown how research indicated apples could be handled, displayed, and merchandised more effectively. Consumers wanted to know why the method of merchandising was changed, and the advantages of the new system. This change in methods of marketing called also for some change in State regulations with respect to display, grade, and kind and size of package. Many people reached by the first demonstrations helped to pass the information on to others. Within 2 years the new practices were in use by thousands of foodstores.

In Minnesota, egg and poultry marketing winter institutes bring poultrymen, hatcherymen, wholesalers, retailers, and other interests together. They include demonstrations, lectures, and exhibits to show the changes in marketing and consumption, merchandising and cutting of poultry meat, selection of high-quality eggs, maintenance of quality, and marketing costs and spread. This educational program has led to quality improvement and to better prices for local eggs in relation to eggs from other areas of production. The attendance at the institutes is 65 to 500.

Some marketing problems are regional in nature, and an educational program must reach producers and handlers in several States. The regional hard red winter wheat marketing program is an example. The unusual demand for wheat during the Second World War resulted in a deterioration in kind, quality, and grade. At the end of the war, millers found it difficult to obtain a suitable quality of hard red winter wheat with high protein and gluten content. An educational program, developed with the millers and the producers, and with premiums paid for the desired qualities, resulted in an increase of 60 to 95 percent in the preferred varieties in 3 years. This accomplishment in the Oklahoma-Texas area highlighted the need to expand the work to include seven States in the Colorado-Texas area and to develop a continuing program of information adjusted to changing conditions in the market and on the farms and ranches. The program in 1952 included grain-grading schools, attended by about 2,400 representatives of the buying trade; State marketing institutes, which emphasized wheat-kernel analysis; and a rather extensive State and county program in the proper use of insecticides on the farms and in country elevators to control damage by insects and rodents.

Large cooperative marketing and purchasing organizations employ experts in several fields to advise them on business-management problems. It is the small cooperatives, and also small private business, that call for and need the counsel and guidance of the marketing specialist. Cooperatives are one of the important channels through which farmers can put to immediate use new ideas and better methods of marketing. Educational work is carried on with thousands of business enterprises engaged in marketing farm products.

Improved marketing of broilers has resulted from the live poultry auction recently started in Delaware. Marketing specialists helped plan, set up, and operate this unique method of selling poultry. All the sales are made from listings posted at the auction by growers. Previous to auction day, the poultry is inspected on the farms by the buyers. Actual bidding takes place Monday through Friday at the auction market. Higher prices to growers, the faster movement of broilers to market, and the development of an organization representing the interests of the poultry industry have resulted from their efforts. During one 21-week period, 17 million birds, or 56 percent of all broilers sold in Delaware during the period, were marketed through the auction. Prices to producers averaged 1.2 cents per pound higher than for broilers sold elsewhere.

Several agencies have recognized a need primarily among independent retailers for training in the care and handling of perishable food products. Training courses have been conducted in a number of States by extension workers. Some have conducted classes in retail stores, as in Florida. Others use mobile classrooms, as in Indiana, and others use the facilities made available by the trade.

State colleges in New England conduct this work on a regional basis, with a specialist coordinating the program in several States. Trade associations conduct similar programs in many parts of the country, with concentrated attention on the products of special interest to the association. These programs are based on information from a variety of sources, including the results of research from the colleges and the Department.

Another objective of education for retailers is to improve efficiency by training in a variety of managerial functions. Michigan State College, New York University, Indiana University, and the University of Chicago have conducted courses in management of retail stores, with the assistance of retail trade associations. Many high schools and colleges, encouraged and assisted by the George-Barden Act of 1946, conduct instruction for retailers.

Extension specialists take this type of training to the retailers in their own communities. Retailers in Indiana have enthusiastically received training in store management and economic outlook offered by the Indiana Extension Service at Purdue University.

Possible accomplishments of this type of education also are illustrated by experience in Illinois, where the extension specialist is in demand by retailer groups to help with store facilities, efficient store organization, labor management, and similar problems.

Extension specialists in marketing and county agents have a responsibility in assembling and interpreting economic information and presenting it so that farmers and others can make informed decisions.

Many illustrations are available of the information provided producers and handlers of many products. Marketing information from several studies served as a guide for Wisconsin farmers in deciding the level to which potatoes should be graded for highest net returns. Producers thus were able to make more profitable marketing decisions. Extension specialists in Illinois and in other Central States periodically distribute letters that present information essential to livestock feeders in developing their grain and livestock marketing plans.

Extension workers in vegetable and fruit producing areas inform producers of changing demands for their products and cooperate with the inspection service in conducting schools on grading and packing. Poultry producers are informed of market conditions and instructed in control and maintenance of quality. There is scarcely a commodity group that does not receive marketing information from extension workers.

High costs of food have given rise to requests from consumers for educational work. The Extension Service program of consumer education in food marketing helps millions of food shoppers to get better food value from the money spent. It also helps to move farm products at the peak of supply. Through discussion and study consumers get a better understanding of the marketing system.

Interest of homemakers during the Second World War centered around programs that helped them to judge the available goods.

Educational programs in relation to food selection included promotion and demonstration of the use of the lesser known foods, home care of food, and nutritive value of food. Interest of city dwellers in such a program was keen, and effort was made to maintain the educational phases of the food conservation programs after the need for national conservation was over.

The Research and Marketing Act of 1946 provided a way to bring to many interested city families more of the market information they were requesting. Localizing such information is important in establishing a program that provides sound information as to the source and availability of food. Twenty-five States and Puerto Rico carried on an extension program in food marketing with consumers in 1954. Marketing tours, producer-retailer forums, and other forms of teaching devices were used.

One of the most important educational developments in relation to marketing has been the recognition that knowledge from many sources and training in many special fields have to be combined to provide the basis for sound educational programs. There must be understanding of the commodity itself, how it is produced, its food value, how it should be handled, and how it will be used. The economic facts that affect the production, the way in which products are distributed, and how they are offered for sale must be part of a marketing program. What the ultimate consumer wants and will pay for, how the product may be stored at home, what new or varied uses may be made of products in supply are also part of the program.

Effective education in the field of marketing is then a cooperative venture. In addition to marketing specialists, other specialists in agriculture, in home economics, and in education can all make valuable contributions. Those who know or have access to overall facts and situations and those who know local conditions, preferences, and customs are needed. Those who are known by and have the confidence of farmers, the trade, and families who purchase must all contribute if a marketing program is to be effective. It is not a one-man or one-woman job. When effective, it is the work of many skilled teachers who can work with producers, handlers, and consumers to the end that each of these persons has a general understanding of the interrelationships in the marketing process and specific knowledge of how his own decision or action will contribute to better marketing.

Improvements in marketing come through the interpretation and application of the research. Education must follow research promptly and be continuing. (*M. C. Bond*, *Frances Scudder*.)

APPROXIMATE LOCATION OF FROZEN FOOD PROCESSING PLANTS IN THE UNITED STATES IN 1952

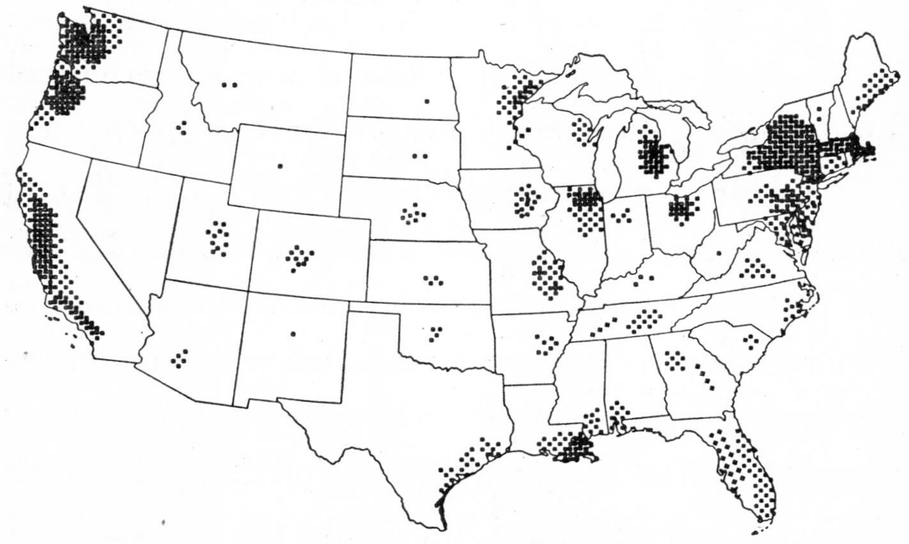

We Who Eat

Seeking consumers' favor, expressed through their purchases, is a major activity of marketing. If consumers do not buy the end product it is fruitless for farmers to produce the raw material from which it is made—or for the processor to manufacture and package it. Producers, processors, and manufacturers have come to appreciate more and more the importance of knowing what consumers want—what products they desire, how and in what sizes products should be packaged, and what services will give the most satisfaction. Americans mostly are well fed from a nutritional point of view. But they could make better food selections, and the food offered could be of higher nutritive quality. To raise the sights of consumers and make possible still better living is a challenge to marketing. When asked about preferences, consumers seldom mention safety and wholesomeness—now they take for granted the efforts of the food trade and regulatory agencies to protect food. Indeed, the American public has the best and safest food in its history.

Food for Families

Most Americans live as members of one or another of the 40-million-odd families in the United States. Food, textiles, and other items are bought mostly for the use of the family group. Plans for saving or investing in household goods of longtime usefulness are made largely on a family basis. Most marketing is for families. The family buyer is the ultimate customer.

Two-person families are the most numerous among the groups that make up the market. They alone account for nearly one-third of all families. Eighty percent of them are families of husband and wife and no others. Families of three persons are one-fourth of the total.

Small families want small packages, sometimes even smaller than the market provides. Small families have also found useful the prepared dishes and mixes that incorporate the seldom-used ingredients that are hard to keep on hand.

Many of the two-person families are older couples. In the early 1950's, in 5 of 10 couples in this country the husband was 55 years of age or older; in 2 out of 10 he was 65 or older. These groups make special demands on the market. Many want easily prepared foods. Here, also, is a group with different food needs, either because they need less food as they become less active or because of diets prescribed for illness.

To market wholly for small families would be to fail to meet the needs of households that must operate on a larger scale. The distribution of families by size in 1950 shows the place of larger families in the national market: Two persons, 33 percent; three persons, 25 percent; four persons, 21 percent; five or more persons, 21 percent.

The continuing long-term trend toward smaller families and the increased birthrate of recent years may seem like a contradiction. It is explained if we keep in mind the other shifts that have taken place. Many young people have found jobs and have established their own households. Aunts and uncles have married or set up their own bachelor quarters. Older couples are both more numerous and

281437°—54——14

more likely to live in separate households. So the average private household now numbers 3 to 4 persons, compared with nearly 5 in 1890. In parallel, the number of households has increased more than the population.

Working wives may make special demands on the market. One married woman out of every four has paid employment outside the home. These women have, in effect, two jobs. They cannot go to market during working hours. In many families the men or older children do the shopping. The time that employed homemakers can spend at home to prepare food is limited. They like foods that can be prepared quickly.

On a nationwide basis, a large share of the market is urban. Of every 100 families, 65 live in urban places; 36 live in cities of 50,000 or more. Farm families number 14 out of every 100; rural nonfarm families, 21 out of every 100. The small family and working wives are most frequent in cities, and marketing in the parts of the country that are dominated by large cities is most influenced by their needs.

Fastest growing has been the rural nonfarm and suburban market, which has different characteristics in different parts of the country. In some places settlements have reached far out into the country. In others many rural people still live a distance from markets. Their needs are less well known than are those of city people.

The market analyst thinks in terms of his own market, here and now. But he also looks ahead and asks whether the small household, the working wife, and the growth of country living are trends that are likely to continue. He knows that the small household and the working wife are closely related to the overall economic situation. Apparently if they have the incomes to support separate households, different generations prefer to live apart. It also seems to be true that if they can find jobs, many married women are likely to work outside the home.

People in this country depend on the market for the largest share of their food, clothing, and other goods. Farm families produce some of their own food, and homemakers still perform at home some services that they could buy on the market. But purchased food and services have become more important, and many consumer goods are available only on the market. One hears occasionally of families that try to escape from the market by enlarged home production and home processing. But they are exceptions; the trend is toward a greater dependence on the market.

To serve the largest numbers of families, marketing must take into account the many families with moderate incomes—particularly in the marketing of food, which takes a large share of the budgets of people with medium and low incomes. Four out of 10 families have cash incomes of less than 3,000 dollars. The middle-income family has 3,700 dollars to cover taxes and living expenses. The middle third of the income range extends from about 2,600 dollars to 4,400 dollars, according to reports from the Bureau of the Census. Those sums must cover all the family outlays—for food, housing, clothing, newspapers, medical care, automobiles, taxes, savings, insurance, and many more.

The division of the consumer's dollar shows the way the market is divided among different groups of goods. In the average budget of urban wage-earner families, food takes about as much of every dollar as do housing expenses, like rent or the costs of home ownership, furniture, heat, light, and household supplies. Clothing for an average city worker's family budget takes only 10 cents of every dollar spent for living; that is less than the sums spent for transportation, which includes the family automobile.

This division of the dollar differs among groups. For example, food takes a smaller share of each dollar at upper income levels. The proportion in which the consumer's dollar is shared among different kinds of goods also changes over the years, but changes are slight and come slowly. The share for food has increased somewhat since the Second World War, in part because of the cost of added processing and restaurant services. The clothing dollar has shrunk slightly, giving way to the popularity of automobiles and durable household equipment.

Changes in the level of incomes and price relationships also affect the division of the consumer's dollar. Even though this division of family expenditures does not change rapidly, small shifts represent large sums of purchasing power and are watched closely by those responsible for marketing.

The division of the food dollar also changes little. Figures for dates before 1942 that can be compared precisely with those in the table are not available. But earlier studies of food consumption show that the order of importance of different kinds of food in the family food budget has not changed. Meat, poultry, and fish have repeatedly ranked first; fruits and vegetables, second; and the milk and flour cereals groups, third and fourth, respectively.

Considering the overall changes in eating habits that have taken place, the differences over the country in tastes, and the great variety of foods offered to an even greater variety of families, it may seem surprising that this division of the food dollar is so constant. To understand it, we need to keep in mind the limits within which the household food buyer operates.

Food is purchased to fit family meal patterns. No matter how appealing the package or how novel the product, the housewife must buy for breakfast and dinner and, less regularly, for lunch or the lunch box. So she goes to market for meat or a substitute main dish, vegetables, beverage, bread and cereals, and dessert, but never simply for "food." The pattern of what makes an acceptable breakfast or dinner, moreover, is largely a matter of habit. It may change, but not rapidly. It differs among groups but not so much as it used to.

More of the food dollar of the low-income than that of the higher income families, for example, is customarily spent for bread and cereal foods. That is not surprising, since breads and cereals are the cheaper foods. The share spent for meat—although not the total amount spent—does not differ among income classes. Smaller shares and smaller amounts are spent by the low-income families for fruits and vegetables and milk products.

The consumer's food dollar in different cities shows the effect of regional food habits. In Birmingham, Ala., flour, cereals, and bakery products take a larger share of the food dollar than in Minneapolis-St. Paul, San Francisco, and Buffalo. (The comparative level of incomes is one explanation.) Moreover, the southern custom of serving hot breads means that more of the consumer's food dollar is spent for flour there than in other parts of the country. Minneapolis and St. Paul families emphasize milk products, influenced no doubt by the dairy section in which they live. Families in San Francisco spend a large share of their food dollar for fruits and vegetables.

What do consumers want? We are all consumers, and we all think we know what we want. Yet few questions in marketing are harder to answer. It is an important question; practical decisions for farmers rest on its answer. Is it worth the extra cost, for example, to produce a more attractive but costly variety, or to take the steps necessary to insure that foods reach consumers in top-quality form? In other words, do consumers "prefer" certain foods enough to pay more for them?

One way—an expensive way—to find out what consumers want is to try to sell something to them. If a product is not a success, it is obviously not what consumers want.

Marketing research has worked out various ways of learning what consumers want. We can ask consumers,

DIVISION OF THE FAMILY FOOD DOLLAR

Food group	1942 (spring) urban U. S.	1948 (spring) urban				1948 winter			
		All incomes	$1,000 to $2,000	$3,000 to $4,000	$5,000 to $7,500	Birmingham	Buffalo	Minneapolis-St. Paul	San Francisco
	Percent	Percent	Percent	Percent	Percent	Percent	Percent	Percent	Percent
Meat, poultry, fish	27.2	29.5	29.4	28.9	30.7	29.2	29.4	26.3	30.2
Fruits and vegetables	20.8	17.4	16.2	16.7	18.4	15.5	15.2	15.9	17.9
Fresh fruit	6.2	5.4	4.7	5.3	6.4	4.4	4.7	4.9	4.8
Fresh vegetables	7.2	6.4	6.1	5.9	6.6	5.0	4.5	4.2	7.0
Canned, frozen, dried fruits and vegetables	7.4	5.6	5.4	5.5	5.4	6.1	6.0	6.8	6.1
Milk, cream, cheese, ice cream	14.8	15.8	15.0	16.3	16.2	14.3	16.3	18.2	15.0
Flour, cereals, and bakery products	11.5	10.3	12.4	10.4	8.9	11.5	11.1	10.2	9.1
Flour, cereals	2.6	3.0	4.5	2.8	2.1	5.2	2.8	2.7	2.5
Bakery products	8.9	7.3	7.9	7.6	6.8	6.3	8.3	7.5	6.6
Fats and oils (including butter)	7.3	6.8	7.6	6.7	6.3	7.8	6.5	7.9	6.3
Eggs	6.4	4.4	4.6	4.4	4.2	5.8	4.8	4.4	4.6
Sugar and sweets	2.8	3.2	3.4	3.5	2.6	4.0	3.9	3.5	2.7
Potatoes	2.5	1.9	2.2	2.0	1.5	2.0	1.9	2.2	1.6
Miscellaneous (beverages, prepared and partially prepared dishes, nuts, soups, condiments)	6.7	10.7	9.2	11.1	11.2	9.9	10.9	11.4	12.6
Total	100.0	100.0	100.0	100.0	100.0	100.0	100.0	100.0	100.0

Source: USDA Misc. Pub. 550 and 1948 Food Consumption Surveys, Preliminary Reports 1–5.

or observe their behavior in specially designed experiments, or arrange for them to try out products in their homes. We can also try out new products in laboratories. Marketing decisions are based more and more on those methods in place of the wasteful trial and error of offering new commodities untested.

When homemakers are asked what they want, several points are found in their replies. Some admit that they do not know what they want or why they made the choice they did. More numerous are those who reply that their choices are mostly on the basis of habit—significant replies because it is apparent that consumers could not survive the complications of the modern market place if they did not have habits to guide them. If every purchase were based on conscious weighing of alternatives, spending the family income might take even more time and effort than earning it.

The expressed reasons for the selections made by buyers usually can be boiled down to three general points—quality, price, and convenience. These are not new ideas, although the great emphasis put on convenience—saving time and labor—is a recent development. The three attributes are not easily defined: Much of the history of buying and selling, its laws and customs, can be summarized as the history of trying to define "good quality" and "fair price" to the satisfaction of both buyer and seller.

THE HOMEMAKER uses exterior appearance of food as her first clue to quality. Packaging, store displays, and some aspects of our grading systems emphasize the appearance of the product. Certainly the household buyer will not select something that is unattractive. But it would be a mistake to assume that a product will win and keep a lasting place in the family food budget chiefly because it is attractive to look at.

Buyers who are asked about quality reply mostly in terms of flavor and cooking quality. Meat should be tender. Fruit should be ripe but not mushy. Potatoes after cooking should be soft but firm. Some vegetables should have proper cooking quality; others should hold crispness for eating raw. All foods should have good flavor when served.

Such a list of wants should not be too difficult to satisfy. But in practice it is hard to identify in products as produced the characteristics that will give the desired taste and quality on the table. Maintaining all the qualities throughout the long process from farm to table is no easier.

Research on food quality contributes in a practical way to marketing. The qualities most important to consumers must be determined, defined, and identified. Then practicable methods of measuring the qualities must be devised. Then the various products and methods of marketing must be rated as to their success in providing the wanted qualities. Testing of foods in laboratories and home kitchens is a last step in the process, based on the qualities that the researcher has defined and using the tests that he has developed.

Nutritive value has come to play a prominent part in the consumer's idea of quality. Earlier generations prized certain foods just because they were thought to be "good for you." Some of those old beliefs had some foundation in the science of nutrition. Others have been shown to be myth.

Large numbers of homemakers now have or are seeking knowledge of nutrition on which to base their selections of foods. When they are asked about their food choices, references to vitamins and minerals are frequent in their answers. Many are specific and accurate about the food value they are seeking. Some still have false ideas about the nutritive value of foods, of course. Exaggerated notions of health-giving properties of some foods are common. But the important point for marketing is that the consumers are nutrition-conscious. Attention to marketing practices that protect nutritive value, testing all along the line to be sure that the values have been maintained, and informing consumers specifically of what has been done are likely to yield good returns in getting consumers to buy the products.

Buyers apparently assume that the food offered for sale is safe and wholesome, for they seldom mention it when they are consulted about their preferences. They seem to take for granted the efforts of the food trade and regulatory agencies to protect food. If that were not so, safety would be high on the list of qualities wanted by consumers. It is a first essential in any complete listing of consumer needs. The fact that it is so seldom mentioned is a tribute to the success of the marketing system in providing safe food.

Recognizing the wanted quality is the heart of the household buyers' problem. The apple pie made last week was exceptionally good. Can it be duplicated? Often it cannot be. The buyer may remember the color of the apple, but, unless she has exceptional knowledge of the cooking quality of different varieties and the season at which they are available, she may not remember the name or cannot find the variety that she is looking for. If the apples are packaged, they cannot be easily examined. If canned apples were used, identifying what is wanted is no easier. Many labels are not specific as to the variety, the proportion of solids and juice, or, if sirup is used, as to its sweetness. Even if she remembers the brand name, and can find that brand again, she is not sure of the same quality. Quality has been shown to vary among different cans of the same brand of the same kind of food.

As we depend more and more on packaged and processed food, the household buyer has increasing problems in identifying quality. Complete and meaningful information on labels becomes increasingly necessary. The household buyer needs to know a number of things: The variety and the uses for which that variety is most useful; the content of the package—both as required by law and in additional terms that have meaning for meal planning—as cups, or half cups, and average servings; the content in liquid and solid for many foods; the ingredients used in mixtures; and quality, with a brief description of the elements considered in determining quality.

How much and what kind of information on labels will best serve the needs of the household buyer is an open question. Grade labeling serves to combine several qualities in one designation. But consumer grades do not serve the needs of household buyers unless accompanied by some guidance as to the uses intended. For example, Grade A canned tomatoes are not necessarily and always "the best," if canned tomatoes are to be used for soups or stews. And grades cannot be expected to serve household buyers well if they put most emphasis on appearance, when cooking quality, flavor, and nutritive value are more important to most consumers.

The influence of price on the household buyer's decision to buy or not to buy a product is disputed. Ideas of how consumers think about prices range all the way from the belief that a buyer will search through many stores for the lowest price to the belief that she buys primarily on impulse. It has even been shown that some consumers, when a choice is offered, select the more expensive item because they assume that the higher price indicates better quality. Since people vary as much in their buying habits as in other respects, there doubtlessly are varied reactions to price. It is also probable that concern for price differs with the goods purchased, and that foods (because purchases are small and frequent) are less subject to price comparisons at each purchase than are big items of household equipment.

When consumers are asked about their preferences for specific foods, price does not rank high among the points listed. In market surveys of reasons for selecting the stores in

DIVISION OF THE CONSUMER DOLLAR, 1952

URBAN WAGE-EARNER AND CLERICAL-WORKER FAMILIES

Figures in percentages

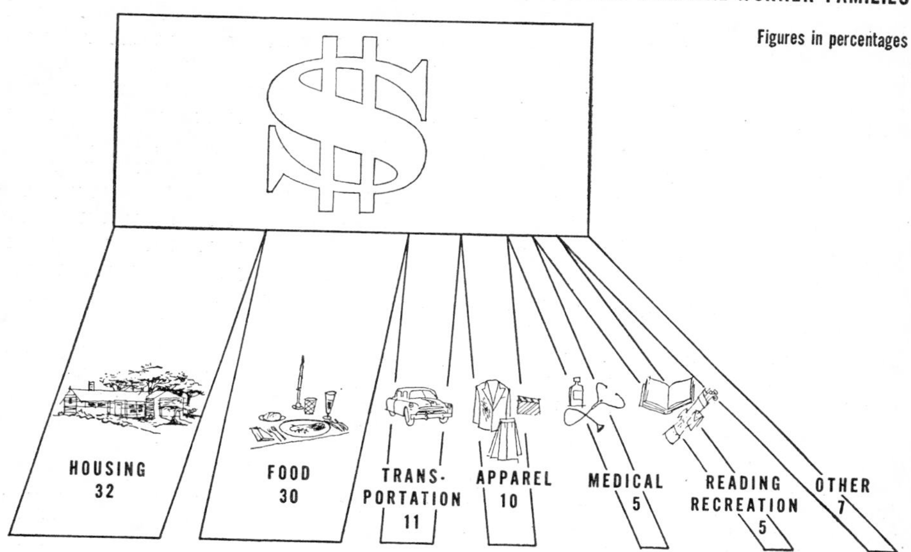

which they habitually buy, however, their judgment as to the general level of the stores' prices is mentioned almost as often as their judgment as to the quality of food carried. Thus it cannot be said that buyers disregard price, even though they may not often mention it.

Trends in the popularity of certain foods give further evidence of the importance of price to consumers. Increased sales of margarine are proof of consumer selection of the cheaper item. The rapid adoption of frozen orange juice concentrate must be attributed partly to its favorable price in some seasons and markets, when compared with the price of an equivalent quantity of fresh fruit. Clearly, consumers want food to be priced as low as it can be, and marketing, from their point of view, is most successful when it continuously lowers the cost of food.

Consumers seldom say that they want plenty of food on hand from which to select. Like safe food, abundant food is one of the advantages that consumers in this country take for granted.

Convenience is a major selling point in retail food markets. When homemakers are asked about the foods they prize, "easy to handle," "quick cooking," "time saving," and "convenient" are frequent in their replies.

Reference to changes in ways of living shows why that is so. Families that include few adults other than the parents have fewer hands for preparing food. Small families and small kitchens limit both the incentive and the possibilities for elaborate food preparation. Caring for large numbers of young children keeps homemakers too busy to undertake time-consuming kitchen tasks. Domestic workers, never a part of the way of living of most families in the United States, are scarce. And as more women have taken jobs away from home, they have sought shortcuts in the work of homemaking.

Is there an element of fashion in the current enthusiasm for saving time and effort? Some reasons for it have been listed. But it is also possible that the popularity of easier methods has outstripped these reasons and that there is an appeal in saving time and effort simply for the sake of saving it. Many years ago the term "conspicuous consumption" was used to sum up the ways people like to spend money, not for apparent value received but for the joy of display. It might be that the fetish of saving effort for the housewife has some element of the same pleasure. The immediate outlay is small, but the pleasure of using the easy way may be far more than proportionate to the actual time and energy saved.

Seeking consumers' favor, expressed through their purchases, is a major activity of marketing. If consumers do not buy the end product it is fruitless for farmers to produce the raw material from which it is made—or for the processor to manufacture and package it. The total sum consumers spend for a group of agricultural products—food for example—is determined chiefly by the number of consumers, the amount of money they have to spend, and the pressures (some of them pressures of habit) to buy other kinds of goods and services. Even when a household buyer chooses among different kinds of food, the habits of fixed meal patterns limit her freedom of choice. But the small changes in buying habits produce large shifts in purchasing power. Market competition for these sums and among foods that serve like purposes is tremendous.

The pursuit of the consumer's favor is costly. More attractive packaging, better products, transportation that protects perishables, and added services result in increased marketing costs. Thus the end product costs consumers more and the spread between what the consumer pays and what the farmer receives for the raw material is larger.

The success of products attractively packaged and easy to use shows that consumers want them. But we must remember that many of these successes came during a period of rising income when buyers were not inclined to question the extra pennies they paid for convenience.

Most advantageous to consumers, and hence most certain of lasting favor, are ways of marketing that enhance products without adding to the retail price. Some processed and packaged foods can be transported and handled at enough saving in cost that they can be sold as cheaply as food that has not been packaged or processed. Finding more cost-saving ways of marketing foods is to the advantage of farmers, also. (*Gertrude S. Weiss.*)

Our National Diet

A high-level consumption of food means an abundance and variety of foods in sanitary condition, of good nutritive value, of high table quality, and in a form that allows them to be made into varied meals with a minimum of preparation.

Better marketing has been responsible for many changes that contribute to high-level consumption of food. But marketing alone cannot take all the credit. Food is abundant today because our farms have become increasingly productive. We have also enjoyed economic conditions under which an increasing proportion of people have been able to have the kinds of foods they want. Average real income (income after adjustment for increases in price) is higher, and the benefits of increased incomes have especially affected families at the lower end of the income distribution. And, finally, people are more generally aware of their need for a proper assortment of foods for good health.

Our national diet today can be described as the kind people choose when the supply of food is ample and they have the money to buy it.

Each of us now eats more of the dairy products (except butter), eggs, poultry, vegetables, and fruit, but fewer potatoes and grain products than people did at the beginning of the century. Consumption of meat is about the same as it was before the First World War. Consumption of fats and sugar is higher than in the early part of the century, although we eat less sugar than we did in the years between the wars.

What do the changes mean in terms of nutrition? First, there has been a slight trend toward fewer calories per person. The increased consumption of some foods has been more than compensated, in calories, by smaller consumption of others, chiefly grain products and potatoes. During the past 40 or 50 years, we have had a shift in the kind of work people do, a movement of population from farms to cities, widespread use of many laborsaving devices in factories, on farms, and in homes, and an increasing proportion of elderly persons in our population. So the trend toward fewer calories is related to a lower average need for food energy. We also have become increasingly aware of the need to control body weight.

The steady increase in the share of total calories in the national diet derived from fat is another trend.

There has been a slight increase in grams of fat consumed per person, and because total calories are down, the percentage from fat has increased rather markedly in 40 years—from about 32 percent to 40 percent. At the same time the percentage of calories from protein has remained remarkably constant—around 11 percent. Whether the shift in the source of our calories—more from fat, less from carbohydrate—is desirable nutritionally is questionable and merits further study.

Largely because of our increased use of milk over the years, there have been long-term increases in the calcium and riboflavin content of the national diet. The intake of vitamins A and C also has increased because of a greater use of leafy green and yellow vegetables and products, such as citrus fruit and tomatoes, that are rich in vitamin C. Supplies of iron and the B vitamins (thiamine and niacin) dropped from the early 1900's to the mid-1930's, and then increased as a result of the rise in the consumption of meat and the enrichment of white bread and flour.

Nutritionists welcomed the increases, particularly of calcium and the vitamins, because those nutrients often were lower than desirable in diets of many people. Actual dietary deficiency diseases, however, are rare in this country today. Rickets and scurvy in children have practically disappeared now that either vitamin D milk (or some other source of vitamin D) and orange or tomato juice are given infants and children every day. Reported deaths from pellagra, once common in the South and now known to be due to a deficiency of an amino acid and a vitamin, have declined markedly.

Beginning in 1941, the bakers have added small amounts of iron, thiamine, and niacin to their bread formulas. Later riboflavin was added, the amounts of other added nutrients were raised, and in 1943, by order of the War Food Administration, all white bakery bread and rolls were enriched. The enrichment of commercial white bread has been made mandatory since the war in 26 States. Much of the family flour on the market is also enriched. Diets of city families in 1948 were estimated to have been 12 percent higher in iron, 16 percent in thiamine, 3 percent in riboflavin, and 13 percent higher in niacin than they would have been without the enrichment of bread and flour.

Cereals, rice, and corn meal and grits are sometimes enriched by the addition of one or more of the nutrients that are added to bread and flour. Vitamin A is added to nearly all margarine. Vitamin D is added to some of the fluid milk and to all of the evaporated milk. Much of the table salt used in homes is now iodized.

Some of the additions (to cereals) have been made because important nutrients were destroyed or removed in processing. Because foods must be treated so that they will not spoil during storage and shipment, some substances that might be beneficial are removed in order to provide safe products for the kitchen. The primary purpose of most processing is to destroy the micro-organisms and enzymes that hasten spoilage. During processing—in canning, for example—some losses of nutrients seem inevitable.

Improvements in canning since the nineteenth century makes products that probably retain more of the original nutritive values than formerly. Better processing also lessens changes in flavor, makes products more acceptable, and means that many foods can now be had the year around, with consequent reduction in the seasonality of the nutritive content of diets.

Better facilities for storage, shipping, and display of fresh and processed products, better refrigeration in railway cars, trucks, in wholesale and retail establishments, and homes have enhanced the table quality and variety of foods eaten. A varied diet is more likely to provide good nutrition than a limited one. Foods harvested and marketed to retain the highest proportion of nutrients probably have the most desired qualities—freshness and crispness in vegetables and full flavor and ripeness in fruits, for example.

Increases in table quality, as distinguished from nutritive value, are difficult to measure. What was thought to be good quality years ago may not be so considered today, because our standards have changed. Most experts in the quality testing of foods agree that there has been improvement over the years in domestic cheeses, canned and processed meats, canned and frozen fruits and vegetables, shortening agents, bakery cakes, pies, and cookies. Canned foods taste better and are

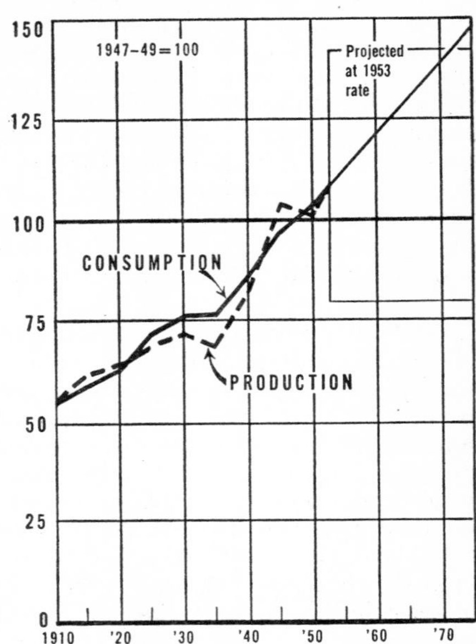

improved in sanitary quality. Milk has a lower bacteria count and a more uniform and delicate flavor. Eggs, graded and handled more scientifically, arrive in most city kitchens in better quality than formerly.

At the beginning of the twentieth century, food preparation required much time, effort, and skill on the part of the housewife. Soup, baked goods, baby foods—to name a few—were among foods that were almost always made at home. By midcentury the picture had changed considerably. The changes have had the effect of transferring to the processor or distributor tasks that used to be performed in the kitchen. Most mothers now buy special baby foods; consumption in 1952 was 51 pounds per child under 3 years of age, or enough for each child to have 2¼ ounces a day.

Commercially canned foods of all kinds are used much more extensively

UNITED STATES MEAT CONSUMPTION, 1910–75

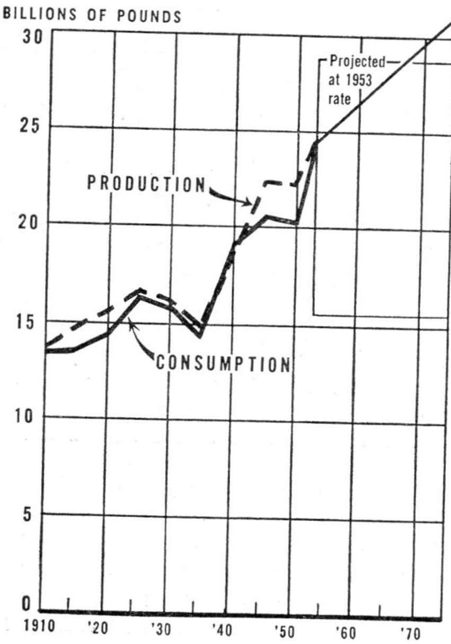

now by all groups of families. Per capita use of canned products increased threefold between 1914–1916 and 1950–1952. They and frozen products take about 10 percent of the average food budget of urban families. They save time in kitchen preparation, as do mixes and ready-for-the-oven and commercially prepared bread, rolls, cake, and pies. Besides, the cook saves time in the washing of pots, pans, bowls, and measuring utensils.

The transfer of the tasks to the processor that formerly were performed by the housewife has not been without cost to the consumer. Adding of services in the marketing of foods usually means that the consumer pays more for the finished product.

Today Americans mostly are well fed from a nutritional point of view. But they could make better food selections, and the food offered could be of higher nutritive quality.

Some groups in the population still do not have food containing recommended amounts of several nutrients. Dietary surveys show that those whose diets are most in need of improvement are low-income families, large families, and those in which the homemaker has the least formal education. The nutrient most likely to be supplied in smaller than recommended quantities is calcium. Also likely to be low are vitamin C and the B vitamins—thiamine, riboflavin, and niacin. Rural diets in some seasons may also be low in vitamin A.

Differences in quality of diet due to economic limitations are not so great as formerly, but problems of getting good diets on low incomes still merit attention.

For higher levels of living, the science of nutrition continues to stress the need for a varied diet—one that includes the following "basic seven" each day:

Leafy green and yellow vegetables—one or more servings;

Citrus fruit, tomatoes, raw cabbage—one or more servings;

Potatoes and other vegetables and fruits—two or more servings;

Fluid milk (or its protein and mineral equivalent in processed forms such as cheese and ice cream)—three to four cups for children; two or more cups for adults;

Meat, poultry, fish, eggs, dried peas, beans—one or two servings;

Bread, flour, cereals, whole grain, enriched or restored—some every day;

Butter, fortified margarine—some every day.

Many families, if they are to have nutritionally adequate diets, need to consume more milk, more fruits and vegetables (especially the ones rich in vitamins A and C), and more of the good sources of the B vitamins. Low-income families would do well to stress the foods that give high nutritional returns for the money spent. Nonfat milk solids, for example, are an excellent source of calcium, riboflavin, and protein. Dry beans and peas are an economical source of protein, iron, and the B vitamins. At the height of their growing season, tomatoes and melons are usually economical sources of vitamin C. The green leafy vegetables and carrots are almost always inexpensive sources of vitamin A.

As long as incomes rise, the consumption of the foods that high-income families like and can afford will probably increase. They are frozen fruits and vegetables; fresh fruit; canned fruits and vegetables; prepared and partly prepared foods like soups; milk and milk products (especially cream and ice cream); meat, poultry, and fish; fresh vegetables; and eggs.

Consumption of bakery products tends to increase with family income (at least up through the middle-income group), but the use of flour and other cereals is likely to decline. Potatoes, fats and oils, sugar and sweets, dried fruit, and dry beans and peas generally do not change much with income. Hence, possibilities of increased markets for the latter foods because of higher income levels in this country are not great.

Only very few persons in the United States are not getting as many calories as they need. Consequently when individuals, groups of families, or the whole population consume more of one product, they necessarily consume less of some other. The large increases in the per capita consumption of fresh fruits and vegetables in this country over the past half century, for example, have been accompanied by decreased use of potatoes. In other words, we cannot expect the domestic market to expand very much per capita, for all foods. Shifts are possible and with higher levels of income, experience shows that they will tend to be toward the more expensive foods, which in general are the ones that require large amounts of agricultural resources (for example, meat, milk, fruits, and vegetables) and of marketing services (for example, processed fruits and vegetables and prepared dishes).

Better marketing contributes to higher levels of nutrition when it gets the consumer more usable nutrients per dollar. Prevention of waste and spoilage in distribution can work toward this end—notably, waste of fresh produce, meats, dairy products, and eggs. Some losses in distribution are probably unavoidable, and elimination of some others would be too costly to justify, but better methods of handling, packing, shipping, storage, and display offer opportunities for substantial savings that would abundantly justify their costs.

Better quality of products will also mean less waste in the home; the housewife has to discard less of the fruits and vegetables when she prepares them for the table. Less fat on meat would mean less waste in the kitchen. If meat were trimmed more at the store, fat might be saved for some useful purpose and not discarded. The marketing system should also pass on to the producer the consumer's demand for meat—especially pork—with less fat.

A hidden kind of waste in distribution is the loss of nutrients that occurs in some foods during storage, transportation, and display. Fresh milk, for example, loses riboflavin when exposed to light. Canned foods stored at warm temperatures retain less of their vitamin C than when they are stored at low temperatures. Fresh vegetables such as broccoli retain more of their original nutritive values when packed in crushed ice than when kept on a grocer's table at room temperature.

When markets are well stocked with foods of high nutritive value and consumers have purchasing power to buy the food they want, good living in terms of good nutrition is available to all. If people are not then well fed, it is because they do not know enough about nutrition to believe that good diets are important or because they do not know how to achieve them. Progress has been made in getting knowledge about nutrition to the public, and families have become increasingly conscious of the importance of good nutrition to health. That is being continued through formal teaching of nutrition in the schools, advice of physicians, adult education programs, writing and lecturing about nutrition, and through advertising.

Marketing can perhaps best contribute to an improvement in the education of the consumer through betterment in information provided both on labels and in advertising. The facts of the real advances of nutrition should not be distorted to mislead the consumer-buyer.

To raise the sights of consumer-buyers and make possible still better living is a continuing challenge to marketing. (*Hazel K. Stiebeling, Faith Clark.*)

How They Tell What We Want

Producers, processors, and manufacturers have come to appreciate more and more the importance of knowing what consumers want—what products they desire, how and in what sizes products should be packaged, and what services will give the most satisfaction to consumers.

The grades and standards of many commodities bear little relation to consumers' desires, levels of information, or ability to distinguish between different grades. Certain technological yardsticks are essential in any proper system of grading, of course, but present standards can be improved by incorporating in them some of the results of studies of consumers' behavior, habits, and preferences.

Those factors may vary with the income of consumers, their educational status, background, locality, and such.

Even when many consumers have similar preferences or behavior, there are always atypical groups that may be small in terms of percentage of all consumers but nevertheless are a sizable body of potential customers. It takes well planned research to locate them and ascertain their wants. As for the "average" consumer, he is largely a statistical fiction.

As the marketing specialist approaches a problem involving consumers and chooses among the techniques available, he starts with the assumption that he must collect data in a way that will accurately represent the statistical universe he wishes to study.

He must look at related inquiries. He must search out technical details about his product. He needs to consider carefully the most appropriate experimental designs. He must decide if a small number of case histories will be adequate or whether a scientific sample of the general population is required. Perhaps his problem will be resolved by a study of a group of producers or a sample of manufacturers who use the commodity at some stage of its fabrication into an end-use product for final consumption. He must judge whether the observations should be limited to so-called objective records such as prices, inventories, or sales records. To understand an economic pattern he might need information on the reasons for particular behavior and on motivations for future behavior. He has to decide at which point or points along the distributive channel he should take readings and whether he should study purchase or use or both. He must decide if a mail survey is adequate or if a personal interview is required.

Consumer wants and needs can be studied directly, or attempts may be made to infer them from studies of behavior. Five principal methods are used in such consumer investigations: Measures of product consumption; retail store records of sales, prices, and inventories; sales experiments in retail outlets; reporting panels; and direct surveys. Each has its special advantages for particular problems, but each has certain drawbacks.

Measures of product consumption are one of the oldest methods of studying consumers' behavior. Their preferences are inferred from the results.

The usual procedure is to obtain data on total estimated quantity of a commodity disappearing into distribution channels and then divide by the total population. This average per capita figure obtained for a period of time furnishes a picture of trends in the average amounts of commodities that individuals use. Such trends often have been interpreted as indicators of changing preferences, but such inferences are open to question. Per capita figures so derived include persons who do not use the commodity at all.

The figures can give no indication of the characteristics of the users or nonusers. At best they can show in a general way over a period what consumers are taking from the market. Preference, though, is a complex of many factors and cannot be measured by gross figures derived from national aggregates.

Studies based on retail store records usually are concerned with a sample of the retail outlets of specific products. Records are kept of the day-by-day sales, the prices paid by customers, and data on inventories as the stocks are replenished. Comparison of the relative amounts of different products sold or the relative amounts of a particular product at different time periods is then used as a basis for inferring the preferences of the buying public.

Such studies can furnish quite reliable indicators of the movement of goods and their selling prices. The data are important as the raw material for certain types of analyses. Retail stores are the usual units studied in such research, but the method can be applied also to wholesalers, distributors, processors, or producers.

It is excellent in its way, but it does have some practical limitations. Even with accurate sales figures, the results cannot be interpreted as reflections of consumers' wants, because the desired goods are not offered for sale on a reasonably equal basis with other market choices in such matters as price, abundance, and convenience. The sample of outlets must be representative of all outlets through which the products are sold, at the level under study; that requirement often is prohibitive in cost or impractical of attainment, because of the impossibility of getting the consent of some large outlets to participate. Even with an effectual sample, there must be constant and complete cooperation between the management of all the sample outlets and those who direct the research for the full duration of the study. That requirement is seldom realized in practice. Finally, the job of recordkeeping is complex, and the chances of error are many.

An argument in favor of this method is that it deals with "objective" data and therefore is superior to surveys whose data consist of "subjective" responses of consumers to direct questions regarding their buying behavior, buying motivations, and preferences.

If one considers the defects of the method in its practical application, he can see that the objectivity of the data may be largely illusory. It does have a place in market research, but he who uses it should neither be tricked by its apparent simplicity nor misled into making unjustified inferences from the data it affords. If its limitations are kept in mind, however, this method can produce valuable information in marketing research.

Sales experiments in retail outlets in many respects are like the methods described so far. They differ in that certain controls are set up, the only variable being the factor that is under investigation—price, type of package, brand, type of display, different characteristics of a product, or any other item. The important thing is that all factors should be held constant while only the item being studied is allowed to vary in some predetermined way.

This is a much more accurate way of measuring consumer behavior and deducing preferences from such behavior than the methods that rely on aggregate statistics. It lends itself to various types of experimental design.

Two main designs have been used.

One, the "matched lot" technique, consists of placing in each sample store two or more separate lots of the product being studied. The lots must vary only in the characteristic under investigation, a requirement usually difficult to satisfy. The relative sales over a given period are used as the measure of consumer preference between the experimental lots.

The second experimental technique is that of comparing sales in test stores with those in control stores. In the sampling procedure, both groups of stores are matched as nearly as possible, but the variable under test is offered only in the test stores.

Controlled experiments of these types seem to offer a relatively simple way of measuring consumer wants or, at any rate, the inference of such wants from buying behavior. But most of the practical limitations pointed out in connection with audits of retail outlets also apply here: The difficulties of adequate sampling, the unlikelihood of securing willing and continuous cooperation with store management, the expense entailed in anything approaching national coverage, and the errors of recording all operate with equal force. In practice, moreover, it is seldom possible to establish and maintain adequate controls to insure constancy in all factors except the test variable. The utility of the method seems to lie in small spot studies of limited and quite specific problems. But it is very useful to and considerably used by chainstore management.

The reporting panels are another method. It consists in setting up a panel of consumers (usually households), which is a sample representing all consumers. The panel members keep diary records of their purchases or are interviewed at intervals regarding certain designated commodities, products, brands, and so on, by kind of product, amount bought, size of package, price paid, and date of purchase. The diaries or interviews are sent to the collecting agency at specified intervals, and the results are tabulated into aggregates and averages for the panel. The data are then usually expanded to furnish totals for the statistical universe represented by the panel. The panel may be on a national, regional, State, or local scale and theoretically will furnish measures of the amounts of various goods and prices paid over a period.

The panel method is more sensitive to changes in individual behavior than are composite measurements. It may be specifically designed for particular problems. It can show areas of competition between products. Diary forms, when they are used, furnish fairly accurate data on consumption or purchases. That is often of such importance in business that management is willing to overlook the defects of the method or to accept them as a kind of calculated risk.

The consumer reporting panel, however, is an expensive operation, particularly on a national scale. It requires constant and expert administration. There is great doubt that a continuously reporting panel can ever be a truly representative sample of the universe it is supposed to depict. The original sample may be sound, but those who refuse to participate will introduce an initial bias. Even when they are replaced, the fact that the replacement members do agree to become members may perpetuate this original bias. As time goes on, more and more members will drop out and cause an increasing lack of representativeness. The dropouts must be replaced to keep the panel up to strength, but the same factors operate again to produce some bias. Many panels have shaken down to only about one-third of their original members. Even though replacements may match the dropouts in such personal characteristics as age and income, the fact that they are willing to assume the responsibility of regular reporting may in itself seriously differentiate them from those who have dropped out.

Another source of bias is the act of recordkeeping itself. The panel members become conditioned to the items in the recording diary and may begin to exhibit a different kind of buying behavior than they would if they were not members of a panel. As far as we know, no adequate method for measuring this bias has been devised.

Moreover, material collected from panels ordinarily furnishes no data for the analysis of buying motivations or the effect on behavior of information or misinformation about the product. Although panels are relatively sensitive indicators of trends, they provide no knowledge of why there are nonusers of a product and hence cannot point out how to capture potential markets. Panels are the most difficult of all types of surveys for which to assure adequate sampling.

Direct surveys rely on collecting information directly from consumers by mail questionnaires or by personal interviews. Both the methods rely on samples of consumers intended to represent the particular universe of people being studied. Specific questions are put to the individuals in the sample, their answers are coded and tabulated, and various types of analyses are applied to the raw tabulations.

The survey by mail is relatively inexpensive and can reach a large number of persons. It can be done quickly and the results become available in a short time. It is a valuable tool in many areas of economic research, but it has limited usefulness in studies of consumers' wants and behavior. Although the original sample to which questionnaires are sent may be perfectly adequate, the rate of response is usually so low that a serious sampling bias occurs. A return of 10 percent is common. Only rarely do as many as half the sampled individuals fill out their schedules and send them back to the research agency. It is fairly well accepted that those who answer mail questionnaires are different from those who will not, and the consequent loss of representativeness is obvious. A second defect is the small number of questions that can be successfully included in a questionnaire. Most of them have to be of a simple check-off type—the answer must be yes or no or selected from a limited list of alternatives. It is not an adequate tool for the study of attitudes, motivations, reasons for likes and dislikes, and the many other items that are involved in research on desires and preferences of consumers.

The interview survey, on the other hand, offers many advantages. Its first cost may seem high, but the outlay per item of information obtained is less than some of the methods previously discussed. It can provide information on use and nonuse, reasons for the behavior, likes and dislikes and reasons for them, levels of information regarding products, factors motivating buying or nonbuying, attitudes toward types and sizes of packages or sales in bulk, attitudes toward different methods of merchandising, amounts bought during specified periods, frequency and recency of use, and many other items. It can provide practical field tests of the results of laboratory experiments on the ability of consumers to distinguish between product characteristics and establish psychological scales of relative preferences. When it is well planned and properly administered, this method will produce answers from more than 90 percent of the original sample and thus reduce to a minimum one of the worst sources of bias in other methods that depend upon sampling.

A good interview survey of this type rests on four essentials. Each is composed of a number of prerequisite elements, and all must be integrated into a functional pattern. The essentials are:

1. Planning and survey design—development of definite objectives to be satisfied; development of specifications of data necessary to satisfy each specific objective; development of a question schedule that will satisfy the specifications of data; pretesting of the question schedule to insure that each question actually does provide information to satisfy the datum specification for which it was designed; and development of detailed, question-by-question instructions to interviewers.

2. Sampling—development of a precise definition of the statistical universe that is to be sampled; choice of adequate sampling methods; determination of size and distribution of the sample in relation to the amount of error that can be tolerated; and development of clear and precise instructions to interviewers on how the sample is to be used.

3. Interviewing—administration of the field staff; use of proper interviewing techniques; and training of interviewers on the question schedule.

4. Analysis—development of an adequate code based upon the original specifications of data and the questionnaire; coding and check coding; tabulation and cross-analysis, correlations, et cetera; and preparation of the final report of the findings.

A NATIONAL INTERVIEW survey may cost between 50,000 and 100,000 dollars, depending on the number of separate regional tabulations involved. In the ascertainment of amounts of products used, prices paid, and frequency of purchase, it is subject to memory bias. There is no convincing evidence one way or the other, but it is generally assumed that while the diary-keeping panel method may somewhat underreport consumption, because of carelessness in recording by panel members, the interview survey has a telescoping effect and produces an overreport. The method has also been criticized on the grounds that the frames of reference in which the questions are asked may not be understood by respondents, so that much variability occurs in the meaning of the answers given.

It is evident that the investigator of consumer wants has a variety of methods to apply in the solution of the diverse problems arising in his field. Different problems require different approaches and it is a part of his skill to select the method or combination of methods which will best fit the particular situation. All the techniques discussed above have defects and some of these have been pointed out. Research in methodology, however, is continually going on and the results applied to the improvement of the basic techniques. They are good now; they will be much better in the future. (*Forrest Clements, Trienah Meyers.*)

281437°—54——15

The Long Fight for Pure Foods

The first laws prohibiting tampering with foods and selling unwholesome provisions were enacted in ancient times. Early Mosaic and Egyptian laws governed the handling of meat. Greek and Roman laws attempted to prevent the watering of wine. In 200 B. C. India provided for the punishment of adulterators of grains and oils. In the same era China had agents to prohibit the making of spurious articles and the defrauding of purchasers. Most of our food laws, however, came to us as a heritage from our European forebears.

In early times foods were few and

very simple, and trade existed mostly through barter. Such cheating as did occur was crude and easily detected by the prospective buyer. In the Middle Ages traders and merchants began to specialize and united themselves into guilds. One of the earliest was called the Pepperers—the spice traders of the day. The Pepperers soon absorbed the grocers and in England got a charter from the king as the Grocers' Company. They set up an ethical code designed to protect the integrity and quality of the spices and other foods sold. Later they appointed a corps of food inspectors to test and certify the merchandise sold to and by the grocers. These men were the first public food inspectors of England. Later on they became officers of the crown, and King Henry III made them custodians of the official weight standards.

Pepper is a good example of the trade practices that brought about the need for the food inspectors. The demand for pepper was widespread, as much for its preservative action as for its value as a condiment. Its price was high; it was handled by various people during its long journey from the Spice Islands to the grocer's shelf. Each handler had opportunity to debase it; the grinders had the best chance, and made the most of it, since adulterants could not be detected in the ground spices by methods then available. Worthless barks and seeds, iron ore, charcoal, nutshells and olive pits, and coconut shell at times were ground along with the pepper berries.

Bread was another food that offered temptation to unscrupulous bakers. The most common cheat was short weight, but at times the flour used contained ground dried peas or beans. In fact, sharp practices by members of the Bakers' Guild brought about the passage of the first protective food law on record. Known as the Assize of Bread, it was proclaimed by King John of England in 1202. A quotation from the law, rewritten into modern English, shows the type of punishment meted to violators:

"If any default be found in the bread of a baker of this city, the first time let him be drawn upon a hurdle, from the Guild hall to his own house, through the greatest streets, where the most people are assembled, and through the streets which are most dirty, the false loaf hanging from his neck; if a second time he shall be found committing the same offense, he shall be placed in a pillory, and remain there at least an hour."

A third offense banished him from his Guild. At times the magistrate ordered a bakery to be torn down and the culprit banished from the city.

In the fifteenth century the explorers opened up the era of colonial expansion. New luxuries—such as tea, coffee, chocolate, and sugar—began to arrive at home ports. Some of these commodities, coffee and tea in particular, seem to have been adulterated from the beginning. They came from countries whose traders had developed skillful and novel methods of adulteration. The Chinese suppliers added to tea destined for export such things as dried leaves from other plants, sand, clay, and even dried spent tea leaves ingeniously dyed and rolled to look like freshly dried tea. The importers further stretched the tea with leaves from their own trees (completely unlike tea leaves) and spent tea leaves from their coffee houses and inns.

Coffee has a similar history; chicory, roasted turnips, barley, acorns, beans, and mahogany sawdust were used as adulterants.

The crown's first interest in this situation came from its loss of excise revenues; more tea and coffee were being served in England than had been taxed at the ports. A law passed in 1718 imposed a fine of 20 pounds for adding foreign substances to coffee.

The nineteenth century in England brought developments in the central processing of foods and with it new forms of adulteration, some of them definitely dangerous to health, such as mineral pigments in candy and spices; and opium, nux vomica, and picrotoxin added to beer to conceal the addition of water. Publication of the scientific findings in the popular and medical journals resulted in the appointment of a committee of Parliament to investigate the extent of such adulteration, both dangerous to health and to the consumer's purse. This resulted in the enactment in 1860 of the Adulteration to Food and Drink Act, the first general food law of England.

The first general food laws in the United States were enacted by the States, Massachusetts leading the way in 1784. California enacted a pure food and drink law in 1850, a year after the Gold Rush. Most of the States had laws of this type by 1900, along with additional laws on special foods, many of them enacted to protect the farmers' basic commodities from competition with adulterated wares. Conditions paralleled those in nineteenth century England. New York inspectors in 1875 found 52 percent of the butter, 56 percent of the olive oil, and 64 percent of the brandy they examined to be adulterated. A Boston Health Department report in 1880 stated that 46 percent of the colored candies sampled contained lead chromate.

Little uniformity existed under the State laws; foods legal in one State might be banned by its neighbors.

The State chemists were among the first to advocate a Federal law to bring order into the chaos.

The pioneer who waged the most effective fight for Federal pure food laws was Dr. Harvey W. Wiley, who came from Indiana in 1883 to be chief chemist of the United States Department of Agriculture. Long interested in the composition of foods, he immediately assigned some of his staff to the problems of food adulteration. Soon a series of Government bulletins emerged; the most important was the 1,417-page Chemistry Bulletin 13, issued in 10 parts from 1887 to 1902, as *Foods and Food Adulterants.*

The first Federal food and drug bill was introduced into Congress in 1879, but the real fight for such legislation began about 1900 and lasted until the law was enacted 6 years later.

By that time the factory preparation of food had become big business, with each manufacturer a law unto himself, as far as the Federal Government was concerned. He could put whatever he chose into his wares, and his only labeling guides were his conscience and his competitor's practices. Few processors knew or cared about sanitation in those days, and commercial refrigeration was in its infancy.

Dr. Wiley, a born crusader, took his message to the public. He became a popular speaker before women's clubs and other organized groups. Reporters began to write front-page stories, which aroused consumers to the danger to their own health inherent in the debased foods of the day. Particularly interesting to the public were reports on the progress of Dr. Wiley's "poison squad," a group of young chemists who volunteered to be "guinea pigs" for a full year and eat nothing but the food prepared in the Bureau of Chemistry laboratories with measured doses of the chemicals prevalent in the prepared food of that period—formaldehyde, benzoate of soda, boric acid, and salicylates. Dr. Wiley became popularly known as "Old Borax."

Stories about medicines in national magazines alarmed every mother and homemaker—reports of infants' soothing sirups containing morphine and opium, of people who became narcotic addicts from the use of medicines with an innocent appearance, of women's tonics that depended on alcohol for their bracing effects, of the tragic consequences to those depending on the cure-all promises of the patent medicines on every drugstore shelf.

In 1906 a chapter in Upton Sinclair's *The Jungle* aroused the public with its graphic exposé of revolting conditions in the Chicago stockyards and packinghouses.

Mark Sullivan, in *Our Times,* wrote: "The women of the country were ripe for the crusade. Enough of them had lived through the transition from home and village food-industry, to large-scale corporation food-industry, to know the taste, odor, and sight of pure products of nature; and to recognize that in what they were now obliged to buy, and what they could not avoid feeding their children, there were elements new and mysterious, and therefore disquieting. These women, by the support they gave Doctor Wiley, by the pressure they brought upon Congress—without votes, without ever thinking they needed votes—did a work greater than anything that women accomplished or attempted during the eight years after women got the suffrage in 1919."

From 1879, when the first Federal pure food bill was introduced, until the law was finally enacted, Congress considered 103 food bills. It passed a tea importation act in 1883, and in 1890 acts prohibiting the *importation* of adulterated food and the certification of certain meat products processed for exportation. In 1891 and 1895 it extended meat inspection to partial protection of domestic consumers by requiring inspection of animals for disease before slaughter.

Despite bitter opposition, the crusade was finally ended when Congress passed the Food and Drugs Act and the Meat Inspection Act. Both were signed on June 30, 1906, by President Theodore Roosevelt, who had fought valiantly for their passage.

Both laws went to the Department of Agriculture for enforcement by the Bureaus, which had small staffs to administer the limited laws enacted in the 1890's—the Food and Drugs Act to the Bureau of Chemistry and the Meat Inspection Act to the Bureau of Animal Industry.

The enforcement of the Food and Drugs Act, which went into effect in 1907, was a stunning blow to the doctrine of *caveat emptor*. Both the Bureau of Chemistry and the affected industries recognized that the new slogan was to be "public interest comes first."

During the first year, before any cases were prosecuted in the courts, the Bureau set up a series of laboratories throughout the country, supplementing the port laboratories already in operation to keep any adulterated foreign products from entering the country. A corps of inspectors was appointed to collect samples of the foods and drugs shipped in interstate commerce. Chemists at Washington headquarters were busy devising new chemical and microscopic methods to supplement the woefully few then available for objective tests of the samples deluging the laboratories.

The industries, too, were putting their houses in order to live with the new law. Labels had to be changed to declare chemical preservatives in processed foods, and to give consumers other information the law required for intelligent purchasing. Almost immediately the processors encountered buyer resistance to foods labeled as containing chemicals that the public suspected would do them no good. The Bureau of Chemistry sent experts into the field to demonstrate how foods could be preserved without chemicals by employing adequate sanitation and suitable raw stock. The processors who adopted those practices found a new, enthusiastic market and prospered. Many others fell into line, preferring to abandon preservatives rather than to declare them on their labels.

In general, factory conditions improved during this period, for it was an era of awakening to the concepts of modern sanitation. The sanitary requirements in meatpacking establishments and the suggestions of Food and Drug inspectors in the plants to which they were admitted (the law did not compel their admission) played no small part in the trend toward the production of cleaner food. Seizures of unfit products in the channels of trade also encouraged more attention to sanitation.

Some compromises had to be made to enact the 1906 law, but for its time it was a good law—the strongest in the world. However, the era of food industrialization had just begun. By the turn of the century there had been a marked change from home production to bulk distribution. The next 25 years brought the package age—not only a change from the cracker barrel to the sealed carton, but from the delicatessen tray to jars and cans. These foods were better protected from contamination, but their contents were concealed from the inspection of the purchaser. More informative labeling was in order.

Other protections to the food consumer were needed, also—official standards defining the composition of basic food products, compulsory sanitary inspection of factories, heavier penalties for illegal practices, a ban on inherent poisons in food as well as added ones.

Stronger controls were needed in the drug field, also, and there was no Federal regulation of therapeutic devices and cosmetics, despite the injurious nature of many products on the market.

Some of the early deficiencies were pointed out by the chief chemist of the Bureau of Chemistry soon after the 1906 act went into effect, and others from year to year as conditions developed that required greater consumer protection.

Meanwhile, a separate enforcement agency was formed in 1927. It employed the staff of the Bureau of Chemistry assigned to administer the Food and Drugs Act. First known as the Food, Drug, and Insecticide Administration, its name was changed in 1931 to the Food and Drug Administration.

President Franklin D. Roosevelt gave a new impetus in 1933 to the reforms the Food and Drug officials had been calling for. A 5-year struggle for a stronger and more inclusive law finally culminated in passage of the Copeland bill in 1938. The best features of the 1906 act were retained, but the new law covered new conditions that had developed and put teeth into the enforcement provisions that had proved weak in the past.

There was little crusading in newspapers and periodicals for the passage of this stronger law such as that which had played so important a part in enactment of the Wiley bill in 1906.

Consumer groups, particularly the large national women's organizations, took up the fight, just as they had done for the first national law a generation earlier. They aroused public thinking on this subject in the cities, towns, and villages throughout the land, despite the general apathy of the press.

The Food, Drug, and Cosmetic Act of 1938 stands today, amended as weaknesses revealed by court decisions or changing conditions (such as the development of antibiotics, which required predistribution testing) were pointed out to Congress. This continuous process of keeping the law alive to the needs of the public should preclude another complete overhaul such as that necessary in 1938.

The new law made instantly effective the provisions designed to protect the public against dangerous drugs, devices, and cosmetics. As originally enacted, the statute was to become fully effective on June 25, 1939. This date was extended by amendment to January 1940, for the new labeling provisions and certain other requirements, with restricted authorization for additional postponements until July 1, 1940. Its complete coverage followed by a day the transfer of the Food and Drug Administration from the Department of Agriculture to the Federal Security Agency. All of the powers vested in the Secretary of Agriculture in the enforcement of the Food, Drug, and Cosmetic Act, the Tea Act, the Caustic Poison Act, the Import Milk Act, and Filled Milk Act were concurrently transferred to the Federal Security Administrator. In 1953 this Agency became the Department of Health, Education, and Welfare.

Where do we stand today in the fight for pure foods? The American public has the best and safest food in its history. We are no longer dependent on geographical location or season to have an abundant choice of nutritious food at any grocery store in the land. We cannot afford to be complacent, however, as we view the advances of the past half century. Most food is perishable or subject to the depredations of insects or rodents at some stage in its processing or distribution. Constant changes in producing and processing methods require comparable development in the regulatory field. There is wide variation among the industries subject to Federal food laws. Some are highly advanced technologically, with excellent control over the factors that lead to violative food, and others still employ methods unsuited to the protection of foods for human consumption.

With only a few hundred inspectors and analysis to cover the operations of 96,000 establishments that are producing and warehousing the commodities subject to the Federal Food, Drug, and Cosmetic Act, spot checking is the only course available. Violations involving direct danger to health receive first consideration in planning enforcement operations. Filth and decomposition are next in importance—and first in the amount of enforcement time actually allotted. Economic cheats affect the consumer's pocketbook, but they can be given relatively little attention. Coverage of the first two categories is woefully incomplete. It is possible to examine and inspect only a small fraction of 1 percent of the total production each year.

Conditions in food factories as a whole have shown progressive improvement throughout the history of enforcement of Federal food laws. The procurement of fit raw materials continues to be a problem. Milk and grain, for example, originate in thousands of farms that ordinarily make no interstate shipments. They are delivered to small collection centers—elevators or cream stations—and the intermingling of lots continues until large deliveries are made to the processors, whose business may be nationwide. The problem is to improve handling and storage conditions at the farms, then to protect the products at each step of the way. Such precautions are equally needed for our fresh produce, which is sometimes handled in city wholesale markets under reprehensible sanitary conditions. The Federal pure food laws can never substitute for adequate local protection of our food.

Another limitation of food protection today, under laws against false labeling and advertising, is the inability to curb the practice of nutritional quackery. Self-styled nutritionists are distorting the facts of the real advances of the science of nutrition and menacing the health of ailing and misinformed persons by making unwarranted therapeutic claims for various "food supplements." People who should be spending their money for readily available and adequate foods, and for competent medical care, frequently divert it to the faddist items promoted by food quacks. This tribe of nutritional pitchmen base their sales talk on myths about soil depletion, misconceptions regarding food processing, and falsely alarming exaggerations about "sub-clinical deficiencies" in the diet.

The food quack has something to sell, but usually he is fully enough aware of Federal laws to keep his claims and promises off food labels. He frequently confines his false teachings to books, magazine articles, and oral promotion which cannot be linked with a commercial scheme of distributing the product. The purchasing public must set up its own defenses against such exploitation.

On the chemical front, the fight for pure foods has been waged in two major battles. The first was a struggle against the recognized poisons used in and on our foods in the past. After passage of the 1906 law, widespread use of formaldehyde and boric acids to preserve foods was soon abandoned. The chief chemist reported in 1909 that a large number of prominent manufacturers had "entirely abandoned the use of any kind of preservatives and openly announced their adhesion to the doctrine that drugs should not be placed in foods."

Arsenic was found in early samples of baking powder, confectioners' glaze, and a few other processed foods, added inadvertently because it was so commonly used in the manufacture of phosphates and phosphoric acid and other commercial preparations purchased by food processors. The primary fight against arsenic and lead occurred in the late 1920's and during the 1930's when those chemicals were widely used as orchard sprays to control insect damage. After turbulent protests against seizures of fruits bearing excess residues when they reached the market, the growers installed washing equipment recommended by State and Federal officials and found that with the exercise of adequate precautions on spray schedules and removal of residues above the informal tolerances set by the Secretary of Agriculture, they could still protect their crops without violating the pure food laws.

Stronger provisions to prohibit or control the known poisons that might contaminate foods were included in the 1938 act. Soon after the new law went into effect, however, and before all of its regulatory provisions could be employed, the Second World War began. With it came an accelerated development of chemicals needed for military supplies in all parts of the world. The second struggle in the cause of pure foods was against chemicals with unknown potentialities.

New insecticides, new packaging and preservative materials, and many other necessary adjuncts of modern warfare were accepted after preliminary tests showed they were safe for emergency use—a calculated risk. There was not time for the 2- or 3-year chronic toxicity tests, without which a pharmacologist could not venture an opinion as to long-range safety in the diet of the general public. Such tests were in progress, but most of the new materials were restricted to temporary military purposes, and permanent, unrestricted use in a civilian economy was a problem of the future.

The end of the war released not only these chemicals but many other new substances developed for technical purposes but later adapted to food uses. Much progress has been made in the study of their long-range effect if ingested day by day in our food supply but there is still much to be learned about them. Additional products continue to appear, much more rapidly than the Food and Drug Administration can study them.

A succession of obviously poisonous additives have been removed from the markets—beer containing fluorine; soft drinks, wine, beer, salad dressings, and sirups containing monochloracetic acid and the quaternary ammonium compounds; frozen peaches with thiourea added as an antioxidant; cheese wrapped in papers impregnated with dehydroacetic acid to prevent spoilage; and numerous other foods containing substances that have been proved deleterious and not required in good production or manufacturing practice. The courts have ruled that it is not necessary to prove that such added poisons are present in the food in injurious amounts. The Government has the burden of proof that the substance is deleterious—and this may take several years of investigation, while the product is being used, with the public serving as "guinea pigs."

In December 1952 a circuit court ruled that the Government may exclude ingredients from standardized foods if there is doubt as to their safety. The court said: "One making a rule for the future which in practical effect will determine whether millions of people shall eat something every day may reasonably refuse to subject the general public to even slight risks and small deceptions."

The Congress, through the Select Committee on Chemicals in Foods, held hearings in 1951 and 1952 to determine whether the public is receiving adequate protection from chemicals used in foods. In a report issued in 1952, it concluded that the Food, Drug, and Cosmetic Act should be amended to require that new chemicals in food be cleared for safety in advance of distribution, similar to the practice established by law in 1938 for new drugs. This would place on the producer the responsibility for establishing evidence of safety.

The Second World War brought a great change in the insecticides and pesticides used to protect food crops. Arsenic, lead, and fluorine, the poisonous sprays of the past, gave way to DDT and its newer cousins. Hearings were conducted by the Federal Security Agency from January to September 1950 to establish residue tolerances for all of the substances required in the production of all classes of food crops. In investigating the problems of poisoning pests without poisoning people, the Food and Drug Administration has received the close cooperation of the Public Health Service, several units of the Department of Agriculture, and many State agencies.

The 1938 act gave a new impetus to sanitation in our food supply. It expanded the definition of adulteration to include production or storage under insanitary conditions that *may* result in contamination with filth. Previously, actions against filthy foods had to be based on contamination that could be detected in the product of the market place. Sanitary inspection of factories gained a new importance in food regulation—not only as an enforcement tool, but also for its educational value.

FDA inspectors invite the management to accompany them during the factory inspection and, when it is completed, leave a written report to the management on observations of insanitary conditions. Usually their constructive suggestions are adopted, and if objectionable products are on hand they are not shipped for human food use. A minority disregard the inspectors' warnings and suffer subsequent seizures of their goods and criminal prosecutions for continued carelessness in preparing food for the use of human beings.

Approximately 80 percent of the court actions involving foods each year are based on filth or decomposition. Major causes have been contamination by insects and rodents, and the use of unfit materials, such as decomposed or high-sediment milk, fruits and vegetables with the spoiled parts not adequately trimmed, and fish and eggs frozen after decomposition had set in.

The effectiveness of FDA's efforts toward a cleaner food supply was threatened by two court decisions. The first temporary setback came in February 1947, when the Supreme Court refused to review an appellate court decision which denied Federal jurisdiction over foods that became contaminated during storage after interstate shipment. An amendment in June 1948 closed this breach in the statute, and assured jurisdiction over adulteration and misbranding of interstate goods until they are delivered to the consumer.

The second came late in 1952 with a Supreme Court ruling that the language of the statute did not give the Government the right to make factory inspections without permission of the owner or manager. The immediate reaction of responsible producers was to invite continued factory inspections, making it abundantly clear that they were a burden only to careless and willful violators rather than to producers with pride in the quality of their merchandise. Early in 1953 amendments to correct this serious threat to law enforcement were introduced into Congress by members of both political parties. The President, in his State of the Union address, urged prompt action to restore FDA's factory inspection powers. Spokesmen of most of the trade associations of the food, drug, and cosmetic industries assured their support of prompt remedial legislation. This was enacted in August 1953.

To protect consumers against economic cheats, the 1906 Food and Drugs Act prohibited shipment of foods adulterated with inferior ingredients, and misbranded with false labeling. The 1938 law provided that labels should be informative—the whole truth, rather than merely a prohibition against dishonest claims of composition.

One of the most important sections of the new law provided for establishing of legal definitions and standards for foods, wherever in the opinion of the Secretary they are needed to "promote honesty and fair dealing in the interest of consumers." The statute calls for a very democratic process in establishing such standards, with every interested party, producer and consumer alike, invited to participate in public hearings and to comment on the proposed standards before the specifications for each item are determined. After such standards become final, foods failing to comply are in violation of the act and are subject to court action.

Food standards are the cornerstone of effective protection of consumers against many economic food cheats. They likewise protect the honest manufacturer and dealer from unfair competition. The standard is a yardstick for the manufacturer and the law-enforcement official alike. While the housewife may not know the exact specifications for any standardized food, she can be confident when she buys a standardized food by name. She knows the law-abiding manufacturer follows the specifications, and that the Government has an effective basis for legal action against the cheating or careless minority that does not comply.

Water is still the commonest adulterant of foods. Court actions in 1952 involved watered oysters, low-fat butter, and frozen turkeys with an average of a quart of water injected into the flesh before freezing. In other instances a 7- to 10-percent ice glaze was produced on poultry by packing wet birds in plastic bags before freezing.

The greatest incidence of fraudulent adulterations came in wartime when food was scarce and many items were rationed. Substitutes and "extenders" appeared on the market, some in disguise and others legally labeled for what they were. Such things appeared on the market as "victory butter," containing only 30 percent butterfat instead of the 80 percent the law demands; an eggless egg substitute; coffee diluted with roasted cereals and even the exhausted grounds found in precontrol days; french dressing devoid of salad oil; and coconut-peanut candy with corn flakes substituted for the coconut and processed wheat for the peanuts. Any product labeled "olive oil" was suspect, for the adulteration of olive oil is an ancient pursuit, even when there is a free flow of imports. Rationing of food oils induced many a mineral oil substitute—a good example of an economic adulteration with a direct bearing on public health. Spices, always subject to adulteration, became much more of a problem when imports of many items were cut off.

Throughout those trying times, however, the general integrity of our food supply was maintained. Enforcement was aimed to insure honest labeling and no concessions were made for expediency that would lower public confidence. As a result, there were few problems in resuming the higher standards of a postwar economy, although high prices prevalent since that period have been tempting to the unscrupulous to take any advantage of the buyer.

There will always be a regulatory problem in the economic adulteration field as long as one product closely resembles another selling at a higher price. A recent example has been the conviction of horsemeat racketeers who removed all required labeling and markings from horsemeat to sell it at triple the price as beef. In a somewhat similar fraud, "butterleggers" surreptitiously repackaged oleomargarine and labeled it as butter, selling for more than twice as much.

The Federal Food, Drug, and Cosmetic Act covers animal feeds and veterinary remedies as well as products for human use. These controls are of great value to the farmer. He depends on the labeled protein content of feeds to determine both the price he should pay and the feeding schedules he should adopt. He is also protected from worthless animal and poultry remedies which, if used, may result in serious loss of stock that could be saved with proper medication.

The story of the fight for pure foods would not be complete without recognition of the part played by the men behind the lines—the chemists, microanalysts, biologists, bacteriologists, and pharmacologists who have developed the objective evidence that has made possible the progress of the past half century. Before a pharmacologist can test the effects of minute daily doses of a substance on laboratory animals, the chemist must develop methods to isolate and measure them. The bacteriologist must study the effects of bacterial contamination of foods, how it occurs, and how it can be prevented. The biochemist has basic responsibilities in the nutritional value of foods, not only in devising testing methods, but in guiding administrative decisions as to enrichment of products and the validity of labeling claims.

In the struggle for pure food, the Food and Drug Administration has had valiant allies in other Federal groups, in State and local enforcement officers, and in the responsible elements of the regulated industries.

The Bureau of Animal Industry, fortified by the Meat Inspection Act of June 30, 1906, continued its elimination of diseased animals brought to slaughter, but added to it post mortem examinations by veterinarians, of slaughtered animals and parts. It was also provided sanitary controls over slaughtering houses and supervision of all meat condemned by its inspectors. All unprocessed meat shipped in interstate commerce now bears the stamp "U. S. Inspected and Passed," and processed meat products are labeled "U. S. Inspected and Passed by Department of Agriculture."

The Public Health Service of the Department of Health, Education, and Welfare establishes uniform sanitary codes used by local health departments in the control of the sanitation of restaurants, and has a comprehensive program to reduce or prevent pollution of the Nation's waters.

State and city officials enforce their own laws and ordinances controlling products distributed within State lines, and work closely with Federal control officials in the planning and operation of food-protective measures that neither could accomplish alone.

Last, but not least, has been the constructive work of the food industry to produce better, purer foods. Its members have drawn themselves into associations which have improved their products, both by sanitation campaigns and collective research to solve technical problems common to all. Most American food manufacturers today have the will and the know-how to produce the pure foods that the public wants. They accept the Food, Drug, and Cosmetic Act as a blueprint of their obligations to the Nation's consumers. (*Charles W. Crawford.*)

Payment for Quality

The simplest way to pay producers is to pay the same price to all, regardless of differences in quality—to pay Farmer A and Farmer B the same amount for a dozen eggs, say, although A's eggs are bigger and fresher, and of the color one wants.

But we do that less and less today.

We pay on the basis of quality for eggs and nearly everything else; Farmer A specializes in producing and marketing eggs, and the eggs he markets are of established grades, so we can choose the grade we want and are willing to pay for.

Quality has come to mean the characteristics of a product that affect the price a buyer is willing to pay. The characteristics may be physical or psychological. In eggs, for example, that may mean size and freshness, plus the color, which in eggs has nothing to do with quality but with habit, preference, or attitudes.

Farmers who participate in an effective quality-improvement program are likely to receive higher average prices as they develop a reputation for high quality. Higher quality also may raise the overall demand for a commodity, raise the level of its prices, lower handling costs by cutting losses due to spoilage and waste, and thus make a larger share of the consumer's dollar available to the farmer.

Quality in food products embraces three major factors.

The appearance of a product may have an important bearing on its selling price. Appearance may have to do with color, shape, size, consistency, glossiness, uniformity, and flaws.

Food products vary with respect to nutritional characteristics. Such variations sometimes are reflected in the values of the products, but for most persons are harder to determine than the variations that can be determined by sight, taste, touch, or smell.

Buyers and sellers of food also are concerned with preservation, sanitation, grittiness or uneven composition, and degree of ripeness.

QUALITY STANDARDS relating to sanitation may be used to achieve objectives other than improvement or maintenance of product quality. Results of a study published in 1953 by the National Research Council showed eight significant factors in milk production and inspection of farms that related to the sanitary quality of milk. It was concluded that—in terms of public health—there is no reason to make accepted health regulations more detailed and rigid.

How a grading program incorporating price differentials for varying qualities can raise prices to producers is demonstrated by a survey of egg marketing in 1951 in Ohio. The study determined the effects on production and marketing of paying producers according to quality, as measured by official grades. In 5 years the percentage of eggs in the top grades increased from 56 to 72 percent for marketing firms using the grading program. Producers who were paid on the basis of quality increased their egg production, produced larger eggs, and received higher prices.

The decline in demand for lard has affected the evaluation of quality of hogs. Hogs now should have a higher proportion of lean pork. To accomplish that, hogs should be marketed at lighter weights because lard production increases rapidly as hogs become heavier. The meat-type hog, specially bred to produce pork with less internal fat, appears to be another answer to the problem. A producers' organization in the Midwest has made progress in the sale of hogs pooled by grade. Six times as many hogs were sold on grade by the association in 1952 as in 1951.

Premiums for extra quality vary in accordance with changes in the general economic situation, market price levels, production conditions, and consumers' preferences. In general, the premium for higher quality must be large enough to compensate the producer fully for increased costs of capital and labor and provide him with an incentive for changing his work habits.

Unless price premiums remain high enough to meet such standards, producers are not likely to make the production changes necessary to achieve higher quality of product.

On a given day, week, or month, a producer may not receive even a small price differential for high quality because on that day maybe not even one quality-minded buyer is at the market, the market may be glutted just then, or consumer purchasing power may have dropped suddenly. Over a longer period of time, however, the producer usually can recover his extra production expense and make a profit.

Since quality is inseparably related to value—even though the relationship may not always be apparent—it is also affected by quantity differences. Price usually reflects the interplay of demand and supply. A change in either will result in a change in value. In terms of technical standards, quality will not be affected by changes in demand and supply, but consumers may be more conscious of quality when incomes are high. Price differentials between qualities also will vary under different conditions of income and supply. Generally the price premium for high quality will be greater when consumers have more money to spend or when supplies of the higher quality are less abundant.

Premiums may be paid the farmer for some factors, such as yield in processing or firmness (fruits, melons), although they are not factors that affect quality as consumers judge quality. For most products, however, payment for quality is based on the same quality factors of the raw product as the finished product. Peas for processing are graded for size, color, and tenderness—factors that are the basis for quality and price differentials of the canned or frozen peas.

Marketing agencies handling food products sold to consumers in their natural form also may reprice products on a different basis from the one on which they bought them. Quality changes often occur during the marketing process because of variation in condition, ripeness, or other factors. Potatoes shipped long distances may drop one grade in quality. Peaches shipped to eastern markets may advance one degree of ripeness.

Usually the separation of a product into various grades or qualities is undertaken by a marketing agency. It may be done when the products are assembled from the farm, at retail, or at some intermediate point. Often products are graded or sorted more than once. In canning, for example, the raw product is separated into various classifications according to prescribed specifications and, after processing, the finished goods also are graded.

Marketing agencies must make the actual quality segregation and to a large degree determine the price differentials between qualities. The prices should be set at levels that will encourage production of improved quality, move the total supply (not just the best or poorest quality), and heighten demand through improved distribution.

Because of the lack of other measures of quality, the customer may select products on the basis of price, which in itself is not always a good guide to quality. In a study in Ohio of price-quality relationships of canned fruits and vegetables, it was found that in one canned commodity only 51 percent of the samples were of the grade expected for the price paid. One-half of the rest graded higher than expected and one-half lower. The brand name was a more reliable guide to quality than price.

On the other hand, a number of research studies have shown that a consumer will pay a premium for products considered to be high quality. The factors that a housewife associates with high quality may not necessarily be the standards of the distributor or producer. Ripeness of many fruits and vegetables is a quality factor, for example. Consumers consider fully ripe fruit to be of the best quality, but distributors are reluctant to handle it because they are more afraid of the risk of spoilage. Wholesalers and retailers usually prefer to market firm fruit even though the housewife likes it less because it is not ready to eat.

Retail store tests of sales of Colorado

peaches of varying degrees of maturity showed that consumers would pay up to 7 cents a pound premium for ripe peaches that had reached the best eating condition. (*Donald E. Hirsch, J. K. Samuels.*)

PERCENTAGE OF TOTAL FEDERALLY INSPECTED SLAUGHTER OF LIVESTOCK PURCHASED AT SOURCES OTHER THAN PUBLIC STOCKYARDS, UNITED STATES, 1923–51

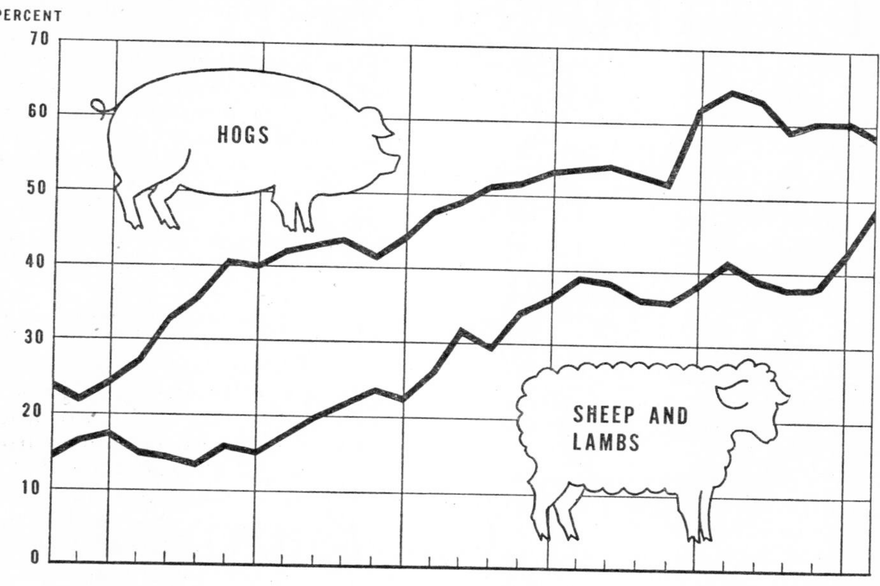

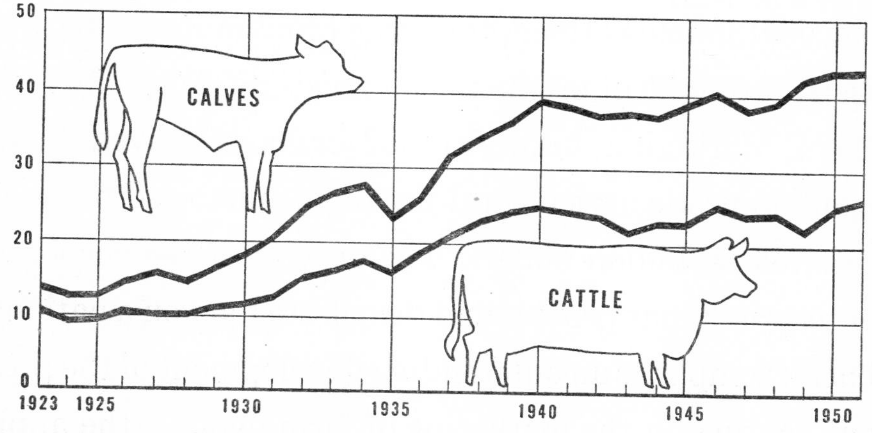

The Industry

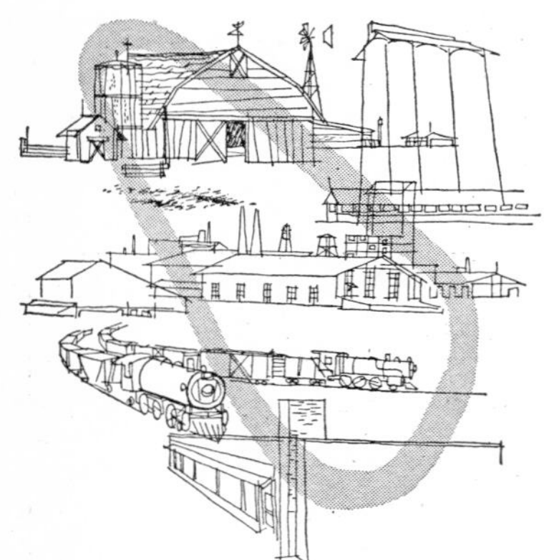

One-fourth of the total number of business concerns in the United States are engaged in marketing, processing or manufacturing, and distributing farm products and goods made chiefly from them. Marketing charges in 1952 for goods derived chiefly from domestic agricultural products amounted to an estimated 50 billion dollars. The growth of the corporate enterprises that process and distribute food on a national basis exemplifies an outstanding development of the present century in the marketing of farm goods—the application of techniques of mass production and distribution to food products. But largeness that carries with it some degree of market control and monopoly power may alter competitive production and consumption patterns, distort the allocation of basic resources, and reduce the ability of the economy to satisfy wants and the public welfare. A challenge for the future in agricultural marketing is to develop means of obtaining the efficiency of the large-scale organizations without excessive penalties from monopoly.

Something About Size and Scope

Marketing, processing or manufacturing, and distributing farm products and goods made chiefly from them are the main activity of more than a million American firms—roughly one-fourth of the total number of business establishments in the United States.

The firms range in size and scope of activity from corner groceries to giant meatpackers, flour millers, and supermarkets. Among the industries that use chiefly agricultural raw materials are several types of businesses that not commonly are thought of as being part of agricultural marketing—textile mills and clothing manufacturers, for example, and the other industrial users of farm commodities, as well as department stores and the other distributors of the products of such industries.

It is not easy to devise a single figure that will represent the overall importance of the business that is based on the farm products. The American consumers in 1953, as an example, bought about 100 billion dollars' worth of food, tobacco products, and apparel. This was two-fifths of consumer income after the taxes, or two-thirds of the consumer expenditure for consumers' goods. But that figure includes many products not of an agricultural origin (fish, for example, and apparel made from synthetic fibers) and products made from imported materials. It does not include exports of farm commodities and the products that are processed from them. It likewise leaves out household textiles and many other industrial products made in varying degree from agricultural raw materials.

The million or more firms comprise about one-half of the total number of businesses engaged in manufacturing and trade. Most of them are in retailing. About 900,000 firms were engaged in 1953 in retailing products derived mainly from farm commodities. They were more than one-half of the total number of all retail firms in the United States. So diverse are they that they usually are not considered together. They are organized into separate trade associations and mostly have separate, though overlapping, manufacturing and wholesaling channels of supply. Despite the wide variety of businesses included, a substantial volume of farm products reaches consumers outside of those channels.

THE FOOD GROUP includes 450,000 firms. Their sales, 41 billion dollars in 1953, accounted for almost half of retail sales of farm-derived products and one-fourth of all retail sales.

Grocery firms dominate the food group in terms of number of stores and volume of sales. More specialized foodstores are also included—meat and fish markets, fruit and vegetable stores, confectioneries, dairy products stores, bakeries, and egg and poultry dealers—and also some general stores that sell food.

In the first two years after the war, when the number of new businesses in all lines was unusually high, the number of firms in the retail food group went up from 450,000 to 500,000.

The postwar peak in the number of retail food firms, reached in 1948, was somewhat below the number in operation before the war. The number of firms discontinuing operations between 1948 and 1953 exceeded the new firms entering the retail food trade in each year, although total sales increased during the period. Most of the drop has been among the small stores. Although the number of failures has not been high—averaging about 2 percent of the total number of discontinued businesses—the small grocery store has lost ground in competition with the larger self-service type of store that handles meats and a full line of groceries. Independent stores and the chains alike have participated in the trend.

EATING PLACES are an important part of the retail marketing of agricultural products. There were more than 350,000 such firms in the United States in 1953. Their sales of food and beverages were about 13 billion dollars in 1953. The total includes the sales of varied types of establishments—regular restaurants and hotel dining rooms, bars, taverns, and nightclubs, dining and buffet cars, school lunchrooms and fraternities, and clubs and industrial lunchrooms. It does not include eating places in other retail establishments such as drugstore lunch counters, restaurants in department and variety stores, hospitals, boarding houses, and clubs.

Some increase in the number of firms whose primary business is the operation of the eating and drinking establishments occurred during the latter part of the war, and the peak in total number came in 1947. Since then the number discontinuing business has exceeded the new units organized. These firms are typically small-scale. Among them are few chain organizations and large individual establishments.

RETAIL FIRMS selling chiefly nonfood farm products include clothing and shoe stores, dry goods and general merchandise stores, department stores, and feed, farm, and garden supply stores. Grouped into separate trade associations, they have little in common.

There were about 150,000 firms in the apparel and general merchandise group in 1953, and sales totaled approximately 30 billion dollars. Two-thirds of the firms in this group sold apparel and shoes.

The individual stores in the apparel group in 1948 varied in size as did grocery-combination stores, except that the proportion of large stores, with annual sales of 500,000 dollars or more, was smaller. The few large clothing stores, however, accounted for a substantial part of total sales. The top 1 percent of the stores had 20 percent of sales for the group; the top 2 percent had 30 percent of sales. Chainstores (with 11 or more units) accounted for about 20 percent of sales in the apparel group.

General merchandise firms numbered 50,000 in 1953; not counted among them were those classified as "general stores with food." Department stores comprise about 5 percent of the total number of stores in this group, but their sales represent 60 percent of the total for the general merchandise group.

Approximately 60 percent of all department stores in 1948 had sales of a million dollars or more. These large stores accounted for 94 percent of all department-store sales in that year, averaging more than 6 million dollars a store. These figures, of course, refer to total sales, not just goods of agricultural origin.

WHOLESALE establishments selling agricultural products numbered about 80,000 in 1948, approximately the same as in 1939. (Those were the years of the two latest censuses; no intercensal estimates are available.) During this period the number of assemblers of farm products dropped about one-third, as the improved transportation tipped the economic scales against the small local assembler. The decrease was most rapid for dealers in dairy and poultry products (from 9,000 in 1939 to 4,000 in 1948), but the numbers of assemblers of fruits and vegetables, cotton, grain, and livestock also dropped. The number of merchant wholesalers of farm products increased substantially in all the main types of trade.

FIRMS PROCESSING farm products constitute between one-third and one-fourth of all manufacturing businesses. Of 95,000 firms engaged principally in processing farm products in 1953, about 40,000 manufactured foods and beverages, 40,000 were the apparel and finished textile concerns, and 15,000 were textile mills and makers of leather products.

The number of food manufacturers has been relatively stable since 1939, but the number of textile mills has increased by one-third. Most of the rise occurred immediately following the Second World War. The apparel and leather firms rose 50 percent by 1947 but have remained relatively constant since that time.

EMPLOYMENT in the types of firms we have described exceeded 11 million in 1953—including part-time workers, active proprietors, and unpaid family workers. Not all of these workers were engaged in marketing farm products. However, the total does not include workers in railroads, trucklines, financial agencies, and other businesses engaged principally in marketing nonagricultural products, even though the employees of those firms perform important marketing functions for farm products.

About one factory worker in four processes products derived principally from the farm. There were 4.4 million employees in industries in 1953 whose chief raw materials were of farm origin. Those who made food and kindred products were the largest group, 1.5 million workers. Another million were employed in each of two industries—textile mills and apparel and finished textile products. Leather and leather-products industries employed 380,000 and tobacco about 100,000.

Approximately one million workers were engaged in wholesale trade in 1953 in firms dealing mainly in farm products.

An estimated 6 million workers were employed in 1953 in firms selling products derived chiefly from farm materials. This includes part-time employees and unpaid family workers as well as active proprietors. Employment in the retail segment of agricultural marketing has risen substantially—around 1,500,000 between 1939 and 1948 and 300,000 more by 1953.

Referring again to the detailed figures available for 1948, we find, of a total of 5,600,000 workers, nearly 700,000 unpaid members of the families of the proprietors and approximately 800,000 part-time workers. This leaves about 4,100,000 workers. Somewhat more than a million of them were active proprietors; the rest were full-time paid employees. About two-thirds of the workers in retail distribution of agricultural products were in foodstores and eating places. Most

281437°—54——16

of the others were in apparel and department stores.

The number of active proprietors increased about 10 percent between 1939 and 1948, with some gain in most of the principal types of stores, except foodstores. The number of full-time paid employees rose 50 percent during the period, from 2 million in 1939 to more than 3 million in 1948. The combined increase in full-time employment was one-third between 1939 and 1948. Physical volume of trade increased by one-half in the same period, suggesting some moderate increase in physical volume of goods sold per employee, though considerably less than the increase in gross output per employee in nonagricultural industry as a whole or in agricultural production itself.

Agricultural processing firms invested more than a billion dollars annually from 1946 through 1953 in new plant and equipment. In 1948, 1.7 billion dollars was invested, compared to 380 million dollars in 1939. Each of the principal agricultural industries—food, beverages, textiles, and tobacco—reached a high point in its capital-investment program in 1948. Spending for plant and equipment for agricultural processing firms then was nearly one-fifth of total capital investment in all manufacturing firms—about the same proportion as in 1939. In subsequent years the rate of investment decreased to about 1.1 billion dollars in 1953, whereas industry as a whole pushed investment to a new high as defense and defense-related industries expanded capacity rapidly.

If adjustment is made for increases in costs of construction and equipment, investment in the agricultural industries in 1953 was two-fifths higher than in 1939. The expansion was general—about the same rate for each of the major groups except beverages, which expanded at twice the average rate. Capital investment other than in manufacturing also has been substantial, especially at the retail level.

Railroads, trucklines, and other carriers are among the most important types of businesses from the farmer's standpoint. Freight of agricultural origin is likewise important to the transportation agencies, although it is far from a major part of their business.

Data on their operations are most complete for the railroads. Products of agriculture (excluding bananas and coffee), animals and animal products, and the main semimanufactured and finished goods made from farm products together accounted for more than 20 percent of railway freight revenue in 1953. Their share in tonnage hauled was less, about 15 percent, reflecting the relatively long hauls of much such freight as well as differences in rate structures.

The proportion of truck traffic is roughly comparable, perhaps higher. Agricultural products in 1936–1937 accounted for about 25 percent of the total number of truckloads. We have no more recent data to show how the figure may have changed since then.

Other types of service enterprises—banks and insurance companies, telephone and telegraph companies, and advertising agencies, to mention only a few—likewise derive appreciable amounts of business from activities relating to the marketing of agricultural commodities.

Economies of Size

Nearly all phases of food processing and distribution are carried on by a great number of enterprises and types of enterprises. They vary in size from small, family undertakings to integrated national corporations whose annual sales run to hundreds of millions and even billions of dollars. Some are independently owned. Some are corporately owned. Some—here the food industries are unique—are cooperatively owned. As a generalization, large-scale enterprise is important in the food field, but does not predominate to the extent found in most nonfood lines of industry.

The integration of different functions within a single firm has also taken several forms in the food industries. There are, for instance, the corporate grocery chains, which specialize in food retailing but which have integrated the wholesale function as well as some food manufacturing and assembling operations.

Integrating in the opposite direction are the large food manufacturers who specialize in manufacturing but frequently distribute their products through to the retail level.

Some companies have expanded their sales horizontally. Others have done so mainly by adding to their line of products. For each type of expansion or integration there are simple and logical reasons.

In any given food-manufacturing field, the typical pattern is likely to be this: There will usually be three or more firms operating on a national basis—the so-called "national brand" companies. Generally they manufacture a large line of related food products—not just one or two—and they carry the products forward to the retailer with their own salesmen and through their own distributive facilities. Examples are the "Big Four" meatpackers, the Borden Company and the Kraft Foods Company for dairy products, and General Mills and Pillsbury for flour products.

Competing with them are 20 to 50 or more companies in any given line that operate on an interstate or regional basis. Generally they have a smaller family of products than their national competitors and they more likely use specialized jobbers and wholesalers to get their products to the retailer. But nevertheless they are large-scale enterprises that use the technologies of mass production and distribution.

And, finally, there are hundreds and thousands of small manufacturing establishments for most food products—local cheese factories, creameries, flour mills, canneries, slaughtering establishments—for the first step in manufacturing food products. Even most of the simplest food-manufacturing processes have become mechanized to the point where a considerable capital outlay is required for efficient operations. The result is that many of the local establishments are owned by incorporated local companies or by producer-cooperatives, rather than by individuals.

The family-size or independently owned enterprise (as exemplified by the independent grocer) retains a position of relatively greater importance in food distribution than in most lines of food manufacturing.

Again we find several large chains (Atlantic and Pacific Tea Co., Safeway, and Kroger) operating on a national basis. Such companies almost always integrate the grocery wholesaling function for their retail units. Frequently they carry on extensive food-manufacturing operations for some of the food products sold under their own brands—baking, coffee roasting, canning, preserving, and manufacturing evaporated milk.

Next below them are several hundred smaller chainstore and supermarket systems, all of them mass distributors of food. They usually operate warehouse units to serve their retail stores. They have their private brands, buy direct from the manufacturer, and are similar in method of operation to the national and regional chains but on a smaller scale.

Nevertheless, the so-called independent grocer still handles more than half of the food products sold to the consumer. The small-business man has retained his position better in the field of food retailing than in any other major sector of the economy, except farming.

For that there are two reasons. First is that only a small amount of capital is required to establish a retail foodstore as compared with, say, a modern milk plant or flour mill. Second, the progressive, independent grocer has been able to obtain for himself many of the advantages of mass distribution by organizing cooperatively into the so-called voluntary or cooperative chains. By so organizing, the small retailers can operate a cooperatively owned warehouse, buy directly from the manufacturer, have private brands, advertise jointly in local newspapers, and standardize and improve their store merchandising and operating methods.

Producer cooperatives are an important segment of our food economy, but their activities mostly are confined to the local assembling and first-processing of food products. Local creameries, the cheese factories, grain elevators, produce assembling plants, and livestock shipping associations are the types of facilities frequently owned and operated by producer cooperatives. Meatpacking, corn processing, flour milling, and fruit and vegetable canning, which require larger capital outlays, are not engaged in by producer cooperatives to any significant extent.

But a number of producer marketing cooperatives are big. One is the California Citrus Exchange, which assembles and packs a large part of the citrus fruits produced on the west coast and operates terminal markets for them. Another example is Land O'Lakes Creameries, a marketing organization for local cooperative creameries and cheese factories in several Midwest States. It assembles butter and cheese from its member factories, packages the products into consumer-size units, has a nationally advertised brand, and operates distributing sales branches in some of the major consuming centers. Cooperative organizations of such a type and scale, however, are the exception and not the rule for most agricultural products.

Why has this development toward large-scale enterprise in the food field taken place? Are there valid reasons in terms of technologies and operating economies, or have the reasons been mainly exploitive, as a few insist? Why does a company expand its operations geographically until it becomes regional and national in its scope? Why does it integrate vertically, or add additional products to its line? What is it that ultimately determines the size and type of business enterprise?

THE TECHNOLOGY of production—the kind, cost, and complexity of the productive processes and the buildings and machinery required to carry them out—is the major factor in determining the size of business enterprise. It is patently impossible to roll a sheet of steel in a blacksmith shop or to assemble an automobile in a garage from parts made in a thousand small machine shops. In those and similar industries, modern techniques of production have long since resulted in large-scale enterprise, which is the only way the techniques could be utilized and applied.

That food manufacturing and distributing technologies have likewise become vastly more mechanized during the past 50 years is a fundamental reason for the growth of large-scale enterprise in this field. But in one important respect the food industries differ from, say, the automobile and steel industries. Technological forces in the food field, important as they have been, thus far have not impelled so strongly toward greater scale as in most other parts of the economy. Medium-sized and even small industry therefore retains a place of relative importance in the handling of food.

Several examples illustrate the point. One can slaughter a pig or make a cheddar of cheese in a small plant with simple machinery and modest investment. Therefore a place remains for the local slaughterhouse and the small cheese factory. But mass production methods can be applied to the dissembling of a pig the same as to the assembling of an automobile. That is why most livestock slaughter today is done in million-dollar plants.

Dairy-manufacturing facilities, while not on the average so large as meat-slaughtering establishments (because milk is perishable), have shown the same trend toward large-scale units and for the same basic reason. For instance, a spray drier to dry the whey resulting from cheesemaking costs about 75,000 dollars. That is why milk plants, corporately or cooperatively owned and costing upwards of a million dollars, are found competing with the small creamery or cheese factory in the dairy areas, and frequently supplementing the operations of the small plants by providing them an outlet for the whey or skim milk which they are not in position to utilize in their plants.

The past half century has brought hundreds of improvements and changes in the technology of food manufacture—most of them requiring larger and larger capital outlays for most efficient application. The reclamation of byproducts, already mentioned, is becoming increasingly important as the chemists discover new and valuable elements in farm products and engineers devise new methods to reclaim and process them.

Most foods are put up by the manufacturer in consumer-size packages. The packaging operation, whether it be filling a container or putting a carton around the product, must be mechanized if it is to be done efficiently. Some types of packaging can be done with small and fairly simple machines, within the range of expenditure of the small operator. But the more difficult packaging operations—done at high speeds and highly mechanized (and this includes most of them)—require plants and machinery that cost hundreds of thousands of dollars.

Another development is the pallet truck, which can lift and transport raw materials and finished goods within a plant, thereby eliminating much hand labor. The result is added impetus toward larger, one-floor manufacturing and warehouse units, in which the pallet truck can be utilized efficiently.

The basic processes used in the manufacture of most food products have been known for centuries, and the more recent of the technological improvements have been mainly those of greater mechanization of a known process. But some of the techniques developed and applied during the past 50 years have given us new food forms—ready-to-eat breakfast cereals, evaporated milk, packaged cheese, and many more. They are handled mostly by the bigger corporate units because of the large capital outlay required to develop, produce, and merchandise a new product.

THUS FAR we have discussed the technological factors that have tended to increase the physical size of the manufacturing plant. Left unanswered is the question of why a chainstore system will integrate the wholesale function for its retail units or why a large food manufacturer will undertake the jobbing and wholesale functions for his products.

One of the chief reasons for such vertical integration is this: Economies can be made by moving a product through the various stages of manufacture and distribution within a single company, rather than by ownership transfers at each stage in the marketing process.

By operating their own wholesale warehouses for their retail store units, the chainstore systems have eliminated the cost of countless salesmen calling on each of their individual stores in order to sell them. Along with this goes centralized buying for the store units, which enables the product to move direct from the manufacturer's plant or distributing unit to the chainstore warehouse.

Other economies are associated with integrated mass distribution—quick turnover, standardized store merchandising practices, careful accounting procedures for the reduction of costs. Their application is not confined to the larger corporate chains. But the savings to be obtained by moving product from stage to stage within a company rather than by ownership transfer at each stage is one of the chief reasons for vertical integration in any field, whether from the retailer back to the manufacturer or from the manufacturer forward toward the retailer.

Next comes the question of why a large meatpacking company, for instance, would want to add butter and cheese to its line, or why some dairy company might add salad dressing or any of a score of products not directly related to milk.

A considerable part of the selling and distributive expenses incurred by an integrated manufacturer and distributor of food (costs of sales branch houses, salesmen's salaries, expenditures for advertising) are in the nature of a fixed overhead, and one of the ways to reduce such costs on a per unit basis is to increase the sales volume by adding products to the line.

Once a company has incurred the expense of building or acquiring a sales branch house, it naturally will try to put through it the greatest possible tonnage to reduce overhead in the branch house. Similarly, when a salesman is calling on a grocer, the cost of his salary as a percentage of the price of goods sold is patently less on an order of 200 dollars for 10 food items than on an order of 20 dollars for one or two.

The same principle of overhead cost applies in many respects to advertising. Having bought advertising space in a national magazine, the cost per unit of increased sales resulting from running any six related products in the advertisement is obviously less than if the same advertisement were devoted to only one or two of them. Here also is one of the main reasons why companies that advertise their products extensively try to obtain national distribution for the products. If they are big enough to use national magazine, radio, or television advertising media, they lose a part of the value of such advertising unless the geographical scope of their distribution corresponds roughly with that of the medium.

In still another way this principle of overhead costs leads a company toward continued expansion and greater size—the growth factor in part resulting from the imbalance of a company's various parts.

For instance, a company decides to modernize or rebuild its production facilities. If it is an up-and-coming company, it will build its plant capacity beyond its current sales volume. Having done so, it tries to run the new plant facilities to full capacity in order to reduce plant overhead. So it adds to its staff of salesmen, redoubles its selling efforts, and perhaps builds new sales branch houses to handle its increased output. Because the costs of the new sales facilities are in part fixed or overhead costs, they in turn lead the firm to add to its line of products and perhaps expand production facilities even further to reduce selling costs, and so the cycle starts again.

IF A FIRM is to maintain or advance its position in a competitive field under conditions of a changing technology, it must spend large sums on technical research and development. A food firm, for instance, is under constant competitive pressure to improve its product, reduce production costs by greater mechanization, improve the packaging of its products, find new uses for them, or to make a better disposition of its byproducts.

Such developments are usually the result of planned research, carried on by specialists and at considerable cost to the company that undertakes it.

Most of the technological innovations in any industrial field therefore come mainly from the larger firms in that field; the innovations in turn contribute to their further growth and expansion.

Many revolutionary discoveries in food technology have resulted from the work of scientists in universities, and colleges, and Government agencies. But the application of the discoveries, first in the pilot plant and then in regular production processes, also is usually a long and costly development, which only a large enterprise is in position to undertake.

Thus the size and type of business enterprise is determined largely by the technology of the times.

Where will it lead? Is there any practical limit to this development—or are we destined ultimately to a situation where large segments of the food industries will be carried on by only a few gigantic companies, with no place remaining for the small or medium-size enterprise?

In some lines of industry that has already happened, but in my judgment it is not likely to happen in foods. The growth of big business in foods since the 1920's has been at a slower and slower rate, and the organizational pattern in foods has not changed greatly in the past 25 years. Some of the major food companies have continued to grow at a slow pace in terms of tonnage, but many of them have held a relatively static position. More noticeable has been the growth of medium-size companies; but, as we have seen, there are thousands of such companies in the food field and the degree of concentration of control (the percentage of business done by one or a few firms) remains low.

He would be rash indeed who would predict the technology of food production in the year 2000. The chemical synthesis of food nutrients into palatable forms from nonagricultural products, as an example, might change completely the nature of the food industries as we now know them. But on the reasonable assumption that present food manufacturing techniques do not undergo revolutionary changes within our time, the structure of the food industries probably will remain much as it now is—an array of small, medium-size, and large firms, all with a rightful place in our food economy. (*A. C. Hoffman.*)

Efficiency, Size, and Monopoly

Among manufacturing and processing establishments, which are large compared to agricultural wholesaling and retailing establishments, have the most important increases in scale occurred.

The number of flour and meal mills dropped from 12,000 in 1909 to 1,200 in 1947, while average employment in a plant increased from 4 to 32 men.

This is a good example of the compelling influence of technological developments; the use of rolls, rather than grinding disks, and air separation of bran and flour required large units to operate effectively and spelled the doom of the local grist mill.

Technological developments have been rapid in the canning, preserving, and freezing industry, and employment in the average plant more than doubled between 1919 and 1947. Large-scale organization in meatpacking occurred at a relatively early date, and was encouraged by greater efficiency and by the economical use of byproducts by the large packers.

Reports for the 1939–1947 period, however, indicate a 50-percent increase in the number of meatpackers. Better communications and transportation contributed to this decentralization, but the war and price control have been factors.

Changes in the number and average size of dairy manufacturing plants are related to four main factors: Improved highways and trucks, permitting the economical expansion of milk collection areas and plant volumes; technological improvements, although in the past quarter of a century they have been primarily in materials handling and allied activities rather than in the basic manufacturing methods; shifts in consumer preferences and demand, especially in the reduced consumption of butter; and wartime changes in milk utilization, which emphasized whole milk and skim milk products and was greatly encouraged by the Government through price controls, price supports, and purchases.

Between 1939 and 1951, the output of creamery butter dropped 32 percent, the number of creameries decreased by 38 percent, and the output per plant increased 9 percent. The number of cheese plants dropped 30 percent while the output per plant increased 130 percent.

The number of concentrated milk plants fell 16 percent, while output per plant increased 60 percent. The total output of nonfat dry milk solids increased by more than 160 percent between 1939 and 1951, the number of plants increased 65 percent, and the output per plant increased nearly 60 percent.

A sharp decline, from 15,000 in 1909 to 1,000 in 1947, has occurred in the number of establishments that manufacture cigars and cigarettes. Most of it was in cigar manufacturing and followed the change from hand to machine methods and a shift in smoking habits to cigarettes. The number of cigarette factories varied from 49 in 1929 to 28 in 1947, when employment reached nearly 1,000 persons in the average factory.

These data on marketing and processing indicate trends in plant size, but they do not reflect changes in the concentration of ownership. Many firms own a number of plant facilities and a substantial share of the total business may thus be in the hands of a small number of corporations.

In agricultural marketing, growth of this type was especially important before 1935. The trend seems to have leveled off in the 1940's, when the major characteristic was a shift from small- to medium-size firms rather than a continued growth of very large, dominant firms. In 1949, the sales of the four largest firms in several food-processing industries accounted for 56 percent of the total sales of dairy products, 46 percent for meat products, 26 percent each for grain-mill products and bakery products, and 23 percent for the canning, preserving, and freezing industry. The five leading grocery chains accounted for approximately 25 percent of total sales by all grocery and combination stores in 1949. Cigarette-manufacturing factories are few in number and large in size; the leading three or four firms account for 80 to 90 percent of the total business.

The conflict between large-scale organization and the public welfare lies in the possibilities for monopolistic control and exploitation.

Largeness that carries with it some degree of market control and monopoly power may alter competitive production and consumption patterns, distort the allocation of basic resources, and reduce the ability of the economy to satisfy wants and improve the welfare.

We have long had a clear policy against monopoly, but legislation to implement the policy has been confused and conflicting. It has varied from absolute prohibition, under the antitrust laws, of any mergers or collusive actions in restraint of trade, to specific permission, under the fair-trade laws, of concerted action to fix prices, and the making of such actions compulsory upon all sellers, whether parties to the agreement or not. It has emphasized protection of competitors from big business, including the use of steeply graduated taxes on chainstores. Such actions implicitly assume that the dangers of bigness or of monopoly power outweigh any advantages of efficiency of large-scale organizations.

In other situations government policy has turned to the regulation of firms as public utilities or to public ownership and operation.

Under public-utility status, some firms are granted monopoly but are regulated with reference to prices that can be charged. The exemption of these activities from antitrust legislation is a frank admission that the efficiencies of large-scale organization are so great as to make any move to smaller firms and larger numbers impractical. Public-utility regulation has been used in such areas as transportation, electric power, and water supply.

Public ownership has had even more limited application, although some items of direct interest to agricultural marketing have been handled in this way. The most common example is the highway system, and terminal and city marketing facilities are sometimes provided by local government agencies. In these cases government participation is limited to providing the physical facilities and establishing certain regulations for the conduct of the market, and does not extend directly into price formation.

Specifically in the case of agriculture, government has intervened in several ways in the free working of the market. To balance the bargaining position of various groups, it has fostered the development of farmers'cooperative marketing associations. Numerous regulatory laws have been enacted to assure fair competition and prevent the exercise of monopolistic power in the market place. The Government has also entered directly into market control through such programs as marketing agreements and orders and price-support activities. Various of these programs, both those of general economic application and those specifically applied to agricultural marketing, are discussed in other parts of this Yearbook.

THE CHALLENGE for the future in agricultural marketing is to develop means of obtaining the efficiencies of large-scale organization without excessive penalties from monopoly. Marketing costs and the price spread between producer and consumer have long been of major concern to our farmers. It is frequently implied that low farm prices and high consumer prices are the result of monopoly and high profit levels. While some monopolistic situations undoubtedly exist, there is little evidence to support this point of view. Marketing costs remain high because of the difficulties of developing and applying an effective technology.

Nor is there evidence to support the contention that "free" competition will result in rapid improvements in marketing efficiency. Many studies have pointed out that the unregulated development of the system has resulted in an excessive number of firms, in duplication of plant and transportation facilities, in excess capacity and a predominance of plants too small to achieve important economies of scale. This is in part a reflection of the slowness with which the system adjusts to new technological conditions, and in part the result of elements of spatial monopoly that cannot be avoided.

PUBLIC CONCERN with marketing costs was reaffirmed in the Research and Marketing Act of 1946. It increased the financial support for research studies of marketing efficiency. If the objectives of the legislation are to be achieved, an increasing amount of research should be devoted to studies of the real economies of scale, and of the combination of marketing, transportation, and processing facilities into the most efficient systems for particular commodities and the geographic areas. Even more important, it means study of the decision-making processes in industry and government to develop effective means of encouraging market reorganization. Finally it requires that we find ways to permit and effectively encourage developments in efficiency and restrict the abuse of monopoly power. Until this challenge is met, I think we can expect little in the way of fundamental reductions in agricultural marketing costs. (*R. G. Bressler, Jr.*)

Some of the Levies Against Marketing

Some factors add to the expenses of marketing food but may be hidden or overlooked because their influence is indirect.

Some indirect costs occur as marketing costs primarily because the concentration of goods in the marketing channel offers a greater opportunity for assessment of levies than exists at the points of production or consumption where large numbers of persons are involved. Excise and processing taxes thus are generally levied against food commodities at the processing or distributing level, because it is less difficult and fewer persons are involved than in the case of levies against farmers or consumers. For example, taxes on tobacco products are levied by the Federal and State Governments at the processing and distributing points. Similarly, a tax on manufactured sugar is paid by the refiner, processor, or importer and is a marketing cost.

In periods of emergency, when price controls and various types of distribution controls are imposed, the point of application usually is a point in the marketing channel rather than the point of production or consumption. Such controls are not levies in the true sense, but their effect is the same; they add to the costs of bookkeeping and accounting of the processors and distributors.

FURTHER COSTS have been added by the efforts of Federal, State, and local governments to protect buyers and sellers. Some of the regulatory measures are financed through appropriations. Some are financed by the collection of fees from dealers and others engaged in marketing. An example: To finance enforcement of the Perishable Agricultural Commodities Act, an annual license fee of 15 dollars is collected from dealers, commission merchants, and others dealing in fresh produce and certain other products. The New York City Department of Markets regulates marketing at the live-poultry terminal in New York and issues licenses to commission merchants, dealers and direct receivers, and operators of slaughterhouses that handle live poultry in New York City, and to truckers who transport poultry in the city. Annual license fees are 5 to 100 dollars. Many States levy warehouse license fees, brand registration fees, and mandatory inspection fees to finance regulatory activities.

Truck transportation has been subject to numerous levies. The cost of interstate movement is affected by taxes on fuel, ton-mile taxes, multiple license or registration fees, and other special levies. Load limits, which may vary from State to State or region to region, sometimes result in circuitous routing or reloading. Bridge and highway tolls have become more and more common.

The free-lance trucker has been the target of particularly vigorous action in some States. Sometimes prohibitive special fees and charges have been levied against them. Many of the levies, apparently imposed as safety measures, revenue sources, or regulatory devices, have actually been designed to protect home-produced goods. But their effect has been to reduce flexibility in distribution and to add to marketing costs.

The cost of moving farm commodities and other goods by rail is influenced by the failure of passenger transportation to pay its way. The railroads have relied on freight revenues to yield a profit. The deficit from passenger and allied services for Class I railroads, 642.9 million dollars in 1952, absorbed 37.4 percent of the carriers' freight service net operating income for that year. To cut down losses on passenger traffic, railroads have sought at times to discontinue unprofitable passenger runs, but opposition by civic groups, labor unions, and others has led public utility bodies to deny many such requests. Industry and Government have studied the situation; if action results that reduces or eliminates the apparent subsidization of passenger traffic by freight traffic, opportunity for reduction in marketing costs will result.

One of the prime objectives of many marketing agencies, Government or private, is the broadening of markets for agricultural and food commodities, yet the process inevitably is a costly one. Research in the development of new products and uses, the development of new types of packages calculated to meet consumer needs and wants, the conduct of consumer preference and acceptance surveys, and other activities involved in market expansion work, all involve substantial expenditures of public and private funds.

Government efforts to aid in the broadening of markets and the orderly movement of commodities should also be noted. The Federal Government and some State Governments sponsor marketing agreement and order programs. The programs, applicable usually to perishable commodities, regulate the rate of shipment of commodities, the quality of commodities to be shipped, and sometimes the price to be paid to the producers by handlers of the product. They are designed to aid both producers and consumers through the stabilizing of markets and the orderly flow of commodities. The administrative organization employed in carrying out these programs is usually financed by assessments levied against handlers of the commodity involved. Here again, a marketing cost is incurred because it is easier to make an assessment against handlers than against producers.

The cost of competition in the marketing of products that have already proved their acceptability to consumers entails a further cost. While advertising of brands may tend to broaden the aggregate market for the various brands of the same commodity, the cost of such competition for individual shares of that market is substantial and may sometimes exceed the benefits derived. The same may also be true of the services offered to tempt the buyer to purchase particular commodities. Such services may include the maintenance of regular delivery routes that duplicate routes of competitors or they may involve more appealing and sometimes more expensive packaging. It is true, of course, that this competitive effort often involves reductions in price as a means of competition and that the price reductions reflect a narrowing of the marketing margin. It is true, also, that the volume benefits resulting from competitive effort tend to result in greater efficiency and, therefore, lower unit cost.

THE FACT that added marketing costs result from the levies and practices described herein does not necessarily reflect discredit on the individuals or groups involved. Nor is it suggested that the levies and practices always are unnecessary or undesirable.

It is not always easy to determine whether the objectives or accomplishments justify the means. It is not possible, either, to state any simple rule or means whereby particular costs can be reduced. It undoubtedly is true, however, that careful and objective review of existing levies and practices on a continuous basis will bring beneficial results. The responsibility for such a review is a joint one, shared in by Government, agriculture, industry, and labor. A close cooperation among those groups, careful appraisal of objectives sought, means of accomplishment, and relative costs can lead to cheaper, more efficient marketing without infringing on the rights of any group. (*George A. Dice.*)

Cooperatives

There were 10,166 service cooperatives in the United States in 1951. They served a membership of more than 7.4 million and did a net volume of business of 9.4 billion dollars. Federal and State statutes encourage the formation of farmers' cooperatives. The statutes guard against any risk that they might become conspiracies or combinations in restraint of trade. The ownership and control of a cooperative is in the hands of those who use its services. Decisions are made and control exercised by the owners as patrons rather than as investors. The basic purpose is to hold costs to a minimum consistent with the quality of services demanded by the patron-owners. A cooperative is a tool fitted to the need for group action. Once the decision is made to go ahead with group effort, the problems to be met are the same as those of other business concerns that perform like functions, plus those of keeping the organization cooperative in character. If both sets of problems are met intelligently and well, a successful cooperative will be the result.

How the Cooperatives Work

If you were to walk into a cooperatively owned grain elevator you would find that the grain is weighed and dumped, handled through the elevator, and loaded into railroad cars very much the same as it is in any other elevator operated under some other form of ownership. The real differences lie in the way in which the business is owned and controlled and in the basic objectives and policies for organizing and carrying it on.

Ownership and control of the cooperative is in the hands of those who use its services. The decisions are made and control exercised by the owners as patrons rather than as investors. The basic purpose is to hold costs to a minimum consistent with the service wanted by the patron-owners.

Over the years, farmer cooperatives have developed ways to assure that they will be patron-controlled at the time of organization and that they will continue so. Every member has the same voice in control of the organization as any other, under the rule of one man, one vote.

Another less often used practice is to proportion ownership and control according to patronage. However the votes are counted, the right to vote generally is limited to active patrons, even though others may own capital in the organization. Most cooperatives also give control of the transfer of the capital shares to their boards of directors and limit such transfers to those who use their services.

Another basic principle of cooperative organization is this: Business operations are so conducted that they approach a cost basis. That means that provision is made in some way or another to return to patrons on an equitable basis any amounts over cost of performing the marketing, purchasing, or other services that the cooperatives are set up to perform.

Cooperatives are often referred to as nonprofit business concerns—all business proceeds beyond the costs of operation are credited to patrons. Yet the motive for profit or gain is a force in the organization and operation of every farmer cooperative just as in any other business concern. It is the basic incentive that prompts the individual member-patron to invest in and patronize his association. He hopes to gain from this sort of group action aimed to improve the market for his products or to lower the costs of supplies or services he needs.

Still another basic concept of cooperative business is that of limited returns on share capital. In a profit-seeking business the primary motive for investment is to obtain as large a return as competition or other limiting factors permit. This concept is significant mainly because of the distinctive character it gives to risk capital in the cooperative.

In terms of amount, the capital needed by a farmer cooperative may be no different than for any other form of business of like nature and scale of operation. But the element of risk as a factor influencing investment may have a different significance. In the cooperative the patron-member supplies share capital primarily to obtain and gain from its services. Risk and possible returns on the investment as such are only secondary. In the noncooperative business the return factor is a dominant consideration. The risk is assumed deliberately by the investor who weighs the chances for gain and loss involved in the alternative investment opportunities for funds and then makes his choice.

The difference in status of share capital in cooperatives as against other business concerns shows up in some of the practices used by cooperatives. For example, cooperatives commonly put a top value (usually par) on their capital shares. Likewise they usually limit the ownership of voting shares to active patrons. Such practices reduce the speculative value of shares. Possibilities of value increases, ease of transfer, and ready salability are desirable characteristics of the capital shares of most noncooperative corporations having many owners. The need for capital is just as urgent for a cooperative as for any other form of business, but the methods of getting it must be adjusted to the fact that share-capital returns are definitely limited, and sources of risk capital are restricted.

Other businessmen besides farmers have found the cooperative useful in joint efforts to improve their competitive position or better the quality of needed services. Grocers, druggists, and hardware dealers are among those who have developed retailer-owned wholesales. Many newspapers are members of a cooperative news-gathering agency. Mutual organizations, with some of the characteristics of cooperatives, exist in the insurance field. These developments are evidences of the integration that has taken place in American business—integration being the tendency to group together the functions of producing and marketing commodities in one concern or in closely related organizations.

Agricultural production has been in terms of family-size farms, which are pretty small business units in these days of big corporate firms in other parts of the economy. When they go into the market as individual sellers they deal with few buyers—and with buyers who are likely to know more about price-making factors. As individual buyers they are likely to be in a similar weak bargaining position.

Furthermore, the units of volume in which an individual farmer buys or sells are too limited to provide cost-cutting opportunities. Hence, when need has forced them, farmers have used cooperatives to improve their positions as to costs as well as prices. By making the cooperatives their marketing and purchasing departments, farmers are integrating some of the off-farm with the on-farm aspects of their business. Yet it is a form of integration that permits them to operate their farms independently.

In cooperatives we find corporate or group ownership of productive property, but that ownership rests with individuals whose property rights are determinable. They are voluntary organizations in which the individual may choose freely to invest or not to invest his capital, to use or not to use their services within the terms of any contractual arrangements he may choose to make. They compete with other business firms. They facilitate the efforts of the individual to obtain economic rewards proportionate to his abilities and initiative.

An estimated one-fifth to one-fourth of American farm products moving into commercial channels in 1954 went through farmer-owned cooperatives at one or more of the marketing stages.

The services that farmers require of their cooperatives vary widely. The services most often performed are those involved in the first movement from farm to market. As the products move forward through marketing channels, a decreasing proportion is handled by the cooperatives.

WHAT ARE the services rendered by cooperatives in the area of local markets? Here, too, are wide variations between commodities and within commodity groups. The most common functions are the ones involved in actual physical handling of the products at the local shipping point. For example, between a third and two-fifths of all the grain moving into commercial channels is handled by cooperative grain elevators. The functions performed nearly always include weighing, grading, unloading from trucks, and handling through the elevator into railroad cars or out-going trucks, and (less frequently) cleaning, drying, mixing, blending, and storage. Then there is the important function of price determination when ownership of the grain is transferred from the farmer to first buyer.

The local handling of some products may involve processing or a material change in the form of the products. Dairy products are an example. Close to 45 percent of the farmers' milk or cream that is processed into butter is manufactured in cooperative plants. Cooperatives process about 20 percent of the cheese. Of processed fruits and vegetables, the overall proportion manufactured by cooperatives is probably about 15 percent. For a few individual products the percentage is much higher; in processed cranberries it may be as high as 75 percent, and in processed citrus it is nearly a third.

An important but relatively simple marketing function of cooperatives is that of bargaining for price. Very well known are the bargaining cooperatives for fluid milk at large centers of population. Another commodity for which farmers utilize this type of cooperative is sugar beets. It is also used in a few areas where there is heavy production of fruits and vegetables for processing. This type of cooperative also gives its members the assurance of correct grades and weights. Sometimes it handles the accounting and settlement of the transaction between farmer and processor or handler.

A significant trend in cooperative development has been the tendency to follow the products beyond local markets. It is another step in the process of integration. Most of the cooperatives of grain farmers, which—to repeat—handle a third to two-fifths of the grain that moves into commercial channels, in turn are members of regional cooperatives, which provide a wide variety of marketing services—handling, storage, merchandising—at subterminal and terminal grain markets. It is estimated that close to 55 percent of the grain that the local associations ship to distant markets is marketed through their regional associations.

MANY LOCAL DAIRY cooperatives also have joined to form cooperative sales agencies of the federated type. The same is true for fruits, vegetables, nuts, and a number of other products.

Another type of large-scale cooperative, the centralized association, does a comparable job of marketing on a regional basis or in terminal markets. Terminal livestock cooperatives and some of the fruit and nut cooperatives are examples. In such a cooperative the farmer is a member directly of the large association, rather than of the local association, which in turn is a member of the regional or terminal association. Here, too, there is integration of local market functions with those of terminal handling and sales but in a single organization.

The relative merits of the federated and the centralized types of association in doing the farmers' marketing beyond the local shipping points are impossible to determine. Points of strength in one may be the points of weakness in the other. The basic consideration for each, however, is primarily that of adaptation to the conditions under which it operates and the efficiency of its operations if the farmer-members' interests are to be served.

Some of these attempts of farmers to retain control over the marketing of the products beyond their fences and local shipping points have failed, not necessarily because they have used the cooperative form of organization. Failure has been due, instead, to some of the ills which can beset any business concern and which sometimes are lumped together in the term poor management.

But many large-scale farmer cooperatives are successful. Some are among the leading merchandising organizations of the country with widely known brand names—Sunkist, Land O'Lakes, Diamond, Eatmor, Calavo, Challenge, Sunmaid, Ocean Spray, Dairygold, Donald Duck, and Blue Goose.

When economic need—too wide handling margins, too narrow outlets for their products, excessive price changes, or like reasons—has forced farmers to organize cooperatives, they face the problems of any business concern. They must assure themselves of capable management. They must have adequate volume to hold unit costs down. They must make effective use of their labor force. They must meet the usual problems of business efficiency.

The cause or causes that lead to the organization of any cooperative usually tend to disappear in a relatively short time. Its organization often is the corrective force since its competitive influence soon is felt. From that point on it must depend on its own efficiency to survive in the competitive race.

But there is another set of problems other than those relating to business operation which these farmer-controlled organizations must meet. These are the distinctive problems which arise from the mere fact that they are cooperative in character. They largely grow out of the member-patron-owner relationships peculiar to cooperatives. Hence, a present and ever-continuing problem of cooperatives is the one to which they apply the term membership relations. It is involved in the organizational pattern, the financial structure, and the day-to-day operations. It is no simple undertaking to maintain a cooperative as a member-controlled association, one in which the members know enough about it to give it intelligent direction.

The cooperative is simply a tool fitted to the need for group action. Once the decision is made to go ahead with group effort, the problems to be met are the same as those of other like business concerns plus those of keeping the organization cooperative in character. If both sets of problems are met intelligently and well, a successful cooperative will be the result.

There usually are some valuable byproducts of successful cooperative performance other than dollars-and-cents values. Farmers, through their active part in owning and operating a segment of the marketing machinery, have a better understanding of the off-farm aspects of a commercialized agriculture. And by being active owners and operators they can give themselves greater assurance that the job of marketing is not being done too badly. (*Harold Hedges.*)

Beginning With Ben Franklin

Mutual insurance was the first form of organized cooperation in the United States. The Philadelphia Contributorship for the Insurance of Houses from Loss by Fire was formed in Philadelphia in 1752. Benjamin Franklin printed the notice calling for subscriptions and headed the board of directors. This first and oldest cooperative in the United States still is active.

Farmers organized mutual insurance societies early in the 1800's—perhaps earlier. Earlier still, the custom developed for farmers informally to make contributions of livestock, forage, building material, or furniture to a neighbor who had suffered a loss by fire.

The next step was the building of factories for the manufacture of cheese and later of butter. The first cheese factory, constructed and operated on a cooperative plan, was initiated in 1851 by Jesse Williams on his farm near Rome, N. Y. The first report of the United States Department of Agriculture, issued in 1863, contains an account of the Williams plan and the progress made in the establishment of "associated dairies" in nearby counties. The account cited as advantages of the new method the savings from the purchase at wholesale of manufacturing supplies, which equaled or exceeded the cost of manufacture, and "superior quality and uniformity," which resulted in an improved price for the product.

In the annual report of the Department of Agriculture for 1865, X. A. Willard described the associated dairies, which by then had spread to other States. He reviewed a suggestion that the associated dairies might jointly sell their "choice factory brands" to European firms through an agent in New York, and concluded that "when associated with others in neighborhoods, in towns, in counties, and in the State, he [the dairyman] becomes formidable, and meets on equal terms the community of dealers with whom he is operating."

The first associated dairy designed especially for the manufacture of butter was built at Campbell Hall, Orange County, N. Y., in 1856. A dairy specialist stated about that time that farm-produced butter could be classified under these grades—"tolerable, poor, and terrible." Improved and more uniform quality and savings in the cost of supplies were factors in the extension of the cooperative system of manufacture. An organization, which later became the American Dairymen's Association, was formed at a convention of representatives of the associated dairies in 1866. R. H. Elsworth reported that "by 1867 more than 400 co-ops were processing dairy products."

Cooperatives for marketing other products were organized during the 1850's and 1860's. The Dane County Farmers Protective Union was formed in 1857. A farmers' elevator was erected at Madison, Wis. It went out of business after the first year because its manager sold the grain and decamped with the proceeds. The earliest reported association to market fruit and vegetables was formed at Hammonton, N. J., in 1867 and operated for more than 30 years.

The Prairie Farmer, Chicago, reported in February 1860 that 17 farmers in Bureau County, Ill., had "for four years fattened and dressed their hogs with great care, clubbed together and brought them to market at the close of the season. Last week these gentlemen brought to this market 504 hogs."

The early period of cooperation saw the formation of a few hundred local associations, usually unincorporated. A more ambitious program was in the making with the organization of the National Grange in December 1867.

Oliver Hudson Kelley, the man who conceived the Grange organization, was first a farmer and later an employee of the United States Department of Agriculture. After an official trip to the South to check on agricultural conditions following the Civil War, he considered the possibility of improving farming conditions by the establishment of a fraternal order. In the first 3 years fewer than 100 charters were issued to local granges. Kelley then decided that the Grange could be expanded to deal with farmers' economic problems. Organization of locals increased rapidly; almost 12,000 were formed in 1874, the peak year. The total was more than 24,000. With the passing of the depression period of the early 1870's, interest in the formation of local granges subsided.

The effect of the Grange on the establishment of farmer cooperatives was dramatic. The political influence of the Patrons of Husbandry (Grange) became recognized. The national organization engaged in battles to curb the power of the railway corporations, and at the same time began to build farmers' buying and selling cooperatives. S. J. Buck, in his book, *The Granger Movement*, published in 1913, wrote: "By 1870 the farmers had become largely producers of staple crops for market and nearly as dependent upon outsiders for supplies as were those engaged in other occupations. . . . The result was the establishment of an almost incredible number of cooperative, or pseudo-cooperative enterprises, under the control of the farmers' organizations. These enterprises included local, county and State agencies for the purchase of implements and supplies and the sale of farm products, local grain elevators and cooperative stores, the manufacture of farm machinery, banking, insurance, and even organizations for bringing about direct trade between the American producer and the European consumer."

Many local Grange organizations, as Buck suggests, were not truly cooperative in that earnings were distributed on the basis of stock holdings rather than patronage. This factor contributed to the short life of most of them. The feature of the Rochdale system of cooperation, which requires distribution of savings in proportion to patronage, was introduced in the organization of some of the later Grange cooperatives. At least three of those organized during the second half of the 1870's were in business in 1954. Another helpful feature introduced about that time was the practice of making the sales at the current retail price in the community served, thus avoiding the intense opposition of the local merchants.

Responsibility for the decline of the Grange movement, however, must be shared by its large-scale cooperative ventures. Many of the State purchasing and marketing agencies got beyond their depth and had to be liquidated. The manufacture of farm machinery resulted in heavy losses. Lack of local repair shops to service the machines is given as one of the primary causes.

Grange banking and insurance activities appear on the whole to have been more successful. The Granger's Bank of California, established in 1874, had deposits of 2 million dollars a year later, and is reported to have saved the farmers of the State a large amount of money at a time of depression in the wheat market by lending them 3 million dollars and thus enabling them to hold their wheat for a rise in the market. Two other banks were established in California during the same year, and in 1883 a Patrons Cooperative Bank was established at Olathe, Kans., where a successful cooperative store already existed.

Grange fire insurance companies, as a rule, followed the plans of farmers' mutual fire insurance companies, a number of which were in existence before the founding of the Grange.

Life insurance societies were less successful. They went out of business as the death rate of their aging membership increased.

Fruit growers during the 1880's planned and organized several large-scale cooperatives, none of which survived until the end of the nineteenth century. A few locals later became members, or forerunners of members of some of the present marketing federations. California deciduous fruit growers formed the California Fruit Union, which operated from 1885 to 1893. California citrus producers organized the Orange Growers Protective Union in 1885.

At least two local cooperatives were incorporated in the early 1890's to pack and sell the fruit of their members. A general plan, adopted in 1893, led to the establishment of local associations and district marketing exchanges in all districts, coordinated by a central board, which met in Los Angeles. Competition between the district exchanges was responsible two years later for the organization of the Southern California Fruit Exchange and the centralization of sales in this Los Angeles office.

This cooperative in 1954 is the Sunkist Growers, Inc., which markets some 75 percent of all citrus fruit shipped fresh from California. Other large-scale citrus cooperatives formed during this period are the Mutual Orange Distributors, Redlands, Calif. (1906), and the Florida Citrus Exchange (1909).

After the failure of practically all local elevators formed by the Grangers, farmers began again in the early 1880's. Altogether 54 cooperative elevators formed before the end of the nineteenth century were reported active in 1950.

Opposition to farmers' elevators on the part of grain dealers and line elevator companies was intense during the first 30 years of the period. Charges by farm groups of unfair competition, low weights and tests by local marketing agencies, and boycotts of cooperatives by terminal receivers were common.

A device adopted by a farmers' elevator at Rockwell, Iowa, in 1889 was the maintenance clause, which provided that members should pay the association a small amount per bushel for all grain sold outside the organization. The plan helped maintain the cooperatives, but even more effective was the formation of associations of State farmers' grain dealers. The first was formed in Nebraska in 1903. By 1919 practically all farmers' elevators in the central region were organized in State associations.

Dairy cooperatives continued to increase and constituted more than 70 percent of the total number reported at the end of 1900.

Farmers had learned much about the strength of the opposition to cooperatives by 1900. The old belief that a farmer's business interests should end at his front gate still was strong. On the other hand, farmers learned much about business methods in their early attempts to cooperate, and later cooperatives were tempered by the mistakes and failures of the past. They also tasted the strength of organization and acquired cooperative experience that their fathers did not possess. Consequently cooperatives increased rapidly between 1900 and 1920.

Nearly 7,000 cooperatives for marketing farm products and about 1,300 associations for purchasing supplies were formed between 1910 and 1920. More than a third were formed to market grain, one-sixth for dairy products, one-seventh for livestock, and one-tenth for fruit and vegetables.

There was one conspicuous failure in this era of progress. Farmers, beginning about 1913, invested some 4 million dollars in the construction or purchase of meatpacking plants at four points in Wisconsin, two in Minnesota, one in North Dakota, and one in Illinois. All of them were out of business by 1924, with practically total losses to the investors.

The decade, 1910 to 1920, was one of stirring changes for agriculture. The increase in the number of cooperatives meant shifts in the programs

ESTIMATED NUMBER OF ASSOCIATIONS, MEMBERSHIP, AND BUSINESS OF MARKETING, PURCHASING, AND RELATED SERVICE COOPERATIVES, 1951–1952 [1]

State	*Number of associations with headquarters in State*	*Number of associations doing business in State* [2]	*Number of members in State*	*Net business after adjusting for duplication* [3] *$1,000*
New England:				
Maine	[4] 25	[4] 31	22, 490	46, 259
New Hampshire	[4] 14	[4] 22	11, 432	32, 066
Vermont	39	50	25, 142	70, 276
Massachusetts	[4] 45	[4] 49	34, 068	66, 815
Rhode Island	5	10	3, 490	6, 987
Connecticut	[4] 29	[4] 38	17, 814	51, 082
Total	157	....	114, 436	273, 485
Middle Atlantic:				
New York	388	400	172, 398	471, 414
New Jersey	65	72	39, 914	129, 393
Pennsylvania	182	200	158, 294	278, 954
Total	635	....	370, 606	879, 761
East North Central:				
Ohio	311	324	366, 325	491, 411
Indiana	156	182	371, 815	360, 672
Illinois	582	606	597, 841	661, 181
Michigan	238	256	186, 562	261, 454
Wisconsin	[4] 871	[4] 898	417, 997	550, 323
Total	2, 158	....	1, 940, 540	2, 325, 041
West North Central:				
Minnesota	[4] 1, 334	[4] 1, 356	582, 853	641, 890
Iowa	718	747	398, 618	540, 656
Missouri	291	309	430, 058	309, 784
North Dakota	556	573	218, 472	286, 547
South Dakota	317	333	146, 939	183, 223
Nebraska	415	439	218, 543	281, 647
Kansas	360	380	173, 051	280, 264
Total	3, 991	....	2, 168, 534	2, 524, 011
South Atlantic:				
Delaware	15	19	17, 197	20, 141
Maryland	59	68	79, 310	85, 362
District of Columbia	1	....	....	....
Virginia	133	141	240, 036	151, 956
West Virginia	45	56	46, 865	18, 858
North Carolina	86	97	381, 657	128, 526
South Carolina	33	36	48, 374	18, 360
Georgia	79	84	116, 085	84, 939
Florida	110	115	18, 964	112, 856
Total	561	....	948, 488	620, 998
East South Central:				
Kentucky	80	94	374, 814	130, 211
Tennessee	112	126	194, 310	56, 923
Alabama	60	64	80, 826	35, 073
Mississippi	132	142	116, 091	114, 807
Total	384	....	766, 041	337, 014

ESTIMATED NUMBER OF ASSOCIATIONS, MEMBERSHIP, AND BUSINESS OF MARKETING, PURCHASING, AND RELATED SERVICE COOPERATIVES, 1951–1952[1]—continued

State	*Number of associations with headquarters in State*	*Number of associations doing business in State* [2]	*Number of members in State*	*Net business after adjusting for duplication* [3] *$,1000*
West South Central:				
Arkansas	115	129	64, 061	69, 920
Louisiana	58	66	22, 629	35, 861
Oklahoma	203	218	154, 832	145, 092
Texas	553	566	210, 679	375, 244
Total	929	....	452, 201	626, 117
Mountain:				
Montana	181	198	57, 210	99, 549
Idaho	109	125	61, 448	142, 742
Wyoming	26	39	16, 410	26, 047
Colorado	118	131	75, 048	166, 274
New Mexico	32	43	11, 342	31, 583
Arizona	13	19	41, 507	25, 676
Utah	74	79	32, 586	86, 585
Nevada	5	6	951	5, 398
Total	558	....	296, 502	583, 854
Pacific:				
Washington	193	207	107, 308	266, 739
Oregon	130	142	71, 768	162, 654
California	470	479	126, 705	843, 038
Total	793	....	305, 781	1, 272, 431
United States	10, 166	....	7, 363, 129	9, 442, 712

[1] Preliminary.

[2] These figures include associations doing business in States other than those in which their headquarters are located and cannot be totaled because of duplication.

[3] This figure represents value at the first level at which cooperatives transact business with farmers. It does not include wholesale business of farm supply cooperatives with other cooperatives or terminal market sales performed for local associations.

[4] Includes incorporated local associations without facilities affiliated with an operating regional association.

of State and Federal agricultural agencies. The system of county agents was inaugurated; State and the newly organized Extension Services took over the program of the farmers' institutes. A Commission on Country Life was appointed by the President in 1908, and its report encouraged "a vast enlargement of voluntary organization among farmers themselves."

The Office of Markets was formed in 1913, and its first project dealt with cooperative purchasing and marketing. That was the genesis of the research and service assistance to cooperatives now administered by Farmer Cooperative Service. Many county agents were active in the formation of local and large-scale cooperatives. A considerable number went on to become managers of associations they had helped build, and a few of them have remained in positions of responsibility.

By 1920 there were large federations, whose members were local associations, for the marketing of farm products. Other groups were undertaking to replace the local associations with branch offices and plants of large-scale centralized associations serving an entire producing district or an entire State. Others were attempting cooperative selling in the terminal markets. New cooperatives were formed at the rate of five a day in 1920, the peak year.

The American Farm Bureau Federation was organized in 1919. It set up special committees to prepare plans for establishing national marketing cooperatives. The committees dealt with livestock, grain, fruits and vegetables, and other products. The National Livestock Producers Association was organized in 1921, and is still active. Most of the rest have been succeeded by other cooperatives.

Early in 1920 farmers were given a new slogan, commodity marketing—an implication that through cooperative control of a large percentage of a crop, farmers would in effect fix prices of their product. It was a dominant idea in many cooperatives formed in 1920–1925. There were 16 large, centrally controlled cooperatives with approximately 50,000 members, at the end of 1920. Associations of this type had increased to 74, with more than 879,000 members, by 1926. Cotton, wheat, and milk were the main commodities represented. Membership contracts, which could not be canceled over a 5- or 10-year period were used to insure that members would deliver their crops.

Farmers discovered at least two weaknesses in the "monopoly and prosperity" theory. First, cooperatives never obtained control of a percentage of any crop sufficient to make an attempt to fix prices. Second, such a theory of cooperation did not lead to careful and economical management. It seemed unnecessary to save pennies when the program promised a pot of gold at the end of the rainbow.

Several large cooperatives, active today, were formed during this period, however, including some that began as commodity marketing associations with long-term, "ironclad" contracts. Following the agricultural depression, which became acute in 1922, farmers continued to look to their cooperatives for assistance.

Cooperatives also began to set up some legislative and educational associations to promote their cause. The State farmers' grain dealers' associations have been mentioned. The National Milk Producers' Federation was formed in 1916; in 1923 "Cooperative" was added to its title. The forerunner of the National Council of Farmer Cooperatives was organized in 1922.

The American Institute of Cooperation was organized in 1925 as an educational agency. Every year since that time, except during the Second World War, it has held a summer session of a week or longer on the campus of a land-grant college or university.

The Agricultural Marketing Act, passed by the Congress in 1929, provided for a Federal Farm Board, whose members were appointed by the President. On October 1, 1929, the Division of Cooperative Marketing was transferred by Executive order from the Bureau of Agricultural Economics to the Federal Farm Board. Work dealing with problems of cooperatives was destined to remain outside the jurisdiction of the Department of Agriculture for the next 10 years.

In the depression years, the Federal Farm Board, was able to save many cooperatives from failure. It also was instrumental in assisting in the organization of several additional large organizations, many of which still are active. The contributions of the Federal Farm Board to farmer cooperatives generally have been overlooked in analyses of the more spectacular failure of its stabilization operations.

The passing in 1933 of the Federal Farm Board, however, marked the end of the belief in general that cooperation was a cure-all for the economic ills of the farmer. During the 1920's, as a matter of fact, efforts were made to obtain the passage of legislation dealing with the disposal of the farm surpluses. In 1933 and thereafter much special legislation of this general nature was enacted, and farm cooperatives were regarded as one of the methods of transacting the marketing of farm products and the procurement of supplies and other business services. More attention than ever before was devoted to the job of building sound, well-financed business enterprises.

Many cooperatives were assisted in this respect by the establishment of the banks for cooperatives within the Farm Credit Administration in 1933. The organization of a Central Bank for Cooperatives and 12 district banks for cooperatives was especially helpful. The requirements of the banks for monthly reports from borrowers did much to promote the use of more complete and accurate records and were a contribution to improved business practices.

Approximately 10,900 marketing, purchasing, and service cooperatives were operated by farmers in the United States in 1933. The number of members was reported as 3,156,000, and their total volume of business for the year was estimated as 1,365 million dollars.

During the past 20 years the number of associations engaged in marketing has declined steadily. Associations shipping livestock by rail have almost disappeared, but associations shipping by truck have not. Cooperative creameries, grain elevators, and citrus packing plants have merged to gain the advantages of large-scale operations.

At the same time the number of members and the dollar volume of business have increased tremendously. For the crop year 1951, which may be compared with 1933, the total number of farmer marketing, purchasing, and service cooperatives was 10,166. They had 7,363,129 members and an estimated gross volume of business of 12,132,097,000 dollars. (There are duplications in the number of members, as many farmers are members of two or more cooperatives.) It was estimated in 1954 that at least 60 percent of all American farmers were affiliated with some form of cooperative marketing or purchasing activity.

A review of the development of cooperatives since 1930 discloses several trends. The first is their increased financial stability and much larger farmer investments, which for all cooperatives exceeded 2 billion dollars on January 1, 1954. Large modern plants have been built by many locals to serve a county instead of a single community and to achieve material economies and greater operating efficiency. The general acceptance of cooperatives by their trade competitors and by the public also is worthy of note.

Today there is a tendency to coordinate the marketing of consumer products particularly in the hands of large-scale cooperatives that are national or nearly national in scope. Cooperatives handling eggs at several points in the Eastern States, for example, have completed organization of a marketing federation. Cooperatives marketing miscellaneous fruit and vegetables in many States have united to purchase a large, privately owned sales agency as a basis for a national marketing cooperative. This cooperative, American National Foods, Inc., began operations on January 1, 1954.

Latest figures show farmer cooperatives handled at one or more stages of the marketing process a little more than a fifth of all farm products sent to market. The percentage of production supplies distributed by purchasing groups is about a sixth. (*Andrew W. McKay.*)

The Co-ops and Legislation

The first cooperative corporations were formed by special acts of the legislature or were incorporated under the general corporation law of a State.

A statute for the formation of such

corporations was enacted in Michigan in 1865. But it was some years later before the States generally had statutes that were especially adapted to the incorporation of cooperatives.

Aaron Sapiro, a California lawyer, encouraged the enactment of a standard cooperative marketing act. With some modifications, it was enacted in many States about 1920. Every State now has at least one special statute for the formation of agricultural cooperative marketing corporations.

When farmers' cooperatives were small local organizations, their legal right to exist was generally accepted. Nobody seriously contended that they were combinations or conspiracies in restraint of trade.

But that changed about 1916, when Aaron Sapiro began organizing centralized cooperatives on a commodity basis—getting all the growers of prunes or rice or tobacco or whatever to join a marketing association. The growers were asked to enter into contracts that required them to market through the cooperative all of the particular commodity that they might produce for market. Those contracts were called "ironclad," but the reason was somewhat uncertain, because one of the standard definitions of a contract is that it is an agreement enforceable at law. Probably the term arose because the contracts specified that the grower who violated his marketing contract was liable for damages for all of the commodities that he failed to deliver to the cooperative. The contracts also specified that the cooperative could bring a suit against a grower for an injunction to bar him from selling his commodities to others and could also maintain an action for specific performance against the grower to compel him to deliver the commodities grown by him to the cooperative. The contracts usually ran for 10 years.

Arguments arose that such cooperatives made it possible for farmers to fix the prices of their products and to get an economic status comparable to that of a manufacturer of a needed article. Some called them monopolies. Many regarded their legality as uncertain, at least from the Federal standpoint.

In the standard cooperative marketing acts under which most of the cooperatives were organized was a provision reading like the one in the Virginia act: "No association organized under this Chapter shall be deemed to be a combination in restraint of trade or an illegal monopoly; or an attempt to lessen competition or fix prices arbitrarily, nor shall the marketing contracts or agreements between the association and its members, or any agreements authorized in this Chapter, be considered illegal or in restraint of trade."

Such State statutory provisions quite clearly established farmers' rights to organize cooperatives within the laws of their States, but they had no effect on Federal antitrust acts. Section 6 of the Clayton Act (15 U. S. C. 17), enacted in 1914, purported to authorize farmers to act together, but the section applied only to the nonstock organizations.

National farm organizations urged the Congress to enact legislation that clearly authorized the organization and operation of farmers' cooperative associations, with or without capital stock. The result was the Capper-Volstead Act (7 U. S. C. 291), approved on February 18, 1922.

The act established the right of farmers to act together in large or small associations. It authorized associations to have marketing agencies in common if they were composed of farmers. Voting was to be on the basis of one man, one vote, unless the dividends on stock or membership capital were not over 8 percent a year; then voting might be upon any legal basis. The amount of business an association could do for nonmembers must not exceed in value the amount done for members.

The act gave the Secretary of Agriculture restricted jurisdiction over the cooperatives. If he has reason to believe that an association monopolizes or restrains trade in interstate or foreign commerce to the extent that it raises unduly the price of any agricultural product, he may issue a complaint against the association. If the Secretary believes after a hearing that the association has monopolized or restrained trade, he may issue an order directing the association to cease and desist from doing so. The order, if not obeyed, is enforceable by the Federal district court in the district in which the association has its principal office.

No complaint has been issued by a Secretary of Agriculture under the act.

THE ACT does not put cooperatives outside the antitrust laws. It assures farmers the right to form and operate cooperatives to market their products that do not by reason of their organization violate the antitrust laws. Just as businessmen may form corporations through which they may engage in business, farmers were seeking a like right. Equality with industry, and not special privilege, was furthered by the Capper-Volstead Act.

After a cooperative is organized, however, it is subject to the antitrust laws in its dealings with third persons as are other business concerns. For instance, the Robinson-Patman Act (15 U. S. C. 12), which prohibits price discriminations, is as applicable to the selling policies of cooperatives as it is to the business of any other seller. If a cooperative association conspires with third persons to restrain trade, it is amenable to prosecution under the Sherman Act.

In the case of the *United States* v. *Borden Company et al.* (308 U.S. 188) the Supreme Court recognized the right of producers to act together but said: "The right of these agricultural producers thus to unite in preparing for market and in marketing their products, and to make the contracts which are necessary for that collaboration, cannot be deemed to authorize any combination or conspiracy with other persons in restraint of trade that these producers may see fit to devise."

By 1935 fear had mostly ended that farmers, by having substantially all the producers of an agricultural commodity market that commodity through a single cooperative, could determine the price of the commodity. People had come to realize that one food product can be substituted for others; that each food, broadly speaking, competes with all other food products; that consumers tend to buy a cheaper product if they regard the price of another one as too high. Moreover it was found that production could not be controlled, for more could be produced if growers' returns were increased.

An instance is an experience of tobacco cooperatives, which for a time got better prices for their members. The higher prices stimulated the growing of tobacco in marginal areas and by nonmembers. The big tobacco companies generally bought no more than they had to from the cooperatives and as much as possible from the nonmember growers. At the end of a marketing period, the tobacco cooperatives found themselves with huge carryovers and were unable to make final settlement with their members. When tobacco cooperatives were organized, farmers in a community brought pressure on all growers to observe the contract requirement that they deliver their tobacco to the cooperative. But the attitude changed; toward the end of the active life of the tobacco cooperatives that had been formed about 1920, the farmers seemed in sympathy with contract violators. In an effort to force farmers to market their tobacco or other crops through cooperatives, hundreds of suits were filed against the members, and many thousands of dollars were collected as liquidated damages from farmers who had violated their contracts. Such an experience showed the impossibility of control by legal strictures.

Cooperatives pay real estate, personal property, social security, and

ESTIMATED BUSINESS IN SPECIFIED COMMODITY AND SERVICE GROUPS OF MARKETING, PURCHASING, AND RELATED SERVICE COOPERATIVES, 1951–1952 [1]

Commodities	*Number of associations handling*	*Gross business*	*Net business after adjusting for duplication* [2]
Products marketed for patrons:		*$1,000*	*$1,000*
Beans and peas (dry edible)	82	42, 612	35, 888
Cotton and cotton products	567	437, 626	380, 375
Dairy products	2, 132	2, 589, 181	2, 202, 257
Fruits and vegetables	862	910, 675	595, 766
Grain, soybeans, soybean meal, and oil	2, 759	2, 463, 229	1, 616, 427
Livestock and livestock products	706	1, 757, 943	1, 647, 093
Nuts	74	128, 475	92, 367
Poultry products	759	356, 708	320, 596
Rice	52	149, 677	111, 585
Sugar products	65	147, 313	147, 313
Tobacco	29	173, 399	173, 399
Wool and mohair	217	46, 170	42, 031
Miscellaneous [3]	289	54, 064	45, 962
Total marketing	[4] 7, 303	9, 257, 072	7, 411, 059
Supplies purchased for patrons:			
Building material	790	72, 953	40, 255
Containers	921	44, 905	17, 767
Farm machinery and equipment	1, 792	126, 137	76, 278
Feed	4, 249	1, 068, 700	810, 153
Fertilizer	3, 376	296, 771	183, 615
Insecticides	1, 111	33, 153	24, 649
Meats, groceries, etc	859	45, 787	37, 675
Petroleum products	2, 657	653, 610	421, 524
Seed	3, 436	128, 788	94, 997
Other supplies	4, 522	289, 785	210, 304
Total purchasing	[4] 7, 418	2, 760, 589	1, 917, 217
Receipts for services:			
Trucking, storage, grinding, locker plants, miscellaneous	3, 411	91, 511	91, 511
Cotton ginning	513	21, 146	21, 146
Livestock trucking	208	1, 779	1, 779
Total services	[4] 4, 127	114, 436	114, 436
Total marketing, purchasing, and service	[4] 10, 166	12, 132, 097	9, 442, 712

[1] Preliminary.

[2] This figure represents value at the first level at which cooperatives transact business for farmers. It does not include wholesale business of farm supply cooperatives with other cooperatives or terminal market sales for local associations.

[3] Includes forest products, fur pelts, hay, hops, nursery stock, tung oil, and other farm products not separately classified.

[4] Because many associations are engaged in more than one type of business, these totals are less than the number that would be obtained by adding the number of associations handling individual items or performing individual services.

sales taxes like all other business firms.

Under section 314 of the Revenue Act of 1951, farmers' cooperatives are subject to the Federal income tax laws. Cooperatives that comply with rules and operating methods that before 1951 relieved them of liability for income taxes are permitted to exclude patronage refunds and to make certain deductions and other adjustments in the computation of net income under the Internal Revenue Code. Almost half of the farmers' cooperatives choose not to comply with those rules, with the result that they are taxed under the same laws that apply to corporations generally. Both "exempt" and "nonexempt" cooperatives may exclude patronage refunds from their income tax computations when the refunds are made in compliance with a prior, mandatory, contractual obligation under which an accounting to patrons is required for any amounts in excess of authorized expense deductions. The farmer-patron takes into account the patronage refunds if they affect his income from his farming operations and if he is notified of the amounts credited to him. If he is not notified, the amounts are taxable to the cooperative at the regular income tax rates.

The public policy of the United States toward cooperatives is shown by the statutes enacted by the Congress respecting them. Several have been mentioned. Another is the Cooperative Marketing Act (7 U. S. C. 451) of 1926, which directed the establishment in the Department of Agriculture of a division authorized "to promote the knowledge of cooperative principles and practices and to cooperate, in promoting such knowledge, with educational and marketing agencies, cooperative associations and others." This act is now administered by the Farmer Cooperative Service, established in 1953.

In 1927 the Congress enacted a statute (15 U. S. C. 431) forbidding boards of trade and exchanges (except markets designated as contract markets), on which agricultural products are bought and sold from excluding the duly authorized representative of any lawfully formed and conducted cooperative association "composed substantially of producers of agricultural products," provided such associations comply with certain prescribed conditions. The act further provided that no rule of a board of trade should be construed to prevent the payment of patronage dividends by a cooperative association of producers.

Similar recognition of the distinct character of patronage refunds is contained in the Robinson-Patman Act (regulating price discriminations), the Packers and Stockyards Act (regulating commission men and their charges) and the Commodity Exchange Act (regulating commodity exchanges).

In 1929 the Agricultural Marketing Act (12 U. S. C. 1141) was passed, which created the Federal Farm Board. Section 1 of that act specifies: "That it is hereby declared to be the policy of Congress to promote the effective merchandising of agricultural commodities in interstate and foreign commerce, so that the industry of agriculture will be placed on a basis of economic equality with other industries, and to that end to protect, control, and stabilize the currents of interstate and foreign commerce in the marketing of agricultural commodities and their food products . . . (3) by encouraging the organization of producers into effective associations or corporations under their own control for greater unity of effort in marketing and by promoting the establishment and financing of a farm marketing system of producer-owned and producer-controlled cooperative associations and other agencies."

The Farm Credit Act of 1933 (12 U. S. C. 1134, 1134 (f)) provided for the establishment of 12 regional banks for cooperatives and the Central Bank for Cooperatives to make loans to farmers' cooperatives.

Agricultural cooperative associations now have as well defined and certain a legal status as other types of business organizations. (*L. S. Hulbert.*)

Fair Dealing

Regulations for the marketing of farm products are designed to promote the public welfare. As the needs of the Nation change, the regulations must be modified or altered to meet them. Cities, States, and the Federal Government adopt regulations for the marketing of farm goods. About some of them there is argument. We discuss two controversial issues—interstate trade barriers and fair-trade legislation. Many regulations are concerned with sharp trading, for which the marketing of farm products is a fertile field. Several of the regulatory statutes administered by the Department of Agriculture are designed to establish reasonable codes of conduct for the buyers and sellers. The Packers and Stockyards Act and the Perishable Agricultural Commodities Act are two of the most important. The intelligent grower, alerted to the tricks that may be played on him and aware of the aid provided by the statutes, can evade some of the pitfalls and rogues that may be waiting for him along the trail leading from farm to market.

The Wide Range of Regulation

Cities, States, and the Federal Government have found it necessary in the public interest to adopt regulations for the marketing of farm products.

It is said that "the health of the people is the first law," and legislative enactments provide generally for the regulation, including inspection, of the sale of agricultural products in which disease-bearing organisms can survive. The regulatory measures are to guard against the diseases that can be transmitted through impure, unwholesome, or adulterated food.

The need for such regulation has been recognized for a long time.

In 1903 the Court of Appeals of New York said: "In great cities, where, in certain sections, life exists under crowded conditions that cannot be fully comprehended unless seen, and where many articles for table consumption by all classes of the community are liable to pass through processes and conditions little short of appalling unless regulated by law, the full and vigorous exercise of the police power in the interest of the public health and welfare is absolutely essential. . . . The vesting of powers . . . in various officials and boards is necessary, if the work of prevention and regulation is to ward off fevers, pestilence, and the many ills that constantly menace great centers of population." (*People ex rel. Lieberman* v. *Vandecarr*, 175 N. Y. 440, 445, 67 N. E. 913, 914, affirmed *sub nom. Lieberman* v. *Van De Carr*, 199 U. S. 552.)

One of the earliest functions of a municipality in the United States was the regulation of markets and marketing. The city charter for Philadelphia in 1701 and the new charter in 1789, as amended in 1804 and 1810, authorized the city council to erect market houses and specify appropriate regulations for the marketing of agricultural products and other foods.

In 1854 the Supreme Court of Pennsylvania, in a case involving market regulations by the city of Philadelphia, said: "The necessity of a public market, where the producers and consumers of fresh provisions can be brought together at stated times for the purchase and sale of those commodities, is very apparent. There is nothing which more imperatively requires the constant supervision of some authority which can regulate and control it. . . ." (*Wartman* v. *City of Philadelphia*, 33 Pa. St. 202, 209.)

The city of Charleston, S. C., in 1808 established one public market, owned by the city, and provided regulations to govern the marketing of agricultural products and other foods. The Court of Appeals of South Carolina in 1844 said that the public market in Charleston was policed "with great vigilance by the commissioners of the market," and explained that: "In dense populations, dependent for daily food upon the public market, not merely general convenience, but the public health and necessity, require such regulation and caution. . . . And in this way, the butchering of cattle and the vending of meats becomes a regulated municipal calling for the common convenience and safety." (*State ex rel. Wilkinson* v. *City of Charleston*, 2 Speers 523 [old volume, 623], 525–526 [old volume, 626].)

The legislature may vest in a municipality all of the delegable powers of the State as to the regulation of marketing, thus making the municipality in this respect a miniature State within its locality.

Municipal authority to regulate marketing generally is of wide scope, and municipal regulation is applicable to a variety of trades or businesses. The rule-making authorities in some municipalities have exercised the power by enactments to attain what they have regarded as an appropriate economic goal, even though the objective may have been of controversial character and the means of attaining it may have been of debatable legality.

An example is the ordinance enacted in 1826 by the city of Mobile, Ala., "to license bakers and regulate the weight and price of bread, and prohibit the baking for sale except by those licensed."

With respect to that ordinance, the Supreme Court of Alabama said in 1841 that: "Where a great number of persons are collected together in a town or city, a regular supply of wholesome bread is a matter of the utmost importance; and whatever doubts may have been thrown over the question by the theories of political economists, it would seem that experience has shewn that this great end is better secured by licensing a sufficient number of bakers and by an assize of bread, than by leaving it to the voluntary acts of individuals. By this means a constant supply is obtained without the fluctuation in quantity which would be the inevitable result of throwing the trade entirely open, and the consequent rise in price when from accident or design a sufficient supply was not produced." (*Mayor and Aldermen of Mobile* v. *Yuille*, 3 Ala. 137, 141–142.)

It was contended on behalf of the Mobile baker, in the Alabama case in 1841, that a lawful trade or business could not, under any circumstances, be regulated by the State or by the municipality, but in rejecting the argument the court said, with respect to a business that affects the public interest:

"Free government does not imply unrestrained liberty on the part of the citizen, but the privilege of being governed by laws which operate alike on all. It is not, therefore, to be supposed that in any country, however free, individual action cannot be restrained, or the mode, or manner of enjoying property, regulated."

Trade which "affects the public interest" may be regulated, said the court, "for the good of the inhabitants," and by way of summary it was stated: "Upon this principle, in this State, tavern keepers are licensed and required to enter into bond, with surety, that they will provide suitable food and lodging for their guests, and stabling and provender for their horses; and the County Court is required, at least once a year, to settle the rates of innkeepers. Upon the same principle is founded the control which the legislature has always exercised in the establishment and regulation of mills, ferries, bridges, turnpike roads, and other kindred subjects. So, also, all quarantine and other sanitary regulations, all laws requiring houses to be built in cities of a certain material, to guard against fire, depend for their validity on the same principle."

Some municipalities have provided that cotton and some other bulky articles must be weighed on the city scales by a public weigher before they can be sold in the municipality. The purpose is to prevent fraud. The need for regulation varies from time to time and place to place. The determination as to the public need is vested in the governing groups in municipalities.

IN THIS INDUSTRIAL DAY, the large municipalities generally have extensive regulations that (in brief) relate to the marketing of meat and meat products, fish, vegetables, fruit, and milk and milk products. All such foods are subject to inspection by a representative of the city's department of health; any food that is unfit for human consumption may be seized or condemned. Also the products intended for human consumption must be stored, transported, and displayed for sale so as to be protected from dust, dirt, flies, or other contamination, and all buildings, plants, rooms, and stalls used in the marketing process must be clean, sanitary, and maintained in a wholesome condition.

Slaughterhouses are subject to licensing requirements, under some circumstances, and also subject to inspection and supervision under municipal regulations.

Elaborate regulations generally apply with respect to the milk approved for sale in a metropolitan area. In many places, dairies must be approved by city departments of health. The dairy cows must be physically inspected from time to time by an approved veterinarian. The dairy barns, equipment, and facilities must be in accord with sanitary standards. The people engaged in the handling of milk must be free from communicable disease. The milk must be within the specified limitation as to bacteria, and must be cooled and otherwise handled in conformity with the various requirements, such as pasteurization.

States also have requirements. The New York legislature, for example, has concluded that the production, marketing, storing, and distribution of agricultural products intended for human consumption, as well as other foods, and also fertilizers, feeding stuffs, materials, and apparatus or machinery used or needed in connection therewith "are matters of public interest and proper subjects for investigation, encouragement, development, and regulation by the state to secure an abundant supply of pure and wholesome food, to protect the health of the inhabitants of the state, to secure the exchange of such food and instrumentalities upon a fair basis and at market prices uncontrolled by speculation, to prevent frauds in the traffic therein, and so far as may be to eliminate waste and loss in distribution thereof." (McKinney's Consolidated Laws of New York, art. 1, sec. 3 of the Agriculture and Markets Law. Also see ch. 651 of the Laws of New York 1946.)

THE AUTHORITY OF THE STATES to require inspection of agricultural products extends to numerous factors in addition to that of wholesomeness or quality.

The ambit of the authority was defined in 1882 by the Supreme Court in upholding a Maryland statute that prescribed the packaging requirements for Maryland tobacco. The Court said: "Recognized elements of inspection laws have always been quality of the article, form, capacity, dimensions, and weight of package, mode of putting up, and marking and branding of various kinds, all these matters being supervised by a public officer having authority to pass or not pass the article as lawful . . . as it did or did not answer the prescribed requirements. It has never been regarded as necessary, and it is manifestly not necessary, that all these elements should coexist in order to make a valid inspection law. Quality alone may be the subject of inspection, without other requirement, or the inspection may be made to extend to all of the above matters. When all are prescribed, and then inspection as to quality is dropped out, leaving the rest in force, it cannot be said to be a necessary legal conclusion that the law has ceased to be an inspection law." (*Turner* v. *Maryland*, 107 U. S. 38, 55.)

The power of a State to prescribe standard containers for horticultural products in order to facilitate trading, to preserve the condition of the products, to protect buyers from deception, or to prevent unfair competition has been said to be based on the police power, and such "regulation of trade is a part of the inspection laws; was among the earliest exertions of the police power in America; has been persistent; and has been widely applied to merchandise commonly sold in containers. . . . Latterly, with the broadening of the field of distribution and the growing use of containers in the retail trade, the scope of the regulation has been much extended." (*Pacific States Co.* v. *White*, 296 U. S. 176, 181.)

Different agricultural commodities require different types of containers, and as to each commodity there may be differences of opinion as to the type best adapted to the protection of the public. Whether it is necessary to provide a standard container and, if so, whether the type specified should be made mandatory are issues of fact and of policy, the determination of which rests in the State legislature or in the administrative agency to which may have been delegated the rule-making function.

The Constitution of Illinois as revised in 1870 authorized the legislature to require the inspection of grain and, also, to specify the regulations for the governance of the operators of warehouses or elevators, so as to provide "for the protection of producers, shippers, and receivers of grain." (Art. XIII, sec. 7. Also see art. XIII, sec. 1–6.)

Thereupon the State legislature established the ceiling or maximum charges for the storage and handling of grain in warehouses in large cities in Illinois. The validity of the regulation was sustained in 1876 by the Supreme Court of the United States in a case with respect to the grain elevators in Chicago which, according to the Court, "stand . . . in the very 'gateway of commerce' " and as a virtual monopoly exact a toll for the passage of each bushel of grain. (*Munn* v. *Illinois*, 94 U. S. 113, 123–132.)

The Court concluded: ". . . the [grain elevator] business is one of recent origin . . . its growth has been rapid, and . . . it is already of great importance. And it must also be conceded that it is a business in which the whole public has a direct and positive interest. It presents, therefore, a case for the application of a long-known and well-established principle in social science, and this statute simply extends the law so as to meet this new development of commercial progress," and although the warehouses may be instruments of commerce nonetheless "until Congress acts in reference to their inter-state relations, the State may exercise all the powers of government over them."

It has been held by the Supreme Court that the "Constitution does not guarantee the unrestricted privilege to engage in a business or to conduct it as one pleases," and, for example, a State may, in view of economic maladjustments in the dairy industry, delegate to an administrative agency the authority to fix the price of milk. (*Nebbia* v. *New York*, 291 U. S. 502, 527–539.) The private character of a business does not necessarily remove it from the realm of State regulation with respect to charges or prices. The legislature is primarily the judge of the necessity for such regulatory enactments.

THE MARKETING PRACTICES in the various States are not in all respects alike, and the States have somewhat different regulations with respect to the marketing of agricultural products.

In general, however, the regulatory measures by the States relate to the suppression or eradication of infectious or communicable diseases that affect domestic animals; the use of accurate weights and measures for determining the quantity of a commodity or article for sale; the prohibition of adulterated or misbranded products; the licensing of cold-storage warehouses, the marking of the food products therein, and the period of time that products may be kept in cold storage; provisions for plant quarantine and pest control; meat inspection; grades and standards for fresh fruits, vegetables, and other products of the soil; the licensing of agricultural warehouses and provisions as to the issuance and negotiation of warehouse receipts; the licensing of the produce dealers and the processors of farm products.

Seventeen States provide for the classification and pooling of milk, for use as fluid milk in metropolitan areas, and the specification of a minimum price which the dealers must pay to the producers. It has been said that legislation "which has for its purpose the regulation and stabilization of the milk industry, even to the extent of fixing prices for which it may be bought and sold, is not any new development in our social legislation. While it is of recent enactment in this State [California], it has been in force in other States for many years. . . ." (*Jersey Maid Milk Products Co.* v. *Brock*, 13 Calif. 2d 620, 659, 91 P. 2d 577, 598.)

Some States prohibit the marketing of "filled milk," as defined in the statutes, and also specify sanitary requirements with respect to the processing and marketing of some milk products.

Some States have regulations as to the containers used for packaging farm products, and prohibit deceptive arrangements, displays, or packs. Thus the honest dealers, as well as the consumers, are afforded protection against unfair trade practices.

Some States prohibit false, deceptive, or misleading statements or misrepresentations concerning the quality, size, maturity, or condition of fruits, nuts, or vegetables.

Some States provide for regulation by grade, size, and quality of fresh fruits and vegetables, so as to effect and maintain orderly marketing.

A SIGNIFICANT LIMITATION on the authority of a State or municipality is that the Congress is empowered by the Constitution to regulate the interstate commerce or commerce with foreign nations. The ties or the relationships among markets, in the recent decades of great expansion in mass production and distribution, are generally interstate in nature. The commercial and industrial forces of the Nation have given to our marketing system a national character, and agricultural products are distributed, under present-day conditions of mercantilism, on a nationwide market. Also our emergence as a world power in international trade affords an even broader public interest in the marts of trade and commerce. Under the commerce clause of the Constitution, numerous statutes have been enacted by the Congress, applicable to the varying phases of our economic life, in order to promote orderly marketing and the economic stability and prosperity of the Nation.

The national nature of one of our channels of commerce and also the avowed congressional purpose of market regulation are revealed in a case in the Supreme Court in 1922 with respect to the Packers and Stockyards Act. The opinion of the Court by Chief Justice Taft states: "Thousands of head of live stock arrive daily [in the large stockyards] by carload and trainload lots, and must be promptly sold

281437°—54——18

and disposed of and moved out to give place to the constantly flowing traffic that presses behind. The stockyards are but a throat through which the current flows, and the transactions which occur therein are only incident to this current from the West to the East, and from one state to another. Such transactions cannot be separated from the movement to which they contribute and necessarily take on its character. . . . The origin of the livestock is in the West, its ultimate destination known to, and intended by, all engaged in the business is in the Middle East and East either as meat products or stock for feeding and fattening. This is the definite and well-understood course of business. The stockyards and the sales are necessary factors in the middle of this current of commerce." (*Stafford* v. *Wallace*, 258 U. S. 495, 515–516.)

The object to be secured by the regulation of the marketing at the stockyards, said Chief Justice Taft, "is the free and unburdened flow of live stock" in interstate commerce, and the "chief evil feared is the monopoly of the packers, enabling them unduly and arbitrarily to lower prices to the shipper who sells, and unduly and arbitrarily to increase the price to the consumer who buys. . . . Another evil which it [i. e., Congress] sought to provide against . . . was exorbitant charges, duplication of commissions, deceptive practices in respect of prices, in the passage of the livestock through the stockyards, all made possible by collusion between the stockyards management and the commission men, on the one hand, and the packers and dealers on the other. . . . The shipper whose livestock are being cared for and sold in the stockyards market is ordinarily not present at the sale, but is far away in the West. He is wholly dependent on the commission men. The packers and their agents and the dealers who are the buyers are at the elbow of the commission men, and their relations are constant and close."

The Packers and Stockyards Act authorizes the Secretary of Agriculture, in accordance with the procedure prescribed by law, to regulate the rates, charges, and practices at the stockyards that are within the limits of the statute, and also a person engaged in the business of buying or selling livestock at any such posted stockyard must register, as a dealer, and give bond, and a person engaged in the business of furnishing stockyard services must also register and give bond. Accurate weighing of livestock is required. Consigned livestock must be sold under competitive conditions. The commission firms must account fully and correctly to their principals, and persons subject to the act must not engage in unfair, deceptive, or discriminating practices.

The Secretary of Agriculture is authorized to issue, on the basis of evidence at a public hearing, cease and desist orders against violators of the act. Also reparation orders may be issued by the Secretary, and registrations may be suspended or revoked.

Transactions in commodity futures on boards of trade are regulated under the Commodity Exchange Act, the amended name of the Grain Futures Act of September 21, 1922. The Congress found, in the enactment of this regulatory legislation, that transactions and prices on boards of trade are susceptible to speculation, manipulation, and control, and that regulation of such trading is conducive to the protection of interstate commerce and the national public interest.

The act prohibits the manipulation of the price of wheat, cotton, rice, corn, oats, barley, rye, flaxseed, grain sorghums, millfeeds, butter, eggs, Irish potatoes, wool tops, all fats and oils, cottonseed meal, cottonseed, peanuts, soybeans, and soybean meal. Also the legislation prohibits an "attempt" to manipulate the price of any of those commodities in interstate commerce or for future delivery on a board of trade. A corner or an attempt to corner is likewise prohibited. Futures commission merchants and floor brokers, as well as boards of trade, are subject to regulation, in various respects, under the statute.

The Secretary of Agriculture is directed by the Sugar Act to determine for each calendar year the total amount of sugar needed to meet the requirement of consumers in the continental United States. After that determination has been made, the Secretary is to establish quotas for all sugar-producing areas by allocating the total need of the consumers in the continental United States among continental sugar-producing areas, Hawaii, Puerto Rico, the Virgin Islands, the Republic of the Philippines, and foreign countries. The allocation is determined by standards set forth in the act, and also the Secretary is authorized to allot any area quota among the persons who market sugar in that area.

The statute prohibits the importation of sugar or the marketing of sugar in excess of the quota limitations or allotments. The central aim of this legislation is to rationalize the mischievous fluctuations of the sugar market by the familiar device of a quota system, and thereby secure a harmonious relation between supply and demand.

In upholding quota legislation for sugar, the Supreme Court said: "The complexity of problems affecting raw and refined sugar in widely separated and economically disparate areas, accentuated by the instability of the differentiating factors, must have persuaded Congress of the need for continuous detailed administrative supervision. In any event, such is the plain purport of the legislation." (*Secretary of Agriculture* v. *Central Roig Co.*, 338 U. S. 604, 611.)

UNDER THE Agricultural Marketing Agreement Act of 1937, the marketing of milk, fruits, vegetables, and certain other commodities is subject to regulation by marketing orders issued by the Secretary of Agriculture for the purpose of establishing orderly marketing conditions and achieving the economic goal set forth in the statute.

The Supreme Court has said that the "fluid milk industry is affected by factors of instability peculiar to itself which call for special methods of control" (*Nebbia* v. *New York*, 291 U. S. 502, 517) and "the economy of the industry is so eccentric that economic controls have been found at once necessary and difficult" (*Hood & Sons* v. *Du Mond*, 336 U. S. 525, 529).

The milk orders are designed to stabilize the market by establishing a uniform minimum price which all dealers or handlers shall pay to producers for milk delivered during each month. The milk is classified according to its use by the dealers or handlers, and a "use value" is assigned to each class. A marketwide pool or an individual-handler pool is established by a milk order, and a uniform blended price is paid to each producer in the pool.

All provisions in an order are based on evidence adduced at a public hearing, and the up-and-down pattern of milk production in many production areas coupled with rapid changes in economic conditions calls for frequent hearings in order to effectuate the necessary changes in the classification and pricing of milk.

The statute authorizes Federal orders in conjunction with State orders and the milk program for the New York metropolitan marketing area is a joint Federal-State program. The market administrator for that regulatory program is the appointee of the Secretary of Agriculture and also the appointee of the Commissioner of Agriculture and Markets of the State of New York. The "exquisitely complicated" character of milk marketing or milk regulation has been frequently referred to, and it has been said that the milk problem in conjunction with milk marketing orders "is so vast that fully to comprehend it would require an almost universal knowledge ranging from geology, biology, chemistry, and medicine to the niceties of the legislative, judicial, and administrative processes of government." (*Queensboro Farms Products* v. *Wickard*, 137 F. 2d 969, 975.)

The Congress recognized, in the enactment of the statute for milk orders, that a rigid and inflexible method of regulation cannot be applied effectively to the mutable conditions in the various milk-marketing areas, and in order to counteract the virulent effects of disorderly marketing the Secretary of Agriculture is authorized to include, in milk orders, regulatory provisions within the broad outlines of the statute.

The methods of regulation generally follow the plans and practices employed by cooperative associations of producers before the enactment of this legislation, and the Congress has provided that, in the administration of the act, the Secretary shall extend such recognition and encouragement to the producer-owned and producer-controlled cooperatives as will be in harmony with the congressional policy, in other acts, and as will tend to promote efficient methods of marketing.

This statutory measure is an example of enabling legislation which, standing alone, imposes no regulation but instead directs the issuance of regulations from time to time, whenever the evidence at a public hearing justifies the necessary findings of fact and conclusions by the administrative official. This method of regulation is in contrast to regulatory statutes which merely enumerate certain prohibited practices.

Some fruits and vegetables and specialty crops are also subject to regulation under the Agricultural Marketing Agreement Act of 1937. Many orders are in effect with respect to marketing them. The orders do not fix prices, but limit the quantity, grade, or size of the commodity that may be handled. An order may provide for the apportionment of the total quantity to be handled among handlers or producers. The orders generally contemplate the issuance of regulations at weekly intervals during the marketing period. A surplus pool may also be established under an order.

The purpose of the Perishable Agricultural Commodities Act, originally enacted in 1930, is to suppress unfair and fraudulent practices in the marketing of perishable agricultural commodities in interstate or foreign commerce.

The Congress seeks to accomplish that purpose by requiring commission merchants, dealers, and brokers to be licensed, requiring licensees to keep records of transactions, prohibiting improper practices, requiring accounting, and authorizing the investigation of complaints, the issuance of reparation orders, the publication of facts concerning violations, and providing for the suspension or revocation of licenses and imposing penalties for operating without a license.

Under the Agricultural Adjustment Act of 1938 it is declared to be the policy of the Congress to conserve national resources, prevent the wasteful use of soil fertility, assist in the marketing of agricultural commodities for domestic consumption and for export, and with respect to cotton, wheat, corn, tobacco, rice, and peanuts provide for the orderly, adequate, and balanced flow of such commodities in the interstate and foreign commerce.

When supplies are excessive, as described in the act, the Secretary of Agriculture is required to establish farm marketing quotas for these basic agricultural commodities.

If, for example, a national marketing quota for cotton is proclaimed by the Secretary and approved by farmers in a referendum, the quota is converted to a national acreage allotment on the basis of the national acreage yield and apportioned among the States, counties, and farms on the basis of the statutory formulas. The marketing of cotton from the farm in excess of the farm marketing quota, that is, production from the farm acreage allotment, is subject to a penalty provided for by the statute.

The legislative aim, in part at least, is to maintain a balance between supply and demand and thereby stabilize prices in the interest of both producers and consumers.

Various other enactments by the Congress provide

(1) for the issuance of cotton standards, the licensing of classifiers, and the issuance of regulations as to the sampling and grading of cotton;

(2) for the issuance of grain standards and the compulsory use of those standards, generally, for grain in interstate or foreign commerce which is sold, offered for sale, or consigned for sale by grade, and such grain must be inspected and graded by a licensed inspector;

(3) for the issuance of standards for tobacco and the designation of auction markets, where tobacco is bought and sold at auction, and the inspection and grading of tobacco sold at auction markets; and

(4) for the investigation of quality and condition of farm produce received in interstate commerce and the authorization of inspectors and the issuance of certificates of inspection.

Acts of Congress provide the specifications for standard barrels for fruits, vegetables, and some other agricultural products, and also standard baskets, round stave baskets, hampers, splint baskets, and some other containers.

The line of demarcation between the authority of the States, in this field, and the authority of the Federal Government is not always easy to discern in the practical affairs of business, but the guiding principle was stated by Chief Justice Hughes, in an opinion for the Supreme Court, as follows:

"Inspection and the establishment of standards for commodities has been regarded from colonial days as appropriate to the regulation of trade, and the authority of the States to enact inspection laws is recognized by the Constitution. . . . But the inspection laws of a State relating to exports or to articles purchased for shipment to other States are subject to the paramount regulatory power of Congress. . . . And Congress has long exercised this authority in enacting laws for inspection and the establishment of standards in relation to various commodities involved in transactions in interstate or foreign commerce." (*Currin* v. *Wallace*, 306 U. S. 1, 12.)

In another case, the Supreme Court said that our "system, fostered by the Commerce Clause [in the Constitution], is that every farmer and every craftsman shall be encouraged to produce by the certainty that he will have free access to every market in the Nation, that no home [state] embargoes will withhold his export, and no . . . [other] state will by customs duties or regulations exclude them. Likewise every consumer may look to the free competition from every producing area in the Nation to protect him from exploitation by any. Such was the vision of the Founders; such has been the doctrine of this Court which has given it reality." (*Hood & Sons* v. *Du Mond*, 336 U. S. 525, 539.)

THE UNITED STATES WAREHOUSE ACT authorizes the Secretary of Agriculture to issue a license to a warehouseman if his warehouse is suitable for the proper storage of the particular agricultural product or products for which a license is applied for, and if the warehouseman agrees to comply with the terms of the statute and the regulations thereunder.

The license may be suspended or revoked if the warehouseman violates the act or the regulations. The Secretary may also license inspectors to classify, grade, or weigh agricultural products in a licensed warehouse, and to certify the condition, grade, class, and weight of such agricultural products. A licensed warehouseman is prohibited from discriminating between persons with respect to the acceptance of agricultural products for storage if the products are in suitable condition for warehousing.

Numerous provisions in the statute relate to the mingling of fungible goods in a warehouse, the issuance of receipts for products stored in a licensed warehouse, the contents of such receipts, the records to be kept by the licensed warehouseman, and the issuance of regulations by the Secretary of Agriculture.

A licensed warehouseman is required, in the absence of some lawful excuse, to deliver, without unnecessary delay, the agricultural products, stored in the warehouse, upon appropriate demand by the depositor or holder of a receipt. A licensed warehouseman is prohibited from making any unreasonable or exorbitant charge for service rendered. Although the act is permissive, it provides that the "authority conferred upon the Secretary of Agriculture . . . shall be exclusive with respect to all persons securing a license hereunder so long as said license remains in effect."

Various farm products are subject also to regulation under the Federal Food, Drug, and Cosmetic Act. Also to prevent the use in interstate or foreign commerce of meat and meat products for food that are unwholesome, unhealthful, or unfit for human use, the Secretary of Agriculture is authorized by the Congress to provide for the inspection of all cattle, sheep, swine, and goats that enter any slaughtering, packing, meat-canning, rendering, or similar establishment in which they are slaughtered and the meat and meat products for food disposed of in interstate or foreign commerce, and also post mortem examination and inspection of the carcasses of such animals is provided for, as well as the sanitary inspection and regulation of the establishments in which the livestock may be slaughtered and the meat prepared for shipment.

The Congress has also empowered the Secretary of Agriculture to put under quarantine any area in which any cattle, or other livestock, or live poultry are affected with any contagious, infectious, or communicable disease.

Somewhat similar legislation is designed to prevent the introduction into, or the dissemination within, the United States of plants, plant products, or other articles that carry insect pests or plant diseases.

Unfair methods of competition and unfair or deceptive acts or practices in interstate or foreign commerce are prohibited by the Congress in the legislation that established the Federal Trade Commission. Contracts, combinations, and other conspiracies in restraint of trade in interstate or foreign commerce are prohibited by the antitrust acts, and the normal flow of commerce is to be protected from the coercive or subversive influences of monopolistic practices. It has been said, under the antitrust acts, that "[m]any people believe . . . immunity from competition is a narcotic, and rivalry is a stimulant, to industrial progress; that the spur of constant stress is necessary to counteract an inevitable disposition to let well-enough alone." (*United States* v. *Aluminum Company of America*, 148 F. 2d 416, 427.)

THE FOLLOWING is a list of the regulatory statutes administered by the United States Department of Agriculture, and these acts generally provide for the issuance of regulations: Commodity Exchange Act (7 U. S. C. 1952 ed. § 1 *et seq.*); United States Cotton Standards Act (7 U. S. C. 1952 ed. § 51 *et seq.*); United States Grain Standards Act (7 U. S. C. 1952 ed. § 71 *et seq.*); Naval Stores Act (7 U. S. C. 1952 ed. § 91 *et seq.*); Federal Insecticide, Fungicide, and Rodenticide Act (7 U. S. C. 1952 ed. § 135 *et seq.*); Plant Quarantine Act and Related Legislation (7 U. S. C. 1952 ed. § 141 *et seq.* and 7 U. S. C. 1952 ed. § 441, and 7 U. S. C. 1952 ed. § 1651); Packers and Stockyards Act (7 U. S. C. 1952 ed. § 181 *et seq.*); United States Warehouse Act (7 U. S. C. 1952 ed. § 241 *et seq.*); Honeybee Act (7 U. S. C. 1952 ed. § 281 *et seq.*); Capper-Volstead Act (7 U. S. C. 1952 ed. § 291 *et seq.*); Farm Products Inspection Act (7 U. S. C. 1952 ed. § 414);

Wool Standards Act (7 U. S. C. 1952 ed. § 415b *et seq.*); Poultry and Turkey Improvement Authority (7 U. S. C. 1952 ed. § 429); Cotton Statistics and Estimates Act (7 U. S. C. 1952 ed. § 471 *et seq.*); Produce Agency Act (7 U. S. C. 1952 ed. § 491 *et seq.*); Perishable Agricultural Commodities Act (7 U. S. C. 1952 ed. § 499a *et seq.*); Tobacco Statistics Act (7 U. S. C. 1952 ed. § 501 *et seq.*); Tobacco Inspection Act (7 U. S. C. 1952 ed. § 511 *et seq.*); Tobacco Seeds and Plants Exportation Act (7 U. S. C. § 516 *et seq.*); Export Apple and Pear Act (7 U. S. C. 1952 ed. § 581 *et seq.*); Agricultural Marketing Agreement Act of 1937 (7 U. S. C. 1952 ed. § 601 *et seq.*); Anti-Hog-Cholera Serum and Hog-Cholera Virus Marketing Agreement Act (7 U. S. C. 1952 ed. § 851 *et seq.*); Peanut Statistics Act (7 U. S. C. 1952 ed. § 951 *et seq.*); Sugar Act (7 U. S. C. 1952 ed. § 1100 *et seq.*); Agricultural Adjustment Act of 1938 (7 U. S. C. 1952 ed. § 1281 *et seq.*); Federal Seed Act (7 U. S. C. 1952 ed. § 1551 *et seq.*); Standard Containers Act of 1916 (15 U. S. C. 1952 ed. § 251 *et seq.*); Standard Containers Act of 1928 (15 U. S. C. 1952 ed. § 257 *et seq.*); Meat Inspection Acts (21 U. S. C. 1952 ed. § 94 *et seq.*, and 19 U. S. C. 1952 ed. § 1306 (b)); Dairy Products for Export Act (21 U. S. C. 1952 ed. § 94a); Animal Quarantine and Related Acts (21 U. S. C. 1952 ed. § 101 *et seq.*, 19 U. S. C. 1952 ed. § 1306 (a) and (c), 19 U. S. C. 1952 ed. § 1201, par. 1606, and 46 U. S. C. § 466a and b); Virus-Serum-Toxin Act (21 U. S. C. 1952 ed. § 151 *et seq.*); Cotton Futures Act (26 U. S. C. § 1920 *et seq.*); Renovated Butter Act (26 U. S. C. § 2320 *et seq.*); Twenty-eight Hour Law Relative to the Maximum Period of Time Livestock May be Confined in Railroad Cars or Vessels (45 U. S. C. § 71 *et seq.*).

These general references to some of the major legislation by the Congress for the regulation of marketing should manifest the concern to protect and encourage the normal and free flow of trade and commerce, to safeguard the health of the people, and to promote the stability and prosperity of our agricultural economy in view of an awareness that, as Chief Justice Hughes said, "when industry is grievously hurt, when producing concerns fail, when unemployment mounts, and communities dependent upon profitable production are prostrated, the wells of commerce go dry." (*Appalachian Coals, Inc.* v. *United States*, 288 U. S. 344, 372.)

The regulation of marketing is designed to promote the public welfare, and, therefore, is to be modified or altered from time to time to meet the changing needs of the Nation. (*Neil Brooks.*)

Warning! Let the Buyer Beware!

"Let the buyer beware" expresses a type of warning that became crystallized in the early common law of England and later in America as the doctrine of *caveat emptor*—"let the purchaser examine the article he is buying and act on his own judgment and at his own risk." The seller had no obligation under the ancient rule to reveal discoverable defects.

When a man sought to buy something he was expected to examine the article himself and discover whatever inferiority of quality or any defects it might have. He had no legal recourse to recover the loss or to get his money back because the law told him to be wary when he bought.

The expression came into use centuries ago in England when seller and buyer met in person, usually in the public market place or at a fair or bazaar. With the goods at hand, open and available for inspection by the purchaser, the parties haggled. When the price was finally agreed upon, the sale was closed. In the circumstances, opportunities for finding out the true quality of the article were about equal as between purchaser and seller. Nothing was sold in sealed containers, closed packaging, or similar conveniences, which make it hard or impossible for the purchaser to inspect the product itself.

Transplanted to America, *caveat emptor* is said to have become popular in the frontier days. The United States Supreme Court as late as 1870 applied the doctrine to a case in which the buyer was obliged to suffer the loss from rotten and damaged wool that deceitfully had been packed inside some of the bales comprising a shipment of South American wool offered for sale by a broker in Boston. At the time of purchase, the buyer opened and inspected four bales of the lot; finding them satisfactory, he agreed to the purchase without going to the trouble of opening the other bales. He assumed the unopened bales were of the same quality as those he inspected. Some months later he discovered the concealed rotten and damaged wool, and he sued the seller. The high court, however, ruled that *caveat emptor* relieved the seller of any obligation to make good the loss. (*Barnard* v. *Kellogg*, 77 U. S. 383.)

The English common law courts are said to have regarded the let-the-buyer-beware doctrine as good philosophy because it tended to sharpen the wits of buyers.

As a maxim of the law, *caveat emptor* tended to subject marketing to conditions of suspicion and distrust between buyer and seller. It has long since been learned, however, that the important economic function of selling should be conducted on a basis of confidence and mutual respect between seller and buyer—that the truly sound principle of frank and full understanding of the product and its character and quality and what it can be expected to do should prevail.

The wisdom of the seller, as well as his obligations under new laws, is today leading him in the direction of not waiting for the buyer to discover information about the product offered for sale, but of making facts available to enable the purchaser to buy with understanding and full knowledge. In fact, we find the idea of keeping the customer satisfied so prevalent in business today that often merchants proclaim as their policy that the customer is always right. That may be a bit of exaggeration, for as yet it cannot be said that the ultimate of equitable dealing has been reached in all sales transactions. There is still need for the buyer to exercise a certain degree of wariness.

Personal inspection by the purchaser, as was expected under *caveat emptor*, is no longer practicable or feasible as a means of ascertaining the condition, composition, or quality of the different articles and commodities daily offered for sale. The purchasers do not have much opportunity to examine products for themselves. Modern packaging renders impossible any preexamination of many of the articles placed on the market. Furthermore, most manufactured products are made under such highly developed technology that useful examination requires scientific expertness which the ordinary purchaser does not have. Even learned professionals with highly developed laboratory equipment often find it difficult to determine the components of products and evaluate their potentialities. In reality, the buyer becomes daily more dependent upon the manufacturer or seller for the information he needs for choosing his purchases with understanding and intelligence.

Progress has brought many improvements. A major part of the advances come from an accumulation of special statutes enacted by Congress and by State legislatures since just before the beginning of the twentieth century. In legislating, the idea of requiring informative labeling has been adopted for special lines of commodities, including food products, seeds, fertilizers, wool and fur clothing, and various other products.

Closely related—but more widely applicable—are legislative prohibitions designed to protect the buyer from misrepresentations or deceptive conditions arising from action of the seller. Sale of adulterated or unwholesome products intended for human consumption has been specifically prohibited. Special safeguards are provided to protect people in respect to commodities that contain poisonous or deleterious substances. Various administrative regulations and orders also have been issued providing minimum standards of quality or construction and requiring disclosure of certain facts to prevent confusion or misunderstanding on the part of purchasers.

Heavy reliance has likewise been placed on implementing by law the idea of assuring to the buying public and to our private enterprise economy the benefits of free and fair competition among sellers, thereby affording a progressive stimulant to better selling methods.

LEGISLATION respecting informative disclosure of contents and the exclusion of unfit goods is illustrated by the national pure food and drug law. The original statute was enacted in 1906, and was a culmination of the great efforts of Dr. Harvey Wiley. The Congress improved and strengthened the law by enacting in 1938 the provisions known as the Food, Drug, and Cosmetic Act.

Within the area of interstate commerce it applies to all types of foods and medicines for "human or other animals," as well as to anything (except soap) that is "rubbed, poured, sprinkled, or sprayed" on the human body for "cleansing, beautifying or promoting attractiveness." All types of misbranding are prohibited.

Adulteration or use in the product of any unclean, deteriorated, poisonous, or deleterious substance is also forbidden. Reducing the quality by abstracting some valuable constituent or coloring the product to conceal damage or an inferiority likewise is prohibited.

Packaged foods that may be substandard in quality but nevertheless are wholesome may still be sold but only upon disclosure to the purchaser that they are below standard or are imitations.

Certain food products sold under common names have been placed under "Standards of Identity." Standards of identity provide basic specification of ingredients, and have been issued for bread, flour, macaroni, fruit butters (jellies and preserves), butter, oleomargarine, canned corn, canned tomatoes, cheese, milk chocolate, mayonnaise, condensed milk, whipping cream, liquid eggs, and many other prepared or processed foods. For them the label need not state the prescribed ingredients, but specifications of the ingredients are made available by Government publication. Any departure from the prescribed standard of components is prohibited.

Reforms thus brought about enable the buyer to select his purchase with assurance of its essential quality and purity and with knowledge of components. Besides having the benefits of scrupulous labeling, the purchaser also has protection against false or misleading advertising under another statute—Federal Trade Commission Act (15 U. S. C. A. 41–58)—which applies generally to articles of commerce, as well as to foods, drugs, curative devices, and cosmetics.

Marketing has likewise been materially advanced by national legislation in other fields. Under administration of the Department of Agriculture, the Congress has provided standards for the classification of cotton, "by which the quality or value may be judged and determined." Similarly, "standards of quality and condition" have been established for corn (maize), wheat, rye, oats, barley, flaxseed, soybeans, and other grains, and are required to be used for official inspection when those basic commodities are marketed by grade in interstate commerce. Standards of minimum quality of apples and pears sold for export are required to be met. A system for inspection and certification of perishable agricultural commodities for interstate shipment has been made available. Official tobacco standards have also been authorized and official grading is mandatory on designated auction markets.

UNDER THE FEDERAL SEED ACT (53 Stat. 1275) the Congress has taken steps to assure that the farmer or planter shall be enabled to buy his agricultural and vegetable seeds with knowledge of essential facts. Label disclosure is required to be made to show the true name of the kind or variety of the seed, the percentage of its purity and of its germination, and also the amount of noxious weed seed present. In a seed mixture the percentage of each principal component must be stated specifically. If the germination of vegetable seed is below the standard prescribed, the container must be marked "below standard." False or misleading labeling or advertising are also prohibited.

Strict regulations are imposed to protect the buyer from adulterated foreign seeds. Where the country of origin of foreign seed has an important bearing on the crop which it will produce, such as alfalfa and red clover, the seed must be stained. That imported from South America is required to be stained 10 percent orange red; from Canada, 1 percent violet. Ten percent of a mixture of foreign seeds whose origin is not established must be stained red.

Agriculture is also the principal beneficiary of new legislation by the Congress relating to the sale of pest-control sprays, powders, and compounds known as insecticides, fungicides, and rodenticides—61 Stat. 163. The seller must not only see that these products are up to standard but he is also required to disclose their poisonous nature and to make available information showing what is an effective antidote for the poison. A distinguishing color must be applied to certain types of these products to guard against mistaking them for something harmless, like flour or meal.

In the field of wool and fur products, impetus to improving the basis of sales transactions was further supplied by the Congress in special legislation that became effective in 1941 and 1952. (Wool Products Labeling Act, effective July 1941, 54 Stat. 1128; Fur Products Labeling Act, effective August 1952, 65 Stat. 175.) Articles of clothing or other textiles that contain or purport to contain woolen fiber in whole or in part are required to be truthfully tagged or labeled and to reveal thereon the respective percentages of each different type of fiber contained in the fabric, exclusive of ornamentation not exceeding 5 percent. To the extent they are present, the label must show the percentage of "wool," "reprocessed wool," or "reused wool," and the percentages of nonwoolen fiber, such as cotton, silk, linen, rayon, nylon, or other synthetic fiber. "Miscellaneous Fibers" may be used to designate those present in less than 5 percent.

The buying public need not guess or be misled by appearances or otherwise as to whether the cloth is all wool or what other components it may have, nor whether the woolen fiber in the material is reused (secondhand) or whether it is virgin or new wool, or "reprocessed" fiber never before used by an ultimate consumer.

In the fur-labeling act, the Congress undertook to put an end to the practice of giving false or fictitious animal names to less costly furs dyed and dressed to simulate the more expensive kind. Rabbit fur at different times had been sold to the buying public under no less than 50 purported animal names, not one of which revealed to the purchaser the truth that the product was in reality rabbit fur dyed in simulation of something else. Under the new law an official name guide of all fur-bearing animals has been established. Sellers must reveal to the purchaser by tag or label the true name of the animal; if the fur has been dyed or bleached, or if it is secondhand or damaged, or if the garment is made of paws or other small pieces, those facts also must be revealed. No misrepresentation in labeling, invoicing, or advertising is permitted.

State legislatures likewise have been helping to elevate the basis of sales transactions and to that extent taking the game of chance out of marketing.

Many States have adopted the so-called model advertising law, which provides that "any person who, with intent to sell, disseminates an advertisement which contains any assertion, representation or statement of fact which is untrue, deceptive or misleading shall be guilty of a misdemeanor."

Pure food laws and other similar legislation that States have enacted tie in closely with the Federal law. With the national laws devoted primarily to interstate transactions and State law to local or intrastate business, they complement or supplement each other in the task of reducing the possibility of jurisdictional and other loopholes that would allow some offenders to escape.

Factual labeling under State authority is provided quite extensively in respect to some commodities. Such action is perhaps most fully exemplified by the fertilizer laws, which exist in all the States and require that the seller by tag or label must furnish to the buyer a meaningful description of the content of the product. The buyer is thus afforded a basis of fact on which to make his purchase and to select the fertilizer his soil needs for the crops he intends to grow. The percentages of nitrogen, available phosphoric acid, and potash must be revealed, as well as the weight and the name of the brand and the producer. Some States require more than others. In addition to the ingredients, two States require that the seller must inform the buyer as to whether the material is "acid-forming" or "non-acid-forming." In at least one State special information must be furnished when the fertilizer is to be used for tobacco.

State laws for labeling bedding articles and paint products are further examples of specific legislative action to provide the buying public with honest information.

The so-called uniform sales act, adopted by a number of States, contains a clause to the effect that "if the buyer has examined the goods, there is no implied warranty as regards defects which such examination ought to have revealed." Therein survive vestiges of *caveat emptor*, despite the trend pursued for generations of discarding it as not a fair or equitable rule to govern modern marketing. It is wholly at variance with the principle underlying the various labeling laws, which proceed on the basis that the seller shall furnish the essential facts about the article and not leave such to be discovered by the purchaser upon his own inspection and at his own risk.

The factor of competition, which our Federal and State laws seek to preserve, affords a counteracting influence tending to alleviate the rigors of *caveat emptor*. Competition exerts a far-reaching force in buying and selling. Obviously a greater degree of bargaining power rests with the purchaser when he has a choice among several sellers, each competing with the other to gain his patronage as a customer. The type of service which the seller will afford, his willingness to acquaint the purchaser fully with the quality, character, and performance of his product, his desire to render the purchaser satisfaction, the reasonableness of his price, his readiness to stand responsible for any defects the product may develop—all are influenced favorably toward the buyer by the operation of free and fair competition.

The idea that competition shall be kept free to operate vigorously and fairly is a basic principle of our private enterprise economy under which our industrial and commercial development has made phenomenal strides. There is truth in the saying that "competition is the life of trade."

Our Federal antitrust law (the Sherman Act) dating from 1890, was designed to preserve competition in business by prohibiting monopolies and industrial or commercial combinations that restrain trade.

To safeguard further the operation of competition, the Congress in 1914 established the Federal Trade Commission and charged it with the duty of stopping the use in interstate commerce, by persons, partnerships, or corporations, of unfair methods that suppress or injure competition. By such means it was felt that monopolies could be checked in their incipiency. Monopoly-breeding methods in business have been stopped in numerous cases prosecuted by the Commission in the 40 years of its existence.

The original Sherman Act and the Federal Trade Commission Act, followed by a series of supplemental acts of Congress, stand in recognition of the importance of competition in commercial activities. Under them, competing manufacturers or sellers are not permitted to agree or to conspire among themselves to fix prices or to limit the amount of production so as to keep prices high through artificially created scarcities or to divide territory so as to avoid competing with one another.

Likewise a manufacturer or distributor is not permitted to injure, prevent, or destroy competition by discriminating in price among his competing dealers or in the services he furnishes to them for promoting the resale of his products. Nor is he permitted to lessen competition materially by requiring them not to handle the products of competitors. A corporation may not limit competition substantially by buying up its competitors, and it may not have one or more persons serve at the same time on its own and its corporate competitor's board of directors, unless they are comparatively small concerns.

Implemented by such laws is the basic principle that sellers have no right through monopolistic practices or combinations in restraint of trade to deprive purchasers of the benefit of competition as a governing influence in sales transactions. The view is generally accepted that the driving force of competition in the distribution of goods from producer to consumer will bring to the buyer the greatest abundance and variety of merchandise at the lowest price and with the best quality for the money.

Congress also enacted the policy, enforced by the Federal Trade Commission, that competition although free shall not be allowed to degenerate into or become corrupted by practices that are tinged with elements of deception, bad faith, or fraud, whether brought about by misrepresentation on the part of the seller or by his concealment or nondisclosure of material facts which tend to mislead or deceive the buyer. A great variety of selling practices of this sort have been ruled unlawful by the Federal Trade Commission.

Advertising is today the great salesman. Television and radio have been added to the art of printing as vehicles to carry the sales message to buyers everywhere. Business is spending at a rate of more than 7 billion dollars a year on advertising to induce customers to buy. To preserve the constructive character of such a powerful force and to protect the buying public, the Federal Trade Commission Act requires advertising not to carry anything that is false, deceptive, or misleading in the circumstances in which it is to be used. Such applies in interstate commerce to articles of virtually every description.

The inhibited deception is not confined merely to those selling claims that are actually false, but may include statements which, although literally true, present a misleading inference. The Supreme Court has said "deception may result from the use of statements not technically false or which may be literally true." (*United States* v. *95 Barrels of Vinegar*, 265 U. S. 438, 443; 1924.) Furthermore, a manufacturer must see to it that whatever he says or does in marketing his product shall not lead to deception of the ultimate purchaser even though his own customer, the dealer, is not deceived. When underwear made of cotton with 10 percent wool was marked by a manufacturer with the words "natural wool" he was held to be using an unlawful practice although his customers, the dealers, knew the product was not all wool and were not deceived. The practice was deemed unfair because the misleading brand on the boxes enabled the dealer to deceive the ultimate consumer. (*Federal Trade Commission* v. *Winsted Co.*, 258 U. S. 483; 1922.)

Failure to reveal to the purchaser the secondhand nature of typewriters, used refinished felt hats, and of various other used articles which had been rebuilt or refinished to have the deceptive appearance of being new was ruled to be unfair and illegal.

If a manufacturer constructs or finishes his product in such way as to give it the appearance of that which it is not, he is pretty well obliged to make an affirmative disclosure of the real nature of the article in order to avoid the probability of purchasers being confused or deceived by its appearance. Buffet trays surfaced with a processed paper to simulate walnut wood were held to be "almost certain to deceive the buying public." (*Haskelite Mfg. Corp.* v. *Federal Trade Commission*, 127 F. (2d) 765, 766.)

Not all progress, however, has been forced by Government regulation or the host of new statutes touching the subject. The record on the part of business itself shows noteworthy action in support of a high standard of scrupulous and enlightened sales methods.

Some trade groups have established codes of ethics for their members to apply in selling their products. Merchants of various communities throughout the country, particularly in our principal cities, are supporting such organizations as better business bureaus, advertising clubs, and boards of trade, which usually include among their activities programs for improving sales methods by holding in check practices that are unfair or deceptive to purchasers.

Some manufacturers and dealers pursue a policy of employing commercial testing laboratories, or of maintaining testing laboratories of their own, to analyze and evaluate the quality and performance of products in which they deal. Generally such testing is performed as an aid to their own buying and to assure themselves of the quality and performance of the articles which they wish to offer to their customers. To the extent factual information about the quality and character of the merchandise thus obtained is made available in reasonably complete form, buyers are benefited.

From time to time certain organizations supported by members of industry and trade have also set up minimum standards of construction and performance of products, particularly textiles. Such efforts often help to bring assurance to purchasers and consumers that when they buy products coming under such standards they are getting a reasonable quality.

In a competitive business where the purchaser has a choice of several sellers, competition among them compels each to try to exceed the other in furnishing quality, service, and satisfaction to the buyer. Indeed, their chance of remaining in business depends in large measure on their respective capabilities to supply the customer's needs or desires with the best quality and service at the best price, thus retaining the buyer's goodwill, that indefinable inclination that makes individuals want to come back and purchase again from the same source. The businessman's desire to retain the customer's goodwill exerts a strong influence.

Our courts of justice have gone far in receding from the ancient doctrine of "let the buyer beware." They give substantial effect to a doctrine that there must be complete honesty in whatever the seller does in the course of offering his product for sale. Our highest tribunal has said: "There is no duty resting upon a citizen to suspect the honesty of those with whom he transacts business. Laws are made to protect the trusting as well as the suspicious." (*Federal Trade Commission* v. *Standard Education Society*, 302 U. S. 112, 116.)

The seller has no right to mislead or deceive the buyer even for his own good, and it is no excuse or defense to a charge of deception to say that the article furnished was as good or better than what the buyer thought he was getting, or that it saved him money because the article delivered was lower in price.

To use again the words of the Supreme Court: "Fair competition is not attained by balancing a gain in money against a misrepresentation of the thing supplied. The courts must set their faces against a conception of business standards so corrupting in its tendency. The consumer is prejudiced if upon giving an order for one thing, he is supplied with something else." (*Federal Trade Commission* v. *Algoma Lumber Co.*, 291 U. S. 67, 78.)

In the Standard Education case mentioned above, the Supreme Court also stated: "The best element of business has long since decided that honesty should govern competitive enterprises, and that the rule of *caveat emptor* [Let the Buyer Beware] should not be relied upon to reward fraud and deception."

The march toward the better day, however, has not yet reached the end of its journey of usefulness. There remains in our vast marketing structure areas in which much room for improvement exists, although the advance achieved in the past 70 years has been substantial.

Informative labeling laws leave many products untouched. As our industrial production becomes more scientific and technological, as discoveries of new materials and new uses and combinations of old materials are made, it becomes more pressing than ever that information essential to intelligent buying be made available to purchasers.

Progress on the basis of enlightened thought must continue if our sales policy is to maintain its upward trend toward the wholesome ultimate in which the buyer with full confidence and trust can make all his purchases on an informed basis of honest information and completely fair and aboveboard dealing. (*Henry Miller.*)

A Fraud by Any Other Name

"Fraud" and "deceit" are short and hard words even though we try to soften them to "sharp practice" or "irregular conduct." Somebody takes unfair advantage of somebody else, and intends to do it—perhaps as part of a calculated pattern of doing business. The victim suffers a loss, sometimes small, sometimes ruinous.

The marketing of farm goods may be a fertile field for sharp trading—witness the fact that the statutes of all of the States and the United States are liberally studded with provisions to discourage irregular marketing practices and to punish the malefactor by the imposition of fines, imprisonment, or even economic death in the form of revocation of license. In California, for instance, you can get a year in jail and a criminal fine of a thousand dollars for handling farm products as a commission merchant, dealer, buyer, broker, processor, or agent, without first obtaining a license and posting a bond.

One who holds a valid license as commission merchant, dealer, broker, processor, or agent can lose it or have it suspended for such offenses as nonpayment within the time set forth in the contract between the parties or for failure promptly to make proper and true accounting. Other offenses, upon proof of which a license is placed in jeopardy, are making false statements as to the condition and quality of farm produce received or in storage and intentionally making false statements as to marketing conditions.

A licensee may be called to account for such acts as making fraudulent charges or returns for the handling, sale, or storage of farm products, fictitious sales, or being guilty of collusion to defraud the producer. A commission merchant may not make a reconsignment and charge more than one commission for making the sale without the written consent of the consignor. A licensee may be disciplined for refusing to file a schedule of his charges for services in connection with produce handled on account of the shipper, or, in fact, for indulging in any unfair practice.

One of the most powerful provisions of the code regulating the marketing activities of wholesale handlers provides that a license may be revoked because the licensee has rejected, without reasonable cause, or has failed and refused to accept, without reasonable cause, any farm products bought or contracted to be bought from a producer. He must not fail to furnish or provide boxes or other containers, or hauling, harvesting, or any other service contracted to be done in connection with the handling of farm products bought or handled or contracted to be bought or handled. He must not use any other devices to avoid acceptance, or unreasonably to defer acceptance of farm products bought or handled, or contracted to be bought or handled. One provision states that the licensee may lose his license if he is found to be guilty of fraud, deceit, or willful negligence in any form. He may not fail to carry out any lawful contract with a producer, without reasonable cause.

The acts or omissions thus briefly stated from the pages of the California Agricultural Code illustrate the wide range of irregularities sought to be controlled or discouraged by special statutes in the several States.

The Committee of the National Association of Marketing Officials on Laws to Prevent Misrepresentation, at the Association's convention in 1952, recorded their findings and recommendations as follows:

"The NAMO recognizes the fact that there is no program more vital to agriculture as a whole than to maintain an alert, continuing, and effective crusade against misrepresentation in the marketing of agricultural products. Misrepresentation, generally speaking, costs producers and consumers untold millions yearly, not only from direct losses traceable to fraud and chicanery in their various forms, but in the necessary maintenance of Federal, State and local agencies whose duties are to discover, prevent and punish deceit, and to enforce laws conceived and enacted to discourage and eliminate unfair practices destructive to our economy.

"Misrepresentation is a vice appearing in many phases. A product or package is mislabeled as to the grade, size, weight, condition or even the contents, to the disgust and dismay of the consumer. Producers themselves will deliver 'stacked loads' to processors. Receivers in terminal markets misrepresent to the shipper the condition of a shipment on arrival, in the hopes of securing an unwarranted price adjustment. Buyers misrepresent the condition of the market, or the status of current price schedules. Packers place low-grade or even cull products in cans or other containers, and label or advertise these products as top-grade. Unscrupulous commission merchants make false returns. Unscrupulous weighmasters make false certificates of weight and measure."

The process of marketing is surrounded also with rigid requirements touching fruit, vegetables, and nuts, honey, livestock, and eggs, meat, and poultry products. Producers and consumers alike are protected by agencies engaged in testing the accuracy of weighing and measuring devices, and in discouraging such frauds as deceptive packing. Still other agencies inspect milk, meat, poultry, and canned or frozen foods and require them to be produced, processed, and delivered under sanitary conditions. The evasions made by some to avoid the sanitary and packing requirements have been characterized by the courts as fraud.

THE VARIOUS FRAUDS and deceits used by the fast traders are legion. Not all are practiced by the handler or receiver against the grower or shipper. The grower is not above reproach. In the unsavory lexicon of chicanery, the following instances are characteristic.

Grapefruit grown in the Coachella Valley in California bear the mark "Coachella" stamped on each fruit. The boxes bear a like legend. Inferior grapefruit produced in other parts of the State nevertheless have been stamped "Coachella." Inspectors followed the loads and noted their origin and destination. Court action and heavy fines put a stop to it.

In packing asparagus, growers have been known to pack large stalks on the outside because they make a better looking package and so bring more money. When these deceptive packs are intercepted, fines follow.

During the Second World War dealers bought oranges at 5.5 cents a pound on the trees. They found they could not make commission charges. Accordingly they packed 150 oranges in a box, but used the 176 size; the latter has a diameter of 2.84 inches, while the 150 size calls for a 3-inch diameter. All boxes were properly marked as to count, but the fruit did not average up to the required diameter. More than 17,000 boxes were rejected at one packinghouse.

The "stovepipe" method of packing, an old practice, is to put the smallest and defective potatoes in the center of the sack and the largest and best on the outside and top. Inspection by cutting the sack on one side or opening the top usually does not reveal the defective or undesirable potatoes.

Growers and packers of strawberries have persisted in placing the larger and better strawberries on the top or in the face of the basket and the little ones in the bottom. One grower, appearing in court for such a violation, pleaded that the big strawberries on the top did not hurt the little ones in the bottom!

A few years ago some growers and handlers of sweetpotatoes began to dye them to attain deeper color, to get higher prices, and also to cover some defects. Some of the dyes would dissolve in the water during preparation for the table. In a test case, the court sustained the law against deceptive dyeing and ordered the destruction of a large quantity of sweetpotatoes. Dye also has been applied to pale-colored red varieties of Irish potatoes to increase the red color, and in a few instances, but with little success, to white Irish potatoes to make them appear red.

Black varieties of juice grapes of lesser value than the Zinfandel variety have been labeled Zinfandel grapes and shipped to eastern markets. Prosecution of violators has discouraged the practice. In some eastern markets shipments of juice grapes in containers not labeled as to variety have been similarly mislabeled. In some instances proper variety markings have been obliterated upon arrival in eastern markets, and misstatements of variety placed upon the containers in order to enhance their value.

In the official inspection of canning tomatoes in California, where representative samples are taken from a load for the purpose of determining compliance with the law, it has been necessary to vary the positions from which the sample containers are taken from the load in order to discover the loads that have been stacked. Stacking a load is arranging the containers so that inspectors will take for their sample containers of tomatoes of better quality than those in the rest of the load. The same situation exists in reference to deliveries of many kinds of fruits and vegetables that stop for inspection at highway inspection stations.

In a prosecution for the sale of apples packed and wrapped in containers with misstatement as to count of the number of fruits, it was found that the dealer or his agent, upon filling an order for certain sizes of apples, merely removed the previous count markings, which apparently had been correct, and applied the count on the containers as specified in the order.

A shipment of eggs to a Government agency was found to contain a substantial percentage of inedible eggs. The shipment had been inspected before delivery and had been found to be satisfactory. It was proved that after inspection the eggs had been removed from the cases; the defective eggs had been substituted and delivered to the agency.

Many attempts have been made to avoid inspection in order to ship frozen oranges to markets. Because freezing damage is not visible from the outside appearance, some handlers have sold frozen oranges to dealers. At one packinghouse lookouts were posted to give a signal when an enforcement officer approached, whereupon the packed frozen oranges on hand were hidden quickly. Another time officers followed a load of frozen oranges that were delivered to a packinghouse, which apparently was closed. They discovered that supplemental packing equipment had been installed on the second floor of the building, and that frozen oranges were being packed there behind blackout curtains.

Another type of fast dealing was the false delivery of canning tomatoes to a cannery. Truckloads of tomatoes were received and inspected and presumably delivered to the cannery; a weight receipt, inspection certificate, and delivery receipt were filed in the cannery records. With the knowledge or instruction of an employee, the tomatoes were taken to the unloading platform but, instead of unloading, were taken away from the plant. After an interval, to let it seem like another load, the same tomatoes were again presented for inspection, weighing, and acceptance by the cannery.

An instance of sharp practice: A trucker is hauling baled hay from a grower's barn for delivery to a dairyman. The grower is not at home when the trucker loads the hay, but the instructions are for the trucker to have the hay weighed by a licensed public weighmaster. The trucker goes to the grower's barn and loads the truck with 110 bales of hay. The public weighmaster has already determined the tare weight of the truck, and when the trucker returns to the scale with his loaded truck, the public weighmaster determines the gross weight. The trucker tells the weighmaster that he has 100 bales on the load and that a note to that effect should be made on the weighmaster's certificate. The weighmaster makes the notation, subtracts the tare from the gross, and notes that the net weight is 13,750 pounds. On the way to the dairyman, the trucker stops at his home place and removes the top 10 bales. He continues to the dairyman, delivers the 100 bales, and presents the weighmaster's certificate, complete with license number, gross, tare, and net, properly signed—a certified count of 100 bales with a net weight of 13,750 pounds. The buyer counts 100 bales of hay after they have been stacked. He mails his check to the grower for 6.75 tons of hay.

The dairyman who bought the hay might wonder why his 6.75 tons did not last as long as he had planned, but it is possible that the trucker has been delivering hay to him for many years and the dairyman has become one of the trucker's regular customers for short-weight deliveries.

Another phase of sharp practice involves dealings between the buyer, or commission merchant, and the grower. The handler may take advantage of the fact that complete information generally is lacking regarding production and harvesting costs, particularly for perishable crops.

Until the crop has been harvested and the total amount obtained from the sale considered in relation to expenses of production and harvesting, one cannot determine the price per unit to be obtained in order to assure a profit on the season's operation. Therefore the producer tries to get the highest price offered for his produce, hoping to place himself in a favorable position in relation to his cost. He thereby becomes a target for the operator whose method is to offer more than the market justifies and who thus is often successful in securing the produce in competition with legitimate buyers. It is not until settlement time arrives that the producer realizes his mistake in seeking to obtain unrealistic prices.

The operator's method is to withhold a part of the purchase price, create a controversy with the producer over grade, quality, or size, and wear the producer down to accepting less than the amount due, in order to avoid a long delay or possible litigation. The deliberate adoption by the buyer of such a method is unethical, but his actions are not illegal in themselves. He thus gets farm products at reduced prices, and the producer has been placed in the position of finally accepting less than he might have received from a buyer who offered a legitimate price.

Another practice is that a buyer pays promptly for the first few loads of produce he receives but does not return to pay for the last load. There is the buyer whose checks are worthless and who makes them good only when he is caught. There are the buyers who, although unknown to the producer, can fast-talk the farmer out of a load of produce with nothing but promises to return and make payment.

Consider also the promoter who promises more than top prices to the producer if he will send his produce on consignment. The prices do not materialize, but substantial handling charges do, and the grower at the end ruefully regards an account of sales that shows only red ink as the reward for a season's work.

Safeguards against traders' attempts to profit from lack of knowledge on the part of the grower or shipper and against false claims for adjustments based on the alleged failure of the commodity to meet contract specifications are provided in the reports of prevailing prices, market conditions, demand, supply, carlot movements, track holdings, cold-storage holdings, and other related information collected and sent out by Federal and State market news and crop reporting services. Help also is given by shipping-point inspection service, which, at the request of the shipper, examines fruit and vegetables as they are being graded, packed, and loaded for shipment. It issues certificates describing in detail the quality, condition, grade, size, and pack. Its certificates are used largely as the basis of sales f. o. b. at shipping point, and are admissible as evidence in the courts.

Deceptive packaging is a fraud practiced against the consumer. In a carton that can hold 10 ounces of a food are placed only 8 ounces. Dried beef often is packed in glass jars. Usually they are properly filled; but it has been known to happen that a label, carefully placed to go completely around the jar, hides the contents so that the unscrupulous packer can avoid filling the jars entirely. The buyer could see the "slack fill" if he turns the jar upside down and strikes the bottom sharply with the palm of the hand. But that simple way to determine whether the jar is completely filled is not ordinarily practiced by the customer. Thousands of cases of a certain brand of dried beef were sold in California before the practice was discovered.

DESPITE FREQUENT WARNINGS, frauds are practiced with materials that are misrepresented as fertilizers. A case in point is the salesman who filled with sand secondhand sacks bearing the label of a well-known fertilizer manufacturer. He went from door to door in the best residential districts, selling the sand at a high price as a product of the reputable manufacturer. In the end he went to jail.

A group of peddlers selling peat as fertilizer once operated throughout the country. Peat helps improve the physical condition of poor soil, but it has comparatively little fertilizing value. It is mined from natural deposits and, where it occurs, is relatively cheap. The peddlers located various deposits. To gullible householders they sold it at the high price of 75 cents a basket, applied to a lawn. A purchaser who agreed to buy enough to cover his lawn got a bill for several hundred dollars, the peddlers insisting that more than a thousand baskets had been applied. Anyone could see that the truck could not have held that much peat, but the purchaser was threatened until he paid. Some of the purchasers consulted regulatory officials before paying, however. When warrants were issued for the peddlers, the racket was stopped.

Sometimes growers seem to insist on having the right to be cheated. A promoter developed a radio device which he said would kill pests at a distance, if a picture of the field to be treated was inserted in the device. When the farmers were warned that there was no evidence that such a device was of any value, they took up a collection and gave it to the promoter to help him continue his research. Later, when his tests did not succeed, they went to the district attorney and wanted their money back. The promoter by then had left the State.

A popular type of wholesale thievery is known as the pack-out method of handling fruit or vegetables. The buyer writes a tight contract, setting up extremely high grades, with small tolerances. He agrees to pay the grower on the basis of the weights of the finished product. The grower may deliver 600 pounds of cauliflower, in a regular field cart or container, to the freezing processor, and may be told later that his net pack-out was about 200 pounds or less of the specified grade. He has no way to trace this fraud—his cauliflower is weighed as it is received and before processing.

A confidence game is operated by the man who approaches a grower with a proposition to grow lily bulbs, for instance. After a glowing talk, the farmer can hardly wait to affix his signature to a contract whereby the supplier will furnish the planting stock at a suspiciously low price. The farmer, in consideration, will grow commercial bulbs from the stock thus furnished. The sales of the finished product will be handled by the supplier or promoter. The farmer is assured that from the proceeds he will pay for the stock he bought from the operator and have a tidy profit.

The farmer has failed to read a fine-print clause that gives the supplier a chattel mortgage on the stock of bulbs he supplies. At the end of the growing season he learns to his sorrow that he has not raised enough merchantable bulbs to pay off the amount due for those purchased at the start. He faces foreclosure and must pay, unless he can point out the fraud; even then he cannot recover the use of his land or the months of hard work. The fraud? The bulbs sold to the farmer were culls, worthless for commercial plantings. Substitute Shasta Daisies, ivy, or another plant for bulbs, but the answer is essentially the same: An inexperienced farmer is lured into a trap, where he finds himself in debt for the worthless commodity used as bait.

It has happened that the farmer has come back for more. He is told that "something must have gone wrong with the first venture, and that nothing can prevent the success of another crop." So he signs a new contract embracing the indebtedness of the old one and goes further into debt. He again plants his good acres with useless stock and does all the irrigating, cultivating, and harvesting. The crooked operator then handles whatever crop the grower may get, questionable as it may be, and retains all the proceeds of the sale for himself, because there is not enough to liquidate the purchase price of the bulbs, seeds, or plants with which the operator started. The balance still due on the contract gives the promoter the whip hand over the grower.

To this sorry record of fraud and deception there is no ready answer. But education may avert disaster: The intelligent grower, alerted to the tricks that may be played upon him, and aware of the aid provided by regulatory statutes, may evade the deadfalls and ambushes waiting for him on the dangerous trail leading from farm to market. (*C. J. Carey.*)

Some Rules for the Produce Business

The services of the commission merchant, broker, and dealer make it possible for a producer to concentrate on production.

Some problems have attended the increase in utilization of agents' services. They have had to do with the determination of an agent's reliability and responsibilities; setting up standard trade terms; provision for impartial determination of quality; verification and evaluation of an agent's accountings and actions; and providing for handling contracts and disputes.

At first, some undesirable individuals were attracted to the produce business because large amounts of credit could be obtained and profits could be made quickly. The buyer, seller, and agent were usually far apart, and the absence of regulations made it hard to check the statements of a dishonest operator. If a dispute arose regarding the quality of merchandise, the shipper had difficulty in proving that the goods met contract specifications. If legal action became necessary, the shipper would have to sue in the receiver's State. Early State laws pertained mostly to movement of goods within States but did not regulate commodities in interstate commerce.

At the turn of the century, commission merchants, dealers, brokers, and producers were greatly concerned over the loose manner in which the business was being conducted. Honest dealers found it difficult to carry on their business in competition with the minority of dishonest operators. One result was the formation of trade associations, which served to identify and evaluate the operation of members.

Shortly before the First World War, interest developed in the possibility of Federal legislation to regulate the marketing of fresh fruit and vegetables. Preliminary studies to that end were conducted by the Department of Agriculture and representatives of growers, shippers, and receivers. A report was issued in 1917 by a joint council of trade associations concerning bills before the Congress designed to make certain practices unlawful and to authorize the Secretary of Agriculture to take steps to facilitate distribution, to license handlers, and to prescribe regulations governing the conduct of the business.

In the First World War, the United States Food Administration formulated regulations requiring the licensing of all handlers of fresh fruit, vegetables, and certain other products and prescribing rules to be followed. The regulations became effective November 1, 1917.

Conferences were held in 1921 by the Department of Commerce and the Department of Agriculture with representatives of the various trade associations. The result was the adoption of rules for the conduct of the produce business—including such matters as the correct form of records, the facts that would be shown on accounts sales, and the enrollment of persons, firms, and associations which would agree to be bound by the rules.

To bring about a further standardization of trading practices, the Department of Agriculture in 1925 developed a plan of voluntary registration and arbitration of disputes. The plan proposed that the Department would enter into cooperative agreements with handlers of fresh fruit and vegetables in wholesale quantities, whereby they agreed to be governed by the standard trading rules, to keep adequate records, to allow examination of the records, and to settle disputes by arbitration. By November 11, 1926, agreements had been signed by 788 persons, who handled more than half a million cars of produce a year. The plan was abandoned, however, when the Produce Agency Act was passed in 1927.

That act makes it a misdemeanor, punishable by fine or imprisonment, or both, for any person who receives fruit, vegetables, dairy or poultry products, or other perishable products to be sold for somebody else to make fraudulent accounting or false or misleading statements, with an intent to defraud, or to dump produce without good cause.

As the act applied only to the handling and disposition of products received in interstate trade for sale on consignment, some persons believed that further regulatory measures should be enacted to apply to all types of contracts involving the purchase, sale, and consignment of fruit and vegetables.

After several years of study by members of the industry and legislators, the Perishable Agricultural Commodities Act became law in 1930. It was designed to suppress unfair and fraudulent practices and to promote more orderly marketing of perishable agricultural commodities in interstate and foreign commerce. It applies to all persons doing business as commission merchants, dealers, or brokers who handle fresh or frozen fruit or vegetables in interstate or foreign commerce, except if the commodity is of the individual's own raising or purchased in small quantities solely for sale at retail. They must hold a license issued by the Department of Agriculture or be subject to fines. License fees of 15 dollars a year are deposited in a special fund and used to defray the expense of administering this act, the Produce Agency Act, and the Export Apple and Pear Act.

The Perishable Agricultural Commodities Act prohibits such unfair practices as rejection without reasonable cause (goods might otherwise be rejected if prices are falling fast); failure to deliver without reasonable cause; making false and misleading statements (for example, untrue statements made to induce a person to make a contract he would not make if he knew the true details); making incorrect accountings on consignments; failure to pay promptly for commodities purchased or received on consignment; misrepresenting the grade, the quality, condition, or State or country of origin; and altering Federal inspection certificates.

Persons and firms licensed under the act are required to keep for 2 years accounts and records that will adequately disclose all transactions involved in the business.

Any person who has reason to believe that the act has been violated may file a complaint with the Department. Appropriate investigation is made. If deemed necessary, an audit of the books and records of the party complained against is made by an agent authorized by the Secretary.

If a violation of the act is found, the person is informed and given opportunity to make settlement. In recent years, more than 2,500 complaint cases have been filed each year. About 90 percent of them have been settled informally. More than 1 million dollars each year has been recovered for the complaining parties.

If the investigation shows a probable violation of the act and the party complained against refuses to settle, a formal complaint is accepted from the complaining party. A copy of the formal complaint and a copy of the report of investigation made by the Department are served on the party complained against. He is given 20 days in which to settle or file an answer. If settlement is not made, the case is then referred to the Solicitor of the Department for legal action.

An order issued later by the judicial officer may dismiss the proceeding for lack of proof or other causes or may award reparation to the complaining party. If the party against whom reparation is awarded does not pay the award, or file an appeal with a United States District Court, within 30 days from the date of the order, his license becomes suspended by operation of law and it is illegal for him to operate as a commission merchant, dealer, or broker in fruit and vegetables. The Department is prohibited from issuing a license to any person who has failed to pay a reparation award issued against him within 2 years of the date of the application for license.

Disciplinary proceedings are authorized in the act. They are instituted by the Secretary of Agriculture or persons to whom he delegates authority.

Following requests by a majority of members of the fruit and vegetable industry for speedy disposition of bona fide disputes, the Department has undertaken informal arbitration of controversies. After all parties have signified in writing their willingness to arbitrate a complaint filed under the act and after facts and evidence have been submitted, the Department's staff in Washington studies and evaluates the facts and reaches a decision, which is accepted as final by the parties to the complaint. The entire matter is settled quickly and inexpensively and without publicity or lengthy litigation.

An average of 2,335 cases a year have been handled since 1930. More than half of the complaints alleged failure to account and pay. About a fourth alleged rejection without reasonable cause or failure to deliver.

Trade terms and definitions were promulgated, as provided in the act, and are used as a basis for making contracts for purchase and sale of perishable farm goods. The United States Standards established by the Department for fruit and vegetables are also widely used as a basis of trading.

Eight amendments have been made to the original act. The latest authorized an increase in the license fee from 10 dollars to 15 dollars a year. The others were designed to strengthen the position of the honest dealer.

The act has afforded protection to the grower, shipper, commission merchant, broker, and dealer. It has reduced the number of arguments, minimized risk, prevented losses, and lowered marketing costs. (*Ted C. Curry.*)

Agents and Buyers

A common cause of disputes is the seller's misunderstanding of the status of the agents or buyers with whom he is dealing.

A producer who ships his products to a distant point should first make sure whether the party with whom he is negotiating is representing him as his selling agent or is merely a buyer bargaining with him for the purchase of his product.

The legal obligations of anyone who holds himself out to act as selling agent for producers differ considerably from those the law imposes on one who is dealing with a producer on a buyer-seller basis.

A producer has a right to expect expert selling services from his agent, the assessment of no more than reasonable charges, complete and accurate accountings as to all details of the transactions handled by the agent for the producer's account, and the agent's loyalty throughout the entire period the principal-agent relationship exists.

A producer who gets in touch with a buyer to offer his products for sale should recognize that the buyer owes him no agency responsibility and that it is up to the producer to protect his own interests in the trading that ensues. The producer has a right to expect, of course, that the buyer will not pose as an agent, or, in bargaining, will not engage in other deceptive or unfair practices.

Regardless of whether a producer ships to an agent, or deals with a buyer, before he completely relinquishes control of his product he should assure himself that he is going to receive payment for it. Agents and buyers in some industries are required by regulatory acts to provide bonds to assure they will meet their financial obligations. Others, though not providing bonds, are subject to disciplinary actions if they fail to make prompt settlement with principals or sellers.

Several regulatory acts, administered by the Department of Agriculture, are designed to establish reasonable codes of conduct. Among them are the Packers and Stockyards Act, the Perishable Agricultural Commodities Act, the Produce Agency Act, the Standard Containers Acts, the Federal Insecticide, Fungicide, and Rodenticide Act, the Tobacco Stocks and Standards Act, Federal Seed Act, United States Grain Standards Act, Cotton Standards Act, Naval Stores Act, Tobacco Inspection Act, Export Apple and Pear Act, United States Warehouse Act, and the Cotton Futures Act.

The Packers and Stockyards Act was enacted in 1921. Extensive congressional investigations had shown that the large meatpackers owned dominant interests in major stockyards and thereby exercised considerable control over the market agencies to which producers consigned their livestock. Charges were made at congressional hearings that the packers assessed unreasonable marketing charges against patrons of public markets, discriminated between them in the furnishing of stockyard facilities and services, attempted to influence the movement of livestock to market, tried to control the prices received by producers for their livestock, and engaged in other unfair and monopolistic practices.

The passage of the act signaled the end of a long fight by livestock producers' organizations to obtain, through Federal legislation, an effective means of regulating in the public interest the practices of meatpackers engaged in interstate operations and the marketing of livestock through public stockyards.

Soon after the act was passed, market agencies and dealers at public stockyards challenged its constitutionality as it applied to their operations. In a test case (*Stafford* v. *Wallace*), the Supreme Court held that all livestock being handled at markets meeting the definition of a "stockyard," as given in section 302 (a) of title III of the act, is in the current or flow of interstate commerce and, therefore, market agencies and dealers operating at such markets are subject to Federal regulation.

The act and regulations issued under its authority provide, in effect,

that the services and facilities furnished consignors of livestock to public stockyards shall be adequate,

that the yardage, commission, feed, and other charges assessed by stockyard companies and market agencies shall be reasonable and applied on a nondiscriminatory basis,

that all livestock consigned to public markets shall be offered on the open market and sold under competitive bidding conditions,

that the weighing of such livestock shall be accurate,

that full and correct accountings shall be furnished consignors and buyers of livestock for whom the market agencies act as selling or buying agents,

that meatpackers shall not engage in any act for the purpose of manipulating or controlling livestock prices or the movement of livestock or meats and meat food products in commerce,

and that stockyard companies, market agencies, dealers, and packers subject to the provisions of the act shall not engage in unfair, deceptive, unjustly discriminatory, or monopolistic practices.

A small staff of specialists in Washington directs enforcement of the act as to rates, trade practices, and scales and weighing.

General market supervision and day-to-day supervision is carried out by field forces stationed at 20 major livestock markets.

A marketing specialist, known as the district supervisor, is in charge of each field office and directs enforcement of the act in a district, which may include one State or several States.

Members of the district supervisory forces observe daily operations in the stockyards to ascertain the adequacy of their facilities and the yarding and selling services and to take whatever corrective action is needed. They investigate complaints of irregularities and obtain evidence of violations of the act. If the Secretary finds, after affording a market agency or dealer an opportunity for hearing, that such registrant has violated the act, he may issue a cease and desist order or, if serious violations are involved, he may suspend the registration for a reasonable time.

Outlying markets in the districts and plants of packers subject to the act are visited periodically by marketing specialists and, as conditions require, by scale technicians, accountants, and other specialists. Accountants are stationed at those field offices where the auditing work is heaviest. A staff of three service and facility engineers and a scale specialist are stationed at Kansas City.

A stockyard, to be subject to the provisions of the act, must have an area of 20,000 square feet or more (exclusive of alleys) normally available for handling livestock, must be operated for compensation as a public market, and must be engaged in handling interstate shipments of livestock. At such yards notices are posted to inform operators and the public that they are subject to the act. They are commonly known thereafter as "posted stockyards." Of the 322 stockyards that in 1954 were posted, 66 were terminal markets and 256 were livestock auction markets. At terminal markets, market agency salesmen sell livestock received from producers on a consignment basis through direct negotiations with buyers. Livestock consigned to auction markets is offered to buyers in sales rings and sold by auction methods.

All market agencies and dealers engaged in business at posted markets must register with the Secretary of Agriculture. Market agencies are individuals or firms that offer selling, buying, or other services to the public on an agency basis. They are commonly known as commission firms. Dealers are individuals or firms that buy and sell livestock for their own accounts or for the account of others on other than a commission basis. Dealers are also known as "traders" and "speculators." Registered to operate at markets posted under the act in 1954 were 2,300 market agencies and 2,700 dealers.

The act at first did not authorize the Secretary to require bonds from commission firms or dealers to assure performance of their financial obligations, but from 1924 to 1943 the authority to require such bonds was given to the Secretary in riders to the annual appropriation bills. In 1944 it was covered in permanent legislation.

Market agencies and dealers registered under the act were bonded in 1954 in amounts totaling 46 million dollars. Furthermore, the accountants make periodic audits of their records to assure that the firms remain solvent and that the market agencies handle proceeds of sales of producers' livestock properly. Such safeguards have undoubtedly had a stabilizing influence on the livestock marketing industry. In some years patrons of certain nonposted auction markets have suffered losses because such markets became insolvent, but producers consigning livestock to posted markets have suffered practically no losses through defaults of registered commission firms, who handle annually billions of dollars of producers' proceeds of sales.

The market agencies at some markets have taken joint action to require packers with uncertain credit standing to furnish bonds in an amount sufficient to cover their livestock purchases. Although agencies at several markets have incurred losses through failure of packers to pay for livestock purchased, these losses have been covered by the market agency and dealer bonds or have been absorbed by the market interests instead of being passed on to livestock producer-patrons.

An important provision of the act is the one that places in the Secretary responsibility for determining the reasonableness of yardage and commission charges. Livestock producers and other patrons of the posted stockyards pay to the livestock marketing industry in yardage, commissions, feed, and other charges more than 70 million dollars annually.

Labor costs are the chief operating expenses incurred by both stockyard companies and commission firms.

Stockyard companies and commission firms, which have had to meet large increases in wages and costs of construction, repair, equipment, and supplies, have requested approval of increases in their rates. In general, increases in yardage and commission rates have been restricted to levels that have offset approximately the additional costs.

Marketing costs at posted markets vary, but yardage charges for cattle at posted stockyards average about 80 cents a head and selling commissions for cattle average about $1.10 a head, or a total cost of about $1.90, exclusive of feed. Comparable charges for calves, hogs, and sheep are 95, 70, and 45 cents, respectively.

Feed at most posted terminal markets is furnished at inventory cost, plus reasonable margins to cover the handling, storage, and delivery.

To encourage needed improvements in stockyard facilities and services and to effect reductions in marketing costs through elimination of inefficient operating methods and obsolete construction and equipment, marketing specialists and engineers were assigned to study the facilities and services furnished by each yard company. Since 1947 supervised stockyards have spent millions of dollars in modernizing and improving their facilities so as to give better service to patrons. The studies made and the official position taken that no increase in yardage rates will be approved while inadequacies in facilities and services exist contributed to the improvements.

In measuring the effectiveness of the job done by market agencies—commission firms—in selling livestock for producer-shippers, the following standards have been applied: To what extent do the market agencies stimulate and obtain active competition in bidding by buyers on all consigned livestock? Are they providing expert salesmanship in disposing of such livestock to buyers? Are they furnishing their principals—livestock producers—with full and accurate accountings of all sales made for their accounts? Are they maintaining complete loyalty to the shipper throughout the entire period the principal-agent relationship exists?

A few years ago a Federal statutory court, hearing an appeal from an order issued by the Secretary against a market agency, supported the addition of a fourth element to this yardstick. The court stated: "A marketing agency should maintain a position at all times which would assure absolute loyalty to its shippers. No interest should be allowed to interfere between the agent and his principal." Before approving proposed increases in the rates of market agencies, commitments are required from the agencies that existing inadequacies in their selling and buying services will be remedied promptly.

Stockyard scales are key facilities and must be installed, maintained, and operated so as to assure accurate weights. Scale technicians supervise the installation, maintenance, and operation of the 800 scales in use in weighing the livestock at the markets posted under the act. The 1,200 additional scales used by packers subject to the act in their direct purchases at their plants or buying stations are also required to be tested and inspected periodically. The accuracy requirements for livestock scales are more strict than those prevailing in any other field of industrial or commercial weighing on large capacity scales. Stockyard managements are required to select men of integrity to perform the important functions of weighing, and the managements are assisted in the proper training of weighers. When conditions warrant investigations are conducted of weighing operations at posted stockyards and at buying stations operated by packers subject to the act to assure accurate weights to livestock producers.

All livestock consigned for sale must be offered on the open market and sold at the highest bid obtainable. Turn systems in bidding, speculation in consigned livestock by market agency personnel, consistent selling of consigned livestock to one dealer or packer, and other methods of selling that tend to restrict competitive trading are prohibited and action taken to prevent their recurrence when discovered.

Packers subject to the provisions of title II of the act are mainly those who buy livestock in interstate commerce for purposes of slaughter or manufacture meats or meat food products for sale or shipment in interstate commerce. More than 1,900 packers were subject to the provisions of the act in 1954.

In administering the packer provisions of the act the most emphasis has been placed on eliminating from buying by packers at public markets, and at other points, any practices that are unfair or have the effect of limiting or restricting competition in bidding between buyers.

Many investigations have been conducted of alleged unfair or deceptive practices in the pricing, distribution, and sale of packers' products. Whenever information has been obtained indicating that a packer has engaged in a monopolistic, unfair, unjustly discriminatory, or deceptive practice in the labeling, advertising, distribution, pricing, or sale of his product, prompt investigations have been made and appropriate informal or formal corrective proceedings have been initiated.

If the Secretary of Agriculture finds that a packer has violated the act, he is required to issue an order directing the packer to cease and desist from engaging in the practices found to be objectionable. Failure to comply with such an order makes the packer liable to prosecution and possible fines and imprisonment.

Any person who complains he has been injured by violations of specified provisions of the act by stockyard companies, market agencies, and dealers may (under sections 308 and 309 of title III) file a reparation claim with the Secretary of Agriculture. The Secretary, after having given the parties opportunity for hearing, may issue an order awarding reparation to the injured person. The act does not authorize the Secretary to entertain claims for reparation against packers.

In 1926 the act was amended (proviso in section 304, title III) to authorize the Secretary to register as a market agency a duly authorized State department or agency that does the weighing of livestock at a stockyard. Such registration can be revoked if the State agency fails to comply with the Secretary's orders under the act.

After investigations had disclosed that live poultry marketing in some large cities was burdened with exorbitant charges and bad practices, the act was amended in 1935 by the addition of title V to authorize the Secretary to regulate the marketing of live poultry in certain large cities where practices detrimental to the interests of producers exist and the volume of poultry handled is large enough to warrant Federal supervision. Commission merchants, dealers, and other handlers of live poultry in designated cities have to be licensed. The rates and charges of licensees are subject to approval of the Secretary, and their trade practices must conform to the standards set out in sections 307 and 312 of title III of the act. Scales used there must be tested periodically and be operated in accordance with instructions. The Secretary may suspend or revoke poultry licenses for serious violations.

In 1942 the act was amended (section 317 of title III) to permit the Secretary to authorize an approved livestock association or State agency to conduct inspections at posted markets of brands, marks, and other identifying characteristics of livestock originating in or shipped to market from the State receiving the authorization and to assess reasonable fees for such services. The purpose of the amendment is to assure that livestock moving through stockyards posted under the act is not burdened with duplicate brand inspections and fees. Authorizations have been issued to livestock associations or State agencies in Idaho, Oregon, Nebraska, North Dakota, Montana, Oklahoma, South Dakota, Texas, Utah, Washington, and Wyoming.

Section 407 of title IV of the act authorizes the Secretary to make whatever rules, regulations, and orders are needed to carry out the provisions of the act. The regulations in effect in early 1954 were promulgated in 1943. Changes in the regulations to reflect new conditions and practices were proposed and discussed by groups from industry and producers over the years. In 1952 notice was given to the public, through the Federal Register, of recommended changes. Thereupon public hearings were conducted at nine places to give interested persons opportunity to state their views. Proposals for amending the regulations were prepared and published in the Federal Register with a view to promulgating new regulations in 1954. (*M. J. Cook.*)

So As Not To Spoil the Market

Forty-five States have fair-trade legislation on their books. Missouri, Texas, Vermont, and the District of Columbia have none.

In 24 States any seller can specify the minimum resale price of his products. In 21 States only the owner of a trade-mark or brand name or his authorized distributor may do so.

Usually a contract with a single dealer is enough to bind all resellers even if they have not signed, provided the seller affixes a notice of resale prices to the original price lists, sales contracts, or invoices.

Such fair-trade agreements applied at first only to commerce within a State. But the Miller-Tydings Act in

1937 exempted resale price agreements affecting interstate commerce from the Federal antitrust laws when agreements of that description are lawful as applied to intrastate transactions under the applicable State law or policy. To qualify for such exemption, the product has to carry the trade-mark, brand, or name of the producer or distributor. It must compete freely and openly with similar items made or distributed by others. It may only be fair-traded vertically, not horizontally—that is, a seller may set resale prices for his own outlets and for their customers, but not for fellow manufacturers or sellers. No reseller may undercut the established minimum, except when the product is below specifications, or is sold under court order, or is damaged, or is being closed out.

The history of fair-trade legislation goes back to the price and trade practice codes of medieval merchant guilds. Businessmen have traditionally exerted pressure upon each other "not to spoil the market." Nearly two centuries ago Adam Smith discussed at length in his *Wealth of Nations* the drive of merchants and manufacturers to restrain rigorous competition and to raise prices, "even on occasions of merriment."

When a farmer brings his crops to market and is paid, his main worry about prices is over. Not so the manufacturer selling a commodity bearing his brand, trade-mark, or other identification. He still has a property right in his product. He may have spent large sums persuading the public that his brand stands for dependable quality at a stable price. Resellers offering the item at varying, or special, or "loss-leader" prices cause consumers to doubt its genuine origin or quality and also deprive the manufacturer of sales outlets that are unable or unwilling to handle it at cut rates.

To safeguard his property rights, the manufacturer first stipulated terms and conditions of resale in his sales contracts. But in 1911 the Supreme Court in the case of *Miles Medical Co.* v. *Park & Sons Co.* declared resale price agreements in violation of the antitrust laws. Other measures were tried, such as refusing to sell to price-cutting distributors, setting up exclusive representatives, licensing, and financing retail inventories. The only way out seemed to be legislation.

THE SUPPORTERS of fair trade, especially retailers' associations, maintain that resale-price maintenance helps to keep the small, independent, local retailer in business. A uniform price prevents large department and chain operators, who can afford "loss-leader" sales, from driving their smaller rivals out of business, merely because of length of purse. The large distributors have their private labels on which they can police any price setup they please. Without "fair trade" they would cut prices only on products that are also handled by their smaller rivals whose volume may be too small to warrant a private brand.

Resale-price maintenance, say the manufacturers, makes it unnecessary for us to enter the retail field and supplant small business: Our responsibility for the product does not end at the factory door. We frequently keep up consumer demand, if, indeed, we do not create it, by our expenditures for research, development, and national advertising. Throughout the life of the product we often provide refills, spare parts, and technical servicing. We have a perpetual stake in the quality, reputation, and performance of our product. To get and keep distributive outlets that will push it requires stable prices and dependable profit margins.

Uniform, well-publicized resale prices put all competition on an even footing. The one-price-to-all practice economizes time of consumers and retailers, lowers distributing costs, and eliminates price cutting.

Furthermore, as former Senator Tydings, co-author of the Miller-Tydings Act, pointed out, there must be "free and open competition" before the right of resale-price maintenance is available. It is similar, he argued, to the collective and cooperative right that farmers exercise through their produce and milk associations. The producer-farmer makes contracts with processors and distributors, stating the prices of tomatoes, milk, and numerous other agricultural products. The large, integrated concerns, such as the manufacturers of automobiles, electrical appliances, or agricultural implements, are able by agency, consignment, or in their own stores to announce and maintain the resale prices of their products. Federal and State fair-trade enabling acts merely permit independent manufacturers, wholesalers, and retailers to do the same.

THE OPPONENTS of resale-price maintenance insist that it is a cartel device: What the retailers collectively cannot do by agreement among themselves, one of their number achieves by contract with a manufacturer. Though the latter may possess no knowledge of retail costs, he sets up a system of administered prices controlling all distributors of his product without the investment of a single dollar or the assumption of any distributive financial risk. The retailer, on the other hand, though he have clear title to the goods, is deprived of the elemental right to use his business judgment to price his property according to his particular market opportunities and operating economies.

Resale-price maintenance, the opponents say, removes the keystone of the American competitive enterprise system. How else than by sovereign choice of consumer buyers will those producers succeed most who give the best and most for the money? When prices are identical, the consumer cannot test, shop around, and choose. The price is the same for each store, irrespective of its location, size, equipment, or lines of merchandise; no matter what may be the wage differentials, the service, or customer. The consumer gets no benefit from new techniques or mass distribution at lower margins. Competition is transferred from attractive pricing to services that the consumer may not want, advertising, extravagant showrooms, and display facilities. Incentive markups sufficient to induce retail "pushing" result in prices that limit buying power and living standards. With high prices come the twin evils: Low volume and mass unemployment. Without the governor of consumer sovereignty, the competitive system fails to weed out the inefficient and to reward those who serve it best.

Maintenance of resale prices not only eliminates the price competition among retailers in price-maintained goods. It makes easy the private policing of horizontal agreements (open or tacit) among manufacturers, especially when three or four can command one-half of the market or more. Each need find but one distributor. The nonsigning distributors have no choice. They cannot appeal to courts, should an uneconomically high price drive customers away. They become the victims of a system of private law that gives them no recourse to public justice.

THE EVIDENCE is that fair-trade legislation raises and stabilizes resale prices. Ewald T. Grether documented this finding in 1939 in his volume, *Price Control under Fair Trade Legislation.*

It was corroborated by a number of other surveys, including one, *Fair Trade*, by Edgar H. Gault, of the School of Business Administration of the University of Michigan, who concluded: "There can be no doubt that consumers in Michigan who formerly purchased drug products at cut prices are paying from 15 percent to 30 percent more for price-controlled items under Fair Trade. Michigan's present minimum Fair Trade prices are higher than the competitive prices for the same items in the State of Missouri where there is no Fair Trade."

The Federal Trade Commission issued a report, *Report on Resale Price Maintenance*, in 1945 after a long investigation. Although some of the outlying independent credit-and-delivery stores may lower prices slightly, it said, large-volume, cash-and-carry mass distributors in densely populated areas had to raise their prices 15 to 30 percent. Such differences have persisted for over a decade between free-trade Missouri on one side of the Mississippi and fair-trade Illinois on the other, and between the District of Columbia and Maryland.

The opponents of resale-price maintenance—department stores, large farm, consumer, and labor organizations, and many economists—agree that the independent distributor needs protection against "loss-leader" selling and predatory price cutting. But the way to cope with that practice, they contend, is through enforcement of the Federal Trade Commission Act (which prohibits such "freezing out" tactics), through the Robinson-Patman Act prohibitions against discriminatory prices destructive of competition, through individual manufacturer-distributor contracts, and through civil suit for damages where trade-marks or brands have been injured—not by fair-trade legislation that coerces nonsigners.

THE SCOPE of fair trading is small. It is most important in the drug trade, but it has spread to liquor, books, cigars, jewelry, sporting goods, small garden tools, kitchenware, cooking utensils, and some electrical appliances. In 1948 the manufacturers belonging to the American Fair Trade Council estimated that fair-trade legislation affected about 4 percent of the retail trade in the United States.

Little use of resale-price maintenance is made in the grocery trade. Farmer's crops, including most fruits and vegetables, are usually not branded or trade-marked. Food processors and distributors market hundreds of brands, but each is reluctant to place his product under resale-price contract unless the rest do at equal or competitive prices. Because prices of processed food usually fluctuate with the prices of raw materials, no fixed-price line is firmly placed in consumer thinking.

Thus only such products as soap, canned milk, flour and cereal products, and vegetable shortenings are fair-traded to any appreciable extent.

Except for the processed foods just named, cigars, and alcoholic beverages, the produce of the farmer does not reach the consumer as a fair-traded item. With little to gain and much to lose as purchasers, farmers and their organizations have consistently opposed fair-trade legislation. Moreover, quick, effective distribution makes imperative a free competitive market with varying prices flexibly adjusting the amounts offered and sold. (*Theodore J. Kreps.*)

Barriers to Trade Between States

A trade barrier is any artificial restriction on the purchase, the sale, or movement of goods or services.

Interstate trade barriers are any State laws or administrative regulations that unreasonably discriminate, directly or indirectly, against the sale or importation for sale of goods produced in another State. They are designed to improve the competitive position of producers in one State over producers in another State. They attempt to do so generally by directly or indirectly limiting the volume of goods that may be imported, thereby maintaining or increasing the prices on the available supplies.

The Thirteen Original States granted to the Federal Government the power to regulate foreign and domestic commerce only when they were faced with a virtual economic paralysis. Trade wars that developed after the American Revolution so disrupted commerce between the States that something was necessary to avoid economic self-destruction. So the Thirteen States granted to the Federal Government in the United States Constitution the power to regulate foreign and domestic commerce (art. I, sec. 8, par. 3) and agreed to a limitation of their own powers by accepting the provision that "no State shall, without the consent of the Congress, lay any imposts or duties on imports or exports except what may be absolutely necessary for executing its inspection laws . . ." (art. I, sec. 10, par. 2).

The transition period between 1787 and 1825 was not easy. Growing industries sought protection for their home markets, and only through the interpretations by the Supreme Court of the commerce clause of the Constitution was the basis built for removing the problem of State trade barriers from the area of controversy. A fairly active foreign trade, a rapid expansion of the national boundaries toward the Pacific Ocean, the relative freedom from unemployment, and later the Civil and the Spanish-American Wars pushed into the background the notion that internal trade restrictions were a necessary part of our economic institutions. On the other hand, the issue of free foreign trade versus protectionism assumed major importance in the political and economic thinking of people. The impact of import tariffs was felt mainly on the manufactured goods that competed directly with growing American industries. The idea of protecting the American market for American manufacturers spread rapidly as our industries grew, became more specialized, hired more workers, and sought larger markets at home and abroad in order to get the advantages of large-scale production.

An expanding market for manufactured goods and farm products has existed in the United States since the formation of the Republic. The increased productivity of the American manufacturers, farmers, and laborers found an outlet largely among the people within our national boundaries. The population rose from about 5.3 million in 1800 to more than 160 million in 1954. The fact that the United States was a relatively free trade area afforded to American industry and agriculture opportunities to take full advantage of specialization in the use of labor, land, and area resources. At the same time, the productivity of our economy enabled the American people to improve their plane of living.

Farmers turned more and more to our domestic market as foreign trade declined after the First World War. With sizable farm surpluses built up as a result of a decline in European market demand, farm prices dropped rapidly in 1921. The economic adjustments faced by farmers were severe. In an effort to protect themselves against further price declines and loss of markets, organized farmers sought and got higher tariffs. They sought but were denied further relief during the 1920's through two-price plans like the McNary-Haugen bill, only to get temporary consolation in the high tariffs of the Smoot-Hawley Act. Our farmers soon learned that import tariffs of the ordinary type gave little economic relief for those producers who were dependent on foreign markets to absorb their domestic surpluses. The virtual collapse of all prices in all countries between 1929 and 1935 brought to the forefront every conceivable scheme to raise the farm prices, eliminate foreign competition, and prevent new products from being placed on the market in competition with established farm goods.

The germ of the protectionist idea of keeping domestic markets for domestic farmers spread rapidly after the First World War as foreign trade in food and fibers became less important. From that point it was not difficult to proceed with further tests of the theory that a protected market is the surest market. Therefore the development of barriers to protect agriculture and other industries within a State from trade from neighboring States by setting up impediments to the free flow of trade came in natural order. Similar types of restrictions also were imposed by some municipalities that guarded zealously their rights to do business within their boundaries.

The regulation of trade is a basic function of Government. Uniform laws and regulations prescribing the conditions under which trade can be carried on legally may be helpful to traders and may encourage trade development. Our entire system of laws relating to contracts, negotiable instruments, bailment, and conditions for the transfer of title to real and personal property are designed to stimulate trade by having the same uniform system of rules for all persons. This concept of encouraging trade through uniform laws and regulations designed to protect sellers and buyers was carried over into other areas. States and the Federal Government encouraged the development of uniform standards and grades for farm products to remove the need for inspection by the buyer before purchase. Most of the laws regulating trade are of the facilitating type. The regulatory function, however, also has been used widely for restrictive purposes.

Several arguments are offered on behalf of interstate trade barriers.

Foremost is the desire of a State to stimulate the agriculture and industry within its borders. Such a policy assures its tax base by protecting property rights and insuring employment to its citizens. This concept is tied closely to the theory that the States must maintain a balanced economy and that competition that damages home industries may be particularly damaging to a State's economy. The pace of technological changes in production, processing, and marketing techniques often forces a delay in market shifts and practices to afford time for adjustments. Furthermore, the competitive pricing and merchandising practices of large-scale, low-cost, out-of-State industries conceivably could destroy a small business without leaving any lasting advantage to the local citizenry.

A second argument is that permanent supplies of basic commodities, such as fresh milk, must be assured. Because the public has accepted the idea that a clean, pure milk supply is a prerequisite to the health of growing children, special inducements are offered to in-State dairymen to maintain that supply.

Another argument is that unemployment resulting from competition from out-of-State producers is economically and socially undesirable. Workers dislike and resist pressures to move from one occupation to another and from one area to another.

J. S. Hillman and J. D. Rowell in a monograph, *A Summary of Laws Relating to the Interstate Movement of Agricultural Products in the Eleven Western States* (University of Arizona Agricultural Experiment Station, Tucson, Report No. 109, May 1952), considered the question of the economic justification of trade barriers and concluded: "State legislative intervention into the marketing picture does not necessarily signify poor economic judgment. The actions in some State and municipal councils may well be taken to measure, counterbalance, or defeat trade practices which, if left unchecked, could have adverse effects on the marketing process and conditions of enterprise. Consequently, care must always be taken to differentiate measures which are necessary to protect the health, safety, and morals of the public from those measures which use governmental sanction to protect entrepreneural inefficiency, to prevent growth through innovation, and which favor other undesirable monopolistic practices. This, of course, is no easy task. Often it is found that there is no precise line separating the two, and that a particular public decree must be weighed in the balances of a large composite of social value considerations."

Discriminatory laws and regulations occur in a number of forms, but the major abuses occur in the use of the powers of States to tax, inspect and quarantine, regulate public safety and morals, and protect their proprietary interests.

In the absence of specific regulation by the Congress relating to the movement of products and services in interstate commerce, States have used their residual tax and police powers to control trade as they have seen fit. It is worth noting, however, that Congress generally has been upheld in its attempts to regulate interstate commerce when it has chosen to do so.

Trade barriers frequently are administrative rules and regulations. Under the Constitution, the States retained broad powers that enabled them to take whatever measures are necessary to tax and to protect the health, safety, and property of their citizens. Authorities of the various subdivisions of States are granted some similar rights within their boundaries.

State legislatures, generally speaking, delegate their authority to administrative branches, which, in turn, promulgate the rules and regulations to accomplish the objectives of the legislatures. That procedure is nearly always followed on matters that relate to public health and sanitation. Municipal ordinances, however, are issued in a most detailed manner. In any event, it is necessary to grant wide discretionary powers to enforcement officials, who can use their authority in a manner to interfere seriously with normal trade procedures. An understanding of trade barriers and their impact on the trade among the States and within State boundaries can be gained only through a study of State and municipal laws and administrative rules and regulations relating thereto.

THE POWER TO LEVY and collect taxes is one of the chief powers of the Congress. It is likewise one of the chief powers of the legislatures of the States. The power of taxation carries with it the power to destroy economically. When the Congress or the State legislatures use their taxing power to discriminate against one group or to favor another, the results can be very far reaching.

The Federal tax of 10 cents a pound on colored margarine was repealed in 1950. For all practical purposes the action foreshadowed the end of special levies on margarine. As of January 1, 1953, 17 States had some form of excise tax on margarine, but 11 of the 17 exempted margarine containing domestically produced fats and oils. For practical purposes only 6 States had effective taxes on the product.

Idaho, Iowa, and Utah were levying 5 cents a pound on white margarine, and Minnesota and North Dakota 10 cents. In Idaho, Utah, and North Dakota, the taxes on colored margarine were 10, 10, and 20 cents, respectively. Wisconsin had a tax of 15 cents on all margarine. Except for the Wisconsin license fees of 1,000 dollars on manufacturers and 500 dollars on wholesalers, State license fees were of minor importance.

States have found their taxing power a fertile field for reducing out-of-State competition. Some States levy heavy taxes on itinerant peddlers who have not produced the goods they sell. Several States assess higher taxes (license fees) on truckers who haul products into the State than on those who haul homegrown products. Other States levy higher special charges on nonresident peddlers.

Truck operators who haul pay loads across State boundaries frequently are required to pay heavy vehicle fees in each State in which they travel. Because such fees usually are graduated upward with the weight of the vehicle, the movement of truck cargoes over any long distance could be very uneconomical. Truckers, motor caravans, and new-car transporters have found license fees extremely heavy in several States. Such taxes tend to reduce the competition for railroads.

281437°—54——20

Wine and other alcoholic beverages—especially those produced in other States—have been singled out by several States for special taxes.

Inspection and quarantine laws are designed ostensibly to protect the health of the citizens of the States and to prevent the spread of plant and animal diseases and pests. Such laws may be socially sound and economically justifiable when they are administered for the purposes stated. Another aspect arises when their health, sanitation, and disease-control features are used as means of protecting local industries from competition.

Perhaps there are more instances of trade impediments in the marketing of milk and dairy products than there are with any other farm commodity. Many reasons could be offered for the restrictions that have developed in marketing milk and dairy products. The fact that public health is endangered by unclean milk has been a justifiable reason for regulation. With this purpose as a point of departure, however, it has not been too difficult to develop stringent sanitary controls, which, when administered unfairly, have kept fresh milk supplies in line with market requirements at a given price level.

Each State and most municipalities have minimum sanitary requirements for fresh milk. The various legal quality requirements vary so widely, however, that the public is confused as to what is actually needed to protect it from communicable diseases. Frequently, too, the established minimums have been set aside temporarily when it was necessary to take fresh milk of lower quality in order to supply the market demand.

The refusal of some cities to permit the sale of milk produced on farms more than 20, 30, or 40 miles from the city center is one type of restriction. Sometimes cities may not specifically exclude milk produced outside a given boundary, yet they prohibit the sale of milk unless the dairy is inspected by the city and then proceed to make such an inspection impracticable if not impossible beyond a boundary.

Further restrictions occur when cities require that fresh milk sold within the city shall be pasteurized in a plant licensed and inspected by the city. This type of barrier was jolted severely by the United States Supreme Court decision in the case of the *Dean Milk Company* v. *City of Madison, et al.* (1951), and the Oregon supreme court decision in the case of *Safeway Stores, Inc.* v. *State Board of Agriculture* (1953). The effect of the decisions was to prevent the State or city from excluding milk pasteurized outside of the community in which it was to be sold.

As many as 26 States have had some form of State milk-control laws which were passed "to protect the health and welfare of its citizens and to assure an adequate supply of pure wholesome milk." The State milk-control laws ranged from the minor matter of establishing legal minimum prices to producers to the major task of regulating minimum producer, wholesale, and retail prices, regulating trade practices, licensing producers and distributors, and issuing market quotas or rights to producers on an historical basis of milk deliveries to market. These controls were designed entirely to assure minimum prices. The administrative agencies were granted a licensing power and the authority to revoke such licenses for cause.

A rather general protest arose against many of the restrictive practices used to keep down the competition for milk producers. But the dairy industry is no more of an offender than many others. Very likely not all of the economic restrictions affecting the dairy industry work to the immediate or long-run disadvantage of consumers. It must be recognized, however, that milk is a more immediate concern to the American family than most other foods, and actions of producers and distributors therefore are subject to close public scrutiny.

The development of ice cream made with nonfat milk solids and vegetable oils has created a new competitive problem for ice cream manufacturers. Laws covering this subject were changing in early 1953; it seemed that 22 States could prevent the sale of vegetable-oil ice cream under their "filled" milk regulations and 12 could prevent its sale on the basis that it was an adulterated dairy product.

MOST OF THE REAL obstacles to the interstate movement of eggs have been dropped. Wyoming in 1954 required that all out-of-State eggs be candled before sale.

Livestock inspection and quarantine laws and regulations are designed primarily to prevent the spread of tuberculosis, hoof-and-mouth disease, and Bang's disease. While there is some opportunity to use the State inspection laws to curtail competition, this situation has not been particularly burdensome.

Fruit and vegetable restrictions can be difficult. Careful checks on weights, grades, and types of containers used and inspections for diseases and insects have been employed to exclude out-of-State trade. As fruits and vegetables are highly perishable, delays resulting from inspection may cause losses to shippers and discourage further shipments.

Nursery stock and some field crops, such as hay, have been subjected to numerous and severe restrictions. Efforts of officials of some State departments of agriculture have been helpful in reducing the number of useless barriers to trade in fruit, vegetable, nursery, and field crops, but the list of plants that are partially or entirely kept out of many of the States is large. The delay, annoyance, and expense required to move some types of plants in interstate trade are formidable obstacles to the nursery business.

STATE LEGISLATURES have found the power to regulate public safety and morals an effective device for protecting their citizens against fraud, deceit, and misrepresentation, as well as insuring them against "unnecessary" hazards from competition from nonresidents and from commercial trucks of excessive length, width, and weight. The licensing power is the legal device used to control nonresident merchants and truckers.

Efforts to protect against fraud, deceit, and misrepresentation have taken the form of laws and regulations requiring the proper grading and labeling of fresh and processed foods and fibers, the use of specified types of containers, and the designation of the State of origin.

One serious obstacle to interstate truck transportation is the lack of uniformity among States on the maximum sizes and loading weights for trucks. Some of the differences appear to be due more to a lack of coordination among States than any other reason. The controls of the size and weight of trucks as a means of preventing highway damage and possible traffic hazards show foresight. The misuse of this power to curb competition is a questionable procedure.

STATES HAVE THE POWER to protect their proprietary interests. Four aspects of that use have important implications in interstate trade: The power to require State funds to be used to purchase farm and other products grown within the State boundaries, to restrict the export of any of the natural resources, to purchase the services of residents only, and to specify the conditions under which the forest, water, and natural mineral and wildlife resources of the State can be used or harvested and its highways employed for private or commercial transportation. With few exceptions States try to favor resident farmers, laborers, artisans, and professionals. They likewise buy products produced locally when possible. In some dairy States they favor the purchase of butter, and in the industrial States they permit the purchase of margarine.

Economic groups are affected differently by trade barriers. The producers of goods and the people who have services to market might gain specific advantage from trade barriers because they are interested in a specific service or a specific commodity. A nurseryman is more interested in eliminating out-of-State competition than a consumer is interested in preventing such restrictions. Likewise, a milk distributor gains far more from a municipal regulation restricting the granting of licenses to other milk distributors than any one consumer loses. In other words, a given producer's interests in a trade barrier is a specific thing, whereas a consumer's interest is quite generalized. It is not surprising therefore that we find farmers, craftsmen, doctors, lawyers, and teachers supporting specific types of trade barriers rather vigorously, while members of the same group in their capacity as consumers have no interest in trade barriers that do not directly affect their income.

It is argued that the indirect price boost given to the local producers and processors will be extremely helpful in some cases and the additional costs to any one consumer will be small. Some persons contend that all consumers in the protected area are better off because they are assured a more stable income when local industries keep operating and sell their products at good prices. Other things being equal, there is some short-run and possibly a long-run economic justification for such an argument.

If one deals with prices only, it is not difficult to show that consumers of farm products in deficit areas pay higher prices when trade barriers limit the supply of out-of-State products they can receive. Conversely, it can be shown that consumers in the surplus-producing area benefit when the out movement of products is curtailed by trade barriers imposed by another State.

Even though selected groups of producers may benefit from trade barriers that reduce competition and maintain or increase prices, the effect on consumers and the State as a whole may be the exact opposite. As far as consumers are concerned, a great deal depends on the extent to which they are forced to pay higher prices for products or to take lower quality products at prices comparable to those charged by out-of-State producers.

The advantage or disadvantage to a State's economy will be determined largely by the extent to which other States follow similar restrictive policies, and as a consequence reduce the available markets for those producers who must sell their surpluses outside their own State boundaries.

The widespread imposition of unreasonable barriers would have a dampening effect on specialization o product and labor and geographica specialization. The likely result woul be less productivity and a lower plan of living. It would seem, therefore that any State that attempts to ai selected groups of producers by usin its taxing and police powers to reduc out-of-State competition should giv careful attention to the possible adverse effects on its entire population.

Many legislators and administrativ officials are giving serious attention t the possible disadvantages to thei population that might be caused b an unwise use of the taxing and polic powers to control economic actions.

Marketing and transportation agencies that thrive on trade from an source generally oppose trade barrier On the other hand, the pressures fro consumers to eliminate such restrictions are practically nonexistent. It i only under conditions of extreme urgency that the opponents of interstat trade barriers get well enough organized to agitate for their repeal.

Restrictions on the free moveme of goods or services in interstate or i local commerce can prove costly to th marketing functions. Such restric tion often results in costly handlin and inspection procedures and le than full utilization of the transporta tion and marketing facilities. Th maintenance of "ports of entry" ha proved costly in relation to the know good that has come from them.

Regulations that discriminate against one method of marketing and favor another are found most often in the selling of fresh milk. Some States, including Oregon and Virginia, maintain minimum retail prices that prevent competition between store and home-delivery milk on a price basis. The practice favors the higher cost system of distribution through home deliveries and charge accounts.

The application of rigid inspection and quarantine procedures on products from a given production area may permanently destroy the market for products from that area of production and divert the trade elsewhere. This was the case in 1932 when the State of New York excluded the importation of most dairy cattle in an effort to eliminate Bang's disease. It particularly affected Wisconsin.

EFFORTS have been made to reduce trade barriers. The responsibility for administering laws that impede the free flow of trade falls to a considerable degree on the heads of the various State departments of agriculture and their staffs. It is to their credit that they have recognized and sought to remedy the administrative abuses connected with trade-barrier legislation. Whenever local conditions permitted, they have sought to revise the regulations that were particularly offensive to normal trading. The officials, through their National Association of Commissioners, Secretaries, and Directors of Agriculture, have been a constructive force. But the obstacle faced by the State officials has been the lack of any real cooperation from the grass roots. Progress, however, has been made, although the advances have not had a real test, for example, to see whether a drop in farm prices and some unemployment will cause a reversal.

Trade associations whose members are affected adversely by discriminatory taxes, inspections, quarantines, and labeling requirements have been active in publicizing trade restrictions. Some have worked diligently to repeal laws they find objectionable or to change administrative regulations.

The educational activities of the various groups seeking to reduce trade barriers have contributed heavily to a more uniform and less severe administration of many State inspection and quarantine laws and regulations. These administrative changes have tended to minimize the discriminatory features of such controls.

The relatively satisfactory level of farm prices between 1940 and 1952 caused farm groups to lose interest in interstate trade barriers as a means of restraining competition. When farm prices began to decline in the latter part of 1952 there was no active campaign to institute new interstate barriers as a defense against lower prices. Instead, organized farmers sought to protect their prices and incomes by seeking Federal price supports, by voting in production controls, and by developing marketing agreements to control the quantity and the conditions under which their products are sold. (*D. B. DeLoach.*)

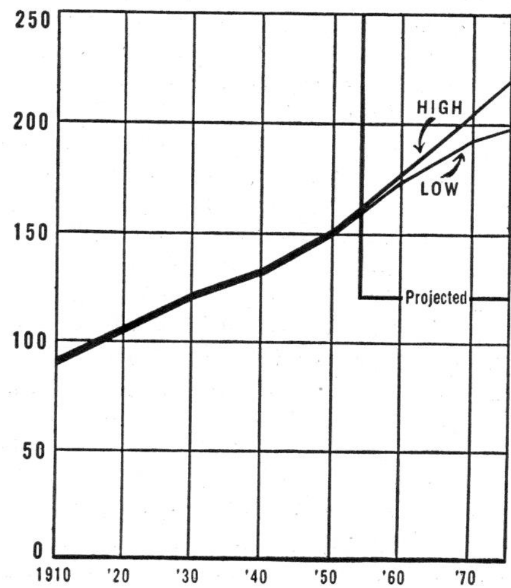

Ownership

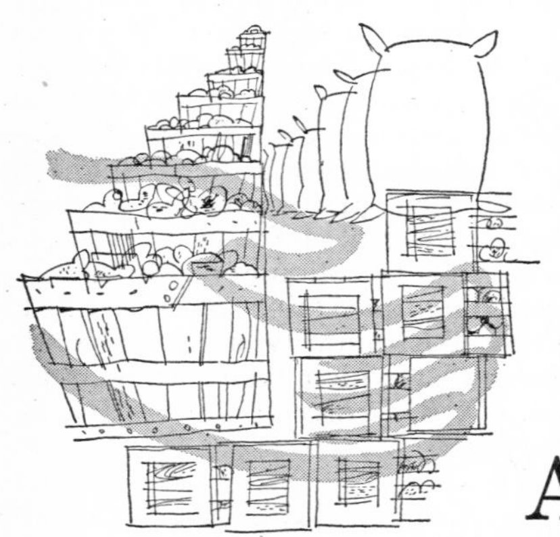

An understanding of ownership is basic to the consideration of such problems as ownership transfer, risk bearing, pricing, and financing. Transfer of ownership of farm products from original producer to ultimate user is one of the main functions of marketing. Risks result from the ownership of farm goods during their movement from producer to consumer. They affect farmer and consumer alike by increasing marketing costs. Maintaining fair play and honest dealing in futures trading is vital because future prices are used as base prices in the buying and selling of actual, physical products. Other types of selling in which the seller puts off for a time some part of his obligation to deliver, transfer title, or perform other duties are contracts for processed fruits and vegetables and forward sales of broiler chickens. The large amounts of financing involved in the ownership of farm products require important decisions with regard to the availability of funds and the benefits and liabilities from their use. Several factors influence the financing of farm marketing.

Rights and Duties of Ownership

The transfer of ownership of farm products from original producers to ultimate users is one of the main functions of marketing.

Ownership includes rights to possess, control, use, and enjoy property and the benefits from it and to sell or otherwise dispose of it according to law.

Certain duties and liabilities also attach to ownership. Owners must control and use their property so as to avoid unwarranted interference with the legal rights of others. Liabilities include risks of losses, declines in prices, and possible damages due to the inadequate control or the illegal use of the property.

Property may be an object (such as a bale of cotton or a cow), or it may be any kind of an intangible, such as a right to receive or recover a debt, or money, or damages for breach of contract.

Large amounts of funds are involved in the ownership of agricultural products, and an understanding of the role of ownership is basic to the consideration of such problems as financing, risk bearing, ownership transfer, and pricing, all of which (plus others) are involved in marketing farm products.

An important attribute of ownership is the power or ability of the owner to transfer to others all or any part of his bundle of rights, duties, and liabilities. Transfers may take the form of sales or bailments. A general description of the effects of the different forms of transfer may be of assistance in selecting outlets, methods, and agencies through which farm goods are marketed.

Legal title to agricultural products, together with the entire bundle of rights, duties, and liabilities incident to ownership, may be transferred by means of sale.

The time and manner of such transfers have legal consequences that may be of prime importance to sellers and buyers. Such consequences may be illustrated by sales "f. o. b. (free on board) shipping point" and by sales "f. o. b. destination," or "delivered sales," two common types of contract terms used in the sale of agricultural products. In sales that specify delivery of the commodity f. o. b. shipping point, the buyer is liable for freight charges and he assumes the risks of loss due to destruction or quality deterioration upon delivery of the goods to the carrier. In sales that specify delivery of the products f. o. b. destination, the seller is liable for freight and retains the risks of loss due to destruction or quality deterioration before the goods arrive at the destination.

Risks of loss due to a price decline, however, are assumed by the buyer as of the time the contract of sale is made, provided the seller substantially complies with terms of the contract.

It is beyond the scope of this chapter to enumerate all the many possible combinations of contract terms, customs, and other factors that may affect the time and manner of transferring property. The general rule is that a contract to sell specified or ascertained goods transfers property in them to the buyer at such time as the parties to the contract intend that it should be transferred. In ascertaining the intentions of the parties, the terms of the contract, conduct of the parties, trade practices, and other circumstances relating to the transaction may be taken into account. If the intentions of the parties are clearly manifest in the contract as, for example, terms stating delivery f. o. b. destination, the terms of the contract are generally decisive with regard to time and manner of passing property.

In the absence of contract terms that clearly show the intentions of the parties, general rules have been formulated for ascertaining the intentions of the parties with regard to the time at which ownership of goods passes from the seller to the buyer. For example, an unconditional contract to sell specific goods, in a deliverable state, passes the property in the goods to the buyer when the contract is made.

A contract to sell specific goods where the seller is bound to do something to the goods, for the purpose of putting them into deliverable state, does not pass the property until such thing is done. Goods delivered to the buyer on approval, on trial, or on satisfaction, or on other similar terms passes property therein to the buyer when the buyer signifies his approval or acceptance to the seller, does any other act adopting the transaction, or retains the goods without giving notice of rejection within a reasonable time.

Although title to goods may have passed to the buyer, the unpaid seller and also the buyer have certain rights that may affect the incidents of ownership. The unpaid seller has a right to retain goods for the purchase price while he is in possession of them; a right of stopping the goods in transit after he has parted with the possession of them, in the case of the insolvency of his buyer; a right to withhold delivery of the commodity; and a limited right of resale of the goods. These rights are contingent upon the possession of goods by the seller after the contract of sale has been consummated, except if the buyer is insolvent.

Such rights of the unpaid seller restrict the incidents of ownership that normally pass to the purchaser.

The buyer, in the absence of contrary agreement, is entitled to examine the goods before the property is finally vested in him. A refusal by the seller to allow opportunity for inspection generally justifies the buyer in refusing to fulfill the contract.

When the terms of bargaining specify that property is to pass before delivery of the goods, the buyer has a reasonable time after delivery in which to examine the goods. If they are not of the kind and quality ordered, he may then refuse to accept them and thereby rescind the contract.

The buyer is deemed to have accepted the goods when he so intimates to the seller or when the goods have been delivered to him and he does any act in relation to them which is inconsistent with the ownership of the seller, or when, after the lapse of a reasonable time, he retains the goods without intimating to the seller that he has rejected them. But the acceptance of the goods by the buyer does not generally constitute a release of the seller's liability for defective performance.

Owners at various stages of the marketing procedure may transfer a part of the bundle of rights, duties, and liabilities incidental to ownership to intermediate agencies for some special object or purpose. Such transfers may include bailments for sale, transportation, storage, or for other purposes.

Important intermediate agencies employed to sell farm products include brokers, factors or commission merchants, auctioneers, and cooperative marketing associations. The employment of them for the sale of agricultural products usually establishes an agency relationship by means of which certain rights, duties, and liabilities incident to ownership are transferred to the agents and others are retained by the principal.

Brokers, used in the sale of agricultural products, are agents whose job is to bring buyers and sellers together for the purpose of negotiating sales. They usually do not physically handle the goods while the transactions are being negotiated. Generally the right to conclude the sale resides in the principal who retains the complete bundle of rights, duties, and liabilities incident to ownership of the goods. Brokers are paid a brokerage fee or commission for their services and they have no lien on the goods.

Factors or commission merchants are agents who are entrusted with the possession of goods of another for the purpose of selling them. It is their duty to exercise reasonable care, prudence, and diligence in handling, storing, and caring for the goods consigned to them for sale, and they are liable for any losses resulting from a breach of this duty.

In the absence of special directions, if the factor or commission merchant pursues the usual and regular course which has been adopted by custom and experience as proper and prudent under like circumstances, he usually would not be responsible for any losses.

Although title to goods consigned to factors or commission merchants to be sold remains in the principal until the goods are sold, a factor or commission merchant usually has the right to sell the goods and to collect payment for them in his own name. He has a lien on the goods for advances made by him and for his commission. Such a lien is a general one in that it secures not only the indebtedness due for services performed on the specific goods concerning which the lien is claimed, but also the general balance of the accounts, arising out of transactions in the regular course of the factor's or commission merchant's calling, owed to him by his principal.

An auctioneer is an agent who is authorized to sell to the highest bidder goods of another at public sale, usually referred to as an auction market. As an agent, the auctioneer is obligated to obtain the best price he fairly can for the goods and is responsible for damages arising from his failure to pursue the regular course of business. Special terms or conditions may be inserted in auction sales as in other contractual arrangements but, unless special terms or customs in the bargain or other circumstances show a contrary intention, the property in the goods passes when the bid is accepted without waiting for delivery or payment. Although the auctioneer is not an insurer of the safety of the goods entrusted to him for sale, he is under obligation to keep them with ordinary and reasonable care. The auctioneer has a special property interest in, and a lien upon, goods of his principal in his possession, and upon the proceeds therefrom when sold, for his advances thereon and for his commissions and other charges.

A cooperative marketing association, a business organization usually incorporated, is owned and controlled by the members and furnishes marketing services on a nonprofit basis for the mutual benefit of its patrons.

Cooperative marketing contracts, which define the rights and obligations of members and the association, may be of the purchase-and-sale type or of the agency type. Under a purchase-and-sale contract, title to the products passes to the association on or before the delivery of the products, in accordance with the stated intentions of the parties. An association which operates under an agency contract does not take title to the products marketed. Under either type of marketing contract, the grower surrenders direct control over the sale of the products and the association is obligated to return to patrons the sale price of the products on the basis prescribed in the contract, less authorized deductions.

Marketing contracts ordinarily provide that the association may exercise its sole discretion and judgment in grading, processing, packing, warehousing, financing, and marketing the products of the members and the responsibility for mistakes of management and for loss in collection must be borne by the members. In addition, they usually specify that the association may enjoin a breach of the stipulation to deliver; that it may mortgage, pledge, hypothecate, or otherwise encumber the produce; that it may commingle the products with those of other producers; and that it may make deductions from the proceeds of sales to meet costs of operations.

The agencies employed to transport agricultural products include common and private carriers. A common carrier of goods is one who holds himself out, in the exercise of a public calling, to transport goods for hire, for whomsoever may employ him. A private carrier, on the other hand, is one who undertakes, by special agreement, in a particular instance, to transport goods without being bound to serve every person who may apply for his services. The distinction is important because of the differences in liabilities involved. In either case, the owner usually retains title to the products transported and transfers to the carrier physical possession along with some other incidents of ownership.

Common carriers are liable for all losses or damages to goods received for carriage, irrespective of negligence and from whatever cause, except losses resulting from the act of God, the public enemy, the act of the State, the act of the shipper, and damages due to the nature of the goods themselves. The carrier may be liable for loss or damage resulting from the excepted causes, if his own negligence or that of his agents, servants, or employees contributed to the loss or damage.

The extraordinary liability of the common carrier attaches when the goods are delivered and accepted by the carrier, and it terminates, generally, when the transportation of the goods is completed and the goods are delivered to either the consignee or to a connecting carrier in accordance with the terms of the contract.

The exception to the general rule of liability that relates to the inherent nature of the products involved is especially applicable to some agricultural commodities. In the absence of negligence, the carrier is not liable for the deterioration of perishable fruits and vegetables in its custody due to natural causes. The carrier is not liable for the destruction of cotton by fire started in the bale at the gin and not discoverable at the time the bale was delivered to the carrier. A carrier of livestock is not liable for their natural tendency to deteriorate or for other loss or damage during transportation due to inherent characteristics of the animal and not to any fault or negligence on the part of the carrier. The measure of the common carrier's duty as to such goods is to exercise reasonable care and diligence to protect them from loss or injury while they are in its custody, taking into consideration the nature of the commodity, the conditions of the weather, and the time necessary to complete the transportation.

The carrier is obligated to guard the goods from destruction or injury by the elements; from the effects of delays; and from every other source of injury which he may avert, and which, in the exercise of care and ordinary intelligence, may be known or anticipated. Live animals must have food and water, when the distance shipped demands it. Fruits and some other perishable products must be transported with expedition and be protected from frost. It has been held that where a carrier undertakes to transport fruit or dairy products, he may be required to ice them during the journey in order to prevent their destruction. The Interstate Commerce Act, applicable to shipments in interstate commerce, now permits the carriers to provide different tariffs for different services rendered by them. If the shipper fails to take advantage of the special services provided, he cannot hold the carrier liable for losses due to failure to supply heat or refrigeration.

Acts of God that exempt common carriers from liability refer to unusual natural causes such as fire caused by lightning, unusual floods, violent wind and rain storms, and hurricanes or tornadoes which the carrier could not reasonably be expected to foresee. The exemption of the act of the public enemy refers only to acts of the public enemy of the State, the armed forces of another nation with which the State to which the carrier owes allegiance is at war. A carrier is not liable for goods placed in its custody when they have been taken from the carrier, without collusion on its part, by legal process, valid on its face, and when the carrier has with reasonable promptness notified the owner or the shipper. Justice requires that, if loss or damage to goods shipped is due to acts of the shipper, the shipper and not the carrier should be liable.

Liability of private carriers for damage to goods transported is much more limited than that of common carriers. As a general rule, a private carrier is not absolutely liable for damages to goods transported, but he is under the duty of exercising at least ordinary care and diligence to prevent damage of the goods entrusted to him, and is liable where injury results from his negligence or failure to use due care.

In the case of a common carrier, the owner's right to possession is conditioned. A common carrier has a specific, but not a general, lien for its freight charges on all goods delivered to it for transportation by the owner. The lien, if any, of private carriers by land is based upon agreement with the shipper.

Storage or warehousing plays a vital role in marketing agricultural products. A warehouseman is a person who is lawfully engaged in the business of storing goods for profit. The warehouseman is not an insurer of the goods in storage but is liable for any loss or injury to the goods as a result of his failure to exercise such care in regard to them as a reasonably careful owner of similar goods would exercise. This liability commences as soon as the goods are received by the warehouseman and it continues until the goods are delivered to the owner or the holder of the warehouse receipt.

The warehouseman has a lien for storage and preservation of the goods; for all lawful claims for money advanced for such items as interest, insurance, transportation, labor, weighing, and cooperage; for all reasonable charges for notices and advertisements of sale; and for the sale of the goods where default has been made in satisfying the warehouseman's lien.

A warehouseman having a lien valid against the person demanding the goods may refuse to deliver them to him until the lien is satisfied. The lien is lost by a surrender of the goods.

The types of ownership of business usually involved in marketing agricultural products include individual proprietorships, partnerships, corporations, and cooperative associations.

Some important legal and economic consequences may flow from differences in type of ownership of business involved in marketing agricultural products. The differences may have important influences on the volume of capital available, nature and durability of the operating unit, concentration of management and control, and the distribution of responsibilities and liabilities.

In an individual proprietorship, the simplest form of ownership organization, ownership is vested in one individual who supplies his own capital, is sole manager and operator of the business, has unlimited liability (except for certain small exemptions) for claims against the business, and is entitled to all profits and other benefits from his operations. The duration of business under an individual proprietorship is limited by the duration of life or legal competency of the individual owner. Usually the volume of capital is more limited and the operations more restricted for individual than for other types of ownership.

A partnership is a voluntary association, based on contract, of two or more persons to carry on as co-owners a business for profit. Special forms of partnership include joint-stock companies, business trusts, joint adventures, and limited partnerships, among others. Every partner usually is an agent of the partnership for the purpose of its business. The partners are jointly and severally responsible for every debt incurred on behalf of the partnership. Since the dissolution of a partnership usually may be brought about at any time by the expressed will of any partner, by the death or legal incompetency of any member, or by other means, the duration of the association is uncertain.

A corporation is an artificial person or being, endowed by law with the capacity of perpetual succession. The owners may be few or many. The characteristics of a corporation are the concentration of management, transferability of ownership interests, making the perpetual succession a possibility; power to take, hold, and convey property in the company name; power to sue and be sued in the company name; and limited liability of owners.

Cooperatives take the form of corporations and unincorporated associations. There are three basic principles that make cooperatives different from other forms of business enterprise. The first is ownership and control of the cooperative by those who use its service. Control is exercised by the owners as patrons rather than as investors. The second is that the provision is made to return to patrons on an equitable basis any amounts over the cost of performing the marketing, purchasing, or other service which the cooperative is set up to perform. The patronage refund is the best known of the devices used by cooperatives to attain operation at cost. The third of the three basic concepts of cooperative business is that of limited returns to share capital. In contrast to other forms of business, the capital of a cooperative is invested by the owners as patrons primarily to provide themselves with needed services. (*L. D. Howell*, *Charles W. Bucy*.)

Selling: The Transfer of Ownership

Sale by private negotiation or agreement, the striking of a bargain between a buyer and a seller or their agents is the oldest and commonest way to change title to farm products.

It is used in each of the stages from the farmer's local market to the retail store.

Its general characteristics include face-to-face negotiation between individuals in markets where there is relatively little organization, where the products bought and sold are available for inspection, and where there often is need for buyers and sellers to seek each other out and haggle over prices and the other terms of sale.

Transactions usually are for cash and title passes immediately from seller to buyer. Often the sales are in small lots of diverse kinds and quality.

Posted price sales, such as those at retail stores and restaurants, although lacking many of the above characteristics, are still to be classified as ownership transfer on the basis of private treaty. The seller or the buyer accepts or rejects what is offered on the basis of the listed prices. In modern retail foodstores, food prices are posted; in fact, they are generally marked on articles except in the case of some unpackaged produce and meats. Increasing quantities of food products are reaching final consumers through hotels, restaurants, and other eating places. Prices are listed on the menu. The buyer either buys at the indicated price or refrains from buying. The retailer adjusts prices to expanding or lagging consumer demand, particularly for perishable goods. If the retailer is a member of a chain, his major pricing policies are likely to be determined by a central office.

Grain elevators, crushers of oilseeds, and other agencies that buy directly from farmers commonly post the prices at which they are prepared to buy whatever quantities farmers may elect to deliver. The seller elects to sell or to refrain from selling on the basis of the prices as posted. Prices are in terms of a particular grade, and on sales to distant points they may be for immediate or deferred shipment. The quantity may be in general terms, such as a carload, and there must be an understanding as to permissible excess or deficit on actual amounts delivered, who pays the costs of transportation, and when payment is made.

Terminal-market grain merchants frequently make "bids to the country" to buy grain "on track" or "to arrive." In the first instance the price is for grain loaded on cars at the country point. The seller guarantees the quality, but the buyer pays the freight and assumes the risk of price changes. On grain sold "to arrive," the seller pays the freight and assumes the risk of accidents to the grain in transit, but the buyer assumes the risk of price changes.

The use of grades and standards, such as the sale of grain on the basis of class and grade, cotton on grade and staple length, or hogs on carcass weight and grade after slaughtering, usually reduces the area for negotiation between buyer and seller and improves the accuracy of pricing.

Methods of transfer of ownership in livestock marketing would be strongly affected if sale on the basis of carcass weight and grade should become general. This method, used experimentally by a few packers, involves paying the farmer on the basis of the grade made by his hogs, cattle, or sheep after slaughter. Stock purchased on this basis have been bought primarily from farmers delivering direct to the slaughtering plant and payment has been delayed only a few days or less. Perhaps it would be practicable to sell to distant markets and through one or more middlemen, but then a system of maintaining the identity of individual animals would need to be developed, and advances to producers might be necessary if there were considerable delay between sale to the first buyer and slaughter.

Brokers, commission men, and agents often are used when quantities bought and sold are relatively large, when it is necessary to buy or sell in a distant market, or when a highly specialized knowledge of marketing conditions is desirable.

Under those conditions, farmers, handlers, and processors have often found it economical to utilize the services of marketing agencies that specialize in buying and selling for others. Some operate in local markets. They are particularly important in wholesale and terminal markets. They take the product of a farmer or secondary seller and find a buyer, disposing of the product at the best price afforded by the market. They may operate as agents of a buyer, who may be a wholesale receiver, a manufacturer of cotton or woolen textiles, or other processor or manufacturer.

The agent does not acquire title, but is given such authority by the principal as is necessary to perform the buying or selling operation. The broker or commission man, then, is an agent who facilitates transfer of ownership.

The growth of large-scale marketing and processing has led food manufacturers, processors, and others to make greater use of selling or buying agents or of manufacturers' agents. The former may sell or buy exclusively for one firm. Such agents may be entirely separate organizations, or the agency may be owned or controlled by the parent corporation.

THE MANUFACTURER'S AGENT is between the free-lance broker and commission man and the exclusive selling or buying agent. The manufacturers' agents usually receive commissions but represent a limited number of principals and usually operate in a definite territory. Marketing firms of this kind are more important in the handling of industrial goods of nonfarm origin, but are of some significance in buying and selling finished or semifinished textiles and foods. For instance, a manufacturer's agent may handle the products of a number of cloth manufacturers, dyers, and converters. Another agent may sell a line of breakfast cereals for one manufacturer, cake flour for another, and sauces and salad dressings for yet another.

Forward contracting for farm products has increased in recent years.

Although the contracts of an individual processor are commonly standard in form, some of the conditions, particularly the acreage, prices, and time of delivery, are negotiated individually with each producer. Ordinarily the producer agrees to maintain specified production practices and to deliver the product after harvest.

Agreements may also cover grades, dockage, service charges, liability, prices, time of payment, and advances of credit. Because ordinarily the quantity of products cannot be determined until harvest, title to the actual products does not pass until delivery is made. In effect, however, the basic determinations incident to transfer of ownership are made when the contract is entered into.

Such contractual arrangements have been an important factor in the production and processing of canning crops. They played a significant role in the rapid development of the broiler industry, although they are usually less formal and more flexible as to price than in the canning industry. Contracts for forward sale and delivery between farmers and the first handlers are also used in the marketing of irrigated cotton in the Southwest, feeder cattle in the West, and Florida citrus fruit for concentrating.

Numerous variations of sale by contract occur. Some are so informal as to approach transfer through consignment. For instance, most of the butter in the North Central States is sold on the basis of some kind of advance sales agreement. Some of these are written contracts and some are letters, but others are merely verbal agreements.

In selling goods through cooperatives, growers nearly always participate in some sort of pooling arrangement. That may include only a pooling of handling margins, as in the case of sales of cash grain to cooperative elevators. Or the grower's lot may be pooled with the production of many other farmers and at the time of delivery, the grower receives an advance of a percentage of the basic price of the specific quality delivered. The final price is based on the proceeds of the entire quantity within the pool. In some cooperatives the grower may elect one of a number of different agreements. He may also retain certain rights that affect the ultimate receipts for his products, although title has passed to the cooperative. For example, in some cotton cooperatives the grower may have the right to fix the basic price over a considerable period after his crop has been delivered to the cooperative.

Improving the farmer's bargaining position rather than rendering marketing services is the primary purpose of some cooperatives. They act only as agents in negotiations with buyers, and title passes directly from farmer to buyer. A number of these bargaining associations exist in the milk field.

Representatives of such a bargaining association meet with the distributors and, within any applicable Federal or local regulation, come to an agreement on the prices to be paid the farmer. Ordinarily the agreement is in effect until one of the interested parties initiates a proposal to change the basic agreement, but commonly provision is made for interim automatic adjustments during the life of the agreement when specified economic conditions change.

Generally the farmer is subject to a monthly marketwide pooling arrangement under which all producers receive the same price, with differentials for location, quality, and butterfat. Farmers deliver their milk to distributors, and payments are made by the distributors directly to the producers, usually with a small deduction or checkoff of so much per hundredweight, which goes to the cooperative association.

ORGANIZED MARKETS are focal points in the transfer of many agricultural products, but the extent of organization varies substantially.

In some respects present-day State and county fairs and industry and trade expositions are survivals of the fairs of medieval Europe. State and county fairs provide space for the display and sale of livestock, produce, fruits and vegetables, home craft wares, and other farm products. Transfer of ownership under these conditions more nearly resembles sales by private negotiation or at farmer's markets. Ordinarily the samples displayed at trade or industry expositions, however, are merely the basis upon which sales of the product are made.

Although fairs and expositions are organized as to rules and means of display, they lack some of the most distinctive features of the more highly organized public markets. At such markets the bids and offers of numerous buyers and sellers are focused during specified trading times and agents commonly make transactions for principals.

The auction method seems to be increasing in local marketing of farm products. Auctions almost completely dominate the tobacco marketing scene; more than 95 percent of the United States tobacco crops are so sold. Local livestock auctions have increased greatly in numbers.

Ungraded goods and various kinds of small and odd lots can be sold at auction. Unlike private negotiations between individual sellers and buyers, however, auction sales are open to the public and anyone is free to buy and sell in compliance with the rules under which the sales are conducted.

When numerous buyers and sellers are attracted to one place, there is likely to be a closer approach to a freely competitive market than is the case when negotiations are between two individuals. Producers apparently have tended to favor the auction method of selling when the belief has been widespread that a few buyers have dominated the market for certain commodities and when there is evidence that buyers are better supplied with market information than are sellers. In many small auctions a limited number of buyers may make it possible to buy articles cheaply, but here the tobacco or livestock farmer feels that he is protected by his right to accept or reject the highest bid made. The auction company and the auctioneer have a general responsibility to maintain satisfactory marketing conditions, both the physical facilities for effectively and honestly handling the products offered for sale and fair competitive bidding.

Variations of the typical auction methods of selling developed in several areas in 1952, notably in the Delmarva Peninsula (Delaware, Maryland, Virginia), in the marketing of broilers. The birds are not brought by sellers to a central place for inspection by buyers. Rather the latter visit the farms and inspect the flocks with respect to size, condition, and their readiness for market. Buyers and sellers meet daily in an auction room where buyers are given lists of the flocks to be offered for sale that day. When the auctioneer has received the final bid on a flock, the owner stands and indicates whether he accepts or rejects the bid. If he accepts, he and the buyer execute a sales contract, which provides that the buyer must pick up the birds at the producer's farm within a specified number of days. Title passes to the buyer when he takes delivery of the broilers.

Commodity exchanges or boards of trade are organized markets for trading in agricultural commodities under formal rules and standardized contracts. Of the approximately 65 exchanges, 20 provide facilities for trading in futures contracts and on most of these there is also trading in cash commodities. The other exchanges are cash markets only. Trading in futures and cash commodities on the leading exchanges provides a pricing basis for cash transactions on the other exchanges and in the country.

The exchanges operate under a State charter or corporation law, which vests authority in the exchange to elect officers, hold property, make rules, and to exercise other corporate authority, and usually to arbitrate commercial disputes between any of the members.

In size and scope of services, exchanges range from smaller markets, with services limited largely to provision of market information, to the larger grain and cotton exchanges, which provide rather complete services and facilities for trading. They range in number of members from fewer than 20 to 1,400, and in paid employees from 2 to 200.

Members are individuals elected by the exchange and usually membership is acquired by transfer from a retiring member. Members include representatives of merchants, dealers, farmers' marketing cooperatives, and processors interested in the cash commodity. The membership of exchanges where futures trading is conducted also includes representatives of futures commission merchants or brokerage firms and persons primarily interested in speculative trading in futures.

Only members may trade directly on the exchange. In making transactions for nonmembers they act as agents. They may also trade for themselves, commonly at half nonmember rates, and usually a member who is a partner in a firm or an officer of a corporation may confer on the firm or corporation the privilege of membership rates.

Exchange rules customarily fix the hours for trading and the rates of commissions or brokerage for cash and futures transactions. On futures markets, minimum margin requirements, permissible limits on daily fluctuations in prices, and procedures for trading are established by rules, and a clearinghouse performs an essential function in the clearing of trades.

Rules for cash transactions specify the terms and conditions under which sales may be made on the exchange or under its rules. Provisions for drawing of samples and for resampling are customary. In grain, rules also cover the hours and methods of making "to arrive" bids to the country. Other rules provide for the weighing of grain, the permissible variation in carlot weights, the time allowed for unloading of cars, and procedures for surrender of documents and payment. Unpaid-for grain unloaded into private elevators is weighed and placed thereafter under the jurisdiction of a custodian employed by the exchange, who holds the certificate until payment is made.

In connection with futures contracts, exchange rules prescribe the grades of commodities that may be delivered, the amounts of premiums or discounts at which various grades are deliverable, and procedures for the issuing of notices of intent to deliver. Where authorized by charter or corporate law, rules provide for arbitration of commercial disputes and the making of awards by an exchange committee, and establish procedures for handling of appeals and for enforcement of the award by the filing of claims in a court of law by a party to the dispute.

The amount and arrangement of space used by exchanges varies widely. Smaller exchanges maintain offices for the receipt of price quotations from other markets, and for inspection, weighing, and other services. Many exchanges have a traffic department or bureau to assist members with rates and routing of shipments.

Typical of the more highly organized exchanges is a large high-ceilinged room, with boards for quotations and open floor space for continuous trading in cash commodities or futures during prescribed hours, or for trading at "calls," the latter resembling auctions in many respects. On grain exchange floors, tables are used to display a sample from each car, with an identifying ticket showing the class and grade and grading factors. Cotton samples drawn from each bale require more space than is available on exchange floors, and cotton merchants maintain sample rooms, commonly in the exchange building.

Data on the transfer of cash commodities on exchanges are incomplete, but cash sales of grain and cotton under exchange rules are substantial. In wheat, for example, more than 70,000 cars of grain, or approximately 115 million bushels, were reported as sold on six of the larger grain exchanges during the year ended June 30, 1953. Reported cash sales of corn on five of the leading corn markets during the year ended September 30, 1953, totaled more than 33,000 cars of grain, or about 55 million bushels.

Futures trading overshadows cash sales on exchanges. In the year ended June 30, 1953, for example, the volume of trading on all exchanges in the United States aggregated 3.8 billion bushels of wheat, 2.8 billion bushels of corn, and 3.3 billion bushels of soybeans. Futures trading in cotton totaled 91.3 million bales. In terms of dollar value, futures transactions in the year ended June 30, 1953, aggregated more than 45 billion dollars for the commodities regulated under the Commodity Exchange Act, which covers most agricultural commodities in which there is futures trading.

There is relatively little transfer of title to cash commodities through delivery on futures contracts, as most futures contracts are closed out by the making of an offsetting contract rather than fulfilled by making delivery.

For example, futures contracts in wheat settled by delivery on the three largest grain exchanges averaged approximately 29 million bushels a year during the 5 crop years ended June 1953.

Besides the price-basing use of futures markets in cash transactions, the transfer of ownership of cash commodities, particularly to central market merchants and to processors, is facilitated by hedging. This is the entering into of a futures transaction opposite in type to the cash transaction. For example, a merchant sells wheat futures as an offset against price changes in cash wheat purchased. In major grains, the quantity of short hedges tends to be related, both in amount and in seasonal variation, to privately owned commercial or terminal market stocks. Hedging transactions in cotton are usually made in connection with fixed-price transactions and fixation of "on call" sales. A partial measure of the importance of hedging is shown by the fixed-price

281437°—54——21

sales and fixations of the larger merchants and cooperative organizations, which in the year ended July 31, 1951, were equivalent to approximately 73 percent of total domestic consumption and exports.

VARIATIONS in methods of transfer of ownership are influenced in part by physical and price characteristics. It is difficult in some cases to isolate the factors that account for differences in the relative importance of the various methods used in the buying and selling of one commodity as compared with another, and these factors are frequently mixed in their influences.

When the lots to be sold are small and no processing is required, and particularly when there is unusual buying sensitivity to quality, sales are likely to be made from farmers to local buyers or direct to consumers. Eggs are an example. Frequent and wide price fluctuations during the season have led many farmers to sell through the pooling arrangements of cooperatives.

When buyer inspection of individual products is particularly important and trucking of small lots to the local market is economical, auctions tend to be important. Auctions also provide opportunity for farmers to witness the bidding of representatives of various buyers for their products and those of their neighbors. This is believed to minimize the influence resulting from fewness of buyers. Durable, storable commodities that are adapted for sale on the basis of sample and description and can move to considerable degree through major centers of storing and processing are particularly well adapted for sale through the central market wholesalers and the exchanges.

For a number of commodities where two or more methods of transfer of ownership exist side by side over a long period, there is basis for believing that methods of buying and selling also are determined to a large extent by subjective factors that are difficult to isolate. For instance, large producers of western livestock sold much of their stock through terminal market commission men, while small farmers and ranchers tended to rely more on local buyers and on auction markets. The economic basis was that the large producers were in better position to ship in carload and truckload lots, but a number of farmers and ranchers, large and small, said they patronized terminal markets because they believed that competition was keener and prices received were higher. But others gave exactly the same reasons for doing their buying and selling at auctions.

Changes in the relative importance of the different methods of buying and selling and changes over time are affected by changes in marketing institutions, methods, and technology. Contracting for crops has increased as more and more fruits and vegetables are marketed in processed form.

Development of meatpacking plants at interior points within the livestock-producing areas and the increasing sale of livestock directly from farmers to packing plants has been sufficiently important to lead to the use of the term "direct marketing." Price-support programs have led producers of some products to sell directly for cash to Government buyers, or pledge storable commodities as security for nonrecourse Government loans. Sometimes such products may be redeemed by the producer-borrower and sold through commercial channels, and sometimes the Government takes title at the maturity of the loan.

Integration of retailing and wholesaling and the use of motortruck transportation has reduced the relative importance of sales of fruits and vegetables through terminal market auctions and has affected the position of the merchant wholesaler and commission man. In processed goods, integration now often involves two major integrated stages, with retailing and wholesaling under single ownership, and the processors of meats, canned and frozen foods, textiles, or other products extending their ownerıip all or most of the way back to the ırmer. In some cases integration has roceeded to the point where legal tle to goods may pass only in the sale y the producer to the processor and ıe sale by the processor to the con- ımer. Within the integrated concern, owever, a process closely akin to wnership transfer occurs if products re separately accounted for as they ass from, say, a purchasing division ɔ a processing division and then to roduct sales divisions. And each divi- ion may be as zealous in championing :s "price" and quality in intracom- any transfers as it would be in selling r buying in the open market.

The efficiency with which buying nd selling are carried on is of concern ɔ buyers and sellers and to society. Methods of purchase and sale that are xpensive in terms of time and effort nean loss of production and income to ndividuals and society. The methods vhich result in prices that do not ccurately reflect underlying condi- ions of demand and supply can lead o unwarranted differences in prices mong both individual producers and roducing areas. This means loss of atisfaction to consumers and a waste f resources by producers, as the latter lo not receive from the price system he proper guides to the allocation of esources.

The persistence of wide variations n methods of transfer of ownership uggests that there is no one best nethod suited to all conditions. The nethod actually used may be even less mportant from the standpoints of conomy and efficiency than is the xtent to which both buyers and ellers have knowledge of the market onditions.

It is not so much a matter of whether ɔuying and selling takes place in local narkets, wholesale markets, direct to etailers or consumers, through coop- ratives, or through the utilization of pecialized buying and selling agen- cies. Rather it is the knowledge of lemand, supply, and prices possessed ɔy buyers and sellers and the extent to which grading and standardization enable buyers and sellers to know what is being bought and sold.

The closer such knowledge comes to perfection, the more quickly buyers and sellers come to terms and the more satisfactory are pricing results. (*Bennett S. White*, *W. Edwards Beach*.)

The Danger of Loss

Risk in the commercial sense commonly means the danger of loss arising from the uncertainty of future developments.

Risks are an important element in agricultural marketing. They have direct effects on marketing agencies. They affect farmers and consumers alike through increased marketing costs and affect early-season prices of many commodities because they restrict the accumulation of inventories.

Under primitive conditions, each family carried its own risks of inadequate food, clothing, and other things. Under modern specialized production, the risks of farm production are taken over by the farmers, and the risks of marketing are assumed by marketing agencies.

Risks of marketing appeared when the first few farm products were purchased for resale. They increased in each commodity market as the distances between the producers and consumers became greater, commercial processing grew, and inventories expanded.

MANY KINDS of risks are incurred in the marketing of farm products. The principal kinds, by major groups, are:

Destruction or deterioration of property (principally products handled): Fire; flood; storm; earthquake; wreck (ship, train, truck); insects, rodents, birds, et cetera; disease, rot, mold; excessive heat or cold.

Personal risks: Illness, injury, or death of owner or manager, or a partner; illness, injury, or death of associates or employees.

Risk of dishonesty: Theft (burglary, robbery); embezzlement, et cetera; breach of contract; manipulation of prices; failure of others to pay debts.

Business risks: Changes in value of money; liability for injury or damage; variations in the production of commodities handled; variations in production of competing commodities; political interference; any technological changes; shifts in demand; war; inadequate supplies; loss of customers; intensified competition; delays.

Price risks: Declines in prices of property owned (principally products handled); advances in prices of property contracted for delivery.

THE STORY of marketing hazards is that of a race between development of new marketing conditions in expanding markets and efforts to control the sharp practices of a few dealers or processors. For example, when berries came to be consigned to distant commission merchants, there was more need for legislation and for trade-association efforts to set forth the minimum responsibilities of commission merchants and give protection to shippers than there had been when most growers were close at hand. Obviously, legal safeguards may reduce such hazards but cannot eliminate them entirely, just as funds are embezzled from time to time despite the punishment of embezzlers.

The risk of inadequate supplies may be vital to a company that depends on continued business. Adequate supplies of essential ingredients are important to a company that has developed a brand and has devoted considerable energy and money to getting that product accepted by a body of consumers. For example, a mill will pay substan tial premiums for high-protein whea when it is scarce in order to maintai the quality of its flour brands.

THE EXTENT of risks varies amon farm products.

Proportionate risks might seem to b greatest among highly perishable com modities, such as melons and berries That is not so. Risks there are far fron unimportant, but deterioration ha been reduced by improved technique of handling and prompt movement o products to consumers. Florida or anges, for example, usually are in th hands of consumers within 2 week after picking. Furthermore, prices ar kept closely adjusted to what the con sumer will pay.

Greater aggregate marketing risk actually occur in the less perishabl commodities because they are ac cumulated by marketing agencies fo comparatively long periods. Accumula tion is the building up of inventorie by dealers and processors during th periods when farm marketings ar seasonally in excess of the consumers requirements and the subsequent with drawals from inventories. Seasona production and the demand thus ar adjusted.

Consumers play a much smaller par than formerly in carrying food forwar from harvest. Sixty years ago mos families of substance laid in a season' supply of flour in the fall. Now man buy bread every day or two. The each family filled a bin with potatoe in the fall. Now most families bu potatoes in small amounts.

The trend toward less home storag of food is offset only partly by the us of lockers and home-freezers by som families. Lack of storage space i apartments and industrial housing the larger proportion of marrie women who work for wages and hav less time to prepare food, and generally higher standard of livin contribute to greater reliance of con sumers on the accumulations of dealer and processors.

Many farmers also have a smaller part in carrying their products forward. Often they want to sell their crops at harvest. In wheat, for example, the use of combines cuts down the time required in harvesting, the use of trucks permits the wheat to be hauled to market without rehandling, and the combined wheat frequently needs more postharvest conditioning than most farmers can provide advantageously. Generally similar conditions are found in many other commodities. The trend is offset only partly by the actions of some farmers in placing their crops, unsold, in commercial warehouses.

Dealers and processors accumulate large inventories of annual crops, such as cotton and wheat. The other important accumulations may include canned, frozen, and dried fruits and vegetables, refrigerated and frozen eggs, and frozen orange concentrate. For the commodities in the latter group the accumulations make the commodities available to consumers over longer periods. For all commodities accumulated, the accumulations regulate the rate of movement into consuming channels.

Three main characteristics of accumulations affect marketing risks.

First, in contrast to the short periods that perishable commodities commonly are owned in marketing, most accumulations are owned by dealers or processors for an average of several months or more. Stocks of such commodities as cotton or tobacco frequently are owned longer. The longer the period of ownership, the greater the possibility of a decline in price. The inventory also is exposed longer to other risks, including destruction or deterioration, during its ownership.

Second, risks commonly are highly concentrated in the accumulating agency. Frequently a dealer or processor may have a peak accumulation equal to the quantities produced by several hundred or, indeed, several thousand farmers, with the result that his risks may be large in proportion to his working capital. Only a comparatively small proportion of the dealers or processors of each commodity accumulate inventories, largely because most of them lack the necessary capital or are not in a position to assume the risks.

Third, prices of the inventory must be estimated largely in advance and are arrived at on the basis of incomplete information. Each dealer or processor accumulating an inventory generally estimates in advance about how much he will buy and the maximum price that he can pay, taking into account the quantities that he expects to sell and the prices that he hopes to get. He can revise his estimates from time to time during the period of accumulation, but ordinarily his peak inventory occurs early in the season while only partial information is available.

Accordingly, the prices at which the inventory is purchased may be either higher or lower than they would have been if full information had been available for their determination.

Hope of advances in price during the period of ownership doubtless is a factor in accumulations, but business reasons often cause accumulations considerably in excess of the quantities that would be held for a price advance.

An example is the crushing of soybeans in 1948–1949. Production had increased rapidly during the Second World War and afterward, and ways of handling risks had not kept pace with the production, largely because the Government had assumed most of the risks of marketing during the war.

Suppose that a typical crusher of medium size expected to crush a million bushels in 1948–1949. He might have a plant valued at about 750,000 dollars, mortgaged for 375,000 dollars, and have working capital of about 600,000 dollars. Since most farmers sold their beans after harvest and he could buy only relatively small quantities later in the season, he might have to accumulate an inventory of about 500,000 bushels by the end of harvest. At 2.50 dollars a bushel, that would amount to about 1,250,000 dollars; he would have to borrow about 700,000 dollars if he put in 550,000 dollars of his working capital.

In such circumstances his risks were great. Doubtlessly he covered all risks like fire by insurance, as far as he could, but he could not obtain insurance against his very large price risks. Soybean prices at Illinois country points actually declined 37 cents a bushel from November 1948 to February 1949. If that decline had been suffered by the crusher on his peak inventory, the loss would have been about 185,000 dollars—or more than 30 percent of his working capital.

Crushers of soybeans accordingly were anxious to reduce their price risks. Most of such reduction they did by means of forward sales of oil and meal: About 70 percent of the oil and 60 percent of the meal in Illinois were sold for forward delivery; the greatest forward sales were early in the season. In November 1948, sales were made for delivery as much as 9 months in advance.

Largely to reduce their risks, crushers made substantial price concessions on their distant forward sales. The average discounts in November 1947 and 1948 for delivery in the following months through June were (in percentages of November prices) for oil: 2.7, 5.7, 7.5, 13.4, 13.8, 15.4, and 16.3. For meal they were 1.8, 4.7, 8.5, 10.4, 12.4, 13.0, and 13.7.

The proportions of oil and of meal sold at the various discounts are not available, but the discounts show clearly that crushers were anxious to reduce their price risks.

Such large discounts represented an extreme condition and could not continue long. Other methods of handling the risks were brought into use, and the discounts were reduced sharply, being quite small in 1952–1953. The large discounts, however, indicate some of the possible effects of accumulation on the marketing risks of a commodity, especially upon the price risks.

Of 28 farm products showing farm marketings of more than 100 million dollars in 1951, only fresh oranges and cattle and calves did not exhibit significant accumulations. Some, including tobacco and cotton, showed large accumulations in commercial channels (but farmers and ranchers themselves do on occasion hold back large numbers of cattle and calves which would normally have moved to market). There was practically no accumulation of fluid milk and ice cream, but there was a moderate accumulation of most manufactured dairy products and of fluid cream. In perishable fresh fruits and vegetables there was no accumulation, but processed products of many had substantial accumulations.

Because most farm products have moderate degrees of accumulation, it is reasonable to conclude that price risks constitute the most important risks in farm marketing, even though we cannot measure them precisely.

Risks increase the cost of marketing farm products directly by the amount of the premiums paid for insurance and indirectly by tending to restrict competition in marketing.

Risks, particularly those of loss of capital, frequently deter persons from engaging in the marketing of a given commodity. Risks keep down the operations of many marketing agencies. Otherwise increased competition would cause smaller margins of profit.

What proportion of the total cost of marketing farm products is represented by risks?

Only a general estimate can be attempted on the basis of the scanty information available. Insurance premiums paid by several hundred cooperative marketing associations of various kinds in recent years averaged between 4 and 5 percent of their operating expenses. Comparable data are not available for private companies, but some observers suggest that

4 or 5 percent may be typical. Those proportions are higher than were indicated by some data in 1925; it seems that more insurance is carried now.

Price risks and other noninsurable risks incurred in agricultural marketing are considered to be substantially greater, on the whole, than those that are covered by insurance. If the insurance premiums average 4.5 percent of the cost of marketing of all farm products, the total risks may average more than 10 percent.

Government price supports change the pattern of marketing risks and tend to reduce such risks when prices are at or below support levels. Their effects upon price risks are mainly indirect. With the exception of a few commodities in which prices are supported by purchase programs, marketing agencies that have purchased farm products outright cannot obtain Government loans or other price supports.

Availability of loans and the other assistance to farmers tends to reduce the after-harvest pressure of a crop upon the market and reduce the peak accumulation. The need for large inventories is less if substantial quantities are held by farmers under loans, because an advance above the support level will be followed by liberal farm offerings. Accumulations may be purchased at higher prices, but the existence of the support level cuts down the danger of a decline below that level later in the season.

The situation is somewhat different in years when prices are well above the support level. Then the supports have little effect upon marketing risks except that they may limit a possible drop in prices.

Risks of agricultural marketing may be handled in five main ways under private enterprise. They may be covered by insurance, reduced through increased information, reduced by combining marketing units, "transferred" to others, or assumed by the marketing agencies.

Many risks incurred in marketing farm products are covered by insurance of various kinds. Such risks are principally those in which the losses can be predicted at least with a moderate degree of accuracy, so that appropriate premiums can be determined.

Risks may be reduced by obtaining additional information concerning the conditions which give rise to the risks, thus reducing the uncertainty. In some instances this research needs to be followed by action to change the conditions.

Some hazards may be reduced by legislation restraining misbehavior or providing additional safeguards among certain marketing agencies, principally those entrusted with commodities or funds.

Risks in interstate shipments of fruits and vegetables have been cut down by the Produce Agency Act, which makes it illegal for a commission merchant to fail to account for or to dump or destroy without good reason the produce consigned to him. The Perishable Agricultural Commodities Act penalizes breach of contract by receivers. The Commodity Exchange Act provides that the commission merchants operating under it shall not commingle customers' funds with their own but shall place customers' funds in segregated accounts to protect the customers' funds if the commission house fails. Several laws provide for licensing and for minimum financial responsibility among marketing agencies entrusted with the property of others.

Risks arising from the uncertainties of the future, including the risks of price changes, have proved harder to reduce than most others, but material progress has been made, both in supplying accurate market information, and in reducing price fluctuations through purchases and crop loans. The work in prices has consisted largely of relating data of supply and demand to prices of a given commodity over a period of time.

Further work of this sort, making use of refined techniques and more detailed data, is needed. The analysis should be expanded to include the actual practices of price determination and the influence of market psychology.

Risks may be reduced also by combining small business units that perform the same types of services. A large unit can handle many risks to better advantage than a small one.

For example, a lettuce shipper who ships a car a day to 10 markets incurs smaller risks than the aggregate risks of 10 shippers who each ship 1 car a day. The larger shipper is less likely to find all his markets temporarily oversupplied or to have a large part of his funds tied up by a wreck of all 10 cars. The 10-car shipper likewise can adjust more readily to daily variations in the quantities harvested by his growers. Accordingly, risks may be reduced by combining small units that give the same services.

Greater advantages result from the combination of business units that render successive marketing service, such as wholesaling and retailing. This vertical integration lessens both the risk of losing customers and of inadequate supplies and, if the quantity handled is the same, it ordinarily reduces the ratio of risks to financial resources. The advantage of vertical integration in risk handling is further increased if the concentration of price risks before integration was great in one of the units, perhaps because of accumulation, but smaller in the other. The concentration is reduced by the combination of the two units.

Price risks and some other risks may be "transferred" to others by means of forward contracts or by hedging on organized futures markets. The word "transferred" is used here in a limited sense to indicate that while the risks may pass from one person to others the aggregate of the risk to the others on any commodity, ordinarily is not the same as it was to the first person.

For example, a processor of frozen eggs may contract in April with a baker for frozen egg whites for future delivery. The processor may be anxious to reduce his inventory risks; the baker may feel that his assumption of the price risks is a small matter, perhaps overbalanced by the risk of his inability to obtain high-quality frozen egg whites later in the season.

Such "transfers" are used most frequently to reduce burdensome inventory risks.

Forward contracts may shade into unorganized trading in futures, which under favorable conditions may ripen into organized trading in futures. As forward contracts in a given commodity are made in increasing volume season after season, both the contracts and the commodities deliverable on them tend to become standardized. It becomes easier to find someone to take the other side of the contract. A little later the contracts may begin to pass from hand to hand, and persons from outside the industry may enter the trading. The danger of breach of contract, however, increases because as contracts become more common, particularly when they pass from hand to hand, it is more difficult to restrict them to responsible persons. Hence organized exchanges with trading rules and scrutiny of responsibility of members.

Hedging as a means of handling price risks is practiced widely in the commodities having organized futures markets.

Here is an oversimplified illustration of a hedge against an inventory. A midwestern grain merchant who has 500,000 dollars may decide at the opening of the wheat season to accumulate 1,000,000 bushels of wheat for merchandising during the crop year. At 2.50 dollars a bushel the inventory would have a value of 2,500,000 dollars. He would have to borrow at least 2,000,000 dollars, or 80 percent of the value of the inventory; his banker would insist that the wheat be hedged

He hedges by contracting to sell in the futures market (in units of 5,000 bushels) quantities equal to his daily purchases of wheat. When he has accumulated the million bushels of wheat, he also has contracts to sell that quantity in the futures market. To the extent that the futures market and the cash market move in unison, any loss resulting from a decline in the price of his actual wheat, excluding commission charges, will be offset by the profit obtained by closing out his futures position at lower prices. As he merchandises his wheat, he closes out his futures position.

As a hedge against price advances, a flour mill having no wheat may sell a baker the flour equivalent of 200,000 bushels of wheat to be ground from a specified blend of wheat. Since the price of wheat may advance before the mill can find its requirements, it may contract to buy 200,000 bushels on the futures market. Then the mill can shop for the wheat required, closing out its futures position as it purchases the actual wheat.

While hedging usually provides protection against heavy losses, the protection is not automatic, and the hedger must remain alert to market changes. Small profits and losses incidental to hedging are common, because cash prices and futures prices seldom move exactly in unison. Occasionally cash and futures prices may diverge sharply and may reduce the protection ordinarily afforded by hedging.

Advantages of hedging include the convenience, speed, and economy of placing hedges and the guarantee of the exchanges that the contracts will be fulfilled. Prices of the contracts, also, are arrived at publicly under carefully worked out trading procedures. Disadvantages connected with the futures markets arise mainly from imperfections of those markets, such as the conditions that permit occasional manipulation of prices and from the inferior judgment of some of the speculators.

The most widely known forms of manipulation are the "corners" and "squeezes," which occasionally may cause sharp price changes, principally in expiring futures. They occur less frequently than in earlier years.

Perhaps the market judgment of many of the numerous speculators who predominate on the buying side in a number of important futures markets is unlikely to be as good as that of experienced dealers and processors who prefer to avoid or shift their risks by hedging.

Further improvement in handling risks is needed to increase marketing efficiency and open the way to additional economies. Substantial improvements have been effected in dealing with the marketing risks of most farm products, as indicated previously, and in the reduction of social hazards by legislation. Available evidence indicates, however, that additional improvement is possible.

The use of organized methods for handling risks contributed to reductions in the marketing margins for refrigerated butter and eggs during the 1930's. Before that period, when hedging was uncommon, sizable speculative profits in most years were expected by dealers. Toward the end of the period, when hedging was general, dealers complained that speculative profits had been sharply reduced.

Other factors, including less seasonality in egg production, also contributed to the reduction in marketing margins, but it was evident that hedging had an important part. Incomplete information points to a similar reduction in the marketing margins for grain in an earlier period.

Other information indicates improvement in handling risks in various commodities, largely as a result of gains in skill in dealing with risks by individual marketing agencies. Collective action required to institute organized methods of handling risks tends to occur less rapidly. The desire to avoid losses in individual agencies impels the persons responsible to strive to become proficient in dealing with marketing risks; in setting up organized methods of handling risks, considerable inertia may have to be overcome. Some persons may not comprehend fully how the changes will help them; some groups may enjoy an advantage and may oppose change. For example, the development of organized trading in butter and egg futures at Chicago was actively opposed by a minority, including some brokers who were losing business to organized trading.

A systematic study of marketing risks and their handling in a representative group of farm products is needed to disclose how further improvements in dealing with risks can best be effected in individual products. The study should be designed to bring out not only the current methods of handling risks in the commodities included in it, but also the effects which improvements in risk handling have had upon other functions, such as processing, in the development of commodity markets. By pointing the way to better risk handling in specific farm products the information obtained by the study would promote increased efficiency and lower costs in marketing. (*H. S. Irwin.*)

Forward Selling

Forward selling means any selling in which the seller puts off for a time some part of his obligations to deliver, to transfer title, or to perform other specified duties. It forms a large proportion of today's business transactions.

It is accomplished by agreements, which usually are binding contracts. Futures trading is the same as a great variety of other forward dealing, except that it is conducted through elaborate special trading arrangements that were explained in the preceding chapter.

The story of the development of forward selling, including futures trading, is a story of the evolution of contracts. Interwoven with it is the historical development of the institutions of private ownership of property rights, money, debt, banking, and, in fact, the whole institutional organization of credit and business today.

Before the sixteenth century, only landlords and a few wealthy people could own property and make contracts that the courts would enforce. Slaves, serfs, peddlers, and the like had few rights of citizenship and were dependent on such special privileges as were granted and enforced by feudal lords and kings. Little buying and selling were done, and that mostly at fairs or local markets.

The importance of peddlers and merchants grew in the succeeding decades as trade expanded in the yeast of many economic, political, and legal events, increased efficiency in production, evolution of property rights, and ideas regarding individual freedom. They gradually acquired rights as citizens and influence as a class.

Originally their trading had been mostly direct exchange of one commodity for another or for money. But as commerce expanded, more and more business was conducted on the basis of promises to deliver goods or make payment at a later time. In settling among themselves disputes that arose over such transactions, the merchants developed customs that came to be recognized by the courts and thus to be part of the common law.

In the process, the institution of legally enforceable contracts was established by the latter part of the sixteenth century. Since then, any party to a contract has rights of legal action to require the fulfillment of the obligations due to him. Those rights are the basis of ownership, and the property owned consists of the promises or obligations of the opposite party.

THE ESTABLISHMENT of contract enforceability was itself a major step, but it did not fully satisfy the merchants' needs. If they were to achieve a reasonable turnover of their capital instead of having it tied up while waiting for final settlement of their transactions, they needed to be able to exchange the contractual promises they owned for other goods or for money. In other words, they needed to be able to make contracts that also could be assigned or transferred to others. Major difficulties had to be overcome first. The idea of ownership and property held up to that time was that they were tangible things—people were unable to think of rights to the fulfillment of promises as property that could be owned and sold.

Promises were considered personal matters that created rights only for the persons to whom they were made.

But the advantages of being able to transfer or sell contractual rights were considerable; such sales were made in practice and became customary among merchants. Gradually they were recognized in the common law through successive court decisions in the seventeenth century. A parliamentary reversal of a final adverse court decision in 1704 completed the innovation of negotiability and provided an essential part of the foundation for modern capitalism.

All these developments are reflected in the evolution of today's various business orders, agreements, or contracts. Collectively they make up a complex system of financial assets and liabilities through which ownership claims are divided, subdivided, layered, and transferred quite independently from the possession, location, or present existence of tangible goods.

As a consequence, everyday business in a highly developed economy is characterized by the buying and the selling of a bewildering variety of contractual claims to valuable rights. Forward selling is an important part of such market activity.

In order to comprehend the real nature of forward selling, especially of the particular type represented by organized futures trading, it is necessary to distinguish the kinds of rights conveyed under at least a few familiar types of claim.

EVERY ACT of buying and selling involves a mutual agreement between parties regarding their obligations and rights. In true spot-cash dealings they are settled at once through immediate settlement by both parties. Such transactions occur in cash-and-carry retailing and somewhat in jobbing and wholesaling when retailers buy, pay for, and carry away produce from public markets.

Cash and carry is familiar to everyone, but by far the largest volume of business today involves deferred settlement in one way or another.

When the seller discharges all his obligations through the immediate performance of delivery, the buyer may have a period in which to make payment—as in the case of the retail customer who charges the item he buys and takes from the store. The item sold is exchanged for a debt claim on the buyer. The claim is an asset to the seller or creditor—a property he owns and can sell to someone else. It is not a claim to ownership rights in any specific goods. It is a general claim in terms of money.

A number of claims to money debt are in common use—accounts receivable, personal notes, bonds, bank deposits, and many others. Some establish claims that encumber the ownership of specific collateral, as in the case of mortgages. But most are general claims against the debtor and hence against all his resources. In all of them the promise or debt is defined in units of money.

While the importance of deferred payment—credit—in doing business is generally recognized, deferred performance on the opposite side of the transaction seems to be less widely understood. As a matter of fact, most business now is based on voluntary binding agreements, under which both performance by the seller and payment by the buyer are deferred.

In retail service, performance by the seller may be completed within a short period, although not always—consumers may contract for clothing to be made to order, cars to be supplied when available, or furniture to be delivered to houses that have been contracted for but not yet built. Contracts for services, for building and the like, involve deferred performance. Industrial enterprises of all kinds procure their materials to carry out their production programs and sell their products on orders that merge into contracts of various degrees of firmness. All involve forward selling.

The production, handling, processing, and distribution of agricultural commodities include extensive systems of forward selling. Even in so-called spot or cash sales on sample, as for grain or cotton, typical contracts are "to arrive" or "for shipment" within specified periods rather than immediate delivery at the time of sale. Still better illustrations are the large numbers of transactions under which feeder cattle may be delivered to Corn Belt farms on forward sales contracted by range producers, sometimes even before the animals are born.

The many forms of the contracts through which the forward selling is accomplished in agricultural markets include both contracts of sale for later delivery and contracts to sell and deliver. The former transfers rights of ownership in the specified goods and defers the physical delivery. The latter may also apply to specified items, but it defers both the transfer of ownership and delivery. The difference between them is important in the law, where it is often necessary to determine the location of title at a particular time. But this difference has little economic significance, as both establish the buyer's claim to ownership and physical control at the date of settlement.

Sellers may enter into either of these types of transaction with respect to goods they expect to produce or acquire as well as those they already possess. Contracts either of sale or to sell thus are made for animals before they are grown, canning crops before they are planted, and fruit before it has ripened on the trees. Likewise the sale of milk is contracted for extended periods into the future, and broilers are produced under contracts covering the financing of equipment, advance of chicks, feeds, and other supplies, as well as sale of the product before the enterprise is started.

Contracts need not refer to particular items or lots of goods. Many transactions are made through contracts that simply stipulate sale and delivery of certain quantities that meet stated specifications as to quality, location, or other terms. In that case the goods are said to be fungible; that is, the tender of any equivalent lot satisfies the terms of the transaction. Such transactions are common in business dealings relating to all staple agricultural products. An example is the sale by an elevator of a quantity of grain of specified type and quality without regard to which lot in its bins it might deliver.

All these forms of contracts and their many variants that occur in different markets involve forward selling in that they provide for some type of deferred performance by the seller. They differ in the degree to which they can be associated with the transfer of title or ownership of identifiable lots of specific goods.

The results are exactly like those of deferred payment, except that the claim is defined in units of commodity rather than in money.

In transactions that relate to goods that are specifically identified, direct claims to ownership or liens upon those items may be established. But when the contract is to sell and deliver items meeting specifications that do not identify any particular goods, then no direct claim to title is transferred. In that case the buyer has acquired a general claim against the seller for a consideration of value defined in commodity units. This is a debt claim precisely like that involved in deferred payment except it is stated in quantity of commodity rather than amount of money.

These commodity debt claims can be assigned to other parties just as are direct claims to titles in physical goods or claims to the payment of money debt: The buyer can sell his claim and the original seller might buy it back. In that event, the transaction would be settled and the claim extinguished by the payment of money. Alternatively, the seller might buy an identical claim from someone else and transfer it to the original buyer in exchange for the claim outstanding against him. That would constitute settlement by offset, probably the most frequent method in actual practice.

It follows, then, that a person does not need to own, or expect to acquire by producing or purchasing, actual stocks of goods in order to be a seller in such a transaction. On the contrary, he may enter into such a contract to sell in the expectation of settling solely for money, either by repurchasing the claim outstanding against him or buying an equivalent claim in the open market and tendering it as an offset. The amount of money required to settle the obligation will depend on the price of the commodity at the time.

The meaning of a wide variety of present-day market arrangements becomes apparent when they are considered in relation to the kinds of transactions and claims that have been reviewed. Contracts enable persons remotely situated from each other, or from the physical commodities with which they are concerned, to deal in transfers of ownership. To do this it is necessary that buyers and sellers have contact or access to each other, know of all available bids and offers, and have the fullest possible information regarding conditions in or affecting the market. Then they must be able to prepare forms of contract suitable to their particular transactions and in them define their obligations and rights in terms that are least likely to be misunderstood. Suitable means of certifying performance must be available, especially when the transaction calls for delivery or other performance at a point quite remote from either party.

A great variety of specialized enterprises have been established to serve buyers and sellers on every conceivable aspect of their transactions, including performance and payment. Market participants have organized to provide places and facilities for trading, for voluntary regulation of business practices or arbitration of disputes among their membership, and for various other purposes of mutual benefit. Effective use of modern systems of communications have made the markets accessible to buyers and sellers throughout the world. Custom has evolved standard forms of contracts as well as business practices.

Both voluntary association and Government action have contributed to the establishment of grading standards whereby the contract obligations with respect to performance can be stated more definitively than would otherwise be possible. Reliable services of sampling and inspection have been made available, thereby greatly facilitating the necessary certification of performance under forward sales contracts. The Government also has extended the development of information pertinent to marketing far beyond the scale and level of reliability that conceivably could have been feasible through organized voluntary action. Public regulation likewise supplements self-regulation in many respects.

All of these arrangements are costly and—with the chief exceptions of public regulation, reporting, and information services—the cost is nearly all borne by the transactions. But altogether they are economical in that for any one trader the alternative of obtaining access to the same buyers or sellers and negotiating direct transactions would be so costly as to force him to restrict his dealings to a much smaller market. The service makes it possible to realize the economic benefits of regional, national, or world markets.

WHEN THE DEVELOPMENT of economical arrangements to facilitate buying and selling has progressed to a point of reasonable adequacy in a significant market center for staple commodities of wide trade interest, there may arise the kind of forward selling characterized as the sale of debt claims stated in units of commodity.

As forward contracting expands in volume, larger numbers of contracts are resold and there tend to be more settlements by offset. With a reasonably continuous market established for representative contracts, it becomes feasible for buyers and sellers in surrounding areas, perhaps quite isolated, to enter into such transactions, since the prices at which contracts sell on the central market provide a basis for cash settlement.

This kind of trading activity seems to become established in periods when contracting expands to relatively large volume. One situation in which such expansion occurs is during war, when countries seek contracts to cover their anticipated military and civilian requirements through both public and private agencies.

The Chicago Board of Trade in 1865 adopted rules covering such forward contracting activity by its membership. Since then have developed the elaborate facilities, rules, and business arrangements that exist now for futures trading in agricultural commodities on a number of organized exchanges.

In current usage the term "futures" has become restricted to contract claims to performance established in transactions on organized exchanges.

In the earlier meaning, however, a future was any claim to a debt defined in commodity terms, but not establishing rights with respect to particular items. At present there seems to be no term that can be safely used to designate such claims in private or unorganized trading, although their aggregate volume must be great.

As now carried on, futures trading represents the evolution of market institutions to the most advanced stage of refinement and development so far attained. It is dependent on all the facilities, services, and voluntary regulation provided by the exchanges for other kinds of trading. It also employs special facilities and is governed by additional exchange rules and public supervision. Each transaction implies adherence to the rules of the exchange. The rules fix the form of contract, including its specific provisions. Only the quantity and price are left open for determination in individual transactions.

ONE OF THE ARRANGEMENTS that characterize futures trading is the modern clearing association, a subsidiary of the commodity exchange.

Typical clearing association operations provide an efficient method of settling both the obligations to deliver and the money accounts of its members. This involves setting against each other, or "clearing," the offsetting purchase contracts and sales contracts of each member, so that only balances remain to be fulfilled through actual delivery and payment.

The clearing association is a major feature of the overall system by which the safety or security of contracts is assured—each trader, whether buyer or seller, is secured against any chance of loss through default by an opposite party. Futures contracts provide for deferred payment as well as deferred sale and delivery. Clearly the property acquired by each party depends upon the assurance that the other can and will pay his debt when due. Hence the reliability or credit position of the seller is just as important to the buyer of a commodity debt as is the credit position of the buyer to the seller who holds the money debt.

In actual trading under modern exchange rules, the clearing association is substituted for the buyer in the contract to the seller and for the seller in the contract to the buyer. Hence the reciprocal commodity and money debt claims are in fact issued by the clearing association, which is responsible for the settlement of the claims acquired by each party. The claim acquired by each is in effect retained as collateral and can be resold if he does not settle his account with the clearing association. Additional collateral is provided in the system of margin requirements throughout the system. Finally, a further security is provided by all the requirements for membership in the clearing association and exchange. From such a point of view, those organized arrangements, taken as a whole, constitute an elaborate credit system providing security comparable to the banking system.

WHY ARE PEOPE interested in exchanging commodity debts for money debts, and vice versa? What bearing does such training have on the organization of production in terms of transfers of real resources?

As in all purely financial exchanges, the direct gains of one party are losses to another. Hence, if there is to be a social gain, the transactions must have some bearing upon the organization of production. The same statement can be made with respect to transactions in money debt—only if they serve some purpose in the organization of production can they yield a benefit to society.

Interpretation and explanation of the purposes served by debt transactions in the overall operation of an economy are not simple. Probably it is safe to say that most people accept transactions in money debt as having importance to business and hence to general welfare. Certainly bankers are not generally condemned for "selling something they do not have" when they make a loan to a client in the form of an increase in his deposit as shown by the bank's books, but for which the bank has no corresponding money in its vaults. But this is exactly what was said at the time banking began, and, with a reasonable modernization of the language, some of the public discussion then could be easily attributed to very recent times if only "futures trading" were substituted for "banking." Regardless of the acceptance of money debt, however, it is an abstract subject not at all well understood. Commodity debt or futures trading may be not far from the position of banking when that important business was establishing itself.

Attempts to explain the economic significance of futures trading usually run in terms of hedging and speculation. Such explanations ordinarily are based upon a concept of risk of price change in the ownership of any commodity—a risk which is proportionate to the variability of price for the commodity and the quantity owned. Speculation is conceived to be a function of specialized risk bearing. On the basis of these concepts, both of extremely dubious validity in the light of present economic knowledge, hedging is explained as an activity whereby owners of commodities shift their market risks to speculators by offsetting their commodity positions through corresponding futures transactions. Hence, futures trading is said to provide a form of price insurance through hedging and therefore a reduction in the costs of commodity business. This, of course, is an overcondensed and oversimplified statement of the case, but it indicates the essential idea.

In one special case a substantially correct, though incomplete, explanation can be developed in such terms—the case of the creditor's risk that his loan to a commodity business will not be repaid. When a bank lends money to a business, it is always concerned about the amount of the equity capital in the business as compared with the amount of its borrowings. Especially when the assets are concentrated mostly in holdings of one commodity, a prudent bank manager will not extend loans to a point where a variation in price might wipe out the owner's equity. But when the balance sheet of the business is altered by exchanging commodity debt claims for money debt claims, as it would be through offsetting or "hedging" sales in the futures market, the risk of the bank is correspondingly reduced. Hence money could be safely lent for expansion of the business beyond the point that otherwise would be possible without the owner obtaining more capital of his own.

In the illustration—an example of a conventional hedging and bank credit relationship—the business acquires additional capital with which it increases its holdings of the commodity further than it could by simply borrowing from the bank against its inventories as collateral. That is accomplished indirectly through a pattern of transactions in which, on the surface, the bank appears to have financed the increased purchases of commodity. But it has done so only because of the security afforded by the claim to a money debt obtained in exchange for the commodity debt sold in the futures market. Hence, although the bank is an important financial intermediary, it does not supply the new credit with which the business is expanded. Instead, the buyer in the futures market emerges as the investor who pledges part of his credit in the form of his debt to pay money in the future transaction. He obtains in return a claim to a debt of the business, which is like that he would have if he lent the commodity directly. So the net asset and liability effects are equivalent to what they would have been if the buyer in the futures market had purchased the commodity itself on credit and then lent it to the business.

Examined in this way, the whole situation comes to look very much like that in which broilers, for example, are produced on contract. Of course there are many variations of detail in practice, but in a typical case the "producer" owns or leases his land and supplies labor. Someone else, perhaps a feed company, may advance him baby chicks, feed, medicines, equipment, or even credit for the construction of suitable buildings. All the advances represent credit extended to the grower, against which he contracts to turn over the finished product to the lending agent for sale. From the proceeds of sale, deductions are made for repayment of the grower's debt, and the remainder is paid over to him.

Under such a contractual arrangement, it is clear that the credit advances constitute a main source of capital for the enterprise. If the goods advanced are charged at firm money prices, and if no firm price for the finished broilers is fixed in the contract, then the situation is simply one of the extension of money credit. The grower must repay a money debt out of his returns, which will depend upon the price when the product is sold.

But the contract may fix a minimum price which the company guarantees in advance for the product. To the degree that it does assure a firm price to the producer, the company is in effect a partner in the enterprise and its returns become dependent on the behavior of the market.

That is also substantially equivalent to another arrangement quite common in agriculture, the share contract, under which capital inputs are advanced, not at fixed money prices, but for a claim to some stipulated share of the product regardless of its price.

It should be possible to discern the real significance of future trading as it relates to a situation such as has been reviewed. It is an integral part of the larger system of credit through which business is financed. Not directly, but indirectly through a pattern of related transactions, buyers in the futures market invest part of their credit in financing the capital requirements of business in commodities. It is a contribution of equity capital similar to that which would be made by a partner buying a share in the business, not loan capital such as would be provided by a bank. Put somewhat differently, through the combined transactions the total business enterprise is divided and part taken over by a new enterpriser, the buyer in the futures market. About the same thing occurs when a firm decides to sell its plant and lease it back, thereby bringing in a new enterpriser as owner of the plant and releasing part of its own funds for some other purpose.

The situation illustrates one aspect of the bearing that futures trading may have upon the capital organization of a business. Even this has not been developed far enough to reveal the full enterprise position of the buyer who invests in futures. Neither does it bring out the relationship of futures trading to the determination of prices and direction of resource use.

IT MAY BE APPROPRIATE in conclusion to recognize some of the difficulties and imperfections to be found in organized futures trading.

Relatively few of them, on the whole, have to do with the facilities or machinery for executing futures transactions, almost all of which have been developed to a high level of effectiveness.

Probably the most important difficulties in futures trading relate to conditions in the market as a whole.

It has been suggested that futures transactions are best interpreted as creating a structure of debt claims. The claims are defined in relation to commodity specifications in a designated market center or centers taken as a representative base. If the system of commodity credit is to function at all satisfactorily, it is imperative that the value of the debt claim shall always be in line with the competitive price of the physical commodity.

The purpose of delivery features is to accomplish that by maintaining a kind of convertibility, whereby any seller can deliver and any buyer can demand delivery if prices diverge so that it is to their advantage to do so. But whenever the volume of debt transactions becomes too large in relation to the deliverable supplies, then the volume of deliveries demanded at times may be so great as to cause undue disturbance of prices.

Similarly, concentration of business within the sector in the hands of a few firms may create a situation in which one or more large operators may be in a position to profit by releasing or withholding supplies in anticipation of the manipulative effects they can have upon delivery or convertibility. Moreover, a variety of imperfections and frictions may differentiate or isolate the sector to a degree that will significantly reduce the precision of price adjustment. Many variants of these conditions may arise and contribute to arbitrary or manipulative deviations in the price of futures or the price of spots. To whatever degree this occurs, the integrity of the unit is destroyed, and the structure of commodity debt is correspondingly disrupted. The overall effect is like that of comparable fluctuations in the value of a currency upon dealings in money debt. (*Harold B. Rowe.*)

The Futures Markets

The futures markets, conducted by such commodity exchanges as the Chicago Board of Trade and the New

281437°—54——22

York Cotton Exchange, stand at the center of the marketing system for a number of farm commodities.

Maintaining fair play and honest dealing in futures trading—the major purpose of Federal regulation under the Commodity Exchange Act—is of vital importance in maintaining equity in the pricing and marketing of farm products on all commodity exchanges and on all markets.

Farmers are directly interested in the futures markets because futures prices are used as *base prices* in the buying and selling of cash or spot commodities, such as cash wheat or spot cotton.

Futures prices influence cash prices—whether the buying and selling of the cash commodity takes place on the floor of the Chicago Board of Trade, whether it centers around thirty-odd commodity exchanges that are not futures markets, or whether it takes place at hundreds of local markets where farm crops are sold.

In cotton, for example, only a few spot sales are made on the New York Cotton Exchange, but the trade in contracts for future delivery is so large and continuous that New York futures prices are used as a base in pricing spot cotton on all the leading spot markets, such as Houston, Dallas, and Memphis. Local cotton buyers at hundreds of country points get the day's opening price on the New York or the New Orleans futures markets before they begin buying cotton from farmers that day.

The vital relationship between futures prices and farm prices, between futures trading and farm marketing, was recognized by the Congress more than 30 years ago. Basic portions of the present Commodity Exchange Act were laid down in the Grain Futures Act of 1922. More than 200 bills were introduced in the Congress between 1884 and 1922 to regulate in some degree or prohibit entirely futures trading in farm commodities. The urge for regulation came primarily from farmers and farm organizations, although recurring corners and price manipulation had caused the public generally to look upon the futures markets as a means of gambling on the rise and fall of prices rather than as an aid to marketing.

Many centuries of history are back of the exchange system of trading in commodities. The first step in the direction of organized markets appeared when members of a primitive society assembled for the exchange of gifts or goods. Some of the earliest written records show the existence of market places. Even today the prime function of commodity exchanges is to provide a place where buyers and sellers may meet and trade.

Trading in organized markets existed in China as early as 1200 B. C. Even earlier there were markets in India, Arabia, and Egypt with some of the characteristics of exchange trading. More definite outlines appear in the early European exchanges, such as those at Bruges, Antwerp, and Amsterdam.

Almost from the beginning some form of licensing and control over markets was exercised by rulers, city governments, and market boards. As early as the fourth century B. C., the city-state of Athens supervised its markets to assure food supplies and prevent manipulation. A market law of rural England before the Norman conquest specified that certain trades must take place in borough towns "before unlying witnesses." Some means of preventing cheating and fraud and maintaining equity in the market place was early recognized as the business of the city or state, and as necessary to the preservation of the markets.

As we approach modern times, there is increasing evidence of dealings in time contracts. The purchase of goods in ships still at sea was an early development in commerce—a practice that might be considered a form of trading and speculation in commodities for future delivery. A merchant, having purchased a cargo of goods at a specified price, for arrival at a later date, would resell or transfer his rights as buyer to another buyer before the shipment arrived at port. The entry of shrewd merchants and speculators into this type of trade came early and provided a short bridge to broader participation in speculation by citizens generally.

THE HISTORY of the Chicago Board of Trade, the oldest futures market in the United States (but not the oldest grain exchange) shows that a large volume of trading and speculation in time contracts came before the adoption of exchange rules for futures trading and the development of hedging as a common commercial practice.

The Chicago Board of Trade was organized in 1848 to accommodate a rapidly expanding cash grain trade. Early instances of time contracts were greatly accelerated in the period of rising prices, speculation, and inflation during the Crimean War (1854–1856). At times during the war speculation in time contracts was heavy and almost continuous. In August 1856, for instance, a single lot of 15,000 bushels of corn in 2 days passed through 14 hands, and in those transfers settled contracts for some 200,000 bushels—time contracts were the subject of speculation then in about the same sense that we now have so-called organized speculation in futures.

This suggests that futures trading as such was not invented, as is often said, to provide merchants and dealers in commodities with hedging facilities as a protection against ownership risks. It developed rather because of the need to find a more convenient and orderly mechanism for speculating in commodities than the time contract afforded.

The pattern of rising prices and accelerated speculation in time contracts in Chicago during the Crimean War was reenacted on a larger scale during the Civil War years. The trading volume and membership of the Chicago Board of Trade greatly increased. Exchange officials and conservative merchants frowned on the excessive wartime speculation in futures, and "hoped that with the return of peace," as the exchange secretary wrote, "this fever of speculation will abate, and trade will be conducted on a more thoroughly legitimate basis."

The fact was that futures contracts had already become so important to members, and the need for some equitable method of settling disputes over contracts so urgent, that the exchange was compelled to act. In a special meeting on October 13, 1865, written rules were adopted governing margin payments and other practices, thereby for the first time recognizing futures trading as a commercial practice.

ACCELERATED SPECULATION in time contracts, which in the Civil War period transformed the Chicago grain trade into a dominant futures market, also manifested itself in the Liverpool cotton trade during the same period.

"Before the American war," Thomas Ellison wrote in 1886 in his study of the British cotton trade, "only a very trifling business was done in cotton to arrive, the operations of speculators being confined mainly to transactions on the spot. During the war, however, but especially towards its close, the arrival business became very important; while, owing to the extra facilities afforded to operators, it has of late years almost entirely superseded speculative transactions in cotton on the spot."

The accelerated wartime speculation in arrival contracts was a decisive factor in causing the conservative Cotton Brokers Association of Liverpool to adopt written rules for the first time (1863) and recognize futures trading.

Conservative British cotton brokers and merchants did not accept the development of cotton futures trading during the 1860's and 1870's without strenuous resistance.

"They ignored the fact that a very objectionable style of speculative business had forced itself into the market," Ellison wrote, "and that it would be to the interest of sober trade to have this class of business put under some sort of control. They objected to periodical settlements in cotton as a species of commercial heresy. . . . The legitimate merchants and spinners of Lancashire were at present only harassed occasionally by the gambling operations of the 'bulls' and 'bears'; but with a system of periodical settlements they would have the market 'cornered' or 'squeezed' every month or every fortnight; so they elected rather to bear the ills they had than fly to those they knew not of."

Yet in time the Liverpool trade came to the same basic conclusion reached earlier in Chicago; namely, that the speculative trade in futures had become so extensive that the "legitimate" trade should recognize it, and attempt to control it, rather than fight it.

It had become fairly common in the 1880's and 1890's for merchants and processors to use the grain and cotton futures markets for the nonspeculative type of trading known as "hedging," that is, to seek protection on inventories and requirements in actual commodities by making offsetting sales and purchases in futures.

Yet the speculative interest in futures trading continued to be so much larger and more obvious that the terms "speculative markets" and "speculative exchanges" were applied to the futures markets to distinguish them from the cash or spot commodity markets. This practice continued until about the time of the First World War, both in common parlance and in economic writings. Even today the statistical yearbooks of the Chicago Board of Trade, in referring to their price tables for wheat, corn, oats, et cetera, retain the language of the early period: "Daily current prices for the leading speculative articles, at Chicago."

Under the commodity exchange act, the operation of futures markets in the commodities covered and the dealings in futures by futures commission merchants and floor brokers are privileges that may be exercised only on the basis of Federal licensing and registration.

That means that it is unlawful in the United States to conduct a futures market in regulated commodities except on an exchange that has applied for and obtained "designation" under the act as a "contract market." The Chicago Board of Trade, the New York Cotton Exchange, and 15 other futures exchanges are designated as federally licensed markets.

The nature of commodity exchanges is such that most of those who trade must do so through brokers and must necessarily place a high degree of trust and confidence in brokers. The Commodity Exchange Act requires the annual registration of all brokerage firms and individuals engaged as futures commission merchants (those who solicit or accept the buying and selling orders of commodity customers), and all floor brokers executing orders for others on the floor of an exchange.

Registrations in 1953 covered the offices of about 1,800 futures commission merchants and agents and about 800 floor brokers.

The annual registration and related compliance work of the Commodity Exchange Authority has a considerable preventive effect in holding down unfair and wrongful brokerage practices. It enables a small regulatory personnel to maintain contact with the hundreds of brokers and agents through whom the buying and selling orders of thousands of "outside customers" reach the markets. It enables the Government to discipline the small but persistent number of registered brokers who willfully violate the act and to prosecute unregistered operators caught swindling the public.

Maintaining equity in commodity brokerage practices is concerned with the manner in which brokers execute the orders of customers and also with the financial practices of brokers in handling and accounting for customers' funds.

The Commodity Exchange Act requires all futures commission merchants to segregate and separately account for the funds of their customers—the use of one customer's funds to finance other customers' transactions or those of the brokerage house is prohibited. Periodic audits are made to enforce the requirements.

Approximately one-third of the language of the act deals with the designation requirements of contract markets. The enforcement of the requirements is an active and continuing phase of Federal regulation. It seldom involves spectacular measures. Seldom has it been necessary to take formal measures to require a contract market to adopt United States standards in commodity grading (as required by the act), to maintain post-trading periods for deliveries on futures contracts (to prevent squeezes), to furnish copies of exchange records or minutes of committee or board meetings (particularly in reference to price decisions and defaults on futures contracts), or formally to remind an exchange of its responsibility as a designated contract market to take effective measures against price manipulation and corners.

The act grants power to suspend the designation of a contract market, but only once in 30 years has a suspension been formally ordered. The purpose on that occasion (in 1932) was not to close the market concerned (the Chicago Board of Trade), but to compel the exchange to recede from its refusal to grant full membership and clearing privileges to the federally sponsored Grain Stabilization Corporation, which wai set up on a cooperative basis to support grain prices. The Corporation was making large purchases in the wheat futures market, and clearing privileges were needed for economical operation. The exchange appealed to the courts, but receded from its position on the cooperative issue before the litigation was completed. No contract market since then has seriously contested the right of farmers' cooperatives to membership on an exchange on equal terms with others.

The high degree of standardization in futures contracts, the heavy concentration of trading on a single floor, the rapid-fire execution of the buying and selling orders, and the continuous stream of price quotations—these services of a modern futures market are made possible only by an intricate network of bylaws, rules, regulations, and resolutions, constantly subject to change. The market designation work of the Commodity Exchange Authority consists largely of careful and laborious examination of the official actions of exchanges, and continuous contacts with market officials to determine compliance with the requirements of the act.

The significance of the work may be illustrated by reference to a single phase of futures-market activity, that pertaining to deliveries on futures contracts. In practice, deliveries on futures contracts are usually not good business for either speculators or hedgers and rarely bulk large in a smooth-running futures market. Yet the maintenance of sound delivery practices and adequate delivery facilities, whereby delivery rights may readily be converted to actual commodities, is the vital factor that ties cash and futures together. The prices resulting from futures transactions otherwise would have no solid connection with the actual commodity. Inadequate or unworkable delivery systems invite arbitrary price settlements, defaults on futures contracts, and manipulative activities that churn and distort futures prices and drive away hedgers.

A consideration of those problems helps to explain why the Commodity Exchange Authority keeps watch on the grades of commodities deliverable, delivery facilities, and exchange-designated points of delivery—why the Authority compiles and publishes grain stocks in federally licensed warehouses in Chicago, why a copy of each delivery notice issued by a short in a contract market must be furnished to the Authority, and why detailed and current information is required on the storage capacity, storage charges, and fire-insurance rates, of the individual warehouses employed in the delivery of commodities in satisfaction of futures contracts.

THE TREND in development of the futures market over the years has contributed to increase the need for market designation work. Not that the number of commodity exchanges has increased appreciably; the number of commodities traded in for future delivery on existing exchanges has increased significantly. The Chicago Board of Trade, for example, has been a designated grain futures market since 1922, but has conducted futures trading in soybean oil only since 1950, and in soybean meal and grain sorghums only since 1951.

Of the commodities now under the act, only 10 had any considerable volume of futures trading 30 years ago, namely, wheat, corn, oats, barley, rye, cotton, cottonseed oil, lard, butter and eggs. Today there are nearly twice that number. Some of the commodities in which futures trading has been started or has had strong growth during this period are soybeans, soybean oil and meal, cottonseed meal, wool tops, eggs, and potatoes.

Wartime conditions and international trade barriers and currency restrictions closed most of the futures markets in the Old World and contributed to restrict the services of American futures markets in international trade, particularly in grains and cotton. Yet there has been a sound development of futures trading in this country, particularly in the produce commodities, fats and oils, and feedstuffs.

Obviously, the maintenance of services and facilities in long-established markets may require as much attention as those of more recent development. In general, however, a larger number of new trading practices, and a larger number of new problems, arise in the latter. Furthermore, when a smaller futures market, or trade market, begins to attract substantial public participation and greater pricing importance, its problems are likely to increase. This has happened in soybeans, eggs, potatoes, and wool tops.

It is hardly surprising that futures markets should experience growing pains in their formative stage and that regulatory problems in newer markets should be particularly difficult when wartime conditions, inflationary forces, and changing supply and demand situations have disturbed all markets. What is more surprising is that some of the more recently developed markets have been able to resist the recurrent tides of speculation and manipulative activity. Undoubtedly the newer markets have gained much from the experience of the older ones and have benefited from Federal regulation.

TO MAINTAIN EQUITY on commodity exchanges, persons responsible for regulation must know what is going on in the markets.

How is it possible for a small Federal agency such as the Commodity Exchange Authority to keep track of traders and trading on futures markets where the trading volume in terms of contract units is more than 8 million transactions a year, and the dollar value of the transactions ranges from 30 billion to 50 billion dollars a year?

Such a task would scarcely be possible had not the framers of the act clearly granted, and the courts sustained, regulatory power to examine at any time the books and records of contract market members, and the operations of traders.

From 1923 onward, daily recordkeeping and reporting requirements have been in force, first in grain and later in cotton and other commodities brought under the act. The main elements of this reporting system are the daily reports from several hundred members of exchange clearinghouses (somewhat similar to bank clearinghouses) and daily reports from 400 to 500 large traders. From the reports of exchange clearing members, showing the transactions and commitments of their customers and house accounts, the Commodity Exchange Authority compiles and releases daily data on the volume of trading and open contracts in the markets. The daily reports from large traders provide essential information on speculative and hedging transactions in the upper levels of market activity.

One reason advanced in the early period of regulation in opposition to the reporting requirements was that such reports would result in the disclosure of business secrets and weaken the legitimate competitive positions of brokers and traders. The original legislation, however, specifically prohibited disclosure of the identities of traders or other information reported in confidence, and from the very first the Grain Futures Administration (now the Commodity Exchange Authority) observed the requirements so carefully that no legitimate grounds for complaint arose.

A factor of concern in the early period of regulation was that Government inspection and the publication of data showing the large volume of trading in futures and the extent of speculative short selling would antagonize farmers. The number of farmers who believed that the volume of futures trading in wheat and corn far exceeded the size of the actual crops (as indeed it did) was greater than the number who understood why. In the absence of specific knowledge on the character and volume of futures trading, exaggerated guesses as to the size of the trading, and the cost of the futures system to agriculture, gained wide acceptance.

Today, and for many years past, volume-of-trading figures showing futures transactions more voluminous than cash transactions are published every day. Letting the public see the figures on futures trading has brought understanding rather than hostility toward the work of the exchanges.

On two occasions the reporting requirements for large traders were suspended—from February 26, 1927, to October 31, 1927, and from October 24, 1932, to July 20, 1933. Both times the reporting requirements were suspended during periods of low farm prices to test the validity of persistent claims by trade interests that reporting requirements were keeping speculative buyers out of the markets. The opposite proved to be the case. In 1927 and 1932, wheat futures prices, following the suspension of reporting requirements, went down instead of up, and in November 1932 fell to the lowest level in the history of the markets. In both instances large speculators were heavily net short before the suspension. Additional short selling after the suspension further increased profits of professional speculators net short and contributed to the decline in prices reflected to farmers. Available records for the depression years show that large speculators were heavily net short most of the time, and that the major portion of the new buying in wheat futures came from the smaller speculators.

The regulatory task of enforcing the recordkeeping and reporting requirements under the act is likely to continue without becoming much larger or much smaller. The principles and objectives involved in this phase of market regulation have been accepted. Responsible elements of the trade have come to recognize that much of the public goodwill which the exchanges today enjoy stems from the routine publication of market data.

The licensing of markets and publication of market information would win little respect, however, if the major threat to competition in the market were not effectively dealt with. Monopolistic forces must be challenged in specific situations. The acid test of futures market regulation is the prevention or suppression of price manipulation, including manipulation in the extreme form known as the market corner. In plain terms, the job of regulation is to uncover the operations of the manipulator, marshall the evidence against him, charge him publicly as provided by law, and put him out of the market.

The record in this phase of enforcement is found in a long series of administrative proceedings and Federal court decisions, going back to the twenties. Not all the decisions sustained the Government, particularly during the early period, but over the years judicial opinion and Federal court decisions have weighed increasingly against price manipulation and cornering.

Keeping open the channels of market competition by suppressing price manipulation is not all a story of litigation, however. Behind it is a change in public opinion. The act of 1922 merely marked a turning point in the gradual change. From the changed public attitude toward market privileges and market responsibilities came the congressional amendments of 1936, which authorized criminal prosecution of price manipulators and cornerers, and the further authorization to put specific "speculative limits" on large-scale operations which may rock price structure—whether or not there is "intent" to manipulate.

As the opportunities for manipulation by the individual speculator and market leader have narrowed, manipulative attempts by groups of speculators and large corporations have come increasingly into view, and present more complex enforcement problems.

In the group manipulative activity, the size and timing of the operations of no one member of the group may give evidence of manipulation, but the concerted activity of the several members may move the price in the desired direction. In some instances officials of commodity merchandising firms have attempted to add manipulative profits to merchandising profits by accumulating large long positions in expiring futures in order to run up the price and "squeeze" the shorts. In other instances large firms have attempted to maneuver cash commodity stocks and short futures positions in such a way as to depress the price of the near future in relation to a distant month—so that cash commodities bought on a depressed market may be carried forward or delivered in the futures market at a relatively assured profit. Such activities indicate why the Commodity Exchange Authority must be continuously on guard against price manipulation in the futures markets.

What are the standards required for the maintenance of equity and integrity on commodity exchanges?

Most of the Federal requirements for the maintenance of equity on commodity exchanges, as provided under the Commodity Exchange Act, may be indicated as follows:

Federal licensing of futures markets and the registration of commodity brokers;

Maintenance of trading records, and required reports by brokers and traders;

Prevention of price manipulation and corners;

Prevention of dissemination of false and misleading crop or market information to influence prices;

Restraints to curb heavy speculation by large traders;

Recognition of rights of cooperative associations to membership privileges on commodity exchanges;

Recognition and safeguarding of the hedging services of the markets;

Protection of the trading public against cheating and fraud in commodity brokerage transactions;

Trust-fund treatment of margin moneys and equities of hedgers and other traders to prevent the misuse of such funds by brokers;

Prevention of wrongful floor trading practices such as "bucketing" and "wash sales," which are fictitious transactions for the purpose of circumventing the competitive market and quoting artificial prices.

But responsibility for the maintenance of equity on commodity exchanges does not devolve solely upon the Federal Government. A great part of the field of trading supervision rests with the exchanges. The Commodity Exchange Act leaves the exchanges virtually undisturbed in their powers to admit members and select officers, to discipline offenders and expel members, to determine delivery months and contract terms, to fix price-fluctuation limits, margin requirements, and brokerage fees and commissions, and to exercise many other important prerogatives.

To fill a joint responsibility, one policy has been continued: To make clear and definite recommendations for legislation as to regulation when needed, and in the administration of existing powers to avoid broad or loose interpretations. In protecting the public interest in the markets, it is better to have regulation that may not prove wholly effective in every conceivable situation than to have regulation not based firmly on the public will and understanding. (*J. M. Mehl.*)

How Marketing Is Financed

A large volume of financing is required to move more than 30 billions of dollars' worth of raw farm products through marketing channels each year.

Financing by banks, insurance companies, cooperative credit agencies, and the like is especially important in meeting seasonal requirements for the movement of many farm products and in supplying a moderate volume of long-term credit for plant expansion and similar purposes.

But very likely two-thirds or more of the funds employed by marketing agencies engaged in the processing and distribution of farm products is supplied by those who are themselves engaged in the marketing, processing, and distributing trades.

The role of the purely financing agency is primarily one of providing supplementary capital, on a short or longer term basis, to enable the marketing agency to function more effectively or on a larger scale than otherwise would be possible.

Some marketing activities for certain farm products are often regarded as "underfinanced," when actually the difficulty is the lack of adequate capitalization by those engaged in the marketing activities. Men engaged in financing must be cautious therefore lest they assume the risks that properly belong to the owners of the marketing agencies.

Several factors have strongly influenced the financing of farm marketing activities in recent years: The generally higher level of prices and costs, the continuous necessity for the modernization of marketing facilities, geographical shifts in areas of production, and changes in consumer preferences as to processing, packaging, or type of retail outlet favored.

The funds required to finance the movement of a crop when prices are high are substantially greater than those required for the movement of the same crop when prices are low. For canned fruits and vegetables the financial requirements for handling the season's pack have been increased because costs of the raw products have gone up and because cans, shipping containers, labor, other supplies, and freight also have increased. Market men have found it necessary or desirable therefore to expand their working capital funds so they could obtain the volume of credit required to carry on a normal volume of business at the higher level of costs and prices.

Capital expenditures by the manufacturers of food and kindred products alone in 1951 and 1952 are estimated at 1,250 million dollars. The total amount of capital invested in industries engaged in processing foods, beverages, tobacco, and textile products was estimated at 25 billion dollars in 1949. That estimate, however, does not include the capital invested in marketing agencies of a nonmanufacturing character, such as country elevators, cotton gins, assembly plants, and the like. Large capital expenditures are required to maintain existing facilities and services aside from the needs of continuing modernization.

Plant modernization—new facilities to provide for growth of markets and to take advantage of new methods, techniques, or equipment—usually requires long-term financing. It may take the form of permanent capital supplied by the owners of the enterprise, or it may be in the form of reasonably long-term loans supplied by banks, insurance companies, or other investors. During most of the time since 1945 there has been an ample supply of long-term investment funds to meet the needs for this type of financing. Furthermore, the prevailing requirements of the income-tax laws have encouraged the financing of expansion and modernization through long-term loans and other interest-bearing obligations, rather than through the sale of common and preferred shares, since interest paid on loans can be deducted from income as a business expense.

Long-term loans usually range from 3 to 15 years. The maximum maturity of such loans by commercial banks is commonly 5 to 7 years. Insurance companies usually limit their loans to the larger and well-established concerns but at the same time are interested in longer maturities.

Long-term financing may take the form of plant and facility mortgage loans or general unsecured long-term notes or bonds. The smaller firms usually pledge their facilities as security. The larger firms can often borrow on the basis of long-term unsecured notes. Rates of interest have reflected the financial strength of the borrower and the general level of long-term money rates. In the early postwar period, a considerable volume of such financing was arranged at rates varying from 3 to 4.5 percent. Rates have increased since then because of the heavy demand for long-term funds and the general increase in money rates.

A LARGE PORTION of the financing required by marketing agencies is for the purpose of carrying inventories. The requirements have varied greatly with the nature of the product and the length of time required for processing and distribution.

A cotton gin, for example, may engage in the marketing of its customers' products and yet may carry practically no inventory by reason of prompt sale of cotton and cottonseed as rapidly as the cotton is ginned. The cotton merchant, however, will ordinarily accumulate a substantial inventory of cotton during the harvesting season and liquidate it gradually throughout the year. He can minimize his market price risks by forward sales to mills or by hedging on the futures market. Because of their ability to minimize the market risks incident to the carrying of inventories, cotton merchants can obtain inventory financing in large volume at relatively low rates of interest and for a relatively high proportion (usually up to 85 percent) of the funds required for carrying inventories.

Similar financing conditions prevail with respect to the carrying of inventories of wheat and other grains where adequate facilities for hedging price risks on inventories are available.

For many processed or semiprocessed products, however, there are no adequate means of protecting the holders of inventories from the risk of substantial fluctuations in prices while such products are moving through the channels of trade from producer to consumer.

Canned fruits and vegetables normally fall in that category. A season's supply of a canned fruit or vegetable usually must be packed during a short harvest season. The inventory accumulated by the canner must then be merchandised over the entire season. The canner's inventory represents not only raw products but expenditures for labor, cans, and other supplies, which far exceed the actual investment in raw products purchased from the farmer. The canner who requires financing in order to carry his inventory can usually borrow from his bank up to 60 or 70 percent of the net wholesale value of his product at a time of packing. The remainder of the funds for carrying inventory the canner must supply from his own funds or from temporary book credits from suppliers, growers, and others.

As to items that are in short supply, the canner can often reduce or eliminate his inventory financing problem by making prompt sales to distributors who are willing to anticipate future needs and protect themselves against possible price advances due to relative shortage. In that event the distributor supplies the financing from his own or borrowed funds and assumes whatever price risk may result from carrying the inventory until it is moved into the hands of retailers or consumers.

Inventory financing is handled on both an unsecured and a secured basis. Much of the bank financing of such commodities as cotton and grains is supported by warehouse receipts for such commodities issued by agencies engaged in storing or warehousing activities. Many food-processing companies establish "field warehouses" on their own premises and turn the custody of their products over to a "field warehousing" agency. It in turn issues warehouse receipts, which may be used to support inventory loans. Such arrangements are used extensively in connection with the financing of processed fruits and vegetables and similar products.

A LARGE VOLUME of inventory financing is handled on the basis of unsecured seasonal lines of bank credit, particularly for such extensive food-processing industries as meatpacking, flour milling, and the manufacture and distribution of dairy products. Such seasonal credits are usually outstanding for relatively short periods and are normally retired within the seasonal marketing period.

The volume of such seasonal loans is not reported. An indication of their importance is that 215 commercial banks reported an increase of 932 million dollars in their loans to food, liquor, and tobacco companies between July and December 1951. Those banks handle about 70 percent of the total of commercial and industrial loans of all banks. The seasonal increase in the second half of 1951 was followed in the first half of 1952 by a decrease of 868 million dollars in the volume of such loans. The second half of 1952 again showed an increase of 752 million dollars in such loans. Because these figures represent only the net change in outstanding loans, it is apparent that the aggregate volume of such lending would be several times larger than the reported net increase figures.

The availability of adequate financing for farm marketing enterprises over any extended period depends primarily upon the success of such enterprises. The financing of a flourishing new frozen fruit juice enterprise does not become a problem until and unless the industry overexpands in relation to available markets to the point where the stability of the industry and the solvency of the enterprises engaged in the industry are threatened. At that point it may develop that "financing" by strictly financing agencies has been overdone in relation to the risk capital supplied by those engaged in marketing. Those engaged in financing new enterprises or new developments in marketing therefore must try to assure themselves that their role in the financing of marketing is a secondary or supplementary role. Financing that goes beyond that point may lead to unwilling ownership or a management responsibility that properly belong to the owners of the enterprise.

Special financing has been available to cooperatively owned farm marketing agencies since the establishment of the Federal Farm Board in 1930 and more particularly since the establishment of the banks for cooperatives in 1934. The 12 banks for cooperatives and the Central Bank for Cooperatives operated under the supervision of the Farm Credit Administration supply credit to cooperative farm marketing agencies. The banks, largely capitalized with Government funds, make seasonal, working capital and long-term facility loans available to eligible cooperatives.

The banks for cooperatives extended loans to farm marketing and farm-supply cooperatives in the amount of 537 million dollars for the fiscal year that ended June 30, 1952. Outstanding loans on June 30, 1952, amounted to 342 million dollars, of which 234 millions were to cooperatives engaged in marketing farm products. Of that amount, 123 millions were long-term loans, 174 millions were short-term working capital loans, and 45 millions were loans secured by commodities. About one-half of the long-term loans and one-third of the working capital loans were to cooperatives engaged in farm supply and business service activities, as distinct from the usual functions of marketing farm products for the account of farmer members.

These specialized lending agencies have some important advantages over privately owned credit agencies in lending to farm cooperatives. As specialized credit agencies dealing with only one class of borrowers, and backed by a substantial Government investment on a no-interest cost basis, the banks have generally offered credit to cooperatives at rates below the competitive market for similar types of loans made by commercial banks and insurance companies to similar marketing agencies, cooperative or noncooperative.

In some areas also these credit institutions have been able to offer cooperatives credit services that would not be feasible for the local banks because of the limited availability of local lending funds or the long-term capital requirement for facility financing. Often the cooperative bank personnel may be able to provide a type of specialized credit and management counsel that would be beyond the scope of financing agencies not customarily staffed to deal with such specialized problems.

The financing of the marketing of several important farm products has been greatly influenced since 1933 by the lending and other price-support activities of the Commodity Credit Corporation. This has been particularly true of cotton, wheat, corn, and certain types of tobacco, although the price-support activities of CCC have not been limited to those crops.

The availability of CCC price-support loans to farmers often has an important bearing on the financing available to marketing agencies engaged in carrying their normal merchandising inventories of such commodities.

During any period in which a large volume of any particular crop is placed under a CCC loan program, the possibility of a drastic decline in prices below the official loan level is minimized or eliminated during the life of the loan commitment. Thus the risk of financing reasonable inventory or merchandising requirements of such commodities for those engaged in marketing them may be minimized.

Likewise in the case of uncertainty as to the continuance of a particular loan program or as to changes in important terms and conditions of such loans, the short-term hazards of normal financing may be exaggerated and normal financing may become unduly restrictive.

The Commodity Credit Corporation loans for designated commodities are available to farmers in most instances either through local banks which act as lending agencies under CCC programs or through local agencies of the CCC itself. Banks that sign lending-agency agreements with the CCC can make loans direct to eligible farmers in accordance with procedures established by the CCC and continue to carry the paper until the maturity of the loan period prescribed by the CCC. Banks following this procedure are allowed compensation on such loans at 3 percent per annum (March 1954). In the event that the producer repays the loan and redeems the collateral, the bank remits to CCC 1 percent of the 4 percent interest charged the producer. The CCC, however, stands ready under the lending-agency agreement to take the loan off the hands of the bank at its face value and accrued interest at any time. The bank therefore has a riskless loan so long as it handles its loans in accord with the provisions of the CCC lending-agency agreement.

The primary objective of CCC loans is to support the prices of the commodities on which such loans are made at some predetermined level. If the available supplies of such commodities do not move into consumption at or above the "support" level, there is a tendency for the excess or most of it to move into the commodity loan or purchase programs of the CCC.

The accumulation of supplies by CCC usually causes the regular marketing agencies to be cautious about their inventories. That in turn may tend to exaggerate the volume of the commodity that is placed under the CCC loan program. Thus the financing that is normally supplied by the regular marketing agencies and their normal sources of credit is shifted to a considerable extent to the Commodity Credit Corporation.

Since the objective of CCC financing is price support or price maintenance rather than marketing as such, it is only natural that the normal marketing and financing agencies will endeavor to shift to the CCC all of the risks involved in financing of this type. There is some evidence to indicate that long-continued activities of this type tend to destroy the normal incentives for marketing agencies and their supplementary sources of financing to perform their normal marketing functions. On the other hand, however, the CCC has endeavored to encourage the handling of much of its paper through private facilities and price support is of course not a function of the private banking system.

The volume of trading in futures markets tends to be curtailed or distorted so that the value of such markets for hedging purposes is impaired. Storage requirements tend to fluctuate over a wider range with pressure upon CCC to engage in marketing functions separate from merely providing financing. In practice, the wide range of experience between conditions of severe depression and wartime scarcities and food management activities have not made it possible as yet fully to clarify the role of CCC as one of the financing agencies with which the marketing and financing agencies must reckon, either as a supplementary supplier of credit or as a competitor.

Capital and credit tend to flow toward successful enterprises. That is just as true in relation to those engaged in the marketing of farm products as it is with respect to other segments of our fast changing economy.

Over-generous financing that leads to unnecessary duplication of facilities and possibly higher marketing costs may be just as harmful in some segments of the marketing structure as inadequate financing and lack of desirable competition would be in other circumstances.

In most phases of farm marketing in recent years the lack of adequate financing of the type that can properly be supplied by strictly financing agencies such as banks, cooperative banks, and insurance companies has not been a major problem. (*Jesse W. Tapp.*)

Prices, Pricing

A key to how well we think the market is doing its job is our satisfaction or dissatisfaction with prices, for prices help decide farmers' incomes on the one hand and consumers' costs on the other. Economists explore many aspects of a controversial issue—competition and pricing—and advance their own opinions, some of which are presented here. Several programs of the Department of Agriculture provide price assistance to farmers. The most important, price-support programs, bring into the market place an additional type of buyer—the Government—a potential buyer with relatively unlimited financial resources. The Government competes with commercial buyers, but unlike them, its objective is to stabilize prices received by farmers rather than to make a profit. Another program is marketing agreements and orders. The agreements and orders provide the means of regulating the prices of fluid milk and the supplies of vegetables and fruits in order to effect orderly marketing and improve prices to producers.

The Place of Competition

The basic factor that keeps markets in line with one another at different levels, in different places, at different times, and for different commodities is competition among the buyers and sellers.

Competition in the performance of any marketing function generally assures that charges for performing it do not get far out of line with the costs involved. If based on accurate information, competition will cause the goods to flow from one market to another whenever the price differential between them exceeds the intervening costs.

Prices of food in different stores in the same community are tied together by the possibility that consumers will shift their purchases from one store to another if the prices and services they offer get out of line. Such competition is most obvious when two foodstores are side by side or in the same shopping center. Competition of a more complex sort occurs between the large supermarket and the small grocery-delicatessen. If the latter's prices get too high, some consumers will forego buying, until their next chance to visit a larger store or shopping center.

Perfect competition means perfect knowledge of alternative opportunities on the part of each buyer and each seller. Not that every consumer needs to know the prices charged for a given commodity by every seller in the United States. It may be enough that he know the price policies of half a dozen retail stores in his community. The cost in time, inconvenience, and actual transportation outlays of grocery shopping in a neighboring town or even in a distant part of the same town is usually so high that only a small number of relatively nearby stores are of real interest to him. He may not even be curious about prices in foodstores in other parts of a large city because of the ties he knows (or assumes) exist between the individual retail stores. He may know or assume that the national chains or local chains of supermarkets maintain common price policies in his area. Also, consumers living a few blocks away from him are shopping in some of the stores which he patronizes and also in two or three stores which are beyond his reach. That factor in itself tends to produce a great deal of cohesion among prices in different stores in a city even though the purchase habits of most individual consumers may be highly routinized.

But the retail food market in a city is tied together in other ways as well. An individual retailer may keep track of the price policies and major price changes of his main competitors. He or a representative may shop the competing stores often enough so that he thinks he knows pretty well what they are doing. In addition, the leaders or best buys of some of the larger competitors are advertised in newspapers each week, so that other retailers and consumers are informed of the more spectacular price changes. Through market news reports and the sales representatives of wholesale grocers and processors, he knows pretty well what most of his competitors pay at wholesale for the products they buy.

Just as the behavior of consumers and retailers integrates the retail market structure of a city, the behavior of carlot purchasers in terminal markets helps to integrate the market structure between major producing and consuming centers. If the same commodity is produced in both remote and nearby areas, the carlot receiver often finds it advantageous to buy from the nearer source. The buyer's main objective is to obtain any given commodity at the lowest cost as delivered to him. When he compares prices at different shipping points he must allow for differences in transportation costs from the various points to his own terminal.

In each producing area or processing center, shippers make similar calculations. The shipper's usual goal is to sell his products in the markets that will return him the highest net price at the point of shipment. When he compares prices at different terminal markets, he must deduct transportation costs to determine which will yield him the highest net return.

Thus the nationwide market is tied together through the action of buyers in all consuming centers trying to buy from the cheapest source and by sellers in all producing or processing centers trying to sell in the most remunerative market.

On perishable products, daily market news reports are issued in many of the large consuming centers and at many of the more important shipping points. When the reports indicate that a certain shipping point is an unusually cheap source for a given terminal, buyers at that terminal will direct most of their orders to the given shipping point. If reports indicate that a certain terminal is an unusually profitable destination for a particular shipping point, shippers there will intensify their selling efforts in the given terminal. The redirection of shipments speedily eliminates unusual advantages to either buyers or sellers. For example, west coast shippers of fruits and vegetables have long availed themselves of the possibility of diverting rolling cars from one market to another in the same general direction. If the price of California oranges in Baltimore on one day is significantly out of line with the price in Washington, D. C., the situation usually can be corrected within 24 to 48 hours.

Besides watching the daily market news reports, large shippers and buyers are in frequent telegraphic or telephone communication with their chief customers or suppliers. Large processing concerns like some of the meatpacking and milling companies maintain branch houses or sales offices in major consuming centers and thus keep in close touch with retail markets in many parts of the country. The purchasing departments of the large concerns keep in touch with the producer and f. o. b. markets for the raw products. Chainstores perform a somewhat similar function in that they watch f. o. b. markets in all parts of the United States as well as retail markets in the communities they serve. Some of the large farmers' cooperatives also keep in contact with the market on a nationwide scale.

A smaller food processor maintains contact with wholesale buyers in the consuming centers which fall within his natural marketing territory. He also maintains contact with farmers and shipping-point markets in the areas which are for him feasible sources of supply. The time and cost involved in transporting raw materials from long distances to a given plant limit the area within which he is an active competitor for supplies.

Similarly, an individual farmer may be particularly interested in the activities of only a few buyers or in prices at only a few markets. Sometimes he may know from experience that the local buyer pays on the basis of some well-recognized central market price. To the extent that the different buyers available to him follow consistent policies he may normally sell to the one buyer whose policies seem most advantageous to him. Also, in the local market, as well as at other levels, potential competition may be more important than the actual shifting of sellers from one buyer to another may suggest.

Most buyers and sellers in the marketing system, from farmers to consumers, do not try to capture the last penny of possible advantage. If a consumer carefully studied the prices of all individual food products in all the stores that were readily accessible to him, for example, he might find that his grocery bill would be lowest if he bought 15 items from store A, 8 from store B, 5 from store C, and 1 from store D. That would mean three additional walks or automobile trips and three additional trips past check-out counters, not counting his initial visits to scout the stores.

Even if a customer made such a comprehensive calculation he might decide that the savings he might make were not worth the additional time and inconvenience. Furthermore, there might well be enough variation in the prices charged by different stores from week to week so that his least-cost market basket in the second or third week would involve a somewhat different combination of stores and commodities. In that sense least-cost shopping would involve a terrific overhead cost in terms of time and mental effort on the part of any consumer who attempted it.

In order to save energy and cut down on mental wear and tear, consumers and marketing firms tend to lay down certain routines, habits, and policies. The policies and terms of trade followed by various wholesale buyers become known to the retailers who patronize them. Most of the time a given retailer may buy a certain line of products exclusively from a single buyer whose policies he feels are by and large the most advantageous to him. Only if a striking disparity appears between the terms offered by his regular supplier and some other supplier will he think it worthwhile to make a change. The fact that he does shift when another supplier offers an unusual bargain serves to keep his regular supplier in line with his competitors.

So far we have mostly considered markets separated in space. In them, market information tells shippers and carlot receivers whether or not different markets and shipping points are in line with the structure of actual transportation costs.

Markets also are separated in time. Sometimes the lapse of time between sale by the farmer and consumption by the individual is negligible, as in the case of fluid milk. As retail milk prices are changed only infrequently in a given city, little or no price risk is involved in the marketing of a given lot of raw milk.

That is not true for fresh fruits and vegetables, even from nearby areas. In response to a high price for fresh peaches on Monday, enough truck-

281437°—54——23

loads may be delivered to the market on Tuesday to cause a sharp drop in price and consequent disappointment to the producers who rushed their fruit to market. Produce shipped from California to the East is in transit several days. Once it is unloaded at a given terminal it is seldom feasible to reload and ship it to another center. Furthermore, it must be moved into consumption within a few days. Hence, temporary gluts of a few days' duration may occur in individual terminals so that certain shippers, wholesalers, and retailers will incur considerable losses on particular shipments and purchases.

Just as prices at different places are related to one another by the structure of transportation costs, prices of the same commodity at different times may be related to one another by storage costs. Seasonal swings in production of eggs and milk are partly ironed out through storage. Stocks are accumulated most actively during the season at which prices are usually lowest and resold during the season when production is low and prices are usually above the average for the year.

The cost of carrying eggs from April to October in a commercial cold-storage warehouse is just as definite as the cost of transporting those eggs from Chicago to New York. But the prices of eggs in two different months are much more likely to be out of line with storage costs than are prices at different places to be out of line with transportation costs. The uncertainties of movement through time are much greater than those of movement through space where commodity prices are concerned.

Much of our discussion has assumed that we were dealing with a single commodity which had only one form at any given market level. We have indicated some of the forces which tie together the prices of such a commodity in different retail stores, at different terminal markets, and at different shipping points. These factors collectively determine the national market structure for a commodity with only one end use. But some farm products reach the consumer in different competing forms, and for them the market structure is more complex.

For example, oranges are marketed in three forms—fresh, as canned single-strength juice, and as frozen concentrated juice. Markets for these three products at retail are tied together partly by competition at the retail level. Some consumers vary their purchases in response to changes in the relative prices of the different products. But the markets are also tied together at the farm price level. In areas where growers are not organized to control marketings, processors of frozen and canned juices must pay the same price as fresh-market shippers for oranges of comparable quality. Given the same farm price for oranges for all uses, and given sufficient competition among firms processing and distributing each of the three forms, the retail price of each form will tend to equal the common farm price plus the specific cost of processing and distributing it.

While this tendency may average out fairly well over a period of years, it does not do so in any one year because of time lags in the distribution of canned and frozen juices. Production of oranges is seasonal, and processors try to concentrate their purchases in the months when fresh-market prices are lowest. The processed products are sold to distributors over a period of months and may not all move through to consumers for nearly a year after the initial processing date. Consequently, in competing for supplies of fresh oranges processors must try to anticipate the demand for their processed products several months in advance. As that can be done only imperfectly, processors are likely to make windfall profits or suffer windfall losses in most individual years.

WHEN producers are able to control the allocation of a raw product between different uses, they sometimes find it advantageous to set different prices for the raw product in each use.

If the supply going into use A is reduced, the retail price and equivalent farm value in that use will rise. If the supply going into use B is increased by the same amount, the retail price and equivalent farm value in that use will fall. A shift in utilization will be profitable to producers if the total farm value of the raw product is thereby increased.

Generally the maximum farm value for the crop as a whole would be obtained by charging different prices for the same raw product in different uses. Thus, orange producers in California have frequently accepted much lower returns on fruit for processing than on fruit of comparable quality for fresh market. Multiple pricing of milk for different uses has been characteristic of many of our metropolitan milk markets, and the practice has been permitted or facilitated by Federal marketing orders and by many State milk-control laws.

Controlled utilization and multiple price programs (which exist for relatively few farm products) create arbitrary breaks at the raw-product level between markets for different forms of a commodity. But prices of any one end product at different locations and levels of distribution may be determined on a competitive basis once the initial allocation of raw product has been made.

For some commodities, such as corn, the end products are so different as to be noncompetitive at the consumer level. Cornstarch, cornmeal, corn oil, and corn sugar or sirup are not directly competitive with one another, although each may compete with products made from different raw materials. Corn processors buy the raw commodity in competition with livestock feeders, manufacturers of mixed feeds, and others.

All those buyers are interested in end products that will be ready for market several weeks or months after the corn is purchased. Here again is a long-run tendency for prices of different corn products (and prices of livestock products which rely heavily on corn as a feed) to equal the price of corn plus the various costs specific to each end use.

But relationships between the price of corn and prices actually realized on finished corn products are quite variable in any one month or year, and the effects of competitive pricing are obscured by the uncertainties involved in trying to anticipate future conditions of demand and supply.

Thus, for products with several end uses, demand at the farm level may be regarded as the sum of a number of derived demands—demands reflected back from the actual or anticipated demands for each final product. Each distributor or processor makes his own estimates as to future demands and prices at the market levels of interest to him, and these chains of actual costs and anticipated price changes are reflected back through the marketing system to the farm price level.

Ties also exist among markets for different commodities. At the consumer level there is obvious and clear-cut competition within certain commodity groups. Price competition is noticeable among beef, pork, lamb, chicken, and turkey. It is evident that consumers, by and large, vary their purchases of meats and poultry in response to changes in their relative prices. This shifting of purchases means, for example, that a large supply of pork will tend to reduce the prices of competing meats, although to a lesser extent than the price of pork itself.

Other commodity areas in which competition at the consumer level is important are canned fruits, canned juices, and table spreads—butter and oleomargarine. Some consumers may make more extreme substitutions among foods. But such substitutions are made only in response to extreme changes in relative prices or in the income position of the consumer. Thus, substitution of eggs for meat in response to price changes cannot be demonstrated from the national market statistics although some individuals may regard them as alternatives for particular meals.

Further ties among markets for different commodities are provided at the processor level. As an example, different vegetable oils, and even vegetable oils and animal fats, are interchangeable for some purposes. Some substitutability is found among different grades and staple lengths of cotton in the production of specified fabrics.

Competition among feedstuffs is much keener than is typical at the consumer level. Other grains are almost perfect substitutes for corn in many feeding uses, although each may have special advantages in some uses. (The nonfeed demands for feed grains, such as barley for malt and corn for cornmeal, are, of course, highly specialized and distinct.) Individual farmers in feed-deficit areas vary their purchases of different grains and protein feeds at least moderately in response to changes in their relative prices. And manufacturers of mixed feeds are continually on the alert for substitutions that will lower the raw-material cost of dairy or poultry rations without reducing their feeding value. (*Karl A. Fox.*)

Prices and Pricing

If we consider them alone, neither price nor pricing has much practical meaning. They must be considered together as parts of the economic system.

Prices and pricing guide the production, distribution, and consumption of commodities. Farmers and handlers are nearly always faced by many possibilities when they make a business decision. They must decide what kind of farm or plant to buy or build; how big it shall be; and what, when, and where to produce, process, and sell.

Prices affect business decisions of producers, marketers, and consumers. Those decisions in turn affect prices. A pricing system that facilitates the making of rational decisions by investors, producers, handlers, and consumers also contributes to an efficient economic system.

Because there are so many decisions of different kinds to make, with alternatives for many of the decisions, there are many different kinds of prices. Each type of price has certain functions to perform.

Prices guide the use of some products even if no actual transfer of ownership occurs. A farmer in the Corn Belt can sell his corn or feed it to his own hogs. His decision depends on whether he expects that the future return from selling hogs will exceed the present cash return from selling his corn by a sufficient amount to cover the risks of deferred sale. In the purchase of farm supplies, buyers shift from one product to another or from one supplier to another in response to relative prices. Thus, both in selling and in buying, prices help the farmer to select from among the alternative products, outlets, or sources of supply available to him those which will yield him the best expected income.

If a certain fertilizer has high productivity, the farmer can pay a higher price for it than for another less productive fertilizer. With given productivities, and with given methods of production, the prices of the factors of production will largely determine their use. Changing productivities of the resources will normally affect their prices.

Some buyers want a product more intensely or have higher purchasing power than others do. Thus some purchasers will bid higher prices for the same amounts of a commodity or are willing to buy greater amounts at a given price.

Prices also help to allocate returns among sellers. Some sellers will exchange their products at lower prices than others will. The pricing process thus distributes the available supply of a product among buyers in accordance with the intensity of their various demands. At the same time the total money receipts are distributed among the various sellers in accordance with their different dispositions to sell.

The prices of farm products and of the resources used in their production both result from the interaction of supply and demand. If either supply or demand is absent, there will be no exchange and no price. Supply reflects attitudes and actions of sellers. Demand reflects those of buyers.

The statement that supply and demand determine price is correct but not very helpful in understanding pricing. Supply, in a particular market for a specific time period, means the various quantities sellers will offer at each of various prices; usually, the higher the price, the more will be offered. Demand, in any particular market over a specified time period, means the various quantities buyers are willing to take at each of various prices; the lower the price, the more buyers will take.

Both demand and supply may be influenced by appraisals of future as well as current conditions. In a given period, however, the quantity bought equals the quantity sold. Thus the price that equates supply and demand and clears the market reflects the influences of both buyers and sellers. While the general factors of demand and supply lie behind the generation of all prices, the differences in the specific conditions of the demand and supply for particular goods or services in particular markets lead to many different kinds of prices.

Distinction is made in price analysis among normal, long-run, and short-run prices. The normal price of a commodity would result if supply and demand conditions remained unchanged for a long period so that the rate of production would equal the rate of consumption. This notion of normal price is a useful concept for analysis of prices, but it is not a real price like those quoted in the papers. It should not be confused with the "normal" price developed for valuation purposes, which is really an average of realized prices over a long period.

If the supply that is offered comes from a fixed base of production, where farmers cannot increase all the factors of production they use and where new farmers do not enter production, the resulting market price is called a short-run price. If, however, farmers can increase their inputs of any and all of the resources they use, and if new farmers can enter production, the resulting price over such a time period is called the long-run price. The farmer is in fact usually faced with both long-run and short-run prices; for him they appear as day-to-day results on the markets where he sells or buys. Thus, to the farmer, the prices he regards most in his daily operations are those that reflect the immediate conditions of supply and demand. But if he is considering entering a business, or expanding an existing enterprise, he must consider the probable long-run prices of the commodities he buys and the commodities he sells.

The types of prices and pricing also vary with different levels of the marketing system. Prices are made and quoted at farm, roadside, local outlets, central markets, and in wholesale and retail channels. There are f. o. b. shipping-point prices, and cost, insurance, and freight prices. The different kinds of prices are determined by the particular type of market and pricing transaction in which the exchange occurs. For example, California oranges may be sold and shipped from Los Angeles with price specified at so many dollars and cents per box delivered in New York. The same oranges could be sold in Los Angeles but on an f. o. b. basis. In this case, the buyer would pay for transportation and delivery to New York.

Many of the prices one hears about are quoted or nominal prices. They may merely be bids or offers or a trading basis quoted by an organized exchange. Distinction must, therefore, be made between a price a buyer is offering, a price asked by a seller, and a price realized in an actual exchange. Realized prices alone reflect actual transactions or affect farm incomes.

Price, as a general notion, is meaningful only when related to a specific commodity, market, and time period. The phrase, "the price of wheat is \$2.00," has meaning only when it is understood that the unit is a bushel, the market is Chicago, the type of wheat is clearly identified, the terms of sale are specified, and that the sale is either for the spot (cash) or futures market on a particular day.

Published prices for a given day or year are often averages of the prices of many individual transactions. The reliability or representativeness of each average must be appraised on its own merits, considering the type of market and product and the number and volume of transactions reflected.

Many prices made in private transactions remain unpublished. For auction prices a public record is made and published. Because auction sales often may reflect a large number and volume of transactions, they are sometimes regarded as a barometer of current markets as well as a source of information of price changes over a period of time.

For the grains, cotton, and soybeans, there are both cash prices and futures prices, which are widely quoted and watched. Both cash and futures prices are indicators of exchange values but for different terms of trade, products, and types of markets.

The meaning and the uses made of prices at markets in different areas also differ. The price of eggs at a Wisconsin country market would be less significant to a New York buyer than the price in a Chicago central market or a Baltimore terminal market. For many products the central markets register the impact of demand and supply conditions from both country shipping points and terminal markets.

Particular markets frequently operate differently, and differences in the meaning and use of the resultant prices are thereby created. For example, Federal or State laws may set particular prices for milk. If the market area is under a Federal control program, the minimum price of milk may be set for the various outlets in which it is used. State programs may specify minimum prices to farmers and to retailers and consumers as well. Here, prices are not generated by free-market pricing processes; they are set by administrative regulation so as to affect either supply or demand or both. Dairy products in various areas are priced without legislative or administrative intervention. Cooperatives in some places bargain with distributors on behalf of the producers. Elsewhere individual producers may contract with individual distributors.

Each method of marketing thus generates a different type of price—often to serve a different function. For some commodities, such as cheese in certain areas, the announced price for a given grade and day may be no more than a nominal quotation by an exchange committee to serve as a trading basis. For other products, as wheat, the terms of sale may incorporate premiums and discounts for permitted variations in the grade or some other characteristic of the product.

Daily prices for many products on major central markets are published in many newspapers. Both Government and private agencies publish averages of prices by weeks, months, seasons, and crop or calendar years. The meaning of prices and the uses to which they are put, therefore, vary with both the marketing stage and the time period to which they pertain.

Fluctuations in farm prices over time are usually wider than those in retail prices because marketing margins are often relatively rigid. Looking at the retail price for some product and remembering the price he received, the farmer may wonder why his return is so much smaller than the retail price. These marketing margins reflect the market-determined value of the marketing services used in bringing the product from the farm to the consumer in the form, at the place and time, and in the package or amount the consumer wants. "The middleman" may be viewed by the farmer as the cause for his receiving a price lower than he believes equitable. The marketer may be blamed rather than the marketing system and its pricing process. Yet, many people—not only farmers—fail to distinguish clearly between prices, the pricing process, and the marketing system.

Middlemen, as wholesalers and retailers, usually follow a system of pricing wherein they add to the price they pay a margin to cover their costs of doing business and making a profit. The size of the margin or markup varies widely between products, between merchants, and over time. The competition faced by the merchants also affects their margin. There is no unique or set method by which distributors' margins are set. But the margin, however determined, is a price the consumer has to pay for the services performed. This affects the amounts the consumer buys and in turn affects the amounts sold and the prices received by the farmer. It is no wonder that farmers are concerned with prices in central and terminal markets and with wholesale and retail prices.

PRICES CHANGE almost constantly. We may note several broad kinds of changes. With no change in general price levels, the relative prices of farm products may shift. The changes may be due to changes in relative outputs or to changes in outputs and prices of competing or complementary products. They may also be due in the short run to changes in weather or other similar factors. There are fairly measurable long-run changes in the prices of some farm products relative to prices of other farm products. Those changes may be due to long-run shifts in tastes, incomes, technology, or outputs of related products. Prices of farm products also react to changes in general price levels associated with business cycles, with protracted depression or with general price inflation from war or other causes.

The flexibility over time in most agricultural prices is in sharp contrast with the behavior of many industrial prices. The producers of many nonagricultural products are price makers. They tend to have fairly rigid prices, adjusting to changes in demand by varying their outputs. Most farmers, however, are price takers and tend to maintain the volume of the output, making adjustments to changes in demand largely through the prices they receive. These distinctions between farm and nonfarm pricing do not hold for all products, but are broad tendencies which prevail generally.

IN OUR HIGHLY DYNAMIC economy, changes in prices or pricing influence supply as well as demand. The effects of any change vary among products, areas, markets, and marketing channels. Special influences may bear upon particular products and markets. The particular product and market at the same time may react to changes in the economy as a whole. Each pricing process thus has its own functions and characteristics, but the prices of all products are related to some degree.

The many differences among products and markets preclude formulation of any single or simple guide to "efficient" pricing. Pricing may be called efficient if for a given expenditure of resources a product of maximum value is exchanged, or if a given value of product is exchanged for a minimum expenditure in terms of value of resources. If this test is met, resources will be well allocated, the market can effectively be cleared, and consumers, handlers, and producers will be aided in making rational business decisions.

To obtain this efficiency, many buyers and sellers must have prompt and complete knowledge of the market and the product. There must be fairly equal bargaining power between buyers and sellers. Uncertainty must bear equally upon all parties.

Both Government and private agencies have developed information and reporting services designed to increase the efficiency of pricing. Both Government and private agencies have developed such devices as standardization of products and packs, minimum grades, uniform trading procedures, inspection, and certification services whereby the requirements for efficient pricing may be met.

In recent years there have been many changes in the organization of American business. There has been concentration of control in parts of the processing and distributing segments of agricultural industries. Firms have differentiated their products by branding, style of pack, or package. Some firms in the food and fiber fields have undertaken large-scale advertising as a means of influencing the prices at which they sell.

Also in recent years, the extent and nature of Government intervention into the pricing processes have been greatly altered. Governments—both Federal and local—have always regulated trade and production in order to minimize fraud and generally to protect the public through health, sanitation, fair practices, antitrust, or similar legislation. Governments have also regulated such trading units as public stockyards, auction markets, commission selling, and organized commodity exchanges. These laws and regulations in the main set the general rules for pricing. All merchants must conform, but they involve no direct effort by Government to set prices. In addition, for many years the Government has also provided services to producers and marketers designed to facilitate pricing and trade. Such services have included the market news, inspection, standardization, research, and extension work.

Two other forms of direct intervention by Government have had striking impact upon pricing of farm products. Price ceilings have been imposed in periods of national emergency. For almost 20 years, Government has set floor prices for many major commodities. These floors have been maintained by Government purchases, nonrecourse loans, purchase agreements, subsidy, export programs, diversion into secondary domestic markets, and market agreements. Those programs have made Government a major determinant of prices in many industries. Sometimes the programs have been designed to assure minimum prices to producers. At other times they have been aimed at guiding production of farm commodities in accordance with national need as determined by Government. In either event, free-market pricing has sometimes been virtually eliminated by Government intervention.

There seems to have developed a system half way between the traditional free-market making of prices and the making of prices by Government.

Government price programs have different effects upon the incomes of various groups of citizens. Price manipulation by Government is viewed by some as interference with the accepted functions of pricing. Others regard such price programs as a means of attaining goals which could not be achieved through a free pricing system. Whichever view be taken, it is clear that the impact of Government has been greatly extended over the pricing of farm products.

Prices are a major determinant of both gross and net income received by farmers. Sometimes the sale of large amounts of a farm product yields a lower gross income than would sale of a smaller amount. It is not easy to control the output of most farm products. Farmers operate in atomistic competition as a rule. The fluctuation of prices and incomes received by farmers is one of the major reasons that Government programs have been developed to stabilize farm prices and incomes.

THUS, pricing and prices of farm products influence the economic activities of producers, handlers, and consumers. There are many kinds of farms producing most commodities. There are many different uses to which most products may be put. There are many different kinds of firms in the handling and processing ends of the food and fiber industries. There are many different kinds of demands among consumers for farm products. Hence, there are many business decisions made in many different markets as the commodities move through many different channels. So there are many different methods of pricing and many different kinds of prices. And each type of price is an element in the search of buyers and sellers to improve their incomes. (*Sidney S. Hoos, George L. Mehren.*)

Pricing by Formula

Examples of pricing devices based on formulas or sales agreements are found throughout the marketing system for agricultural products. Cotton, juice grapes, tree nuts, dried fruits, butter, cheese, eggs, poultry, fluid milk, and evaporated milk are some of the commodities that may be sold on the basis of formulas that yield prices dependent on later market developments.

Formula pricing occurs also at different levels of trade. Formulas for fluid milk prices apply to transactions between the farmer and the fluid milk distributor. "On-call" transactions take place among cotton merchants and cotton mills or other buyers. The "inventory guarantee" of evaporated milk manufacturers applies to transactions with wholesale grocers.

A cotton mill that buys its supplies while the new crop is coming to market runs the risk of paying more than if it waits until it has received orders for cloth. One way of reducing or avoiding this risk is to hedge the purchase by selling a futures contract. Another way is to purchase the cotton on call.

IN A HEDGE each purchase or sale is a separate transaction completed at a known price.

The on-call purchase, on the other hand, leaves the price to be determined later. By agreement, the settlement price will be the price of a futures contract on the day the price is fixed, plus an agreed-upon premium or minus a discount. The price is usually fixed when the mill buys a future for the merchant's account, or notifies the merchant so that he may buy a future or may take settlement at the future quotation of the day on which notice is given.

For example, a mill in October buys ⅞-middling cotton on call at 2 cents a pound below the May futures contract. On March 5, say, the mill elects to fix the price by notifying the merchant, who buys a May future. The price paid for the future, less 2 cents a pound, is the price which the mill pays for its cotton.

A formula pricing device, therefore, typically has a basic source of current price information, a differential in relation to the basic price, and a provision for fixing the basic price that is to be used.

The automatic pricing of butter depends on the daily market quotation for bulk butter of a specified grade. The sales agreement specifies as a minimum the market and grade for the basic quotation, the amount of the premium, and the provision for fixing the price. Most commonly the price fixed is the market price on the day the butter arrives at the market or on the day it is shipped from the creamery.

A TRANSACTION under a typical sales agreement may serve as an example. The agreement provides for the buyer to pay for the butter on the basis of a Federal grade. The price for butter delivered to Chicago is to be one-half cent a pound above the price reported by a commercial market news agency in Chicago on the day the butter is shipped from the creamery. On a day when the price is quoted at 68 cents a pound for Grade A butter, the creamery would be paid 68.5 cents a pound for butter of that grade.

Although a creamery may ship butter every week or oftener, the terms of an agreement may run unchanged for months and even years. Such a system requires little selling effort on the part of the creamery management. Daily price changes are the greatest price risk the creamery has to face. The sales agreement assures the creamery of getting the advantage of price rises but carries with it the penalty of price declines.

In almost all city milk markets, producers sell their milk to dealers at prices that depend on how it is used. To a dealer, the value of that portion of his milk supply that he must use for manufactured dairy products depends greatly on the market price of the products. And, since dairy products may be shipped around the country at relatively little freight cost, prices paid by manufacturers in one part of the country are closely related to those paid in another part.

In the early 1920's the Dairymen's League of New York agreed to sell milk to manufacturers of evaporated milk in New York at prices paid at condenseries in the Midwest. The price was subject to some adjustments for freight and market conditions.

Next, formula pricing was used for the portion of city milk supplies that was used in butter. The basic price of 100 pounds of milk was usually the wholesale price of butter at Chicago or New York, adjusted for the number of pounds of fat in 100 pounds of milk, the amount of butter obtainable from a pound of fat, and the approximate cost of manufacture. Prices of cheese, nonfat dry milk, and cream gradually came to be included in the formulas, and nearly all the fluid milk used for manufacturing came to be priced by formula.

Prices for milk used as bottled milk in most large markets are also fixed by formulas. Formulas were substituted for negotiated prices when it was found that some economic indicators resulted in prices as desirable as those obtained through negotiation. Fewer price conferences were needed, and time and expense were saved especially where governmental regulations were establishing milk prices. The basic prices used for the manufacturing classes were used first, and are still widely used as part of the formulas for bottled or Class I milk. An appropriate premium or difference is added. Prices of milk for manufacturing uses serve to reflect changes in the general price level and to measure the pressure on producers to shift their patronage between fluid milk dealers and dairy products manufacturers.

Prices of manufactured dairy products sometimes move contrary to the general price level, or contrary to the best interest of a particular fluid milk market. Demand-type formulas were developed to fit the needs of markets distant from milk manufacturing areas. The first and best known was adopted in the Federal milk marketing order for Boston, Mass., on April 1, 1948. Changes in department store sales in New England, the United States index of wholesale prices, prices of feed, and wages of hired farm laborers in New England were combined into an index number, which in turn determined the price to be paid by milk dealers for milk for fluid use. The factor of department store sales later was replaced by a factor of income per capita.

FORMULA PRICING devices reduce the frequency of bargaining over price; distribute risk differently than if definite prices are agreed upon in advance; center attention on premiums and discounts or differentials, rather than on price levels; and promote continuity of relationships between the seller and buyer.

Those characteristics have aspects of advantage and disadvantage. The effort saved by the cotton mill in bargaining over price by purchasing on call may be devoted to more aggressive selling of cloth. The creamery operator may be enabled to give closer supervision to operations in his plant. On the other hand, such plans reduce general participation in transactions that establish price levels, and they may encourage efforts to manipulate prices—the chances of successful manipulation being inversely proportional to the number of traders likely to enter the market.

The distribution of risk between buyer and seller is an important function of buying and selling. Ordinarily, the benefit of any gain in value or the danger of a loss in value goes with the title to property. But formula pricing, by delaying the fixing of the price, allows the risk of price changes to remain with the seller.

Considerations other than gain or loss on a particular transaction may influence the distribution of risk.

Processing plants may wish to assure themselves of the continued patronage of suppliers. A formula price arrangement enables them to assure suppliers of prices that are as favorable as the general level of market prices. That has been particularly important for juice grapes and citrus fruits.

The effect of these steps is to promote continuity of relations between buyer and seller. If a product possesses intrinsic values not wholly reflected in established grades and standards, the continuity is a linkage between the source of goods of given attributes and the users who value those attributes. It makes for a more effective marketing system. But once such linkages are established, there is a risk of overlooking changes in market conditions that may warrant a change in the agreement. The buyer or seller may withdraw too completely from the market. Making of bids and solicitation of offers should not stop when an agreement has been concluded.

In transactions between the departments or subsidiaries of a company, and in settlements between cooperatives and their members, prices may be set by one of the automatic pricing devices used in the free market.

Many cooperatives adopt a policy of paying a current return equal to prices paid by competing firms. It is a kind of formula price: A base price is selected; the premium may be zero; and the price fixed is the price paid by the competing firm for the same period.

THE POOL, another device cooperatives use, may be called one of the automatic pricing devices. The basic price source is the price at which the cooperative sells the product; the differential in relation to the basic price is the operating expense charged against the pool; and the basic price fixed is the average price during the life of the pool.

Proprietary firms have adopted the pooling idea in some instances. The producer is paid an advance covering part of the value of his product. When the season is over, a part of the net proceeds is distributed as final payment for the goods. Grapes for juice, citrus fruits, dried fruits, and tree nuts have been sold on such a basis. Some advantages are that it allows handling of a greater volume with less capital tied up; it may result in more favorable tax situation; and it avoids some price risks on the finished product.

In basing-point price systems, one or more locations may be chosen as basing points, usually important processing centers. A base price is announced for each basing point, and prices at other points are calculated by adding a freight allowance, usually the lowest published railroad freight rate. A processor whose plant is located away from a basing point charges the base price plus freight from the basing point. The same processor selling to a customer located at the basing point will charge only the base price and will absorb the cost of transportation.

THE RESULT of systematic use of a common basing point system by all firms in an industry is that any buyer is quoted identical prices by all sellers, regardless of their locations. Some buyers are discriminated against, products are shipped farther than necessary, and the total cost of marketing tends to increase.

The sugar-refining industry is one of those that has used a basing-point system of pricing. Prices in the interior of the United States are based on wholesale prices at seaboard refinery locations such as Philadelphia, New Orleans, and San Francisco. The base prices usually are the same at the Atlantic and Gulf points. At Chicago, the lowest price for sugar is the New Orleans price, plus freight. Refiners located at other points may sell in the Chicago area, but the cost of freight is greater. They charge only the New Orleans price plus freight, and absorb the added freight. Since the Mountain States produce much more sugar than can be consumed locally, a fully competitive price might be expected to be lower than San Francisco price plus freight.

In zone price systems the same price is charged to buyers anywhere within a given zone. Buyers close to the processing plant fail to gain any advantage from their location, while distant buyers within the same zone benefit from freight absorption. Again, total marketing costs may be increased because buyers do not have any price incentive to patronize the nearest seller.

Because some pricing methods and practices may be or have been tools of monopoly, there are laws to curb their use. State and Federal statutes prohibit monopolies and combinations in restraint of trade—the Sherman Act (1890), the Clayton Act (1914), the act establishing the Federal Trade Commission (1914), and the Robinson-Patman Act (1936). Each in one way or another seeks to preserve competition by making it unlawful, among other things, to conspire or combine to monopolize commerce, by prohibiting price discrimination, and by prohibiting any unfair methods of competition.

Industry groups intent on placing restraints on competition frequently attempt to penalize those who sell at reduced prices. By adopting a basing-point or zone system of prices, an industry can more easily detect price cutting. The base on which a formula price rests may be subject to manipulation. Consequently the use of these systems of pricing has been the basis of actions by the Federal Trade Commission, particularly where they were accompanied by other activities that tended to limit or hinder competition.

LEGAL REMEDIES are of value in the cases where competition is most seriously abused by the use of automatic pricing practices. But there are many weaknesses of such practices which can be mended in other ways. Greater price consciousness among buyers and sellers—more shopping around—is one of them. To make it easier, more information should be published concerning the premiums and discounts used in sales agreements. The market quotations that are the base prices for sale agreements can be improved by increasing the volume of trading—the central market made as attractive as possible in comparison with direct marketing channels. Finally, additional or alternative indicators of supply and demand conditions can be adopted where existing base prices are unsatisfactory. The ultimate objective is to establish prices resembling as closely as possible those that would exist in an ideal competitive market. (*Don S. Anderson*, *Louis F. Herrmann*.)

Price Supports and Competition

Price-support programs bring into the market place an additional type of buyer—the Government—a potential buyer with relatively unlimited financial resources.

This additional buyer competes with the commercial buyers, standing ready to give price assistance on all eligible production at prices that are known a whole season in advance. The objective of this buyer, unlike that of commercial buyers, is to stabilize prices received by farmers rather than to make a profit. It sets certain price standards that other buyers must recognize.

Price supports directly to farmers were started in 1933 in an effort to remove some of the price problems that arise in the marketing of farm commodities.

They are programs conducted by the Department of Agriculture to provide assistance to farmers at certain specified dollars-and-cents prices, which, once announced, remain unchanged throughout the price-support period to which they apply regardless of fluctuations in the market price.

Price supports are only one, but the most important, of several programs that provide price assistance to farmers. The others include the marketing agreements and orders (discussed in the following chapter) and "Section 32" surplus-removal operations to develop wider markets in the United States or abroad for limited quantities of agricultural commodities and their products (principally perishable commodities) that are in surplus supply.

The problem of instability of farm prices had been present before 1933. Suggestions for improvement were numerous and varied, depending upon the immediate price situation. Just before and during the early 1920's, for example, a drop in exports of some farm commodities caused concern. The proposals for assistance took the form of "two-price plans" of one kind or another, the export debenture plan, the McNary-Haugen equalization plan (which was passed twice by Congress in 1927 and 1928 but vetoed) and the domestic allotment plan. All the plans were designed to encourage exports by providing a price for foreign sales in competition with exports from other countries much lower than that provided for domestic sales. In fact, the increase in foreign sales was supposed to shorten domestic supplies and raise prices for the portion of the commodities used in the United States.

In the late 1920's there appeared to be a need to strengthen the farmers' position in the domestic marketing of their commodities, and the Congress established a Federal Farm Board under the Agricultural Marketing Act of 1929.

At first the board stressed the development of farmer-owned cooperative marketing associations to provide price stability. When prices continued to decline in the latter part of 1929, emphasis was shifted to direct price action through loans to stabilization corporations (owned by cooperatives) for the purchase of commodities, chiefly cotton and wheat. The price-stabilization actions were abandoned in 1932 after large stocks were accumulated. Most of the board's funds were tied up and operations were discontinued. The board had come to the conclusion that it was not possible to stabilize prices over a period of years in the face of a constantly accumulating surplus.

The Farm Board experience and the heavy stocks of storable commodities and relatively large numbers of livestock on hand did much to shape the Agricultural Adjustment Act of 1933. Under the programs authorized in that act, reliance was to be placed entirely upon production controls for most commodities, although some provision was made for the use of marketing agreements. Production control was to be implemented by levying processing taxes upon the particular commodity to be controlled with the proceeds of the tax returned to cooperating farmers. The act also in effect provided for a two-price scheme, as the processing tax or its equivalent was to be rebated on products exported.

Within a few months it became clear that control of production and marketing through control of acreage and livestock numbers was a relatively slow process—one that would take some time to work itself out in terms of farm prices. The Commodity Credit Corporation therefore was created under the President's emergency powers in the fall of 1933, and the first price-support loans as we now know them were made on corn and cotton that fall.

The Supreme Court in January of 1936 declared unconstitutional the production-control features of the Agricultural Adjustment Act of 1933. There followed shortly the enactment of the Soil Conservation and Domestic Allotment Act of 1936, which (among other things) provided some control of the acreage of the main soil-depleting crops by offering inducements to soil conservation practices.

But the inducements offered under this new act were found to be too weak and too indirect to obtain effective control of acreage, and, when the large crops of 1937 were followed by a recession in business, the Congress adopted the Agricultural Adjustment Act of 1938. That act, which is still basic legislation, except that the price-support provisions have been rewritten, provided for price-support loans—mandatory for the first time on certain commodities at levels ranging between 52 and 75 percent of parity—to hold supplies from the market in years of plenty for storage and return to the market in years of reduced supplies.

The act also provided for marketing quotas, keyed to acreage allotments, which were intended to keep supplies of certain commodities designated as the basic agricultural commodities in line with market demand.

Shortly before the entry of the United States into the Second World War, to encourage increased output by minimizing the price risk involved in wartime expansion, Congress passed the Act of July 1, 1941 (the so-called Steagall Amendment) and section 8 of the Stabilization Act of 1942. Under those laws, as amended, the basic commodities (corn, wheat, cotton, rice, tobacco, peanuts) and 14 others on which production increases had been requested were required to be supported at not less than 90 percent of parity for the war period and 2 years thereafter.

It was the first time that the Congress had required support at a level as high as 90 percent of parity. The requirement was extended for an additional year, with some modifications, by the Agricultural Act of 1948, which also reintroduced the idea of flexible price supports.

The Agricultural Act of 1949 became effective with the 1950 production. It requires the Secretary of Agriculture to support prices of specified commodities, authorizes support of others after considering certain factors prescribed in the act, specifies the percentage of parity or range in percentage of parity at which prices are to be supported, and specifies the methods of support.

The 12 agricultural commodities for which support is mandatory are the six so-called basics and six designated or mandatory nonbasics—whole milk, butterfat, wool, mohair, tung nuts, and honey. Prices may be supported by means of loans, purchases or other operations that will provide support in the market place. Price-support levels for field crops, as far as practicable, are announced before the planting season. For other commodities they are announced before the beginning of the marketing year or season.

PRICE-SUPPORT PROGRAMS have affected the price level, production, and marketing of a rather wide group of agricultural commodities in a number of ways. The effects have varied so much from commodity to commodity and from year to year that it is difficult to make a general statement that is accurate for all situations. It will be possible to discuss only a few of the effects. Furthermore, because the entire program was under review at the time this chapter was written, the authors have tried to describe certain effects without seeking to imply that any specific features of the program are or are not desirable.

Some idea of the scope can be given by a few figures. In recent years programs were announced for about 25 commodities or groups of commodities that represent about 40 percent of farmers' cash receipts from farm marketings. In 1933 they covered only cotton and corn. During the Second World War they covered about 30 commodities.

The size of the operations has varied from year to year, as indicated by the percentage of total output of 7 crops placed under price support from the 1951 and 1952 crops, respectively: Corn 1 percent, 13 percent; Upland cotton 7 percent, 15 percent; peanuts 50 percent, 9 percent; tobacco 10 percent, 7 percent; wheat 22 percent, 36 percent; dry edible beans 18 percent, 15 percent; grain sorghums 9 percent, 4 percent. (The figures include commodity loans later redeemed.)

Most activities have involved storable commodities, principally wheat, corn, and cotton—commodities on which the Department of Agriculture operating agency, the Commodity Credit Corporation, operated on about a break-even basis from 1933 into 1953. For example, more than 65 percent of the total amount of 18.1 billion dollars in price support extended under CCC programs from the beginning of the Corporation's operations through June 30, 1953 (not to be confused with the value of commodities acquired by Commodity Credit Corporation or CCC losses), was on three storables—wheat, cotton, and corn. CCC operations on a few perishable commodities, such as potatoes, eggs, and dairy products (which have been discontinued except those for dairy products) have represented only a small part of the total price support extended. However, these perishables have accounted for around 73 percent of CCC's total loss of about 1.1 billion dollars in the same period—that is, 1933 through June 30, 1953.

THE GOVERNMENT through the CCC has sought to stabilize prices by eliminating much of the price risk farmers themselves carried before prices were supported. It has sought to do this by providing farmers with more specific advance knowledge of future prices on which to base production plans. Price-support levels generally are announced before planting time. After harvest, the Government has sought to lower price risk by loans, purchases, or purchase agreements that give farmers the opportunity to obtain the support price. The loans and purchase agreements seek to make it possible for the farmer to market his crop in a more orderly manner over the course of the season, and to take advantage of any price increases without the risk of accepting price declines below the support level.

Several general observations can be made about the effect of this additional buyer on prices.

One is that when support programs affect prices, the effect extends beyond the specific producers who participate in the loan or purchase program and the specific commodities that are supported. The removal of part of the supply from the market by the Government affects the prices received by all producers of the commodity.

Another observation is that price-support operations on one commodity affect prices of competing commodities. This degree of competition among several commodities complicates decisions that the Government must make with regard to the level of price support and the way in which the support is to be provided. A price-support level for a particular commodity that is higher than the market price for competing commodities may result in some loss of market to the competing commodities.

Furthermore, a support price that holds the price of an agricultural commodity above the so-called economic equilibrium price and thereby results in Government stocks may lead to any one or a combination of situations. If emergency situations occur, the surpluses may become an important asset. Otherwise, the situation may require disposition of the commodity into uses or outlets other than normal commercial channels of trade with accompanying dollar losses. In some instances the situation may lead to strong marketing controls. Among perishables there also is the possibility of a physical waste of surplus stocks because of inability to move them and the possibility of large dollar losses if the stocks are moved outside commercial channels. Large financial losses are also possible in the case of storables, especially if production controls are not employed.

The presence of the additional buyer may have affected the national price pattern for some commodities. There are several reasons. One relates to the grade, quality, and location differentials that are established under many price-support programs and generally are based on historical price relationships. Support prices, including the price differentials, furnish guidepoints that the farmer uses in deciding whether to sell in the open market or participate in the support program. They also affect what buyers offer and the flow of commodities to individual markets. If prices stay close to support levels over a period, the differentials in themselves can establish some rigidity in the market price structure.

The presence of the additional buyer has not always resulted in a market price at or above the support level. The announcement of a program ordinarily tends to keep market prices from falling too far below the effective support level because the farmers know that regardless of the market situation they have the opportunity to obtain at least the support price for eligible commodities.

In most instances the program provides price support directly only to the producer. The degree to which most programs actually support prices thus depends largely on the extent to which farmers voluntarily avail themselves of price support. The extent to which farmers do not participate when prices are at support level is affected by many factors, such as lack of adequate farm storage facilities, small amount of production, poor prospects for market price increases during the loan period, poor storage quality of the crop, and willingness of some farmers to accept slightly less than the support rather than go through the process of taking out a Government loan. In addition, certain portions of a crop will not meet eligibility requirements. Market prices sometimes therefore do go below the support level. Often that occurs temporarily at harvest. In some years, however, prices stay below the support level the entire season—whenever free supplies (that is, total supplies less those immobilized by loans) exceed the commercial market demand at the support price.

Price supports have influenced total agricultural production by cutting risks and have influenced the agricultural production pattern by affecting the competition among different agricultural commodities for production resources.

A production and marketing problem that has arisen under price support is that only certain commodities receive support.

Price supports in 1953 applied to commodities representing only 40 percent of farmers' cash receipts; a larger segment of production—around

60 percent of farmers' cash income—received no direct support. The group that received no direct price support in 1953 consisted principally of hog raisers, cattle producers and feeders, poultrymen, and producers of practically every kind of fruit and vegetable and a number of other cash crops. For livestock and livestock products, it means that in general producers may not be able to obtain one of their basic cost items, feed, at less than support prices; yet they (except for producers of dairy products) sell their output on an unsupported market. In such circumstances there is considerably less opportunity for production costs to adjust in line with selling prices—a condition that can result in livestock production getting out of line with feed supplies. The cost problem appears to have been offset to some extent by the more stable high-level supplies of feeds that have been encouraged while price supports have been in effect. The situation has given rise to many conflicting views among livestock producers, feed producers, economists, and consumers.

Price supports have been a factor in a number of major changes in marketing practices for farm commodities.

The Department of Agriculture has sought to encourage both increased farm storage and development of improved types of farm storage facilities, including handling and conditioning equipment. That was done to help farmers move their crops to market in a more orderly manner instead of being forced to sell them at harvest if prices were low. Another reason for increased farm storage for some crops, such as feed grains, was to save transportation and handling costs because a large proportion of feed grains are used on farms in the area where grown.

Price supports have brought about the use in a number of commodities of uniform warehouse storage agreements. The agreements establish uniform responsibilities of all warehousemen who store commodities under a loan program (regardless of the State in which they are located). They specify the terms and conditions of storage during the loan period and after acquisition by the Government. They were adopted to permit farmers a wide choice in selecting warehouses, and at the same time give the Government the same protection regardless of which warehouse was selected.

The agreements have had certain effects on warehouse storage operations. For example, warehousemen have been given a greater degree of responsibility for the care and safekeeping of the grain. The agreements also require warehousemen to redeliver grain based on quality factors within the grades; warehousemen otherwise may deliver merely the numerical grade specified on the warehouse receipt.

Government price-support loans have resulted in several changes in commodity financing. One change has been the introduction of nonrecourse crop loans. Government loans are nonrecourse because producers can fully satisfy the loan by delivering the commodity regardless of the market price. Nonrecourse loans were developed so that the loan programs could actually support prices. Farmers would probably not have participated in the loan program, on any wide scale, if they had been held liable for any deficiencies in the event of a price drop.

Another change has been the relatively low interest rate, which is paid only if the farmer redeems the loan. For a long time the interest rate on CCC loans was 3 percent. In 1952 it was raised to 3½ percent and in 1953 to 4 percent. On 1954 crops the rate has been announced at 3½ percent. The changes have been made without affecting the channels through which commodity loans generally are made. Most price-support loans are handled by commercial banks or other established credit agencies—usually those with which farmers transact their regular business.

Some persons feel that the existence

of price-support programs has had some effect on the ability of farmers to obtain credit for financing farm operations. They point out that lending agencies are more willing to extend credit to producers who are cooperating and participating in the price-support program because the agencies are better able to determine in advance the probable income of the farmer from his crops.

One major change in selling practices under price support is that the grading of some commodities before sale by farmers has become more widespread. Grading before sale has been encouraged, because the Government's loans or purchases apply to the quantities that meet specified quality requirements. The support rate is adjusted for the various qualities. For cotton, rice, and tobacco, for example, the grade requirement has resulted in the establishment of increased Government grading services.

ANOTHER BASIC CHANGE affecting marketing brought about by price support has been the development (primarily in tobacco and peanuts, and to a limited extent in cotton and wheat) of methods of controlling the amount that individual producers may market during seasons when supplies are excessive. That has been done by means of marketing quotas.

Quotas control supplies by establishing a national marketing quota for a commodity and dividing that into each individual farmer's marketing share. Quotas involve cooperative action of producers as they are put into effect only after approval of at least two-thirds of the producers voting. Once approved, quotas apply to all producers and enable farmers to divide upon an equitable basis the available market at the support price. Only cooperators receive price support.

When quotas are temporary—that is, used for a year or so and then dropped—they generally do not have long-time effects on the production and marketing patterns. Once established on a somewhat permanent basis, they tend to make the production pattern rigid, by areas and producers. There appear to have been fewer difficulties in dividing the market equitably among individual farmers when quotas have been in effect on a rather permanent basis. Difficult problems in establishing an acceptable basis for allocation among individual farmers have been created when quotas have been used intermittently.

Price supports also have affected marketing by shifting to the Government certain responsibilites for carrying stocks and then for disposing of the stocks. Before price support, such stocks were held by buyers for resale and by processors. Those groups still hold stocks as long as prices are appreciably above the support level. Once prices get close to support, the carrying of reserves is shifted to the Government, which makes maximum practical use of private storage. The Government is faced with complications, because, unlike private sellers, it has the responsibility by law of handling disposal in a manner which will not affect the current price-support program or the orderly marketing of the commodity. It lacks the flexibility of commercial sellers because there are statutory provisions that govern the prices at which commodities acquired under price support may be sold by the Government.

The introduction of price-support programs, which gave farmers an effective bargaining means for holding price fluctuations on the downside somewhere near the price-support level, has also introduced a series of new factors into the market that commercial traders and industrial users of price-supported commodities must consider.

BUSINESS REACTION to price-support programs generally has been mixed. Commercial traders generally have felt that the programs introduced an undesirable degree of rigidity into the market. Many of the industrial users have looked upon the stability introduced into the market as a relatively desirable feature. Some of the processors in effect have used the support program as a hedging device and have concentrated their efforts on obtaining profits through more efficient operations. Both the Congress and the Department have recognized from the start that the programs should be so handled as to minimize Government interference and maintain maximum use of private or commercial facilities.

The fact that the support levels are set under Government authority and that large reserve stocks are held on many occasions introduces as a new market factor the question of possible changes in Government disposal, loan, or purchase policies either by means of legislation or administrative decision.

Over most of the past 20 years, the Congress has tended to increase both the permissible and mandatory support levels as a percentage of parity while the parity standard itself over the course of years has tended to increase or remain the same.

Under those circumstances there are a number of instances in which it appears that the normal holding of large stocks under price support has been a strengthening factor in the market, especially when the trade had confidence that the stocks were strongly held.

THE EFFECTS of price support on marketings have extended to international trade as well as to domestic marketings. For several years during and immediately following the Second World War, price-support programs were an important factor in providing the increased production and reserve supplies needed to fill foreign requirements. With the recent recovery of production in Europe and competing exporting countries, price supports have had different effects.

For some commodities, they have kept domestic prices above price levels in some foreign countries. That, in turn, has had two effects: It has tended to discourage exports or to require export subsidies to maintain export outlets; it has led to import controls to prevent competing imports from interfering with domestic price-support operations. The import quotas imposed on several commodities under section 22 of the Agricultural Adjustment Act, as amended, illustrate this situation. As long as domestic prices are at or below support levels which are above world levels, such problems will persist. Similar problems have occurred and would continue to occur when imports tend to depress domestic prices even in the absence of price-support programs. (*Sidney N. Gubin, J. Murray Thompson.*)

Marketing Agreements

Marketing agreement and order programs have been used primarily for fluid milk and fruits and vegetables. Their aim is to bring about orderly marketing and thereby improve prices to producers.

They are authorized by the Agricultural Marketing Agreement Act of 1937. They are used in particular production or marketing areas.

A marketing agreement is voluntary. It is a contract between handlers of a commodity and the Secretary of Agriculture. It is an agreement to control marketing in interstate commerce. The statute provides that the agreements are not in violation of the antitrust laws.

A marketing order is mandatory. It is issued by the Secretary of Agriculture. It applies provisions identical to those of the marketing agreement to all handlers in the area covered by the program.

The act gives wide latitude as to the commodities that may be regulated and the types of regulation that may be used in marketing agreements. The act specifies the commodities eligible for a marketing order and the types of regulation permissible in an order. A marketing agreement alone is seldom effective. It is rarely used without an accompanying order. Thus the commodities for which effective programs may be undertaken and the types of usable regulations are limited by the order provisions of the act.

A marketing order may be issued for a commodity only if at least two-thirds of the producers or those who produce two-thirds of the volume have approved the order. Besides, handlers of at least one-half the volume must have signed the marketing agreement or the Secretary of Agriculture must find that an order is the only practicable way to accomplish the objectives of the act even though handlers of one-half of the volume have not signed the marketing agreement.

Milk orders normally are issued without marketing agreements. Most fruit and vegetable orders are accompanied by marketing agreements. The difference is due partly to the fact that most fruit and vegetable cooperatives function as handlers and therefore are important signers of marketing agreements. That is not true of most fluid milk cooperatives. Another reason for the difference stems from the different types of regulations authorized for the two groups of commodities and the relative need for handler cooperation and participation in the administration of the regulations.

THE GOAL of the act for fluid milk is to achieve a uniform minimum price to producers that will reflect prices and supplies of feed and other supply and demand conditions in the area and that is necessary to obtain an adequate supply of pure and wholesome milk. For other commodities the aim is to achieve parity prices. No regulations are authorized with respect to commodities other than milk when prices are above parity except to maintain or establish minimum standards of quality and maturity in the public interest.

Orderly marketing has never been specifically defined. It sometimes implies a price objective or stability of prices. Usually it refers to the means of approaching the objective. Frequently it connotes unified action by producers or producers and handlers. Effective action normally requires Government approval. Usually it involves a plan of action to take advantage of the characteristics of the demand for the commodity.

The programs grew out of voluntary schemes developed by agricultural industries to meet their marketing problems. Cooperative marketing associations had a dominant role in the programs. Plans similar to those now established under marketing-agreement legislation were developed in the 1920's and were used to improve prices. They were only partly successful. Some producers and handlers profited without participating.

The sharp drop in purchasing power of consumers during the early 1930's depressed prices, so that large amounts of milk and of many fruits and vegetables remained unmarketed.

Marketing-agreement programs were authorized by the Agricultural Adjustment Act of 1933. Marketing agreements were first regarded as an alternative to the production-adjustment approach for basic commodities. Their particular applicability to the marketing of fluid milk and specialty crops was not widely recognized. The Secretary of Agriculture was authorized to enter into agreements with handlers of agricultural commodities in interstate or foreign commerce and to issue them licenses. The thought was that licensing could be used to prevent unfair and inefficient trade practices.

Thereupon industries that needed

help submitted proposals for marketing programs to the Secretary of Agriculture for consideration. Some handlers refused to participate in the marketing schemes. To offset this, licenses were issued compelling all handlers to comply with the provision of the marketing agreements.

Additional legislation was provided by amendments to the act in 1935 and by the Agricultural Marketing Agreement Act of 1937. Orders replaced the licenses of the earlier programs. Conditions governing their issuance, including approval of producers, were established. The types of control that could be effected were specified. The commodities for which orders could be established were limited. The Secretary was authorized to select industry committees or agencies to assist in the administration of the programs. Assessments on handlers were authorized to defray the expenses of the agencies.

An amendment in 1947 authorized for commodities other than milk the establishment of minimum standards of quality and maturity in the public interest.

The programs embrace both voluntary control, represented by marketing agreements, and regulatory control, enforced by orders. They apply primarily to specific areas (marketing areas for milk and production areas for other commodities), whose particular problems they are designed to meet. They do not use public funds to obtain their objectives.

The legislation alone imposes no control. Neither does it assure that control necessarily will be established. It is enabling legislation. Programs may be undertaken for specified commodities provided conditions within the area are such that a satisfactory and practical program can be developed within the authority and limitations of the act. The programs, financed by the interested industry, provide for a large degree of industry participation in their development and operation, with the necessary governmental sanction and supervision to assure effectiveness and to protect the interests of individuals and the general public.

THE TASK at the outset was to adjust prices or marketings to offset at least part of the effect of the depression of the early 1930's. Later they were used to help meet continuing and special marketing problems.

Stability is a basic and continuing marketing problem confronting producers of milk that is to be sold as fluid milk. Such milk costs more than milk to be used for manufactured products mainly because it must meet stricter sanitary regulations in most urban markets. Milk is extremely perishable; it must be in steady supply, production is seasonal, and an adequate supply in winter means too large a supply in summer. Distributors of fluid milk in cities are relatively large and few in number. Prices of milk to consumers do not change frequently. Any surplus supplies of fluid milk must be used for manufactured products. When that occurs, pressures develop to price fluid milk at levels of those products.

To combat such instability and establish orderly marketing conditions, producers in many milksheds formed cooperative associations to bargain with distributors. But the cooperatives were never able to persuade all producers to join. Nor have they been able to bargain effectively with all distributors. The voluntary programs therefore were only partly effective. The regulatory authority of the legislation has been used from the outset to establish orderly marketing and uniform minimum prices to producers.

The pricing of fluid milk is a difficult problem in most market areas. The general nature of the problem is much the same, but conditions in the individual markets change constantly. Pricing must therefore be a continuous process if marketing is to be orderly.

THE MARKETING of fruits and vegetables is subject to a wide range of continuing problems. Each individual fruit and vegetable commodity has its special problem but most of the problems concern the management of supplies and seldom can be met by price regulation.

Fruits and vegetables are produced by the "batch" method—not the "continuous process," as is milk. The batches must be cared for when they are ready. Markets are usually in distant consuming centers. The size, quality, and timing of the batches cannot be predetermined precisely. Bad weather often causes a bunching of supplies that go to market from different producing areas. Marketing costs are high and relatively inflexible. Maladjustments of market supplies in terminal markets cause erratic price changes which are passed back to producers.

The fruit industries, because of the perennial nature of the producing plant and the effect of weather upon supplies in a particular season, experience a most difficult task in tailoring the volume and composition of their available supplies to fit the demands of consumers. To a lesser extent this problem is encountered by the vegetable industries. To that end, marketing agreement and order programs have been developed and used by the fruit and vegetable industries.

Any interested industry group can propose a marketing agreement and order program. After a request has been received, the Department of Agriculture provides information and help in developing a proposal. A public hearing is held if the Secretary of Agriculture finds that the proposal will be helpful in establishing orderly marketing.

Any interested person can give testimony at the hearing regarding conditions in the industry, the need for regulation, the parties to be regulated, and the purpose of each provision of the proposal. After the hearing, time is allowed for the filing of briefs by those who may wish to suggest conclusions from the testimony. Then the transcript is studied and a recommendation based upon the hearing is issued. Interested persons are given time to file exceptions to the recommended decision. The Secretary issues his decision after the exceptions have been studied.

If the decision is favorable, producers vote on whether or not they wish the issuance of an order, and the proposed marketing agreement is offered to handlers for signature. If the requisite approval of producers is obtained and enough handlers sign the marketing agreement, it and the order become effective. Or, under the conditions previously noted, the order may be issued without the marketing agreement, if it has the approval of producers. Procedures to be followed are set forth in the Administrative Procedure Act of 1946 and in regulations issued by the Department.

The wording of a marketing agreement or order covers definitions; provisions for the selection of an agency to carry out the terms of the program in the prescribed area; arrangement for handler assessments to pay the agencies' expenses; regulatory provisions, including those to be issued under the program; reports to be made by handlers; and the effective time and termination of the program.

The control of market supplies under fruit and vegetable programs, as contrasted with the fixing of producer prices under milk orders, requires a different plan of administration. The supplementary regulations necessary in the control of market supplies are not required in milk orders. Industry committees, usually composed of producers and handlers, are selected by the Secretary to help administer fruit and vegetable programs. Market administrators are appointed for milk orders.

The regulatory provisions, as required by the act, differ widely in the two types of programs. Milk programs contain three principal regulatory provisions. First, milk is classified as to use into two or more classes—fluid milk and milk products. Second, a formula is set forth to determine the uniform minimum prices which handlers pay for the milk sold in the respective classes. Finally, a basis for payment to producers incorporating pools, either on an individual handler or market-wide basis, is set forth. Once the order is issued, the methods of pricing and settlement become effective and remain so unless the program is amended or terminated. Effective milk regulation needs a wide latitude for adapting the programs to the varying and divergent situations in different marketing areas.

In most fruit and vegetable programs, regulations are recommended by the industry committees and subsequently issued by the Secretary. Neither the quantity nor composition of the available supplies of fruits and vegetables can be determined with reasonable accuracy until shortly before the start of the marketing season. As a consequence, recommendations for regulations are not made until just before the season begins.

Two principal types of regulations have been used in marketing agreement and order programs for fruits and vegetables—regulation by volume and by grades and sizes.

Volume regulation is a means of limiting the volume of shipments to particular channels during a given period. One approach is to limit the total amount shipped during the season. Another is to limit the amount that may be shipped to a particular outlet and to divert the rest to an alternative outlet. For example, the sales of walnuts in unshelled form may be limited, and the remainder diverted to shelled markets. Or, one or more pools can be established, with the "salable" tonnage limited and the remainder diverted to a "surplus" or a "reserve" pool, as in the case of raisins. Such programs are used when the nature of the demand for the commodity is such that a reduction in total supplies offered for sale or a diversion of supplies from one channel to others results in an increase in returns to producers.

Volume is sometimes controlled to regulate the rate of flow to market. That may or may not reduce the total quantity of shipments. It aims to prevent gluts and to adjust the rate of movement to market demands. Such control, for example, governs the program for fresh lemons to assure a higher and steadier level of prices throughout the season.

Shipping holidays have been used a few times. Usually they have worked well at the start, but after they have been used once or twice, handlers have anticipated them and have shipped heavily in advance, thereby defeating the purpose.

Nearly every program provides for the regulation of shipments of fruits and vegetables by grades, or sizes, or both. Such regulations are designed to improve average prices to producers by restricting the shipments of poor quality—heavily discounted—grades or sizes.

The regulations often prohibit shipments of immature fruit, a practice attempted by some shippers to take advantage of high prices in the early part of the season.

Unfair trade practices have been prohibited in one of the fresh-fruit programs to prevent deceptive methods of packing fruit. Price posting—a provision requiring handlers to post the prices at which sales are made—has been used in two programs. Its purpose has been to prevent destructive price cutting.

One of the many problems in connection with the programs is to apply the regulations uniformly to all handlers and producers whom they affect. Some individuals in any group may feel the impact of regulations more or less than others in the group. For example, a big shipper of fruits and vegetables usually can adjust to quantity regulations easier than a little shipper can, or the producer of high-quality produce may be disturbed less than other producers by regulations as to grades and sizes.

The programs must be adjusted to

PROGRAMS IN EFFECT UNDER FEDERAL MARKETING AGREEMENT LEGISLATION, 1933–34 TO 1953–54 [1]

	Milk			Fruits and vegetables					
Fiscal year	*Fluid milk*	*Milk products*	*Total*	*Fresh and canned fruits*	*Dried fruits, hops, and tree nuts*	*Potatoes*	*Other vegetables*	*Total*	*Other commodities* [2]
1933–34	30	2	32	8	1	.....	.....	9	11
1934–35	51	2	53	12	4	1	4	21	5
1935–36	43	2	45	7	3	1	3	14	2
1936–37	29	2	31	3	2	.....	3	8	2
1937–38	25	2	27	4	2	3	6	15	2
1938–39	27	2	29	5	3	.....	7	15	2
1939–40	31	2	33	7	2	.....	6	15	2
1940–41	28	2	30	9	2	.....	5	16	1
1941–42	29	1	30	11	2	2	4	19	1
1942–43	27	1	28	12	2	4	4	22	1
1943–44	25	1	26	12	2	4	4	22	1
1944–45	25	1	26	12	2	4	4	22	1
1945–46	29	1	30	12	1	4	2	19	1
1946–47	30	1	31	12	1	4	1	18	1
1947–48	32	.....	32	12	1	4	1	18	1
1948–49	30	.....	30	12	1	7	1	21	1
1949–50	37	.....	37	12	6	8	1	27	1
1950–51	41	.....	41	12	7	10	1	30	1
1951–52	46	.....	46	12	7	8	1	28	2
1952–53	49	.....	49	10	7	7	1	25	2
1953–54 [3]	49	.....	49	12	6	7	1	26	2

[1] Before 1935–36 these programs were marketing agreements, licenses, or both; programs issued after August 24, 1935, were marketing agreements, orders, or both. Some licenses continued after that date but subsequently were terminated or reissued as orders.

[2] North Pacific wheat, tobacco, peanuts, rice, turpentine and rosin, alcoholic beverage imports, package bees and queens, and anti-hog-cholera serum. Since 1935 programs for the last item were under the Anti-Hog-Cholera Serum and Virus Act of 1935.

[3] To April 1, 1954.

changes in production and marketing conditions. There is a tendency to resist change despite the dynamics of marketing.

Some dangers are inherent in the application of controls to market supplies: If regulations maintain prices at levels that encourage an unwarrantable expansion in production, the greater supplies will magnify the price problems that the regulations were intended to solve. Experience with most of the programs, however, tends to disprove this concern, since producers are loath to discard any marketable supplies.

Not all commodities qualify for the programs. Under the act, for instance, marketing orders may not be issued for most fruits and vegetables produced for canning or freezing. Also, conditions favorable to the existence of a marketing agreement and order program do not exist in all production and marketing areas.

Several conditions favor the development and maintenance of the programs. The presence of a large cooperative organization, although not a prerequisite, contributes substantially to their development and operation. Similarity of production and marketing conditions in an area is important. Operations are more successful if there is a concentrated production of the commodity within a relatively small area. There should exist common marketing problems and also recognition and acceptance of the problems by producers and handlers. Finally, nature of the demand for the product must permit the formulation of a workable marketing scheme whose value can be demonstrated to producers.

SEVERAL FACTORS have influenced the growth of the programs.

The broad authority for marketing agreements and licenses under the initial legislation and the low prices during the early 1930's caused great interest in the programs. Their total number reached 79 in 1934–1935, compared to 77 in April 1954. Difficulties of enforcement and changes in the legislation were primarily responsible for reducing the number to 41 in 1936–1937.

The number of fluid milk programs declined from 51 in 1934–1935 to 25 in 1937–1938. The number was 49 in April 1954.

There were 21 fruit and vegetable programs in 1934–1935, 8 in 1936–1937, 30 in 1950–1951, and 26 in April 1954.

The number of programs in effect each year for milk, fruits and vegetables, and other commodities under the marketing agreement legislation is shown in the table.

In the middle 1930's, when demand conditions were unfavorable, many commodity groups were eager to curtail their marketings and thereby improve prices. Marketing agreements and orders chiefly regulate marketings, however, not production. As the depression disappeared, interest waned in regulating supplies.

The development of the programs was affected also by the availability of assistance from public funds to remove price-depressing surpluses.

The coordination of the marketing-agreement programs with programs involving the expenditure of public funds is complicated. Each is designed to improve prices to producers. For many commodities the programs are alternative means toward that end. Ideally, when conditions warrant the expenditure of public funds to provide assistance to producers of a commodity, an effective marketing agreement and order program provides a basis for sharing the burden between industry and Government.

The issue is the share of the burden to be carried by the industry and the Government. The difficulty is in the development and administration of industry programs capable of assuming and carrying their share of the burden. The danger is that commodity groups may maneuver the Government into the position of being solely responsible for the program.

Some fruit and vegetable groups have revealed a belief that the programs in themselves constitute adequate marketing programs. Marketing, however, requires extensive individual operations in assembling, storing, shipping, selling, and merchandising the commodity to be marketed. It requires positive, competitive, and aggressive action. Marketing agreements and orders supplement this action by establishing some limits within which it takes place.

The programs provide the means of regulating prices of fluid milk and the supplies or movement of fruits and vegetables in order to effect orderly marketing and improve prices to producers. The benefits are obtained with some loss of business freedom. Any great increase in prices to producers through the programs may mean somewhat higher prices to consumers. Public welfare must be the scale on which all gains and costs attributable to these programs are balanced.

From the experience of the past 20 years, there is little basis to fear that the industries interested in these programs will seek to have them used in a manner which would tip the public scale against them.

The programs enable many commodity groups to sponsor and maintain marketing regulations that supplement their marketing activities and are designed to achieve some stability in prices to producers. They provide a means for agricultural industries to undertake more initiative and responsibility in the field of orderly marketing. They bring into focus the contributions of industry and Government toward stability of prices and orderly distribution of products. (*Donald M. Rubel*, *Budd A. Holt*.)

Efficiency

Only from research can we gain the vision, foresight, and knowledge to reduce gluts and shortages, waste and spoilage, high margins, sharp practices, ineffective or poor service, and similar obstructions to a sound marketing system for agriculture. Much research is directed toward increasing the productivity of labor because the cost of labor constitutes so large a part of the total marketing bill. Labor must be provided efficient methods, equipment, and facilities for doing its work. Research also is aimed at preventing spoilage by bacteria, yeasts, and molds, damage from rough handling, deterioration in quality and nutritive value. Improved refrigeration of perishable foods is one way to reduce the loss. Developing new forms in which to market products can help expand the market for farm goods. Research to determine how well a new product will be received and to answer many other questions involved in its distribution must precede commercial processing, for there are many obstacles a new product must overcome. Trial and error has become too costly a method.

Ways To Save Time and Work

Some products are picked up, set down, and otherwise handled 25 or 30 times while they are en route from producers to consumers. At each stage in the marketing channel they are handled and rehandled, loaded and unloaded, stacked, and broken out of stacks. At one or more of the stages most types of products must be cleaned, graded, sized, and packed—operations that require thousands of workers and millions of man-hours of labor. The labor required for marketing some products, in fact, exceeds the labor put forth in producing them.

The cost of the labor is the largest single item in the marketing bill for farm products. In 1950–1952, labor costs were about half of the cost of marketing farm food products. Since marketing charges accounted for about one-half their retail cost, labor costs of marketing amounted to an average of about 25 percent of each dollar spent by consumers for farm food products.

An illustration of how defective facilities increase the number of times packages are handled, above what is normally considered necessary, can be seen on a number of wholesale terminal produce markets. On those markets, the railroad lines used for bringing in receipts were stopped short of dealers' stores and warehouses. As a result, rail receipts must be unloaded from cars on team tracks to motortrucks and carted to the stores. On markets having properly designed facilities, such as those in Columbia, S. C., and San Antonio, Tex., where rail lines were brought up alongside the rear platforms of the stores, rail receipts are unloaded from the cars directly onto the storage-room floor. No hauling by motortruck is necessary and two handlings of packages are eliminated.

Time studies of actual operations show that to unload manually a carload of 798 boxes of apples from a car on team tracks onto a motortruck, unload the motortruck at the store, transport the boxes 150 feet to the stacking point in the store, and release 6-high stacks of boxes in storage position, when the clamp-type two-wheel hand trucks are used for handling operations at the store, require roughly 15.5 man-hours of labor plus about 3 hours of motortruck time. The exact requirements in both cases depend on the amount of travel time required. To unload and place this carload of apples in storage, from a car spotted on tracks at the store, by use of the same handling equipment, requires 9.5 man-hours of labor. The saving is 6 man-hours of labor and 3 hours of motortruck time. In addition, losses from bruising and spoilage are less.

Improved facilities are not the only avenue for eliminating unnecessary handling. Most oranges and grapefruit used to be individually wrapped as they were hand packed in boxes even though the packed fruit seldom was stored very long and was unwrapped and placed on display counters on arrival at retail stores. Wrapping each fruit as it is being packed by hand is costly. Most oranges and grapefruit (except choice grades) now are packed by permitting unwrapped fruit to run off the end of the packing line into the containers. Hand operations have been eliminated. Additional study is needed all along the line for the purpose of discovering marketing operations that can be eliminated without impairing services or lowering quality of product.

Improved work methods for using the less costly types of equipment, such as two-wheel hand trucks, four-wheel hand platform trucks, and gravity-type roller conveyors, offer possibilities for saving labor. Many handlers of farm and food products own some of those machines and should explore their most efficient use before investing in other types. Improved methods may involve changes in crew sizes for various operations, in duties of crew members, in amount or arrangement of equipment used, and in the sequence with which operations comprising a cycle are performed. Other improvements may be possible by handling two or more packages as a unit rather than each package individually.

An example of how the separation of individual operations comprising a cycle of operations can increase the efficiency with which the operations are performed can be shown by describing an improved method used for receiving bales of cotton in public warehouses. Receiving involves the performance in succession of the following operations: Unloading bales from the railroad cars or motortrucks, weighing, sampling, transporting to the storage, and storing. Because of problems in weighing the bales, many warehouses still use two-wheel hand trucks for performing these handling operations.

Time studies of receiving operations, in which two-wheel hand trucks were used for unloading and transporting uncompressed bales and automatic platform scales were used for weighing them, show that 6 man-hours of labor are required by a 15-man crew for receiving 50 bales when the operations are joined. Of the total labor required, 3.61 man-hours are lost because of delays and other wait time.

The time studies also show that the speeds of all operations are paced by the speed of the slowest operation in the cycle; delays in one operation are transmitted to other operations in the cycle; and the necessity for using two-wheel hand trucks in weighing operations leads to their use for performing other operations.

It was found that by moving bales into and out of temporary blocks, so as to separate the operations in the receiving cycle, the labor required by use of an 11-man crew to receive 50 uncompressed bales of cotton could be reduced to 4.49 man-hours—a saving of roughly 25 percent. The use of temporary blocks requires no change in the types of equipment used for handling and weighing. However, the number of two-wheel hand trucks needed is reduced because four fewer hand truckers are used when the bales are moved into and out of temporary blocks. A disadvantage in separating the operations by use of temporary blocks is that the elapsed time required for receiving a given number of bales is increased.

One of the more widespread fallacies in connection with handling methods is that the unit-load principle can be applied only to the handling of products on skids and pallets, which implies a need for industrial trucks, pallet transporters, or other powered equipment. This principle, in which two or more packages are handled, stored, and withdrawn from storage as a unit rather than each package being handled individually, can be applied to handling methods involving almost any type of equipment and offers possibilities for saving many man-hours of labor.

Wholesale produce dealers employ the unit-load principle in two-wheel hand-truck methods when hand-truck loads are properly arranged inside the car or motortruck and are tipped off, rather than restacked, at the storage point. Time studies of operations performed by use of both methods show that the labor required for unloading and placing produce in storage can be reduced as much as 40 percent when the unit-load principle is applied to hand-truck operations. If the loads are properly arranged, no increase in broken packages or damaged produce results from tipping off the loads at storage points.

Because of increasing wage rates and the scarcity of labor, however, handlers of farm and food products at all stages of the marketing system are seeking methods and equipment that will permit the handling of larger tonnages by use of fewer workers than is possible with some of the more elemental types of equipment even after improved methods are tried. If their facilities permit, many of the handlers are turning to the use of industrial lift trucks as a means of reducing labor requirements. Warehousemen particularly are finding that industrial trucks are effective for handling larger tonnages with less labor, but other handlers find that relatively large investments and operation costs offset some of the advantages of more highly mechanized equipment.

In studies such as that conducted in Pacific Northwest apple packing and storage houses, six basic types or combinations of types of equipment were evaluated for moving fruit into, within, and out of the plants. Comparisons of methods and equipment were made on the basis of total labor and equipment costs for performing the various groups or cycles of operations under actual plant conditions. The most costly method of handling fruit is by use of elevators and clamp-type, two-wheel hand trucks. Labor and equipment costs for handling fruit in multistory facilities by use of belt conveyors and hand trucks are only 60 percent of the costs incurred by use of elevators and hand trucks. About 47 percent of the plants in Washington in 1950 used belt conveyors and hand trucks for performing handling operations and are referred to as "conventional type" plants.

The most efficient type of equipment for handling apples was found to be industrial fork-lift trucks and 48-box pallets. Handling costs by this method are about 60 percent of the costs in conventional plants and about 36 percent of the costs in elevator-hand truck plants. Costs incurred by use of industrial clamp trucks, which do not require pallets, were only slightly higher than for fork truck and pallet handling. Although industrial trucks proved to be most efficient when costs for all groups of operations by use of all types and combinations of types of equipment were totaled, the clamp-type, two-wheel hand truck proved to be more efficient for use in loading refrigerator cars.

It therefore cannot be said on the basis of these results that industrial or powered-lift trucks would be most efficient under all conditions for performing all handling operations. The results of a study made of the operations involved in loading out the delivery trucks of produce wholesalers further substantiates the point. Although less labor per ton is required when industrial fork-lift trucks are used for assembling the produce and belt conveyors are used for loading, labor and equipment costs per ton are slightly lower when four-wheel hand platform trucks are used for performing both the assembling and loading operations. Studies of retail store operations show that the most productive method of receiving grocery orders involves the use of wheel-type gravity conveyors.

A portable mechanical lift has been developed for high-piling and breaking out high-piled boxes of apples. The problem was to find or develop equipment for use in older plants for stacking and breaking out of stacks all boxes above the lower six boxes which are handled as unit loads by use of two-wheel hand trucks. Traditionally, the manual methods were used because suitable equipment was not available. By use of a two-man crew, 5.66 man-hours of labor were required to high-pile 1,000 boxes of apples in 12-box-high stacks and 4.83 man-hours to break out 1,000 boxes from stacks of that height.

By use of a lightweight portable mechanical lift, which was developed by research workers and built by an equipment manufacturer for test purposes, the labor required for high-piling 1,000 boxes of fruit in 12-box-high stacks was reduced to only 1.78 man-hours—only 32 percent of the labor required by use of the manual method. For breaking out boxes from 12-high stacks, the lift is even more efficient as it is possible to break out 1,000 boxes with 0.95 of a man-hour, or about 20 percent of the labor required by use of the manual method. This lift is now widely used in apple houses and other facilities.

Existing equipment often can be adapted to the operations required in handling farm and food products so as to save labor. It need not be handling equipment. In one instance recording and transcribing equipment, which ordinarily is used in connection with office work, was adapted for use in handling operations, with a relatively large saving in labor.

The operations involved were loading the delivery trucks of service wholesalers. A number of firms use a three-man crew and a portable belt conveyor for performing loading operations. One of the crew members is a checker, who calls off each item to be loaded; one worker places packages on the conveyor as each item is called; and one worker in the truck removes and stows the packages. It was found that by using recording and transcribing equipment the checker could be eliminated and the two remaining crew members could maintain the productive rate of work of the three-man crew, with a saving in labor of 33 percent.

There also are possibilities for saving labor employed for performing marketing operations other than materials handling. At assembly and shipping points, grading is one type of operation that requires relatively large amounts of labor. Studies by R. G. Bressler and B. C. French, of the University of California, showed that in apple and pear packinghouses grading operations account for 25 percent of the hourly wage labor employed and 15 percent of total plant costs.

One of the reasons for the relatively high costs of grading operations is that fruit is not moved past the graders on conveyor belts or tables at proper speeds and is not rotated so that the entire surface comes into the grader's visual field. Limited applications of laboratory data indicate that, when lemons are moved past the grader at the proper speed and are properly rotated, this labor can be reduced 75 percent.

One of the problems that looms largest in obtaining the more widespread use of modern laborsaving equipment lies in the fact that many marketing facilities were not designed for the most efficient use of the equipment. Floors that do not have sufficient structural strength to support loaded lift trucks, ceilings of improper height to utilize fully the cube of the storage space when full-size pallet loads are handled and tiered, doors that are not of proper height and width for the passage of loaded lift trucks, layouts that necessitate out-of-line and back hauls are some of the problems in some of the older facilities. Multistory buildings equipped only with elevators for movement between floors also have their limitations.

However, by constructing new facilities or remodeling existing facilities, market operators are overcoming this obstacle to the adoption of improved work methods and equipment. Manufacturers are helping by designing lighter weight equipment that will operate efficiently in older structures and require less aisle space. These market operators are finding that by operating in improved facilities with the right kinds of equipment for the job, labor requirements can and are being reduced—in some cases as much as 80 percent. But much more needs to be done in this field if total labor requirements are to be cut down. (*William H. Elliott.*)

The Efficient Use of Labor

Most marketing operations can be performed by unskilled labor, in the sense that such labor does not require a trade. As a result, wage rates paid to marketing labor are lower than those paid to manufacturing labor.

For comparable work, however, the wages and other benefits received by workers in marketing are in line with those received by workers of comparable skills in other occupations.

The efficiency of labor generally has increased steadily in recent years, mostly because of the technological advances in the form of better machines, equipment, and methods, and not necessarily because of greater effort on the part of the worker.

In retail grocery stores, according to census data, the sales per dollar of wages paid increased from $16.80 to $19.70 between 1929 and 1948. The basic reason for the increase was the development of the supermarket rather than to increased effort and skill on the part of the employees.

The shorter work week has made it necessary for labor to handle a larger volume of products in an hour in order to handle the same total volume of merchandise in a given period. The greater volume is necessary if the standard of living of marketing labor is to advance with that of the rest of our working population.

If the costs of marketing are to be held at as reasonable levels as possible, labor must be efficiently used—it must be given improved work methods, equipment, and facilities with which to do its job. If it is not, someone will have to pay the cost—market labor in the form of lower wages, farmers in the form of lower prices, or consumers in the form of poorer service or higher prices.

The Wagner Act of 1935 stimulated unionization among marketing labor just as it did among manufacturing labor. The combined membership of all trade unions rose from 3.7 million members in 1935 to about 17 million members by 1954. Union membership on the part of marketing labor did not increase so rapidly as among industrial or manufacturing workers, mainly because the smaller size of business units involved in marketing did not provide the same organizing environment.

Inefficiencies in the use of labor resulting from union rules and practices have often been complained of.

One firm found that it could do a more efficient job of candling and cartoning eggs at country points than at its city warehouse and shifted its operations accordingly. Union truck drivers on city routes, however, refused to deliver eggs cartoned in country plants by nonunion labor.

A farmer brought a truckload of 250 bags of potatoes to an eastern city. He sold 200 bags to one buyer. They were unloaded by the buyer's workers. The remaining 50 bags were sold to a dealer on the local terminal wholesale market. Before the farmer was permitted to unload them, he had to pay the union a fee equivalent to one day's full pay for one worker. The farmer paid more than 30 cents for each bag unloaded from his truck regardless of whether he did the work himself or a union member performed the job.

A midwest egg dealer installed equipment that enabled candlers to candle 40 cases a day. The union production rate is limited to 30 to 32 cases. The dealer therefore could not realize the full potential efficiency of his equipment and workers were less productive than they could be.

But that is only one side—examples of situations which it is generally agreed should be corrected. On the other side, unions often contribute substantially toward increased efficiency of workers. For example, unions are a source of skilled and trained workers; an employer who operates under a union contract can get workers with the needed skills through the union office.

On some markets the unions also supply temporary help. For example, a dealer may receive several carloads of perishables, which must be unloaded immediately, and his permanent crew is busy with other work. Through the union he can obtain competent workers to handle the unloading. In markets where there are large numbers of carlot receivers, this use of temporary labor provides steady employment, since workers without permanent or full-time employment are needed from day to day by different receivers.

Most city wholesale produce markets formerly were open nearly around the clock except on Sundays or holidays. Before union officials interceded on one market to limit the hours of trading, dealers started opening at 9 p. m. and stayed open until 5 p. m. the next day. With unlimited hours for trading, the available business was spread over a long period, management and labor worked long hours, and productivity per hour was low. Demands of unions on produce markets for a work week of 40 hours (or 48 hours, with 8 hours paid at time and a half and all extra time paid at overtime rates) has forced some markets to adopt shorter hours. As a result, labor is more productive. Hourly wage rates are higher. Market and store operating costs are reduced. The sales are more concentrated and faster. Prices are steadier.

The inefficient use of labor occurs at many stages throughout the marketing system. Seasonal factors usually force plant operators to employ whatever labor is available at the packing and storage houses during harvest seasons. Most operators cannot get the same workers every packing season, and so the training given workers—even key workers—one season is lost for the next. Housewives living in areas near packinghouses are hired sometimes, but they are not always available in large enough numbers to meet all demands for seasonal workers.

In areas where perishable products are handled on a seasonal basis it often happens that more labor is hired than is necessary so that trucks bringing products to the plant will not be held up for unloading. Much of the time of a large standby unloading crew usually is lost through idleness.

Labor also is used inefficiently sometimes in materials-handling operations—when, for example, containers loaded on skids and pallets designed to permit handling them in large units are unloaded and stacked individually in storage. Other faulty methods include use of crews of the wrong size, misplacement of workers, lack of sufficient equipment to keep all workers employed, failure to combine containers into unit loads at as early a stage as possible, the unnecessary rehandling of individual packages, overloading or underloading the handling equipment, and using equipment not designed for the task.

Many firms with the cooperation of labor have improved working conditions in their plants and thus have achieved higher productivity of labor. Among such improvements are rest periods in the midmorning and midafternoon; clean cafeterias and lunchrooms, where good, wholesome food is available at low cost; good lighting and ventilation of the working areas; adequate heating; the protection of workers from bad weather; proper clothing; replacement of equipment and facilities that cause accidents; the establishment of employee training programs; and the use of new equipment and methods that make the job easier.

Before the Second World War, the types of equipment for handling farm products into, within, and out of the packing and storage houses, cold storages, auctions, wholesale stores and warehouses, and markets were mostly two-wheel hand trucks, four-wheel hand trucks, dollies, and gravity-type roller conveyors. The war requirements for manpower led to the development and adoption of equipment that could reduce the labor required in marketing: One man with an industrial-type truck can do three to four times the amount of work in the same time that he could by use of other methods and equipment and at about one-half the cost. Increased application has been made of the powered belt conveyor in loading operations.

In many of the packing, processing, and prepackaging operations, assembly-line methods have been adopted with a resultant increase in productivity of labor. An example is tray filling of tomato packages, in which the assembly-line method has increased productivity of workers 33 percent to 65 percent.

A survey of 17 different types of food-packaging lines showed that the hourly worker output jumped almost 400 percent from 1928 to 1953.

The shorter workweek has had some impact on parts of the marketing system. In many cases it has encouraged shops to stay open fewer hours daily and to remain closed on Saturday or some other day of the week. The number of services has been reduced, but the practice has forced the elimination of needless and unprofitable ones.

Seasonal peaks in marketing affect subsequent steps in the market channel. Transportation and storage functions increase their tempo. The movement of the product to consuming centers places a heavy burden on transportation facilities and labor. Car-loading and truck-loading operations are performed as rapidly as possible and as a result the most effective use of labor cannot be made. Products to be stored must be unloaded and put in storage quickly before they begin to spoil. Receiving grain at country elevators causes a heavy demand for labor during the harvest; however, new developments in the method of handling by which grain is brought in bulk to the elevator and dumped, instead of by the old method of handling in bags, has made the receiving labor about four times as effective. A similar development in the harvesting of potatoes and hauling in bulk has led to faster unloading of motortrucks with less labor at commercial storage houses.

Since the cost of labor constitutes a large and increasing part of the total marketing bill, continued steps need to be taken to increase labor productivity in marketing.

If this increase in productivity takes place, wages paid for marketing labor should keep abreast of wages in other parts of the economy. If an increase in efficiency does not occur, marketing labor may not expect increases comparable to those received in some other pursuits where improved labor productivity brings about greater total production out of which wage increases must come.

In other words, labor has a real

281437°—54——25

interest in improved efficiency in marketing. As labor is one of the largest groups of consumers of food products, it will also gain from the lower prices that will result from all marketing labor being efficiently and effectively used. Increased productivity should mean that each hour of labor should buy an increased quantity of goods. In this way the marketing system should be able to pay higher wages for marketing labor and at the same time supply more and better services to farmers and consumers at a lower unit cost. (*Joseph F. Herrick, Jr.*)

Management and Control

The mortality rate of agricultural marketing firms is high. Some have made a success. Far greater numbers have failed. A study of the reasons for this and the suggestions given here for efficient operations can help many persons, including farmers, who run businesses.

It sometimes appears that many firms chanced to grow from one-man operations into large multiunit organizations. But not seen are the many organizations that have grown themselves out of business because management failed to keep pace with opportunity and failed to progress from the stage of being concerned with operating detail to one of policy making. As organizations grow, the changed requirements of management call for greater delegation of authority to lesser officials. Growth and the development of adequate managerial controls go hand in hand. Business failure or stagnation is the penalty for not keeping the two in balance.

The application of managerial controls in marketing firms is necessary in order to extract the maximum effectiveness from the firm's basic operating ingredients—labor, materials, and plant facilities. The ingredients, combined in varying proportions by the manager, bring about various degrees of success or failure in terms of profitable operations.

The labor ingredient is involved in such functions as receiving, storing, assembling of orders, distributing, and selling.

The material ingredient pertains to having available the correct varieties in adequate amount and proper quality and price to meet market demands.

The plant facilities are the common denominator for effective utilization of labor and materials. They include the proper building and adequate plant layout, necessary receiving and loading-out facilities, adequate materials-handling and processing equipment, and adequate transportation equipment for distributing products. Most marketing firms, unlike manufacturing firms, bring about little or no physical change in the product and therefore are primarily handlers of materials.

The effective application of managerial control rests upon a combination of organization, adequate record system, management reports for control, and exercise of effective leadership. Proper combination enables a firm to obtain maximum effectiveness from the integration of its labor, product, and facilities.

Organization means the dividing of a firm's work into definite jobs and assigning the jobs to qualified individuals so that they can harmoniously and economically carry out the objectives of the firm. The development of a proper organization is basically the same, whether the firm is large or small. The only difference is one of size. In a large plant one man is assigned the responsibility for one job. In a small plant one man might be assigned several jobs.

The man who develops the organizational structure has to be objective and uninfluenced by personalities and other prejudicial factors. That means dividing the work into logical activities, such as sales, promotion, distribution, purchasing, financing, and warehousing. Those key activities should be broken down into subdivisions in which there is no overlapping or conflict. Closely related functions must come under the same head or administration.

An organization chart, which shows the relationship of the various activities or functions and the names of the persons in the jobs, is desirable.

If the chart shows that the firm is built around a general manager who does not delegate authority, it is probable that the general manager was considered indispensable. The operations of the firm may be successful and orderly, although somewhat inflexible, but its growth has been limited by the capacity of the manager, and his death or retirement will place the firm in peril. Greater growth would probably have been possible had the firm adjusted itself through managerial control to the kind of organization where delegated managerial control exists.

A detailed statement of the functions, authorities, and responsibilities of each position is a constant source of reference in effective managerial control. The statement should be kept up-to-date and include the names of workers assigned to the various positions, activities, or functions and their relationship to the other positions. The statement should be available to all members of the organization. If the management makes certain that all phases of the specification are being carried out, there will be no overlapping of authority. Delegation of the necessary authority to cope with the assigned responsibilities eliminates confusion and leads to an excellence of performance provided personnel selections are made without fear, force, or personal favoritism.

Records that give accurate and up-to-date information about what is going on in the business are essential. A few managers consider records a necessary evil and keep only some notes in their pockets or keep records only for tax purposes. But most managers are convinced that complete accounts are essential for summarizing the results of past experience and giving data for planning and guiding the future operations.

Having the right type of records is a mark of good management. Too few records may lead to errors in decisions. Too many may cost more than the value of the information developed. A properly installed record system will provide a maximum of continuous and reliable management information with a minimum of cost.

Probably the greatest single cause of unwieldy record systems comes from attempts to use uniform systems copied from some other firm. An effective record system must be tailor-made for each firm and management. Very few firms follow comparable operating detail, and the managements of several firms vary in their capacities to utilize performance reports. A good test of applicability of a system is in the use made of it.

Management reports for control are the chief product of a sound record system. They cover the firm's financial and physical performance. Financial reports, largely from the balance sheet and profit-and-loss statement, provide information as to the type and extent of physical operating reports needed to insure low-cost operation.

The reports of physical performance deal with the individual and group performances of men, methods, and machines. To be the most useful, such reports should cover a long enough period to portray meaningful changes; be designed to meet the specific needs of the interested executives; present information as simply as possible; be prepared only as frequently as necessary; be prepared accurately and on time; and be comparable with preceding report periods in order to facilitate comparisons.

The data presented in reports may

be in terms of money values, physical units, ratios, or a combination of them. A person who interprets the data presented in purely monetary terms must be careful to take into account changes in prices, wages, and costs in order to make valid comparisons.

Much information is available from the balance sheet and profit-and-loss statement. They therefore are prepared frequently and kept readily available to ascertain the firm's financial and overall operating effectiveness.

In the balance sheet the figures are best arranged in a tabular form with adjacent columns showing current figures, figures of the previous period, and possibly figures for a like period in the previous year. Ratios as well as absolute figures should be presented.

The working capital and net worth constitute two important items to look for on the balance sheet. The working capital, the net excess of current assets over current liabilities, indicates the firm's ability to meet its obligations. The working-capital requirements vary for the different types of firms and are especially affected by terms of collection and inventory needs. A rule of thumb is that the current assets, to meet bills when due, should be at least double the current liabilities.

Net worth is represented by the capital stock and surplus combined. It is the stockholder's or owner's stake in the business. A continuous review of net worth will help the management know what is happening, not only with respect to operating results, but also as to any changes in net worth that may not show on the statement of profit and loss.

The profit-and-loss statement shows (in more or less detail, depending on its purpose) the gross sales, costs, expenses, and the net result of doing business during a given period. It represents a summary of the changes between the times at which two balance sheets are prepared. Its purpose is to give a true understanding of the net profit or loss when its component parts are analyzed.

The financial reports are the basis of a great deal of analysis. Sales are the mainstay of most marketing businesses. Therefore the total sales for a week or month and sales by product or product line might well be reported. This may take the form of a profit-and-loss statement that treats the income from sales of each product or major product group separately in one statement in order to appraise the contribution of each to total profit. It may also be desirable to know the sales by territories or routes. Such a breakdown gives bases for comparing present sales with forecasts, budgets, or other goals, and for comparing one line or product with another and one territory with the others. Thus it is possible to get behind the total sales figures to find out what and where the sales weaknesses are and to take action to get to the source of the difficulty.

Other items that might make up a sales report for control purposes are the various sales expenses related to the volume of sales developed, units sold per salesman, order backlogs, inventories, and profit margins by products or lines.

THE BREAK-EVEN CHART is an overall management control device. It is available from financial and other records and can apply to a year, a quarter, or a month. It is a device for bringing together diverse facts in one comprehensive picture as an aid in managerial control. It portrays the relationship of volume of sales or production to income and expense. One of its significant features is the break-even point—the level of sales or production that brings in enough income to meet the expenses at that level. If sales are larger, a profit is produced. If sales are smaller than that level, there is a loss. The degree of profit or loss depends upon how far sales are above or below the level.

The break-even chart usually is constructed so that volume in physical units is plotted along the horizontal axis (if a single product is involved) or

in dollars of sales (if many products are involved). Expenses and income in dollars are plotted along the vertical axis. The income line representing the total income is drawn from the lower left-hand corner of the chart. The total expense line is made up of expense items that might be classified as either fixed or variable.

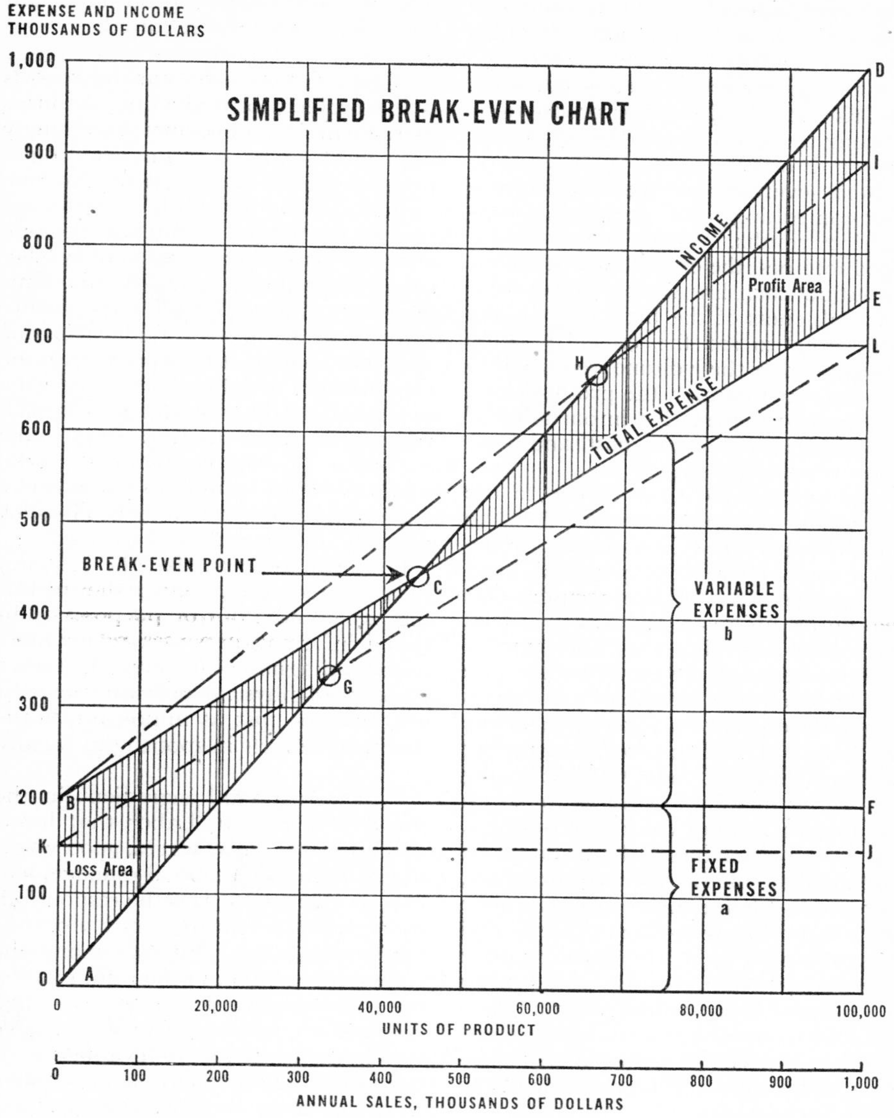

The fixed expenses are due and payable whether the firm is closed or operating at its full capacity. Among them are interest on the mortgage, local taxes, insurance, rent, and depreciation. Among them also are regulated expenses that arise from the operation of the firm and are controllable within limits by the management—

executive and other salaries, and appropriations for advertising, heating, lighting, and standby power.

Variable expenses rise or fall with the rise or fall of sales or production. Among them are commissions, costs of materials or goods, and labor costs.

Break-even charts are effective also for controlling and forecasting operating results. When prepared by product lines, the charts show the contribution each line makes to the total profitableness of the firm. They make it possible to see the effect of price change upon the volume required to break even and upon the profit or loss. They show the relative importance of the principal items of cost and how they vary with volume.

For example, with reference to the hypothetical firm illustrated, when the total expense line B E, composed of the increment of fixed expense a, and variable expense b, management sees an opportunity to reduce the fixed expense items. This new fixed-expense line would be represented by the line K J; since the variable expense is unchanged, the new total-expense line becomes K L and the break-even point is lowered from C to G, thus increasing profits, or making it possible to earn a profit on a smaller volume of business. If, on the other hand, there should be an increase in the variable expenses, the total-expense line would become B I and the break-even point would move from C to H. If the selling price remained unchanged, this would mean that more goods would now have to be sold in order to break even. These are but illustrative of the many types of analyses that can be made with the break-even chart.

The break-even chart enables management to anticipate the effects of its policies and decisions on the profitable operation of the firm as well as the effects of outside influences over which it has no control. For a firm to survive hard times, the break-even point should be low in relation to plant capacity and normal sales volume. For a firm to show excellent earnings in prosperous times, a profit area that has a wide angle is required.

Closely allied to financial reports is the problem of budgeting. As firms increase in size, it becomes increasingly important to have a financial blueprint to chart their course. No one individual can establish an effective budget for a firm of any size because effective budgeting consists of synthesizing past experiences with judgments of future incomes and expenditure trends. The effective budget is one that has been built up from within the organization and has drawn upon the experience and knowledge of each responsible person. In a sense, the budget is a flexible planned guess, designed to be a guide to the effective expenditure of funds and a yardstick of accomplishment.

Financial reports, like the mercury in a thermometer, record the operating experiences of the firm, but additional information is needed for more precise diagnosis in physical terms. Reports of physical operating experience can be just as important as the financial reports in spotting problems.

Labor is a vital ingredient in the makeup of a firm. Labor that has a good purpose, good wages, good working conditions, and good management can do a good job. It is the responsibility of management to furnish a correct amount of labor, plus leadership, the right equipment, and the right method for the various tasks to be performed in the plant. Management should have standards in order to evaluate performance. The evaluation for control purposes is through productivity reports that cover the man-hours expended per unit on such activities as unloading, processing, order assembly, and loading out. Those figures, on a daily basis, when compared with standards or past performance lead to honest evaluations of labor's performance and to constructive courses of action. Knowing which operations are relatively costly should encourage management to seek new methods and equipment to reduce costs.

A firm should strive to meet at least the minimum standards of the industry. Therefore management should be interested in learning the extent of broken delivery promises, short shipments, breakage or spoilage, wrong goods shipped, or poor quality.

The analysis of the records of a firm permit the appraisal of performance in terms of past or anticipated accomplishment. But management needs methods of comparing performance in terms of the competitive environment of the entire industry. A firm's performance may be excellent in terms of the past but still not good enough to maintain its competitive position with other firms. Consequently effective management must know something about the operations of competing firms. Often that information can be had from published information such as that released in financial reports, credit bureau reports, public research agencies, and the like. Trade associations serve as important media for the assembly of industrywide comparative operating costs and sales experience information. It is not uncommon for a number of firms to band together for uniform accounting services, which facilitate the comparison of their operating experience.

Studies of comparative costs among firms engaged in similar activity invariably reveal that no one firm ever excels all others in all aspects of the business. Practically every firm will have some operations superior and some inferior to all others. Thus the comparative information serves not only to appraise the firm's operating effectiveness but also to identify whatever remedial actions are needed.

Management also might need reports on absenteeism and the man hours lost thereby, labor turnover in the firm, and the frequency and severity of accidents. High or rising accident figures should encourage management to seek the causes and apply corrective measures, for they add to costs of doing business.

Getting the information from reports is hardly enough. The next step is action—whether it is to make a decision or set policy. Action may take the form of individual conferences with the interested executive or weekly or monthly meetings with all executives or interested employees. They should be told of the findings as well as the action that must be taken. Any conflicts as to the course of action should be resolved.

The conference can be the source of suggestions for corrective action, particularly when more than one man's responsibility is involved. The conference and the resultant interchange of information among its members should lead to a better understanding of their mutual problems and impart a feeling of being an intimate part of the firm. This will build morale. The members will feel that they had a hand in formulating the decisions; even if a member's advice and suggestions are not accepted, he will feel that he had an opportunity to present his point of view. When a decision is arrived at, he will more readily exert himself to implement the course of action decided upon. (*Frederick C. Winter, Max E. Brunk.*)

Waste and Spoilage

The perishable food lost between the farm and the kitchen would feed millions of people. Spoilage by bacteria, yeasts, and molds, damage from rough handling, and deterioration in the quality and nutritive value take their toll.

Milk, butter, meat, fish, eggs, poultry, and the fruits and vegetables are generally considered most perishable.

Probably the heaviest losses occur in fruits and vegetables because of their susceptibility to decay, mechanical damage, and deteriorative changes in composition.

Railroad freight claims paid for loss and damage in transit provide an estimate of their monetary value. In 1946, a year in which more than a million cars of fruit, melons, and vegetables were shipped, claim payments amounted to about 20 million dollars. In 1951 they were nearly 13 million dollars. Those were the losses paid for by the railroads that could be settled on a claim basis. They represent chiefly mechanical damage and spoilage losses in transit and make up only a small part of the total waste and spoilage. Shipments by highway and boat also suffer damage and loss, but they are not included in the figures.

Some records are available for the amount of loss caused by decay alone. An analysis of about 117,000 inspection records for rail shipments of fruits and vegetables at the New York City market from 1935 to 1942 showed an average of 3 percent of decay. That is not a very high figure, but it would represent a loss of about 3,000 carloads of produce annually in this one market.

By the time the fruits and vegetables are sold by the retailer the damage from decay is much greater. Surveys of spoilage in New York City retail stores gave the following figures: Peaches, 13–24 percent; grapefruit, 9 percent; grapes, 8–15 percent; cantaloups, 8 percent; oranges, 3–7 percent; cabbage, 24 percent; tomatoes, 17 percent; lettuce, 13 percent; and apples, 7 percent.

Decay continues to take a toll after the perishable fruits and vegetables are bought from the retailer. Records kept by 200 housewives in Knoxville, Tenn., showed that they discarded 8 to 15 percent of the fruit and vegetables they purchased because of spoilage. When we add those losses to those of the retailers we have a figure of 18 to 35 percent. The studies give weight to the statement that out of every 5 acres of perishable food produced, the production of 1 acre is not consumed because of spoilage or waste of some kind.

Some other losses are less evident—the losses in quality and nutritive value. They affect the amount of food people eat and the benefit they get from it. Green leafy vegetables may lose 40 to 50 percent of their vitamin C content when they are exposed to warm temperatures for a few days. They also deteriorate in flavor, attractiveness, and other food values. Sweet corn, peas, asparagus, and broccoli lose their fresh quality and some of their nutritive value quickly if refrigeration is inadequate in the marketing channels. Fruit or melons that are picked too green may be discarded as inedible by the consumer, and all the effort and expense that went into their production and marketing are lost. Harvesting fruits and vegetables when they are past their prime also results in poor quality and waste.

What have we done to prevent loss and damage in our perishable food supplies? We have bred better varieties of plants that have disease resistance, higher quality, or particular suitability for canning, freezing, or shipping. We have developed better cultural practices and more effective spray programs for disease and insect control. We have improved techniques for producing higher quality and better yields of many of our food crops. We have developed better methods of harvesting, handling, and packaging that have helped to reduce mechanical damage. Under the stimulus of the high labor costs, harvesting methods have been developed that reduce damage as well as labor.

One of the important harvesting improvements took place in the California lettuce industry. Shallow trailers have been constructed that are hauled to the fields, where they are filled with lettuce. The rubber-tired conveyances then bring the lettuce to the packinghouse, where it is placed gently into the packing bins and is trimmed, graded, and packed. This eliminates handling of individual field crates, reduces damage to the lettuce, and saves labor costs. The system has been applied to the harvesting of other vegetables and melons.

Large portable equipment has been developed for harvesting and packing celery and some other vegetables. The equipment is driven down the rows. A crew ahead of the machine cuts and places the celery on belts, which convey it to the washer and grading and packing belts. The celery is harvested, packed, and washed in a few minutes and is soon on its way to the hydrocooler and loading shed. The refuse is left in the field, many individual steps in labor are saved, and the product is fresh when it is placed in the refrigerator car or truck for shipment.

Improvements have been made in the types of containers used. Among the boxes designed to do a definite job are cell-type cartons for ripe fruits, and smaller, more easily handled boxes for citrus fruit and lettuce. The rapid development of the consumer packages has resulted in packing at the shipping point or at the terminal market in units containing a convenient amount of produce that move through the marketing channels as a unit. This reduces the excessive handling that consumers are likely to give perishable goods and also speeds their flow through self-service stores.

Much has been done to reduce the inroads of diseases on fruits and vegetables. Borax washes for citrus fruits reduce losses from blue and green mold and stem-end rots. Sodium orthophenyl phenate is a newer treatment for citrus fruit and apples and pears. Chlorine compounds are in wide use for fruit and vegetables. Chemicals have been incorporated in wraps or box liners to inhibit the growth of decay organisms. Copper-impregnated wraps are used to prevent the growth of gray mold from pear to pear in the box. Biphenyl-impregnated wraps and box liners are used to retard development of decays in citrus fruit.

Volatile fungicides have been developed for treating fruit and vegetables in refrigerator cars, trucks, or storage rooms. Nearly all of the cars of grapes shipped from California are fumigated with sulfur dioxide before shipment to control decay and to keep the stems from browning. Periodical sulfur dioxide fumigation of grapes in storage more than doubles their storage life.

Fruit and vegetables and most spoilage organisms need oxygen to carry on their life processes. We deprive them of a normal supply of oxygen by replacing some of the oxygen in the atmosphere with carbon dioxide. Storages with atmospheres modified in this way have been developed for varieties of apples, such as McIntosh and Rhode Island Greening, that cannot tolerate low temperatures for long periods of storage. Storage life is lengthened and good quality is retained by the method. Atmospheres so modified have also been used to improve the storage life of meat, fish, and eggs. Dry ice (solid carbon dioxide) is employed to produce an atmosphere of carbon dioxide in the refrigerator car during shipment of some perishable fruits, such as cherries and strawberries. That helps to reduce decay and slow down ripening. Much remains to be done in this field of protecting perishables from microorganisms that produce decay and also to find some way to supplement refrigeration in retarding ripening and deterioration.

Some diseases of fruits and vegetables are brought on by abnormal changes in the plant tissues. Some of them can be prevented.

Apple scald, probably the most important storage disorder of apples, causes a browning of the skin and underlying flesh and usually appears late in the storage season. Its exact nature is unknown, but volatile substances given off by the fruit are believed responsible. Scientists of the Department of Agriculture more than 30 years ago found that paper wraps impregnated with mineral oil, or shredded, oiled paper scattered through the containers would give fairly good control of scald by absorbing the volatile materials. The discovery has been estimated to save more than 2 million dollars a year in fruit that otherwise would have been damaged by the disease. Scald of Anjou pears is also controlled by oiled wraps.

Another physiological disease, soft scald of apples, causes irregular, brown, depressed areas on the fruit. It is controlled by employing a combination of storage temperatures—36° F. for the first few weeks of storage and then 31° to 32° for long storage.

Pears lose their capacity to ripen if stored too long. Storage in atmospheres enriched in carbon dioxide and depleted in oxygen prolong the time they may be stored and still have good quality when ripened. By employing sealed film liners for boxes of pears, and allowing the fruit to build up carbon dioxide and deplete oxygen through respiration, desirable atmospheres can be maintained.

Core breakdown of pears is prevented by picking the fruit before it becomes too ripe. Water core and internal breakdown of apples also are associated with picking too late. Bitter pit and scald are favored by picking too soon. Internal black spot of potatoes, a condition in which the flesh beneath slight bruises becomes gray or black, usually can be prevented to some degree by warming the potatoes to about 50° F. before they are handled. Black heart of potatoes, which makes the center of the tubers gray or black, is caused by lack of oxygen. Losses in boat shipments of potatoes were heavy until the cause was discovered and the ships' holds were ventilated. A similar disease affects apples.

Some vegetables—including Irish potatoes—can regenerate new cells that heal cuts and abrasions and prevent decay, moisture loss, and browning. Temperatures of 60° to 75° F. and high humidities are required to promote healing. This basic information has been applied practically in the prevention of soft rot and browning of potatoes during shipment and storage by using only enough refrigeration to cool the potatoes gradually so they will heal before the temperature is too low. Sweetpotatoes also form protective layers of cells, and curing at 85° to 90° and 90 percent humidity for a week or more is a common practice before shipment or storage.

Refrigeration is an effective tool for preventing spoilage, but it can be overdone. Some fruits and vegetables, usually those of subtropical origin, are injured by temperatures that would be ideal for others.

Mature green tomatoes will not tolerate 32° F. for more than about 6 days. They become susceptible to certain types of rots, subsequent ripening is impaired, and poor flavor develops. The lowest temperature that should be used for tomatoes is about 55°. Ideal ripening takes place at about 65°.

Green peppers behave much like tomatoes in respect to chilling injury. Lemons, bananas, avocados, cucumbers, squashes, melons, eggplant, okra, Irish potatoes, sweetpotatoes, grapefruit, string beans, olives, pineapples, cranberries, mangoes, and papayas are also cold-susceptible. Injury appears as pitting, browning, water-soaked areas in the flesh, development of off-flavors and poor quality, failure to ripen, and greater susceptibility to decay. By adjusting the storage and transit temperatures to the needs of the commodity much spoilage and loss in quality can be prevented.

Much of the damage to potatoes takes place between the field and the packinghouse or storage bins. The rest of it occurs in packing and shipping to the retailer.

Apples are often bruised when they are offered for sale. All the apples in the top layer of the box may have large bruises from the lid.

Lettuce may be hurt in packing and in shipping to the market, and heavy trimming of outside leaves is necessary before it can be sold.

Mechanical damage makes produce

more vulnerable to decay and less attractive to customers. What can be done to prevent it? Improvements in harvesting, handling, packaging, and shipping may all be required.

Another serious fault with fruits and vegetables is that they sometimes lack good eating quality. Perhaps this is because they never had it to begin with. Fruits are sometimes picked either too green or overmature. Sights should be set on the quality the consumer wants. This will mean picking early fruits at a riper stage of maturity and will call for better packaging and refrigeration and faster handling from the field to the market. Improved methods of determining the quality of fruits and vegetables and the maturity at which they should be harvested are needed.

The specific gravity of potatoes is known to be related to cooking quality. Potatoes with high specific gravity are best suited for baking, french frying, and making potato chips. Experimental equipment has been devised for separating potatoes by their specific gravity.

Ripening fruits and vegetables to prime condition before sale offers opportunity for quality improvement. Special ripening rooms are now provided for winter pears. The practice might well be extended to summer varieties, like Bartlett, which will not ripen well at high temperatures. Much of our supply of tomatoes is ripened in special rooms. Quality would be improved if ripening was done at more ideal temperatures and to a riper stage. Melons, like honeydews and cantaloups, are often too hard when purchased to please the consumer. A short ripening period at controlled temperatures would improve their quality.

What has been said about the quality of fresh produce applies as well to the canned and frozen fruit and vegetables. Selection of well-adapted varieties and harvesting them at the peak of quality are essential. Preventing losses before processing by making full use of refrigeration if delays are encountered and using processing methods that do not destroy flavor, texture, and nutritive value are the goals.

Another improvement that could be made in marketing fresh fruit and vegetables is the elimination of unnecessary trimming waste that the housewife experiences in preparing vegetables like cauliflower and asparagus for cooking. Methods of packaging and shipping can be devised that will deliver to the consumer fresh produce ready for cooking. It has been done for some commodities such as spinach, kale, and sweet corn.

There is need to find some way to prevent spoilage and deterioration that is still encountered in certain fruits and vegetables. Continuous refrigeration offers great opportunity for doing so. New types of sprays and chemical inhibitors have been developed, some of which offer promise.

High-energy electrons (cathode or gamma rays) have been used experimentally to sterilize foods. The method may some day have wide application, but problems of secondary effects on the color, flavor, and nutritive value, depth of penetration, and cost have to be worked out.

Growth-regulating chemicals have been used successfully to bring about changes in the physiology of the fruit or vegetable that improve keeping quality. The sprouting of potatoes is inhibited by treating them with dips of some of these chemicals, thus permitting higher storage temperatures to be used that are more favorable to high quality. Sprouting of onions can be delayed by spraying the plants before harvest with maleic hydrazide. Lemon storage is improved by dipping the fruit in growth-promoting chemicals that keep the buttons or stem attachment green and healthy longer.

What has been accomplished to date in preventing spoilage and loss of quality gives encouragement for future improvements. New advances in this field are on their way. (*W. T. Pentzer.*)

Efficiency in Refrigeration

About 75 percent (by weight) of all the food the average American eats in a year requires some refrigeration during its trip from farms and fisheries through processing plants, warehouses, railroad cars and trucks, terminals and markets, and the millions of refrigerated units in retail foodstores to the household refrigerator and the home-freezer.

But all is not fine and dandy. Up and down the marketing line are innumerable instances where facilities are inadequate, poor practices are followed, and handlers do not have the knowledge or interest to maintain proper temperatures for the products they handle. Poor practices result in complete losses, lower quality, or losses of nutritive values.

To understand refrigeration and to visualize its promises for the future, we shall have to look at the basic principles underlying its application to the marketing of perishables.

Two factors are involved—the characteristics of the product and the physical process of removing the heat from air and from matter.

Perishable products vary considerably in their perishability. Apples can be kept longer after harvest than fresh strawberries, for example, and celery longer than tomatoes. Whether fast or slow, deterioration occurs, with losses in nutritive value, natural flavors, and color. Dehydration, the drying out of the food, is a common form of deterioration. The action of mold, yeast, and bacteria sometimes adds to quality losses.

Low temperatures retard deterioration. High temperatures hasten it. The operation principle of refrigeration is to remove heat directly from the product and from the air around it. The rate of deterioration is usually directly proportionate to the temperature of the commodity within limits. At 0° F. the living processes of many products are almost halted; that is the reason for freezing as a method of preserving for many months the ripe quality of fresh foods.

Refrigeration on farms preserves food for home consumption and maintains the quality of products, particularly eggs and milk, while they are being accumulated for sale to the first receivers.

The household refrigerator, the home-freezer, and the rural locker plant have contributed greatly to increasing the comforts of farm life.

There were 1,200 locker plants in the United States in 1938, 3,000 in 1940, 6,500 in 1945, and 11,600 in 1953. The locker plant provides processing and freezing service for farmers' home-produced meat products and space for storing food supplies. Locker plants in the United States provide more than 5 million lockers, or about 32 million cubic feet of freezer space. Plant operators handle—for slaughtering, dressing, cutting, wrapping, freezing, curing, or rendering—more than 1¼ billion pounds of meat and poultry each year. They also freeze annually about 80 million pounds of fruits and vegetables. Locker plants also sell nonfarm consumers meat and commercially frozen foods.

Some farmers use commercial-type refrigerator units to hold eggs and dairy products before sending them to market. Many State agricultural colleges will send information on the construction of such units on request. The Department of Agriculture has plans and blueprints of walk-in units (plan No. 7102 and leaflet No. 320, published in 1951), which may be obtained from the extension agricultural engineer at many of the State agricultural colleges.

A popular size of a farm refrigeration unit for holding foods before marketing and for home use is about 12 x 12 feet. About two-thirds of the space is for the cooler and one-third is for the freezer.

BEFORE PERISHABLE PRODUCTS are started on their long trips from assembly points to distribution centers, field heat has to be removed from fruits and vegetables and body heat from fresh-killed animal products.

The operation is called precooling. Its object is to reduce the temperature of the product as quickly as possible so that deterioration will be retarded. Products can be precooled in the packing plant or warehouse or after they are loaded into trucks or rail cars.

Precooling after the products are loaded into a refrigerated car or truck is done in several ways. One method is to force air through iced bunkers and around the load. Air is circulated either by a portable fan placed in the car or truck, or by use of permanently installed fans. Portable mechanical units are sometimes used to precool loads in refrigerator cars. The equipment, mounted in a motortruck, is placed alongside the car, and cold air is blown over the top of the load and returned across the sides and bottom. When refrigerator cars and trucks are equipped with fixed mechanical refrigerating units, produce can be cooled after loading by stacking the containers so that air will circulate freely through the load.

A method of precooling by vacuum offers the advantage of cooling large quantities of leafy vegetables rather quickly. Steel vacuum chambers for precooling lettuce are about 6 or 7 feet across and 30 to 50 feet long. They hold up to a carload of lettuce. The temperature of the products in the chambers can be reduced from 62° to 32° in 50 to 55 minutes. This rapid and thorough method of precooling allows lettuce to be shipped with only bunker ice, that is, without ice in the shipping containers or over and through the load, as is required for non-precooled lettuce.

To the wholesaler proper refrigeration means maintaining quality of the produce, reducing risk (by allowing more time in which to sell products), reducing waste and spoilage, and affording less chance of contamination of food by foreign matter or micro-organisms.

The wholesaler provides for food refrigeration in two ways—by having short-term holding space at the wholesale store and by using large public or private refrigerated warehouses.

Products that usually do not have a long storage life, such as lettuce and tomatoes, are shipped directly into wholesale stores, usually in single rail-car and truck lots, shortly after being harvested. Seasonal products that can be stored for relatively long periods, such as fresh apples and frozen foods, are held in warehouses and moved into wholesale facilities as needed.

Wholesalers' on-premise refrigerated holding facilities are perhaps the weakest link in the refrigeration chain stretching from farmer to consumer. The inadequacy is more pronounced for handlers of fresh fruits and vegetables than for those handling meats, dairy products, eggs, and frozen foods. Produce handlers are inclined to provide controlled temperatures for only the items whose appearance is readily affected by nonrefrigerated storage. That usually means refrigeration of the minimum number of products rather than the maximum.

Because of the important role of storage in distribution, warehousing is generally regarded as a function separate from wholesaling. Warehousing may be done by a distributor, who operates his own warehouse, or by a public warehouseman, who does not take title to the goods. The amount of private refrigerated space has increased a lot since 1945, particularly among frozen-food packers and distributors, chainstores, egg handlers, and institu-

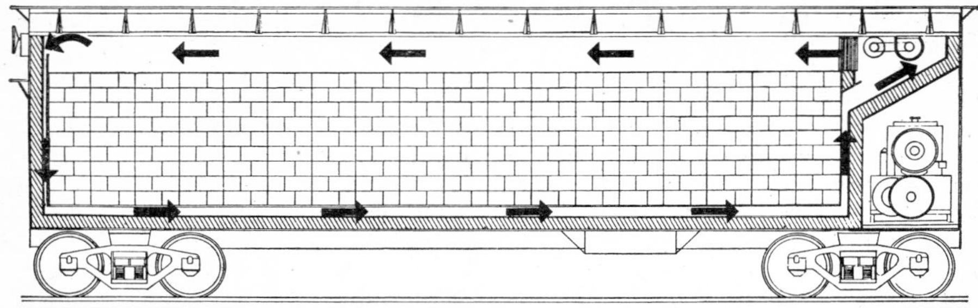

CROSS SECTION OF A MODERN REFRIGERATOR CAR

tional concerns, such as hospitals and commissaries.

Refrigerated warehouse construction began on a large scale about 1915, notably in meatpacking plants, which had 300 million cubic feet of refrigerated space in 1921. The figure has remained about constant ever since.

Public and private warehouses came into prominence about 1920; the 850 public and private warehouses (other than meatpacking plants) then had a total of 250 million cubic feet of space. There were 1,000 such warehouses, with a total of 400 million cubic feet by 1929. The 1,700 refrigerated warehouses (not counting meatpacking plants) had 600 million cubic feet of space in 1951.

Much of the space in refrigerated warehouses designated as "cooler" has been converted to "freezer" since 1945. In 1951, 43 percent of all warehouse space was freezer.

Most warehouses constructed since 1945 are of single-story design and are well adapted to modern equipment for handling materials—especially pallets and fork trucks. Single-story warehouses also offer the advantage of providing a relatively large amount of street-level space from which distributors can carry on their marketing operations.

Because public warehousemen store perishable products for others, there has been a tendency for State and Federal Governments, at the encouragement of storers, to regulate warehouse operations. Many attempts have been made, but only a few controls of refrigerated warehouses actually have been instituted. Some regulations, such as the Uniform Warehouse Receipts Act, appear to have been necessary in order to strengthen the negotiability of warehouse receipts used for collateral in securing bank credit.

Modern retail foodstores have several types of refrigerated facilities: Walk-in coolers and freezers in backrooms for holding items before placing them on display; refrigerated rooms (preferably about 45°) for cutting and prepackaging meats; and refrigerated display fixtures. Backroom facilities depend mostly on volume of business and frequency of ordering items. If delivery of perishable products is made daily, or once every 2 days, the holding facilities might consist of only one refrigerated walk-in unit. If deliveries are made less frequently, several rooms are needed—a high-humidity room for reserve supplies of leafy vegetables; a separate low-humidity room for meats; a room for eggs, milk, and other products; and a freezer room for reserve supplies of frozen foods.

For selling food, the most important refrigerated units in the retail store are the display cases. Considerable emphasis is placed on the display arrangement, particularly in regard to colors. To provide for the best display of products, the fixtures are designed to permit full view of the products and provide adequate lighting so there are no shadows. The characteristics of successful display are freshness, neatness, eye appeal, and ready identification of the product and its price. Rapid turnover is a prerequisite to freshness. Cases for displaying prepackaged merchandise should be held as near 35° as practicable. Those containing bulk produce should be held at 40° to 50°. Cabinets for frozen food must be held at 0°. High humidity must be maintained for fresh leafy vegetables to prevent dehydration, loss of weight, loss of color, and loss of flavor and nutritive values.

William E. Lewis and John C. Hansen, of the Department of Agriculture, studied refrigeration of food in retail stores and offer the following suggestions for prolonging the freshness of produce:

Light sprinkling with water several times daily will reduce wilting and prolong the shelf life of most vegetables.

Produce that has been displayed in nonrefrigerated cases during the daytime should be stored at night in iced produce barrels or in refrigerated storage rooms.

Produce should not be piled above the top front edge of refrigerated cases unless it is expected to be sold in a reasonably short time.

Restaurateurs recognize the importance of proper refrigeration to wholesomeness of meals and to sanitation.

Most restaurants need refrigeration for holding stocks of fresh products before cooking or serving; storing frozen foods and ice cream; holding displays of salads and salad material; holding and dispensing soda-fountain foods and beverages; cooling and dispensing fruit juices, soft drinks, beers, and ales; and cooling and dispensing water. Many large restaurants have refrigeration also for making and storing ice; manufacturing and storing frozen desserts, ice, and ice cream; holding baking supplies; and even refrigerating garbage to help in keeping the kitchen area sanitary.

Even a small restaurant should have at least one refrigerator for holding food before it is prepared for serving. It is good practice to have four separate storage units: A wet room (high humidity) for leafy vegetables; one for eggs, dairy products, and perhaps some fruit; one for meats and poultry; and a freezer room for frozen foods and ice cream. Walk-in facilities mostly are preferred. They should be carefully planned with respect to size, location, and construction. Walk-in units less than 8 x 8 feet usually are not economical.

Temperatures of household refrigerators should be maintained as close to 38° to 40° as possible. The importance of proper temperatures is illustrated in the results of a test on mold growth. The test showed that in a dish of cooked food held for 12 hours at 55°, mold growth had multiplied thousands of times, whereas identical food held at 40° showed no growth at the end of 48 hours.

Several precautions are necessary to maintain the quality of fresh foods in refrigerators. Fresh vegetables and fruits should not be stored in airtight packages, since the "breathing" of fresh food is essential for its proper preservation. Leafy and high-moisture vegetables, such as lettuce and celery, should be stored in special crisper compartments or in bags in which small amounts of moisture can be added if the product is to be held longer than 2 days. Storing bread and other dough products in the refrigerator will hasten staleness, but they can be wrapped in moistureproof paper and stored for long periods in home-freezers.

Freezer space in most household refrigerators is limited to the evaporator, the ice-cube compartment. The air temperature there frequently exceeds 15° and therefore is not suitable for keeping frozen foods more than a few days. Demands for more evaporator space in which to store frozen foods brought the manufacture of dual-temperature refrigerators, which have a frozen-food compartment of about 2 cubic feet, which is normally suitable for at least a week's supply of frozen foods and ice cream. Best results are

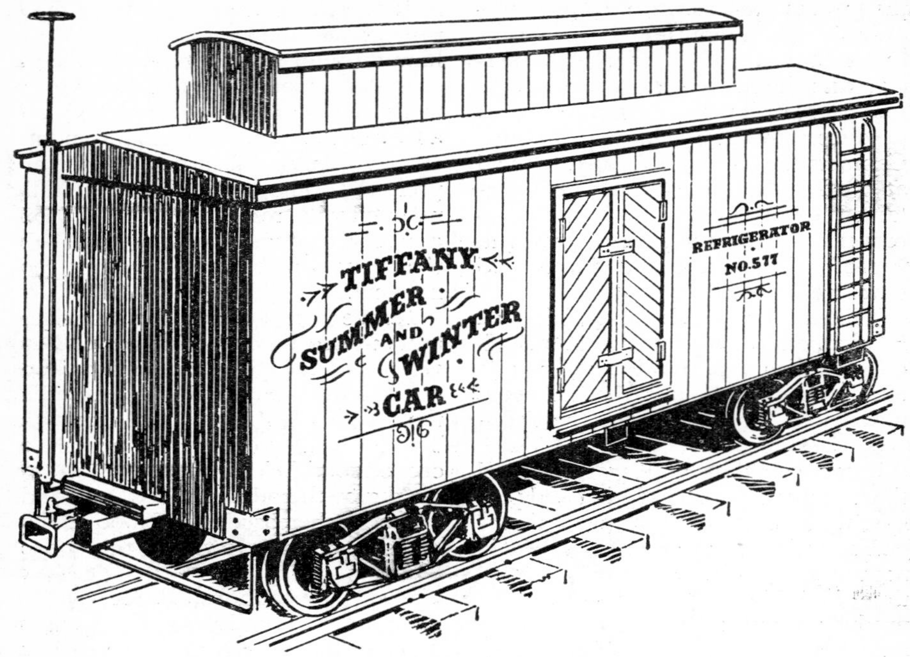

AN OLD-FASHIONED REFRIGERATOR

obtained from the freezer unit of dual-temperature refrigerators if the compartment has separate temperature controls and preferably has a separate door.

The place the refrigerator is put in the kitchen is rather important because in many homes it is opened 100 times a day. It should be as close to the food-preparation center as possible. Because a home-freezer is opened only about 5 times daily, it can be in another part of the house.

The foremost steps in refrigerator design since 1935 have been the production of hermetically sealed units, the streamlining of the compressor unit so that it would fit into a much smaller area, and the development of automatic defrosting.

In two-temperature refrigerators, the placing of coils in the walls rather than in a confined area has helped in obtaining lower and more even temperatures and eliminating, in cooler compartments, the need for defrosting.

The new designs and improvements center around providing more freezer space in dual-temperature units, improvements in humidity compartments for leafy vegetables, special 10° F. compartments for having ice cream at ready-to-dip consistency, special "high temperature" compartment for ready-to-use butter, specially designed space for bottle and beverage containers and juices, outside colors to blend with kitchen color schemes, and the probable application of special light rays to control the growth of micro-organisms.

More than 85 percent of American homes had mechanical refrigeration in 1954. Sales are limited to new homes, old homes in which electricity has been installed recently, and to replacements. Freezers, on the other hand, are to be found in about 9 percent of the homes. About 7 million home-freezers were in use in 1954, and indications were that 1 to 2 million would be added

GROSS REFRIGERATED STORAGE SPACE, BY STATES, OCTOBER 1, 1951

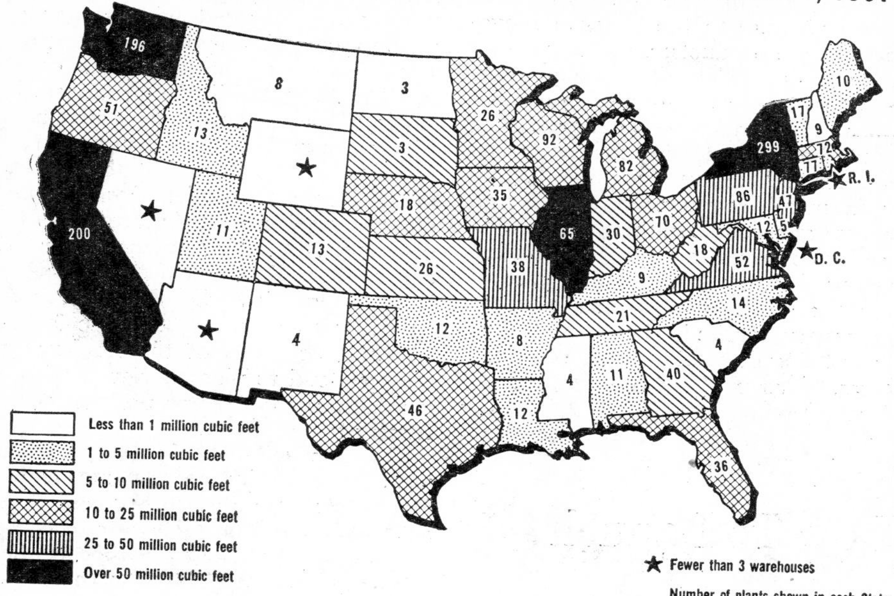

each year for a decade. Future designs of freezers are likely to continue to center around the alternatives of chest and upright freezers and color schemes so they will fit into furniture schemes in parts of the house other than the kitchen.

A GREAT DEVELOPMENT is the rise of the frozen-food industry. Within two decades a whole new enterprise was built through the integrated application of refrigeration principles. The principles themselves are old, but not until technicians learned to apply them to modern needs and wants was a real beginning made.

The commercial frozen foods in 1930 were mainly fish, small fruits, New York dressed poultry, wholesale cuts of meat, eggs, and a few vegetables.

One by one the troublesome technological hurdles were overtopped, and by 1954 to the list of commercially frozen foods had been added shellfish, a large variety of vegetables, fruit juices, baked goods, and many others.

There is also a vast field, yet to be fully explored, of prepared items ready to heat and serve. The most notable growth has been in frozen waffles and frozen french-fried potatoes. Waffles need only to be taken from the freezer and put into the toaster for quick heating. French fries require simply placing under the broiler for thawing and heating. Precooked meals have been frozen and packaged successfully, but distribution problems are harder to overcome—among them economies in commercial preparation and consumer resistance to new, untried forms.

The national markets for some crops have been considerably stabilized because of the expanded outlets offered by frozen foods. A notable example is the citrus industry.

A big job lies ahead for packers and distributors of frozen foods. The immediate challenge is to reduce marketing cost. That can be done principally by less handling of the product, particularly from packer to terminal wholesaler; the establishment of ef-

281437°—54——26

ficient distributing and warehousing plants; the application of advanced flow principles to the physical movement of the products; and the installation at retail outlets of more temporary storage space and more display cabinet space. The long-range challenge is to afford better protection for the frozen product all along the line. More mechanically refrigerated rail cars and trucks are needed. Additional attention needs to be given to product protection during delivery to retail and institutional outlets, while being held in temporary storage in these outlets, and while being displayed for sale at retail stores. (*James A. Mixon, Harold D. Johnson.*)

How To Launch a New Product

Producers and processors seek always a new form in which to market their products, a ten-strike. Hope springs anew in their breasts when they see the success of a product like frozen concentrated orange juice. But a dramatic development like that makes one forget the wreckage of the failures.

The benefits or losses from innovations in distribution of farm commodities may accrue to producers in two different ways: First, assumption of the risk and benefits by producers, through their organizations; second, through development and control of the innovation by large commercial concerns.

In either, the producer is likely to benefit if the product is a success. The benefits are likely to return faster to producers if they themselves undertake the development and marketing of a new product.

The wide dispersal of ownership of agricultural production and of marketing organizations and facilities is frequently associated with a lack of enough capital for developing, producing, and distributing new commodities. The inability of producers to carry out research on new products was recognized in the establishment of four Regional Research Laboratories of the Department of Agriculture under the Agricultural Adjustment Act of 1938. Marketing research which can tie in with physical development is authorized by the Research and Marketing Act of 1946. Those facilities and activities of the land-grant colleges tend to place agricultural organizations in a better position with respect to research.

The Department, in cooperation with the apple industry of the Pacific Northwest, completed studies that exemplify the type of research necessary in placing a new product on the market. The apple industry had attempted to find a profitable means of disposing of C grade and cull Delicious apples. Attempts to can the apples had met with little success because of the exterior characteristics of the variety.

At the Western Regional Research Laboratory near San Francisco a new process of manufacturing frozen concentrated apple juice was developed. It was a modification of earlier methods of essence stripping. It blended Delicious apple juice with juice of apples of other varieties and then concentrated them to a 3 to 1 ratio.

A number of blends were made, and samples of 12 of them were sent to Washington State College for discrimination tests. Three juices were selected for consumer preference tests in San Francisco. The preferred juice was placed on the market in Modesto, Calif., and Tyler, Tex. It was distributed by regular distributors of frozen foods and placed in nearly all stores that had frozen-food cabinets. After about 10 weeks, consumers were asked how they liked the new product. Then its composition was changed.

Tabulation of the results of the interviews in Tyler and Modesto indicated that 70 percent of the initial buyers bought the juice more than once; 40 percent bought it four times or more. Those results were good enough to encourage a manufacturer to undertake distribution in 1952 and 1953 in the Northwest, looking toward the possibility of further manufacture and distribution later in a wider territory.

The experience, in sum, took into account the repeat purchases, the reactions of housewives to taste and use, and the need for changes in the product.

THE FOREGOING EXAMPLE illustrates a fairly simple approach to the appraisal of the possibilities of a new product. But there are still many problems to be worked out before we know whether the new juice will become an actual commercial success.

These additional problems will include: How should the product be packaged in terms of sizes and use? Will the package stand up under storage and transportation difficulties? At what price can the product be sold? What margins are normally required in similar items and at various levels of trade? Are raw materials available in sufficient quantities, and how may they be obtained? What are the problems in distribution? What channels are available for distributing a new product? What is the competitive picture in the field in terms of direct and indirect competitive products and the distributive, promotional, and production policies of competing producers? What investments would be required for production facilities including inventories, distribution, and promotion? What is the size of market? The estimated potential in terms of dollars or volume of product? What is the character of the market in terms of consumers who are the potential users? Will the market be steady or will it be seasonal? Can it be expected to increase?

Market surveys of one kind or another can provide answers to several of the questions. Some of them, however, can only be answered by experience, with part of the answer also depending upon production trends in the raw product (apples) and the strength of the market for fresh fruit.

There is an entirely different group of problems that may not be so easily measurable. Consumption is built on habit; changes from a normal routine are usually hard to get accepted by the consuming public. Health regulations, restrictive trade barriers, and labor rules and regulations also may tend to make change difficult.

Several attempts were made to sell concentrated milk. It was sold on an experimental basis in a dozen markets in Eastern and North Central States. The advertising given it set forth advantages claimed for it—direct use without reconstituting for cereals and coffee, less storage space, added convenience in carrying home a smaller and lighter package, and possible reductions in cost of distribution. In each city where it was placed on the market, sales fell from the "experimental" levels to a small fraction of the total market. In a few months no concentrated milk was sold in any of the test areas.

It had run into difficulties with health regulations, labor organizations, and usual trade practices. In most places it could not be delivered to the customer through retail outlets or by home delivery at less than he would have to pay for the equivalent quantity of regular milk—drivers and salesmen wanted to maintain the same margin for handling concentrated milk as for regular milk.

The truth is that few new products have overwhelming advantages compared to older products. Frozen concentrated orange juice is a notable exception. Even with it distributors overcame the consumers' resistance to change only with large expenditures for advertising. Even with the great expansion in use of the concentrate—2.5 million gallons in 1948 and 48 million gallons in 1953—fewer than one-third of United States families bought it at least once a month in the fall of 1953.

An industrial firm has to devote considerable study before it decides to undertake the manufacture or distribution of a new product. It must fit into the firm's present activities. It might raise unduly or lower the costs of operation. Perhaps it will not fit into the present line of products carried by the organization. The operating procedures in terms of seasonality of operation and availability of labor and raw materials are other points.

Rarely can an organization obtain patent rights or processing franchise on a new product that is fully ready for distribution. More often large outlays have to be made for physical development of processes or the product itself. Yet this is the direction in which progress lies; and anyone who is acquainted with current-day research, merchandising methods, or consumer interests realizes the increasing interest which is going into new and improved uses. (*Shelby A. Robert, Jr.*)

Dynamic, Efficient Research

Research is the application of organized thinking to human needs.

Research in agricultural marketing relates to the entire range of activities that arise in moving products from farms to the final places of use.

Research in agricultural marketing has lagged behind research in agricultural production. And that despite the fact that marketing is but one phase of the process of production, for a product is of little use until it reaches the consumer. Henry Ford's idea that the markets for the Model T could be expanded by a drastic price reduction was a dynamic force in developing the automobile industry and in expanding technical discoveries. It illustrates how a progressive plan in marketing created an opportunity for industrial development.

As far back as 1839 statistics were gathered by the Federal Government to provide information that would help farmers market their products. The aim was to find "ways and means by which the husbandmen shall have a market." In the 1850's the Commissioner of Patents gathered agricultural information on cost of transportation, the cost of production, market value, and methods of harvest, storage, and preparation for market.

The great increase in crop production caused by improved farm machinery, better farming practices, and the opening up of the West led Secretary of Agriculture J. Sterling Morton to assert in 1894, "There is nothing of greater or more vital importance to the farmers of the United States than the widening of the markets for their products."

In his report for 1896 he went on to say: "Science is constantly showing the farmer how to increase the annual product per acre . . . but the great question confronting each tiller of the soil is how to secure satisfactory remuneration for the results of his toil. In view of this, it is a legitimate function of the Department of Agriculture to place before the farmers of the United States as many facts and figures relative to markets as it is possible to obtain."

The work started under Secretary Morton was carried further under Secretary James Wilson. In his first report, for 1897, there was a description of experimental shipments of butter to London. It is here quoted:

"Early in the year it became apparent that a considerable surplus of butter of the higher grades would appear in our domestic markets. . . .

"I therefore decided to make a series of experimental exports of fine

American butter, for the purpose of promoting an increased foreign demand for this article, and in order to get more exact information as to facts and conditions attending such exports than was otherwise obtainable. . . .

"The butter has been obtained from selected creameries in the leading dairy States, prepared with special reference to the ascertained requirements of foreign buyers, and thus far all has been consigned to a representative of the Department at London. It has been disposed of under his supervision, special efforts being made to test the demands of the London market and obtain the opinions of wholesale dealers, tradesmen, and consumers as to the merits of the butter thus sold and its relative position, present and prospective, in that market. Much attention has also been given to the matter of transportation, with the view to shortening the time, improving the accommodations, and avoiding detentions and exposures, so as to make the conditions as nearly perfect as possible all along the line, from the producer, perhaps in our far West, to the consumer in England or on the continent of Europe. . . .

"The shipments made have served the double purpose of securing useful information for those of our own people, whether producers or dealers, who wish to sell abroad, and of aiding to establish a better reputation for butter from the United States among prospective customers. . . ."

The significance of agricultural marketing was given emphasis in 1901 by John Franklin Crowell in the 508-page *Report of the Industrial Commission on the Distribution of Farm Products*. It was a landmark in thinking on marketing problems. It provided a picture of the marketing process and the factors affecting market prices. It dealt with most aspects of the subject, including cold storage, which was growing rapidly in importance.

Before 1907 the principal interest of the Department in marketing related to the foreign market. In that year a bulletin was issued on the cost of hauling products from the farm to the shipping point. That broader approach led in 1908 to the reorganization of the Division of Foreign Markets as the Division of Production and Distribution. Congressional interest in more research and service work in marketing led to the establishment of the Office of Markets in 1913.

The new place of marketing in the work of the Department was recognized in that year by Secretary David F. Houston in his first annual report: "We have been suddenly brought face to face with the fact that in many directions further production waits on better distribution and that the field of distribution presents problems which raise in very grave ways the simple issue of justice."

Great strides have been made in "better distribution" since the statement was made, and many constructive achievements have resulted—the Market News Service; official standards for wheat, cotton, tobacco, and other farm products and for market containers; the United States Warehouse Act; shipping-point inspection of fruits and vegetables; Federal-State cooperation on crop reporting; regulation of the grain futures and livestock market; the outlook program for planning production; the Perishable Agricultural Commodities Act for suppressing unfair practices; and the building of a network of farmer owned and controlled cooperative associations. Since 1913 it has been the policy of the Federal Government to provide research assistance to farmers in organizing and operating cooperatives for marketing, purchasing, or other business service.

Although progress has been made, the dynamic character of our agricultural production and industrial life has constantly brought new problems in marketing. With technological and scientific progress, the problems of distribution have grown in intensity except for intervals of great demand for agricultural products associated with the war and postwar periods.

To CORRECT the disparity between the emphasis on research in production and research in marketing, the Agricultural Marketing Act was passed in 1946. It declared: "A sound, efficient, and privately operated system for distributing and marketing agricultural products is essential to a prosperous agriculture and is indispensable to the maintenance of full employment and to the welfare, prosperity, and health of the Nation."

The act further stated that:

". . . it is the intent of Congress to provide for (1) continuous research to improve the marketing, handling, storage, processing, transportation, and distribution of agricultural products; (2) cooperation among Federal and State agencies, producers, industry organizations, and others in the development and effectuation of research and marketing programs to improve the distribution processes; (3) an integrated administration of all laws enacted by Congress to aid the distribution of agricultural products through research, market aids and services, and regulatory activities, to the end that marketing methods and facilities may be improved, that distribution costs may be reduced and the price spread between the producer and consumer may be narrowed, that dietary and nutritional standards may be improved, that new and wider markets for American agricultural products may be developed, both in the United States and in other countries, with a view to making it possible for the full production of American farms to be disposed of usefully, economically, profitably, and in an orderly manner."

The research work that followed has been largely in three fields: Measurement and analyses of price spreads and costs, which provide basic data for improvement of the marketing system; an extension of research for improving methods of operations from the farmer on through various steps to the consumer; and merchandising and market development work relating to new products, new forms of products, better packaging, quality maintenance, avoidance of waste, more effective retail display, and pricing techniques designed to clear markets.

Besides agricultural marketing research done by Federal and State agencies, much significant work has been done by firms engaged in the marketing of farm products and private agencies interested in serving such firms. Their primary object has been to improve the competitive position of individual firms through increased efficiency in marketing operations.

Greater efficiency in marketing is a broad concept. It implies lower cost in getting products from farmers to consumers; providing consumers with new products or products of better quality; finding outlets for the farmers' capacity to produce; and better guidance to farmers in production to meet the demands of consumers. It implies a system of marketing in which waste and spoilage are kept to a minimum and one which retains the values of the American family farm.

From the standpoint of the individual farmer or firm engaged in marketing, the object of marketing research is simply to increase net income. In a competitive economy the drive to increase individual net income will compel others to meet the competition of the most efficient firms and thus reduce costs of marketing for the benefit of consumers. Any improvement in marketing efficiency by farmers, their cooperatives, or other marketing firms thus tends to benefit consumers.

It follows that a major objective of marketing research is to develop systems of marketing that improve the automatic functioning of a free enterprise system so as to reduce the need for Government controls.

THE METHODS of marketing research are the methods of any research. The problems must be determined and then the methods and techniques to solve the problems must be found and applied.

Some problems call for simple approaches; others require the organized attention of teams of research workers having the requisite abilities and training to help find the answers—economists, lawyers, accountants, psychologists, sociologists, engineers, statisticians, historians, bacteriologists, pathologists, physiologists, entomologists, chemists, and other physical biological scientists.

There is much to be said for research of the pinpointing type, for each research result that is sound helps to improve the strength of the marketing structure. Many research studies provide answers to problems which, in turn, open up new problems. Research in every field is cumulative. The more we find out about any subject through research the larger is our stockpile of knowledge to solve new problems as they arise.

Improved statistical data and more refined research techniques have yielded good results. The methods embrace experimental, analytical, statistical, historical, social, psychological, and technological procedures. A growing interest has been developing in what is known as the operational research approach. In it, a problem in marketing operations is determined and all kinds of possible research approaches with various types of techniques are brought to bear in finding the solution.

A distinction is commonly made between basic, or fundamental, research ("which has as its objective the determination of the various principles and laws which control the physical background and social patterns of behavior") and applied, or practical, research (which "is concerned with the employment of principles evolved by basic research in solving practical problems of man").

An example of basic research in marketing would be a study that would show how population growth may affect various types of marketing situations. Research to determine how a business firm might increase sales by using various types of advertising or of display would be an example of applied research.

Both types of research in agricultural marketing are of practical importance.

Without basic research, applied research would shrivel up. Without applied research, the findings of basic research would not be brought to bear on the solution of immediate problems. A balance in research application must be achieved that will assist farmers in meeting their pressing marketing problems, while providing answers that will alleviate marketing problems in the future before they become chronic.

Both public and private research has a place in marketing. A few large organizations may find it profitable to carry on private research to further their own aims, to increase their own profits, and to retain for themselves the knowledge secured through such research, but not many agricultural producers or small marketing firms are equipped to do marketing research. Government agencies therefore have been called on to engage in such research as a means of serving the general needs of the farming industry and the business community as well as the Nation's consumers. The knowledge gained in research by Government agencies is thus made available to large and small producers and marketing agencies and to all interested persons or firms.

The vigorous growth of our farm production has long exceeded our ability to develop marketing machinery capable of fully meeting the marketing problems imposed. There has been a tendency therefore to be critical of the results of marketing research, even though it is recognized that expenditures in research for marketing have been modest in comparison with those for research in production.

What are some of the results of marketing research? We have made significant progress in setting up terminal markets, in grading, standardizing, packaging, and processing commodities to meet consumer needs, in organizing and operating cooperatives to decrease spreads between the producer and consumer, in reducing risks through improved and timely market information, and in otherwise expediting the flow of products through marketing channels.

Other marketing developments have come from research: Chainstore and supermarket organization and operation, self-service, every-other-day delivery of milk, marketing redevelopment, better location of plants and stores, deep freezers and frozen-food locker plants, frozen fruit juices, dehydrated foods, grade A milk, sweet cream butter, and tenderized and precut meat. In many instances, research paved the way for the establishment of the new product or practice.

Studies of the costs of distribution have been of value by making available knowledge of what it actually costs to perform certain operations.

Such information protects the consumer and improves the functioning of the competitive marketing system. Research in marketing, for example, has brought a better understanding of the economic functions middlemen perform and has provided a better basis for determining the fairness of remuneration for services performed. Research workers also disclosed the fallacies in the commodity marketing philosophy which had wide appeal in the 1920's that farmers, through control of production, could fix prices at cost of production or more. Research studies have shown farmers how prices for farm products are determined by the basic laws of supply and demand. For example, most farmers now know that the demand for supercolossal olives or jumbo special eggs is as limited as the demand for Cadillac automobiles. Again, marketing research, in agriculture as in industry, has aided in determining what qualities and varieties can most profitably be produced.

Consider for instance the impact of research on hybrid corn, which has influenced the marketing of corn and livestock in many ways. This is just one example of production-type research that is revolutionizing our agriculture and bringing new responsibilities to our marketing system. Likewise, the introduction of disease-resistant plants, the mechanization of planting and harvesting, the use of radioactive isotopes on soils, scientific breeding of livestock and artificial insemination, the use of new insecticides, the addition of frozen foods, and similar research-born developments have basically altered the conditions of agricultural marketing.

Some of the problems ahead were listed by Herman Haag, director of research for the Missouri Farmers Association. He asked: "What will happen to the dairy farmer if the price of butter declines to the same level as oleomargarine? What can be done with the large wheat crops ahead? What will synthetic fibers do to the prices of cotton and wool? How much of various products can be sold to American consumers if farmers' prices are held at 100 percent of parity? At 90 percent of parity? What will be the effect of a two-price system on the net prices which farmers receive for their products? Can other uses be developed for the surplus remaining to be sold after the top markets take their share? Will decentralization of industry bring better markets to farmers? How can we best serve such nearby markets? Are we needlessly hauling raw materials to distant markets and finished products back to the farming areas? Can meats be processed and prepackaged in the Corn Belt States to reduce the cost of marketing? Can tests be developed which will accurately measure tenderness and quality in beef and other livestock products?"

Among the fields holding great promise in marketing research is the study of consumer preferences—the economic, social, and psychological factors that control consumer demand. Effective marketing of agricultural commodities in new forms, made possible by prepackaging and processing, depends on adequate research of the needs of consumers and the value and costs of alternative methods. More research is also needed on pricing methods of producers, wholesalers, and retail merchants with special reference to grade, size, and quality and on methods of reducing handling costs while improving services to consumers.

Marketing research can help find out what consumers really desire and farmers can then direct their efforts to produce products that will meet these desires. This insures that resources will be wisely allocated. It is the universal procedure in manufacturing industries to find out what consumers want before production is begun. The same procedure is as essential in agricultural production. (*Joseph G. Knapp.*)

What To Do?—One Man's View

The market is the connecting link between the farmers and the consumers of their products. Farmers expect the market to accept their products when they are ready to sell. Consumers take for granted that the market has anticipated their needs so that the products they want will be available in the quantities and qualities they desire at the time and place they are needed.

Prices become the crystallization of market operations. They help decide farmers' incomes on the one hand and consumers' costs on the other. Prices guide farmers in making their production plans. They help consumers in deciding on their purchases. How well the market meets its responsibilities is important to all of us.

Satisfaction or dissatisfaction with prices is a key to how well we think the market is doing its job. Let us keep in mind that our judgment on this score is not always accurate. We often blame the market for the unfavorable results which really are not its fault because they grow out of the conditions under which the market must operate. The responsibility of the market is to reflect conditions as they exist. To blame the market because the conditions do not please us is like blaming the thermometer or the barometer for disagreeable weather.

Why do we not have a perfect market? One reason is that it is not an automatic mechanism. It depends on human judgments and decisions. The "perfect market" requiring many buyers and sellers, all having complete information and knowledge, and dealing in absolutely uniform products, exists only on the pages of a textbook. In real life there are many imperfections.

Knowledge is far from complete or universal. Man's interpretation and measurement of the influences affecting the market are subject to error. Standardization, especially of farm products, is by no means complete or perfect.

One criticism leveled at markets for farm products is that they are unstable. Farm prices tend to fluctuate widely. An important share of the explanation for this instability is supplied by the nature of agricultural production and of the demand for many farm products.

Farming reacts to depression differently than do many lines of manufacturing. Farmers tend to continue to produce and market about the usual supply when depression strikes and demand falls off. Manufacturing plants tend to curtail output. Neither maintains the former income. The farmer takes a lower price for the same volume; the manufacturer maintains his price better but he has a smaller volume to sell.

The typical farm is a small unit. Its output is only a very small drop in the bucket of total supply. The farmer as an individual has no urge to cut output in the hope that this will improve his prices. The typical manufacturing concern is more important in its market. In fact, if it sells a special product under a trade-mark, brand name, or other distinguishing feature, it has in a sense a market all of its own. An automobile manufacturer does not produce and sell cars in general. He makes and sells a given kind of car.

The farmer and members of the family do much or all of the work on a typical farm. The factory depends on hired workers. The farmer cannot reduce his out-of-pocket labor costs greatly by reducing his operations. The farm often produces materials for use in further production on the farm. Most corngrowers produce corn to feed to livestock. If livestock is curtailed, the outlet for the feed is reduced. Factories usually buy their raw materials. Farmers also are limited in the speed of their adjustments, because they are working with living things. Production cannot be stopped during the growing season without serious loss. It takes time to build a dairy herd. Sheep grow wool when prices fall as well as when they rise. It is not too wide of the mark to say that farmers do not cut output in depression because they cannot afford to, while many other producers curtail because they cannot afford to do otherwise.

The difference is not between the farmer and the manufacturer but between farming and manufacturing.

Agriculture can and does respond to profitable prices by increasing output. The expansion of food production during the Second World War is an illustration. Such increases come mainly from fuller use of present capacity. But on the downside it is very difficult to reduce farm production as explained above. Agricultural supply hence is described as being relatively "inelastic." The physical quantity of farm products moving into consumption, food especially, likewise does not change rapidly. Different foods are in keen competition for the limited space in the human stomach. In a country such as ours relatively few people are at or near the starvation level. Increasing incomes in times of prosperity may cause some to eat more. In many instances, the shift is to higher quality rather than to larger quantity. The total amount of food consumed tends to be relatively stable.

These inflexibilities are not caused by the market but by the nature of agriculture and of the demand for its products. Their effects are reflected in the results obtained by farmers from their markets. The relatively inflexible supply causes prices for many farm products to drop sharply when depression strikes because demand is not available to move the supplies at former prices. The relatively inelastic demand causes prices to fall more than they would if demand were more responsive to price changes. One of the more serious consequences is instability in prices of many farm products and hence in agricultural income.

A word of caution may be in place at this point. If attention is focused solely on prices, the conclusion may be that farmers are the only ones who suffer serious loss in depression. That is not the case. Depression is no respecter of persons. Wage rates may hold up better than farm prices, but many workers experience reduction in hours worked with consequent drop in earnings, while for many others unemployment may mean complete loss of income. The plant operating on reduced schedule experiences loss of income because of smaller sales. Price is only part of the income picture. Volume likewise is important.

Nor are all nonagricultural prices insensitive to ups and downs in the business situation. Some raw materials other than agricultural products also experience sharp price fluctuations.

THE REASONS for changes in demand lie mainly outside of agriculture.

They arise from changes in the level of activity and employment in the rest of the economy and in the export demand. Greater stability in the agricultural markets to an important extent depends on developing greater stability at a high level of production in the rest of the economy. The dependence of agriculture on such stability elsewhere is increasing as farming becomes even more and more commercial and hence even more dependent on the market to provide the funds for operating and living expenses. Farmers are becoming increasingly aware of the fact that there is no substitute for a market kept strong by a high level of productive activity and employment generally.

They cannot place sole reliance on price programs but must be concerned with policies and programs on a wide front. Other lines, in turn, are recognizing the contribution which stability in agriculture can make to general stability.

Stability is marked by the absence of violent swings in market prices. It would be a mistake to conclude from this, however, that all price changes are undesirable. Some price changes are corrective. Others, particularly the sharp, short-run changes, can be disruptive. If price is to continue to do its part in guiding farmers in production and in moving supplies through the market, it must remain free to reflect changing conditions. If price programs are to yield real stability they must reduce disruptive swings without destroying or handicapping the corrective price changes. Price programs too often represent efforts to change the results of certain forces rather than to deal with the forces themselves.

Another criticism of the market relates to the margin or the spread between the prices received by the farmer and those paid by the consumer. One complaint is that the spread is too wide. Another arises over the fact that marketing charges are reduced much more slowly than prices to farmers in a period of falling farm prices.

Farmers recognize that the market performs indispensable services in moving products to the consumers. They want the market to perform those services as efficiently as possible and to do so at the lowest attainable cost.

While farmers are critical of the instability in their prices, they also are critical of marketing margins because of their stability when farm prices drop. The inelastic demand that characterizes most farm products is related to this point. It does not take a very large increase in supply or decrease in demand to cause a considerable fall in prices to farmers. They note that the margins are much more rigid and that consequently the fall in prices at the consumer level is relatively less than that at the farm.

An illustration may help make the farmer's viewpoint clear. Take a given product that sells to the consumer for $1.00 a unit in a period of strong demand. Of that amount the farmer receives $0.50; the other $0.50 represents the marketing margin. Then a serious depression causes consumer demand to fall so that the price has to be lowered to $0.75 in order to clear the market. Because of the rigidity of the margin, the drop comes largely out of the farmer's price, so that he receives only $0.25, or one-third of the consumer's price Had the drop been shared equally, his price would have fallen only to $0.37½ and he would have continued to receive half of the price paid by the consumer.

Handlers and processors point out that they are faced with relatively fixed operating costs, which limit flexibility. Granting this, it still may be suggested that those who are in a position to make decisions with respect to their margins and resale prices might well give serious consideration to sharing with the consumer as quickly as possible reductions in prices paid to farmers.

One of the responsibilities of the market is that of aiding in bringing about a balance between supply of products available and the demand for them. It works in this direction at a given time by arriving at the prices at which commodities on hand will move. This job never will be performed perfectly because man's knowledge and judgment are not perfect. Improvements should be sought in order that the market may perform this function better.

To the extent the prices arrived at in the market truly reflect consumer's preferences and demands, they become effective guides to farmers in determining their production programs. An attractive price is an invitation to expand farm output as long as unused capacity is available. Thus, remunerative prices played an important role in getting production increased to fit the added requirements during the war.

Price relationships likewise are important. If hogs are in a relatively stronger price position than wheat, some of the wheat acreage may be shifted to corn and other feed grains on farms where such a change is practicable. Price also indicates to consumers the relative amounts of different goods on the market. If some foods are relatively higher than others, consumers tend to adjust their purchases accordingly. If food prices in general rise faster than consumers' incomes, some are forced or decide to reduce purchases or to rely more heavily on less expensive foods. In that way, the market helps to attain balance by approaching it from the consumer's side.

The market's performance on this score is not perfect. Knowledge is neither complete nor uniformly distributed. The future cannot be foretold with exactness. Responses are not always immediate or entirely rational. Once a crop is in the ground there is little to be done other than to carry operations on through the harvest. Production conditions vary. An acreage that in a year of severe drought may yield a supply so small that prices rise decidedly may produce a price-depressing surplus in a year of ideal growing conditions. Heat, cold, too much or too little moisture, or coming at the wrong time, diseases, insects, and other variables affect the outturn. Wars, depression, world conditions, employment, business activity, inflation, and other influences lead to decided changes on the demand side. The market does not create those variations. Its function is to reflect the changing conditions as accurately as possible.

THERE ARE TWO situations in which the farm market loses much of its effectiveness as a balancer or adjuster. One is under conditions of decided inflation, as in war. The other is in a period of disastrous depression. During a major war many resources have to be shifted from civilian to war production. The latter stimulates activity and adds to money incomes. Capacity operation is soon reached in many lines of civilian production. Manpower and other resources for increasing capacity are short. Plentiful dollars are in the market seeking scarce goods. The market reflects this in rapidly rising prices.

These prices, however, do not provide a corrective expansion of output once capacity is reached. Neither are they very effective in discouraging demand because spending means are ample. Allowed to run its course, inflation will do serious harm to the economy generally and inflict hardship on fixed-income people of modest means. Price controls and ceilings may have a legitimate place in serious inflation. Greater reliance, however, should be placed on limiting money supply through credit restriction and absorbing excess spending means through heavier taxation. This enables the market to perform its customary role effectively, and avoids supplanting market action with arbitrary controls which tend to bottle up rather than to reduce explosive forces.

Likewise, in a period of serious depression, even a decided drop in prices paid farmers does not lead to major curtailment in output, for reasons already indicated. When only some farm products drop in price, many farmers can shift to others. When all fall, shifting out of all means stoppage of income. Unemployment shuts the door to a shift to nonagricultural lines. Even decided drops in prices to consumers may not expand consumption greatly both because of inelastic demand and because of the lack of buying power. Good public policy may call for steps to prevent market demoralization, pending recovery of productive activity and employment.

These may take the form of supplements to incomes or of floors under farm prices.

Even in relatively good times, some farm commodities may be in distress because the generosity of nature has led to unusual yields in a given season. Such a situation also may arise when farmers have misread market indicators and have accepted earlier favorable prices as an invitation to expand production more than a later market will take except at greatly reduced prices. Potatoes illustrate some decided price swings for such reasons. The somewhat regular cycles in beef cattle and hogs arise, at least in part, from the same source.

Ups and downs in the general level of farm prices, largely as a result of conditions outside of agriculture, and swings in individual prices caused by nature or by errors of judgment, result in some marked instability in farm prices and incomes. While a longtime average of farm income may even out such swings, this offers no solace for those who are bankrupted by violent breaks in the price structure. For example, some farmers who had gone heavily into debt to buy or improve their farms lacked resources to see them through the severe depression of the 1930's. Foreclosure became the lot of many of them. Those who were young enough to get another start may have achieved a comfortable position during the good prices since 1940. Others were too old for this or had been so shaken by their reverses that they had lost their grip.

PRICE INSTABILITY has become of increasing concern to farmers as agriculture has become even more dependent on the market for its cash income. Farmers were more self-sufficient in pioneer days. Farms produced more of the simpler fare of that day. The animal power was raised on the farm. There was more dependence on muscle and less on machines. Taxes and interest required only modest amounts of cash. Living was simple. A commercial farm today needs to have a large flow of incoming cash to meet current operating and living expenses. That cash comes mainly from sales on the market. The interdependence within the economy is much greater than ever before. Farmers are vitally concerned with the level of employment and activity off the farm. They have an important stake in financial, fiscal, and monetary affairs because these affect farm incomes.

The idea of parity and parity price grew out of the concern of farmers with the relationship between agriculture and other lines. Henry C. Taylor and Anne Dewees Taylor in their book, *The Story of Agricultural Economics*, note (page XIII) that the term parity descriptive of this relationship appeared in Wallace's Farmer as early as 1922. Parity price, representing a ratio between an index of prices received by farmers for products sold and one of prices paid for supplies they buy, with 1910–1914 as the base period of 100, was developed by the former Bureau of Agricultural Economics as an indicator of the price relationship.

This indicator was included in the Agricultural Adjustment Act of 1933 as the goal in restoration of farm prices and has been retained in subsequent farm legislation. In response to criticism that 1910 to 1914 no longer represented appropriate price relationships, the Congress modified the formula in 1948. The base period of 1910–1914 was retained to indicate the relationship between the general level of prices received to prices paid but average prices over the most recent 10 years were used to reflect the changing relationship among the different farm commodities. These revised parity prices were lower for some products, such as wheat, and higher for others, such as livestock. In early 1954, however, the new formula had not been applied in the case of any basic commodity where it would result in lower parity prices—that is, amendments to the Agricultural Act of 1948 still provided for deferring until January 1, 1956, use of the new formula where it lowered parity for a basic commodity.

The Agricultural Adjustment Act of 1933 was enacted in the depths of depression, when emphasis naturally centered on raising farm prices as a way of restoring farm incomes. Price supports of more moderate proportions than those of more recent years were viewed as adequate in that period. A sliding scale of support ranging from 52 to 75 percent of parity was in effect for some basics before the Second World War.

War needs shifted concern from price-depressing surpluses to that of meeting increased requirements. This led to a change in the objective of price supports to that of encouraging production of basic and other specified commodities by using supports as a protective floor in the event of a sudden break in the market. Minimum support levels for a number of the main commodities were first set at 85 percent and then to 90 percent of parity to make them effective for such purpose. War demands were strong enough to keep most prices above these levels so supports provided standby protection. Wartime measures extended these supports for 2 years beyond the end of hostilities to give farmers a period in which to adjust to anticipated smaller, peacetime markets. These supports would have ended in 1948 under this provision.

The Agricultural Act of 1948 continued 90 percent supports on basic products and specific supports on certain other commodities for an additional 2 years. A variable scale of supports from 60 to 90 percent of parity was established to take effect for basic commodities—corn, cotton, wheat, tobacco, rice, and peanuts—at the end of 1950. The act of 1949 continued the 90 percent supports through 1952 and these were extended through 1954 by the Congress in 1952. The act of 1949 also raised the minimum from 60 to 75 percent of parity.

Farm prices participated in the upward surge following the removal of price controls after the war. As supplies began to overtake demand, some weaknesses in the farm price structure became evident in 1949 and early in 1950. The Korean outbreak in 1950 renewed inflationary pressures and rising farm prices. The subsequent peak came in February 1951; from then there was a downward trend into the winter of 1953. The decline was more marked during the latter part of 1952 and early 1953 and brought price supports into more active operation once more.

The effects of changes in the economic situation on agriculture may be tempered by price supports. Income payments may be used for the same purpose. Judicious use of such a farm program may help give strength to the economy generally. Farmers will be in a better position to buy production goods and maintain family living on a fairly normal scale in depression.

Instability in prices for individual farm commodities calls for treatment suited to each case. To the extent livestock production responds to each season's feed situation, greater stability may come from programs to maintain a more uniform feed supply by carryovers from year to year. Storage to even out supplies needs to be kept separate from schemes to raise prices. The level of stocks needed rather than prices should be the guide.

Farmers are not free from responsibility for periodic price swings of the type represented by the cattle and hog cycles. Overoptimism when prices are favorable may lead to the production of such numbers of animals that when they arrive on the market unprofitable prices may result. Pessimism over prospects in turn may swing the production pendulum too far in the other direction. More stability in the production programs of farmers will help the market do a better job.

But what about commodities such as potatoes and other vegetables and fruits for which acreage and weather conditions may cause wide variations in output and hence price instability? Should producers be expected to absorb all of such risk or should it be shared by the public? Producers of such commodities are aware of such risks and take them into consideration. The risks are not all on one side. Some years may be decidedly more profitable than others. Growers who get good yields in times of low total output stand to gain. It is reasonable to expect producers to balance out their incomes over a period of years rather than to rely on only one season.

However, a sharp price break in a commodity may spell disaster for some of its producers and public assistance may help strengthen the market. This may benefit the public by discouraging too sharp a reduction in output with inadequate supplies and high prices the following season.

Because these commodities are usually perishables, the price-supporting loans and storage are unsuitable. A purchase and diversion program may be one alternative. This was employed in 1952 to ease the price effects of a large turkey crop. Diversion programs can be used only within limits. If an attempt is made to channel any considerable share of the output to other than regular market outlets, inroads on the latter are hard to prevent. Moreover, public opinion is intolerant of wastage of food supplies and programs which involve loss of products will not be acceptable.

There are limits to the bolstering that can be given prices without serious interference with the proper functioning of the market. A premium must not be placed on continued production of goods not wanted by the market. Such production represents poor use of manpower and other resources. Programs should contribute to stability, not encourage unbalance. That is, they should alleviate, not aggravate, problems. They should seek to improve upon the functioning of the market.

A point inadequately understood is that a program which maintains prices at attractive levels leads to surpluses and, if continued, will call for controls over rights to produce and sell. If the Government is to take away from the market the job of arriving at prices, it necessarily must also take over the function of directing production and consumption. Acreage allotments and marketing quotas do just this.

It may be argued that organized controls have become so general in nonagricultural lines that farmers must look to Government for similar power. The price control enjoyed by others is easily overestimated. Neither monopoly nor competition is perfect. Moreover, to the extent monopoly powers are abused, the more desirable remedy is to curb them, not to multiply them. A point generally missed is that if persons engaged in farming are to be provided gains by giving them monopoly powers, the number permitted to share in these gains must be restricted. A proposal to limit entry into farming is not likely to win much public favor.

The best road to better farm prices and incomes is to be found in increasing efficiency and decreasing costs of production, in improving upon the functioning of the market, and in maintaining good health in the economy generally, rather than in depending primarily on arbitrary supports and controls. (*O. B. Jesness.*)

An Atlas

Presented in the following pages is an Atlas of Marketing, which points out the problems of marketing various types of farm products: Feed grains, wheat, fruits and vegetables, sugar, tobacco, cotton, fats and oils, wool, poultry and eggs, dairy products, and livestock. Some of these commodities are widely grown; others are restricted to highly specialized areas of production. Some are produced the year around; for others the whole year's supply comes on the market in a few months. Some are highly perishable, others can be stored from one year to the next.

Some come off the farm ready to be eaten, and others require extensive processing. Each of these commodities requires its own types and locations of markets, its own methods of handling, its own marketing agencies, facilities, and channels. This Atlas portrays these unique characteristics. It presents facts and figures on where the commodities are grown, how they are sold, the uses made of them. It traces the development of markets for them, especially recent trends and current problems.

Feed Grains

Feed grains are marketed principally through livestock and livestock products. The cash sales of the four feed grains—corn, oats, barley, and the sorghum grains—are comparatively small; they make up only about 5 percent of the gross income of farmers. But cash receipts from the livestock and poultry that are produced from the feed grains and forages account for more than 50 percent of the total farm income.

The surplus feed-grain producing area of the Midwest has become the center of the livestock industry, particularly hogs and beef, which can be processed and shipped to major consuming areas more economically than feed grains.

Some livestock products, notably milk, eggs, and poultry, are produced in quantity near the areas of consumption, particularly the Northeast, which depends largely on Midwest feed.

The production of feed grains has increased steadily since the early part of the nineteenth century. The improvement of the plow for turning the prairie sod was later followed by mechanical power for cultivating and harvesting feed grains. Those developments made possible greater production and released about a fourth of the production of feed grains, which had been fed to work animals, for use in producing meat, milk, and eggs. The extension of railroads into the Midwest facilitated the movement of grain and livestock to consumers in the East and to the coast for export. The rapid growth of trucking has been important more recently in the transportation of feed grains, livestock, and livestock products. Another factor in the increase of feed grains was the improvement in seed, including the development of corn hybrids and new varieties of grains that are adapted to the various regions.

The acreage in feed grains reached a record high in 1932, but has declined since then. In 1948–1952 the acreage was about one-eighth smaller than 20 years earlier, but production, reflecting higher yields to the acre, increased nearly one-fourth.

Grains and the byproduct feeds or-

281437°—54——27

Feed Grains: Production by States, 1948–1952 average

State and division	Corn [1]	Oats	Barley	Sorghum grain	Total
	1,000 tons	*1,000 tons*	*1,000 tons*	*1,000 tons*	*1,000 tons*
Maine	13	58	4	....	75
New Hampshire	16	3	....	....	19
Vermont	78	19	1	....	98
Massachusetts	45	3	....	....	48
Rhode Island	8	1	....	....	9
Connecticut	47	2	....	....	49
New York	796	459	59	....	1, 314
New Jersey	261	23	15	....	299
Pennsylvania	1, 768	424	133	....	2, 325
North Atlantic	3, 032	992	212	....	4, 236
Ohio	5, 291	749	14	....	6, 054
Indiana	6, 637	801	13	1	7, 452
Illinois	13, 936	2, 384	24	....	16, 344
Michigan	2, 019	866	87	....	2, 972
Wisconsin	3, 409	2, 125	159	....	5, 693
North Central East	31, 292	6, 925	297	1	38, 515
Minnesota	6, 745	3, 162	776	....	10, 683
Iowa	15, 731	3, 804	23	1	19, 559
Missouri	4, 655	574	39	16	5, 284
North Dakota	682	798	1, 047	....	2, 527
South Dakota	2, 857	1, 492	465	12	4, 826
Nebraska	6, 621	930	134	78	7, 763
Kansas	1, 974	304	83	1, 004	3, 365
North Central West	39, 265	11, 064	2, 567	1, 111	54, 007
Delaware	146	3	8	....	157
Maryland	565	26	58	....	649
Virginia	1, 144	71	66	....	1, 281
West Virginia	275	26	9	....	310
North Carolina	1, 868	183	25	21	2, 097
South Carolina	744	248	10	3	1, 005
Georgia	1, 300	193	2	8	1, 503
Florida	232	8	....	....	240
South Atlantic	6, 274	758	178	32	7, 242
Kentucky	2, 237	37	36	....	2, 310
Tennessee	1, 717	92	28	....	1, 837
Alabama	1, 310	50	1	6	1, 367
Mississippi	1, 168	84	1	....	1, 253
Arkansas	689	80	2	8	779
Louisiana	438	26	....	1	465
Oklahoma	571	141	16	310	1, 038
Texas	1, 305	317	35	2, 376	4, 033
South Central	9, 435	827	119	2, 701	13, 082

FEED GRAINS: PRODUCTION BY STATES, 1948–1952 AVERAGE—Continued

State and division	Corn [1]	Oats	Barley	Sorghum grain	Total
	1,000 tons	1,000 tons	1,000 tons	1,000 tons	1,000 tons
Montana	74	180	413	....	667
Idaho	51	129	290	....	470
Wyoming	27	72	105	....	204
Colorado	390	94	307	75	866
New Mexico	35	10	12	145	202
Arizona	12	7	155	67	241
Utah	30	34	149	....	213
Nevada	2	5	18	....	25
Washington	31	111	107	....	249
Oregon	30	139	250	....	419
California	68	83	1, 236	103	1, 490
West	750	864	3, 042	390	5, 046
The United States	90, 048	21, 430	6, 415	4, 235	122, 128

[1] Production for all purposes.

dinarily provide nearly one-half of the total feed for livestock. Pasture, hay, and other forages furnish a little over one-half. Corn makes up about 60 percent of the total grain and the byproducts fed to livestock, but only about one-fourth of the total feed, including forages. Hogs and poultry are produced almost entirely from grains and byproduct feeds, but cattle and sheep depend heavily on pasture and other forages.

The North Central States produce approximately 75 percent of the national output of the feed grains. They are especially important as a source of commercial supplies of feed grains, providing about 85 percent of the corn and more than 80 percent of the oats going into commercial channels. An Illinois farmer, for example, sells more than 40 percent of his corn and the Iowa farmer about a fourth, while a Pennsylvania farmer sells only about 15 percent and the Georgia farmer only 10 percent. The North Central States supply about half of the commercial barley. The West Coast States are the second major source. Texas and Kansas are the major sources of the sorghum grains—more than 80 percent—that enter commercial channels.

The normal flow of feed grains is from the Midwest to the East, South, and West. But because each region is a producer as well as a consumer of feed grains, the movement is not uniform or continuous. Year-to-year variations in production and feed requirements in the various regions result in local surpluses or deficits, which change the magnitude of the flow or reverse it. In abnormal years, such as 1936 and 1947, the pattern of movement changes materially, and it may even be reversed as drought areas of the Corn Belt become deficient in production of feed grains. In 1949–1950, a fairly typical marketing year, farmers in North Central States sold about 28 million tons of feed grains, of which 8.3 million tons were shipped out of the region by rail and barge—a little over 40 percent to the North Atlantic region; about one-half to the South Atlantic and South Central regions; and less than 10 percent to the Western States. An additional tonnage moved out by truck, for which data are not available.

COMMERCIAL MARKETING of grain begins at country elevators, which have facilities for marketing, conditioning, and storing grain.

The cost of receiving the grain by truck, placing it in the elevator, and moving it from the elevator at the close of the storage period usually is

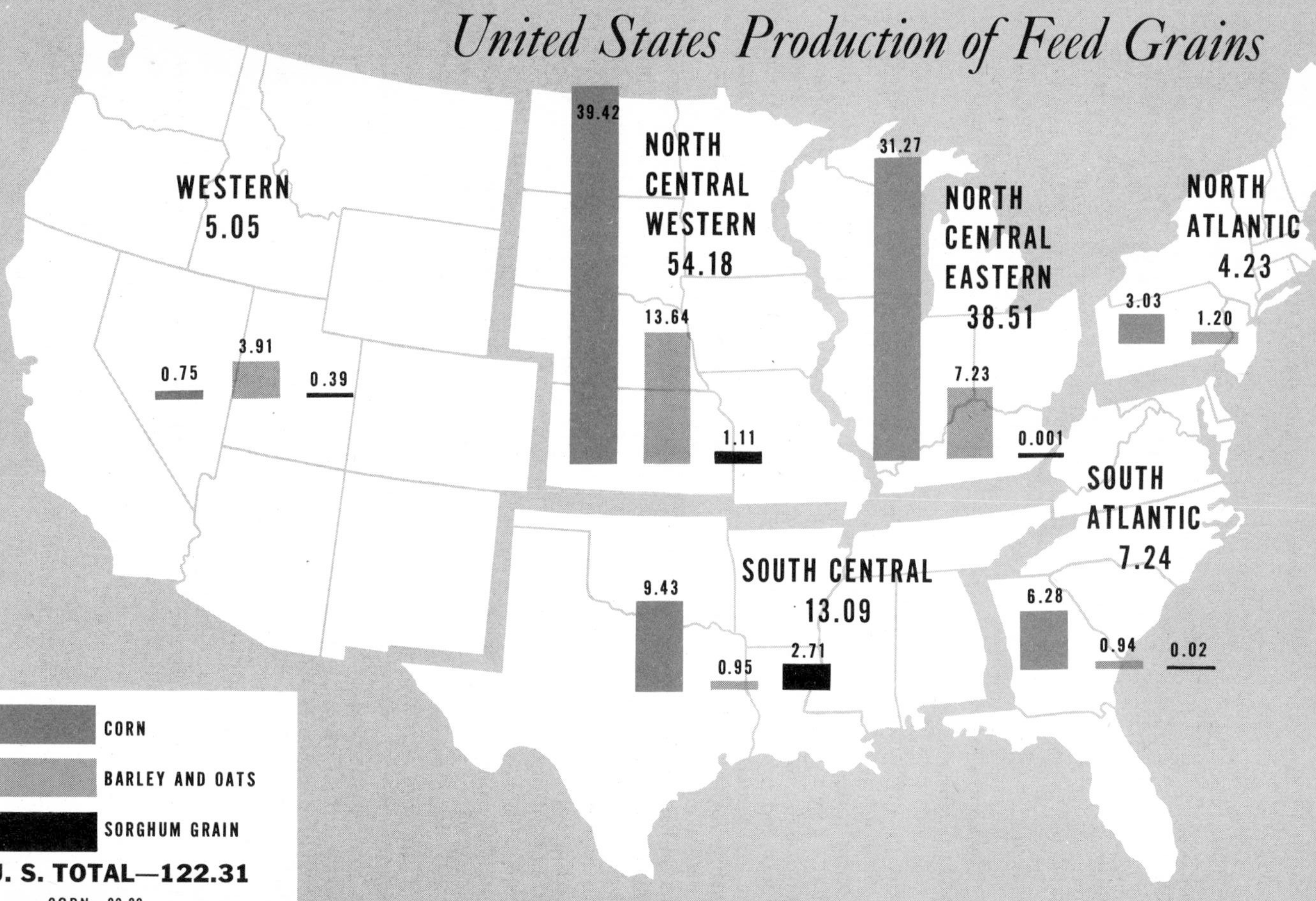
United States Production of Feed Grains
WESTERN
5.05
0.75
3.91
0.39
NORTH
CENTRAL
WESTERN
54.18
39.42
13.64
1.11
NORTH
CENTRAL
EASTERN
38.51
31.27
7.23
0.001
NORTH
ATLANTIC
4.23
3.03
1.20
SOUTH CENTRAL
13.09
9.43
0.95
2.71
SOUTH
ATLANTIC
7.24
6.28
0.94
0.02
CORN
BARLEY AND OATS
SORGHUM GRAIN
U. S. TOTAL—122.31
CORN—90.20
BARLEY AND OATS—27.89
1948–52 AVERAGE IN MILLIONS OF TONS

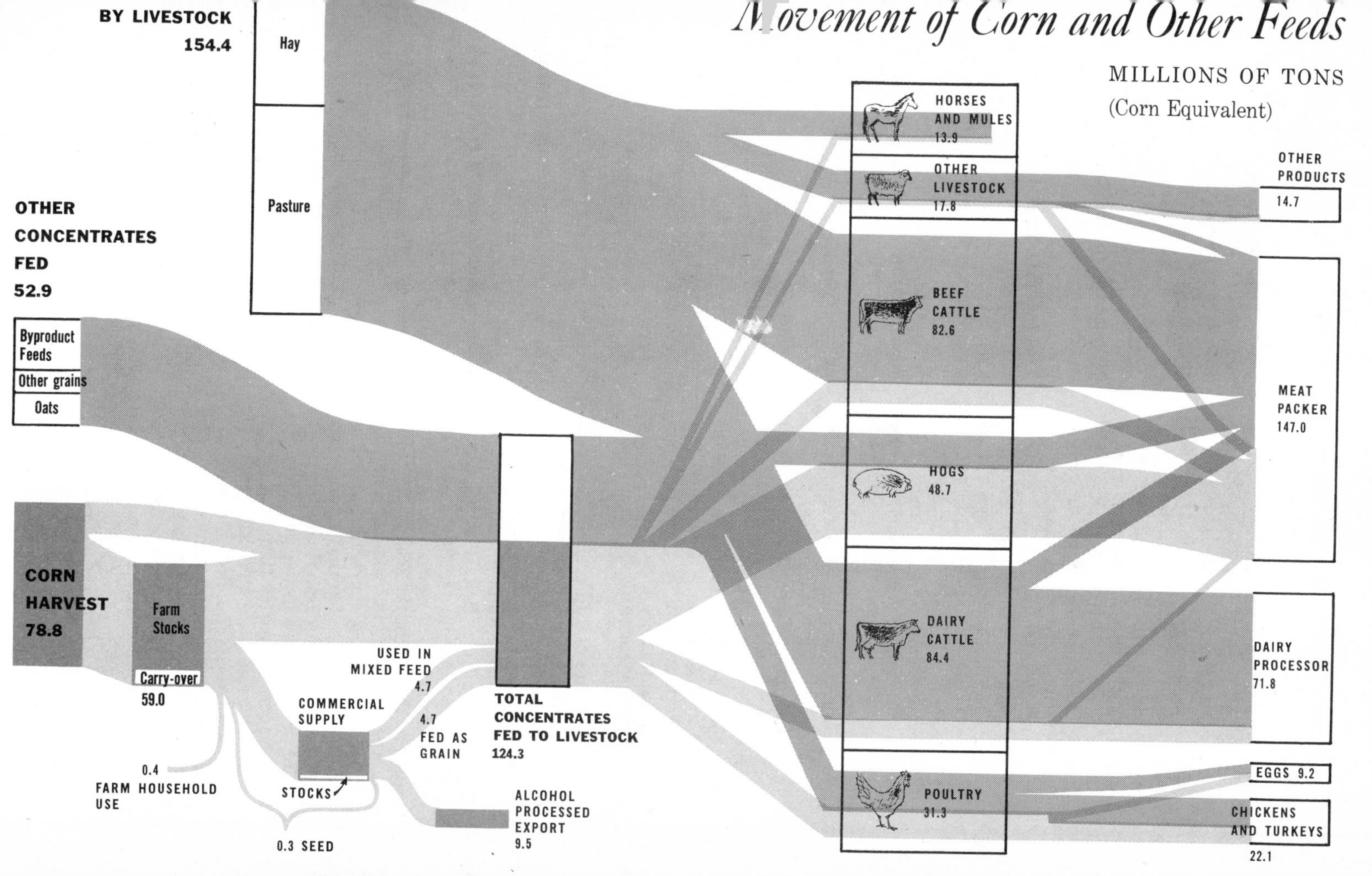
Movement of Corn and Other Feeds
MILLIONS OF TONS
(Corn Equivalent)
BY LIVESTOCK
154.4
Hay
Pasture
OTHER
CONCENTRATES
FED
52.9
Byproduct Feeds
Other grains
Oats
CORN
HARVEST
78.8
Farm Stocks
Carry-over
59.0
0.4
FARM HOUSEHOLD USE
0.3 SEED
STOCKS
COMMERCIAL SUPPLY
USED IN MIXED FEED
4.7
4.7
FED AS GRAIN
ALCOHOL PROCESSED EXPORT
9.5
TOTAL CONCENTRATES FED TO LIVESTOCK
124.3
HORSES AND MULES
13.9
OTHER LIVESTOCK
17.8
BEEF CATTLE
82.6
HOGS
48.7
DAIRY CATTLE
84.4
POULTRY
31.3
OTHER PRODUCTS
14.7
MEAT PACKER
147.0
DAIRY PROCESSOR
71.8
EGGS 9.2
CHICKENS AND TURKEYS
22.1

3 to 8 cents a bushel, depending on the kind of grain and the State or area in which the elevator is located. The usual yearly charge for storage is 10 to 15 cents a bushel.

Country elevator operators have many outlets for their grain. They sell some locally to stockmen, dairymen, and poultrymen. They sell and ship large quantities to millers, feed manufacturers, and feeders in deficit producing areas. But most of the grain handled in country elevators goes to terminal markets.

Terminal markets provide weighing and inspection services, drying and storage facilities, market quotations, services of commission merchants, and services of financing, insurance, and forwarding agencies. Farmers, country elevator operators, or others who wish to ship grain to a terminal market may either sell their grain to a cash grain firm, consign it to the market for sale by a commission merchant, or to a terminal elevator or warehouse for storage. The charges for receiving grain into the storage elevator by rail or water and loading it out into cars range from about 2 to 3 cents a bushel. The storage charge is approximately the same as for the country elevators.

Marketings of feed grains by farmers are seasonally heavy during and just after harvesting.

Marketings of corn are greatest during November–January, after the harvest in the Corn Belt. The prices are seasonally low during November and December. They normally advance during the rest of the season, reaching a seasonal high in August. The seasonal pattern of marketings, cost of storage, and loss of grain in storage are all basic to the seasonal rise in prices. The seasonal rise in the average price to farmers is greater than that in the market price of a specified grade, as the farm-stored corn loses moisture and usually improves in quality during the year. Average prices received by farmers normally rise from a seasonal low of 91 percent of the yearly average in November to a high of 112 percent by August. The seasonal range in price of No. 3 Yellow corn at Chicago, however, is usually about 95 to 108 percent of the yearly average.

Marketings of oats and barley follow a somewhat similar pattern. Heaviest marketings occur during July-September, the period of seasonally low prices. Marketings decline in the winter and spring and the prices advance, usually reaching a seasonal high in April or May.

Heavy marketings of sorghum grains begin with the harvesting of the Texas crop in summer and extend through autumn, when Oklahoma and Kansas crops are harvested. As with corn, the seasonal low in prices of sorghum grains is usually reached in November, but the seasonal high usually comes in May or June, before the Texas crop starts to market.

In the commercial channels of distribution, feed grains are practically always bought and sold by grade. The United States Grain Standards Act requires that in all interstate trading in which grains are bought or sold by grades, the grades used shall be those established by the Secretary of Agriculture. At country points the buyer determines the grade, but at large terminal markets grains are graded by inspectors licensed by the Department of Agriculture, but employed usually by the State or by the grain exchanges located in such markets.

Factors that determine Federal grades for grain are test weight, soundness, cleanliness, purity of type, dryness, and general condition. The best grain is No. 1. Grain increasingly inferior is given grades down to No. 4 or No. 5. Sample grade is applied to grain too poor in quality to meet the requirements of the numbered grades. Grade determines largely the price paid for various shipments of feed grains received in the market, although prices fluctuate from day to day for grain of any one grade.

The quality of feed grains marketed each year is indicated by the percent-

Oats and Corn

Receipts Graded by Licensed Inspectors, by Grade

PERCENT OF TOTAL U. S. RECEIPTS, CROP YEARS 1946–51

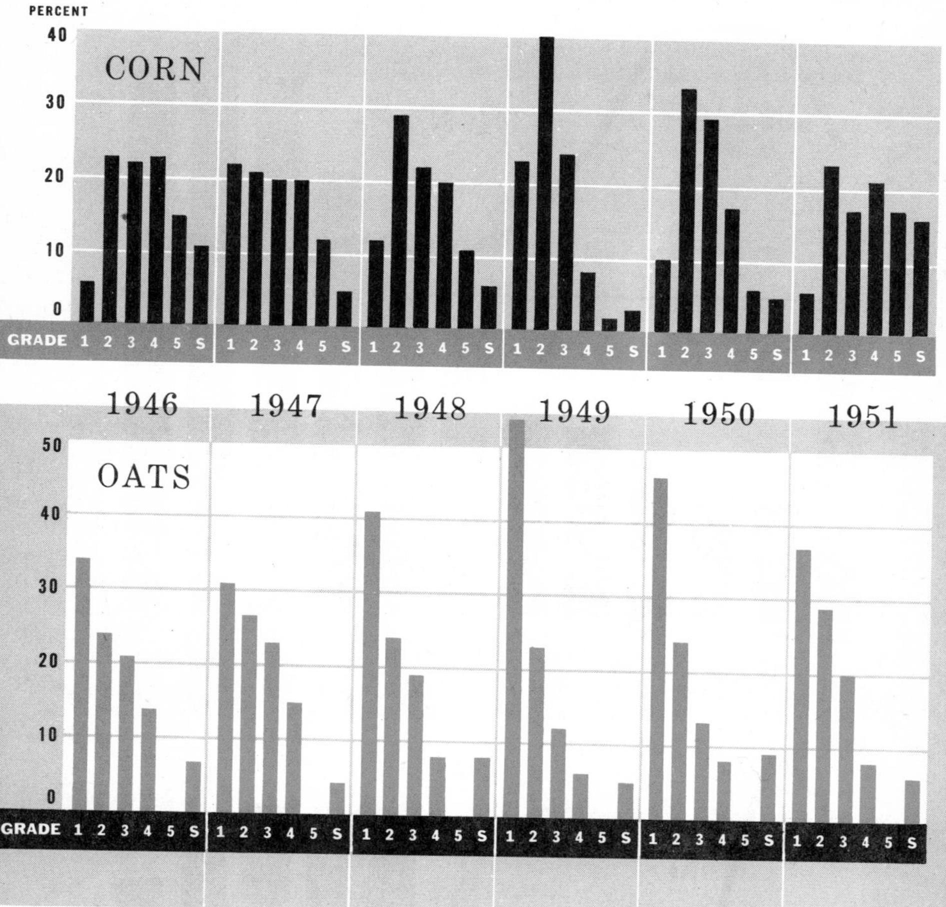

age of the marketings that falls in each of the Federal grades. Percentages of each of the four feed grains, classified by grades, for 1947–1951 are shown in an accompanying chart.

Storage of feed grains from one year to the next is usually comparatively small. The bulk of the storage is from harvest until the grain is used later in the marketing year. The record carry-over of 30.6 million tons of feed grains in 1950 was equivalent to only about one-fourth of the annual production. Usually about 10 to 15 percent of the production is carried over at the end of the year, and part of it is for normal

Seasonal Variation in Prices and Sales of Corn and Oats

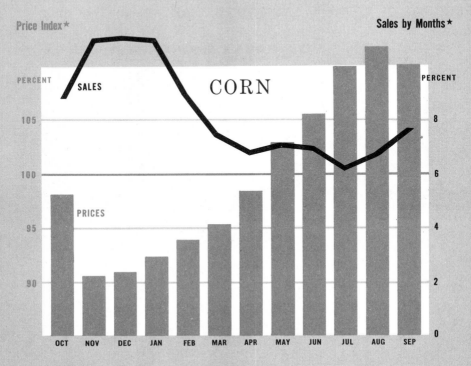

Price Index★ Sales by Months★

CORN

PERCENT PERCENT

SALES

PRICES

105 8
100 6
95 4
90 2
0

OCT NOV DEC JAN FEB MAR APR MAY JUN JUL AUG SEP

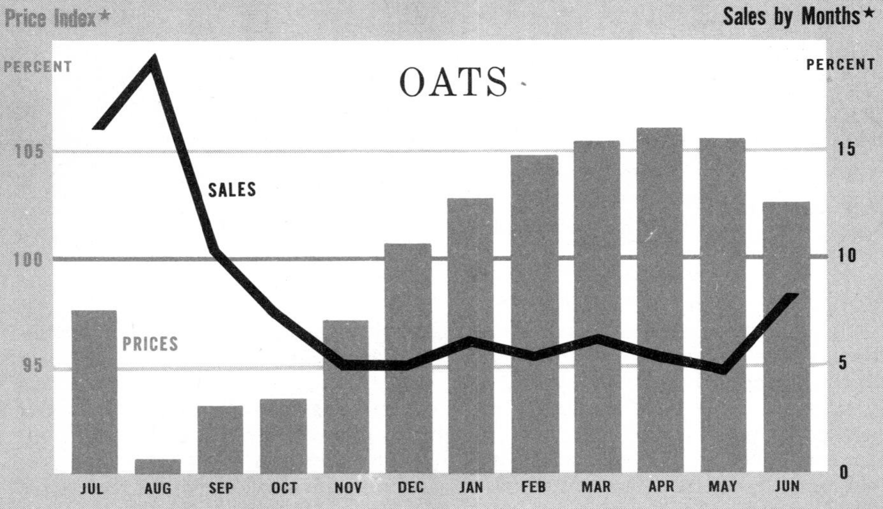

★ Seasonal variation in prices received by farmers, based on the period 1922–41

★ Monthly sales are percentage of annual sales, 1938–47 average

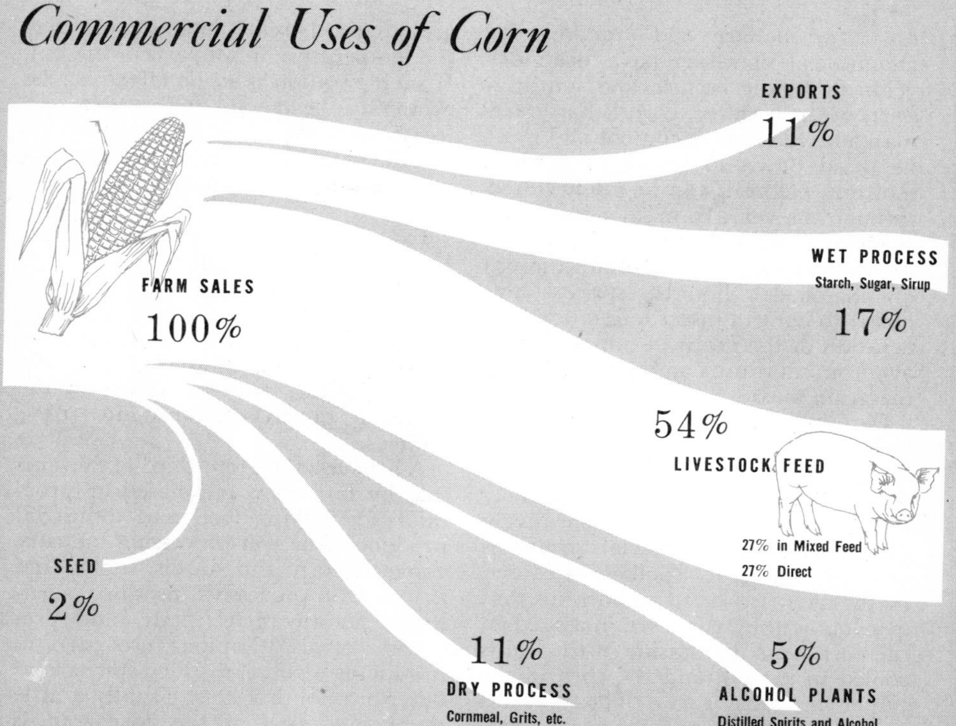

working stocks. More than 85 percent of the carryover stocks of corn and oats ordinarily are held in the north central region.

Most of the corn is stored as ear corn in cribs on farms. Much of it is fed, chiefly to hogs, without shelling. A part of the crop is shelled and stored in bins or sold. Most of the oats is also stored on the farm. Much of the barley and sorghum grain goes into commercial storage.

In 1953 country elevators had a total storage capacity for all grains of 1,466 million bushels. Terminal and subterminal elevators had a capacity of 748 million bushels. About 37 percent of the total commercial storage was in the eight Corn Belt States. The Commodity Credit Corporation has purchased bins over a number of years to provide space for the storage of grains taken over under the price-support programs. In March 1954 the capacity of CCC bins totaled 640 million bushels. Farm stocks of the four feed grains totaled 3,061 million bushels in January 1954. That would mean that farmers have crib and bin capacity, including some temporary cribs, for at least that quantity of feed grains, although it cannot be considered as an indication of the total capacity. About 85 percent of this was in the North Central States.

For successful storage, shelled corn and other feed grains must be in good condition and dry when placed in storage. Artificial drying of grain has increased in popularity in recent years, particularly over the Corn Belt. The equipment usually consists of an oil or gas burner to heat the air and a power-driven fan to circulate it. Small units for use on the farm and large units for commercial elevators have been developed. In the eastern and southern parts of the country, corn is harvested with a high moisture content and must be dried down to about 13 percent moisture before it can be safely stored through the year. In many areas additional steps must be taken to preserve the quality. Chief of these are the use of chemicals (liquids, sprays, and dusts) to control insect infestation and aeration of the grain to prevent spoilage from moisture coming from within the grain mass.

Deterioration of the quality of shelled corn and small grains during storage is a problem almost everywhere. Some spoilage of corn is likely to occur, even when it is comparatively dry, unless some artificial means is used to prevent it. Spoilage is caused by the moisture-laden air currents that develop within the corn mass when the corn near the outside of the bin is cooled in the fall and the corn in the center remains warm. The currents move upward through the warm corn, picking up moisture on the way. As the warm, moist air nears the surface, it cools and deposits some of its moisture on the corn. Increased moisture causes the surface corn to heat, and after a few months a layer of corn about a foot thick on the surface usually is spoiled.

The principle of aeration has been used experimentally to prevent movements of moisture. A low-powered, motor-driven fan or a wind ventilator on the top of the storage structure is attached to a tube inserted vertically so that it extends about half way to the bottom of the grain. The lower part of the tube is perforated. The fan or ventilator draws the warm air from the center of the bin into the tube and exhausts it outside the storage. Warm air entering the tube is replaced with cool air from the area above the grain. That method of aeration removes warm air before air currents are established within the bin and at the same time draws cool air down into the grain mass, thereby tending to equalize the temperature in all parts of the bin. If such aeration is to be effective, the grain must be of good quality, dry, and free from foreign materials and insects at time of storage. The method cannot recondition poor, damp, weevily grain.

FARM SALES AND IMPORTS, which have been fairly important for oats and barley in recent years, make up what is considered the commercial supply of feed grains. Farmers sold about one-fourth of the corn and oats, 60 percent of the barley, and two-thirds of the sorghum grains produced in 1947–1951.

A little less than one-third of the corn sold by farmers is purchased by processors for making food and industrial products. The wet-processing industry converts corn into starch, sugar, and sirup. Dry processors produce cornmeal, hominy grits, flour, and prepared cereals. Distillers use corn in producing alcohol, distilled spirits, and other alcohol products. Usually a little more than half of the corn sold is bought for livestock feed, and includes that going directly to livestock producers and that purchased by feed manufacturers. Thus, including the corn fed on farms, about 90 percent of the total corn produced is fed to livestock.

About 12 percent of the oats sold and 3 percent of the total production is used for making oatmeal. Nearly one-fourth of the commercial oats supply is bought for seed. Most of the remainder is bought for livestock feed.

A little more than 50 percent of the barley sold in 1947–1951 was used in making malt, which in turn is used principally in producing malt liquors, alcohol, and distilled spirits. About one-fourth was bought for feed. Most of the remainder was exported.

The bulk of the sorghum grains entering the commercial channels is bought for livestock feed or exported. In 1947–1951 about 40 percent of the quantity marketed by farmers was bought for feed and about 45 percent was exported. During the Second World War and in some years since, substantial quantities of the sorghum grains have been used to produce alcohol. An additional outlet is provided by the wet-processing plant in Corpus Christi, Tex., which has been in operation since 1949 and has a capacity of about 6 million bushels annually.

Foreign trade in feed grains in most years is comparatively unimportant, as the bulk of our feed grain is produced and consumed within our own country. Although total exports in 1948–1952 were larger than in any comparable period since 1900, they averaged only about 4 percent of the total production and 15 percent of the total sales by farmers. Exports of corn averaged 109 million bushels, or about half of the total tonnage of feed grains exported. They accounted for a little more than one-tenth of the total sales, and about 3 percent of the total production of corn. Exports of oats usually amount to less than 3 percent of the total sales. About one-sixth of the barley sold is exported. Exports have been a more important outlet for sorghum grains. The Texas crop is favorably located for export, and the bulk of the exports are shipped from Galveston.

Imports of feed grains are generally of minor importance. Except in the drought years of 1934 and 1936, imports of corn have been practically negligible. During the Second World War and in some years since, substantial quantities of oats and barley were imported from Canada. Except in the drought years, imports have never exceeded 3 percent of our total production of feed grains.

The 1954–1955 supply of the four feed grains was expected to be a new high record, mainly because of a large carryover of corn from preceding years. Near-record consumption of the grains also was expected, largely because of an increase in the number of grain-consuming farm animals. (*Malcolm Clough, James W. Browning.*)

Wheat, a Food Grain

Wheat is one of the most important crops of the United States. It is the national bread crop. Many farmers grow it. A large acreage of land is annually devoted to it. It constitutes an important part of our domestic commerce. Normally it is one of our chief agricultural exports.

Among field crops, wheat normally ranks fourth in farm value. Since 1945–1946 our country has been the world's leading exporter of wheat and flour.

Wheat is primarily a cash crop. In some areas it is almost the only source of cash farm income. It is grown on about a third of the farms of the United States. In the western edge of the Great Plains region and in the Pacific Northwest are areas in which more than half of the total cultivated land is given over to wheat.

Specialization in wheat growing often occurs in a climate that does not favor the growing of other crops. Anything that affects yields, costs, or prices of wheat in those places affects directly the welfare of the farmers and the whole community.

Wheat is second only to cotton in amount of cash income to American farmers. It enters trade to a greater extent than any other crop except cotton.

Production of wheat in the United States exceeded a billion bushels in 1915 and again in 1944. Production has exceeded a billion bushels every year since 1944 except 1951. The all-time peak was 1.4 billion bushels in 1947. In 1948 and 1952 production was only slightly less.

Changes in acreage seeded before 1938 affected production much less than did changes in yield. The influence of change in acreage since 1938 has equaled that of change in yield. The increased variation in acreage has been due mainly to acreage-allotment programs, which were responsible for the sharp acreage reductions in 1939, 1942, 1950, and 1954. In some years, weather at seeding time and economic conditions also have influenced the acreage seeded.

Yields show no discernible trend in the 1920's. In the 1930's they were abnormally low because of unfavorable weather. From the low level of 8.0 bushels per seeded acre in 1933, yields increased steadily to a record 18.3 bushels in 1942. Since 1942, the yields have averaged about 15.4 bushels per seeded acre. The principal factors, other than weather, that have contributed to the increase in yields have been the use of more commercial fertilizer, improved varieties, more tractors, combines, and other machinery, and more pesticides.

The United States has four fairly definite wheat-producing areas, which overlap considerably.

Hard red winter wheat is grown mainly in the southern Great Plains; the leading States are Kansas, Oklahoma, Texas, Nebraska, and Colorado, the crop in all of which from 1943 to 1952 made up about 40 percent of the total crop in the country.

Hard red spring wheat is grown chiefly in the northern Great Plains, in North Dakota, Montana, South Dakota, and Minnesota. Total production there in the 10 years constituted about 25 percent of the total crop.

Soft red winter wheat is produced in the eastern half of the United States, principally in Ohio, Missouri, Indiana, and Illinois. White wheat predominates in the Pacific Northwest, in Washington, Oregon, and Idaho. It is also produced in Michigan and California. Durum and red durum wheat are grown principally in North Dakota.

Wheat is produced primarily for human food. Each class has particular food uses. Hard red spring and hard red winter wheats are suited especially for bread flour. They contain a relatively large amount of strong, elastic gluten, essential for the best bread flour. Soft red winter and white wheat flour, both low in protein, are used for pastry, crackers, biscuits, and cakes. Durum wheat is used for making semolina, from which are made macaroni and spaghetti. Some red durum wheat is used to make breakfast food, but its main use is for poultry and stock feed.

What the producer does not keep for food, feed, and seed goes to distributors or consumers. Farmers sold about 85 percent of the wheat crop in 1943–1952. That can be considered the commercial crop. Under ordinary conditions, each of 17 States has more wheat than is required for its own needs for food, feed, and seed. The extra quantity is drawn upon by the other 31 States and Territories, whose production of wheat is below their consumption, and it also provides quantities for export.

The movement of winter wheat to market begins in the latter part of May in Texas and becomes general in the main Wheat Belt in June and July. The new crop of spring wheat in North Dakota does not begin to move until August, and the peak occurs in September. In the Pacific Northwest, movement starts in mid-July. For the entire crop, the peak of flow from farms is in July and August. More than a third of the crop was marketed in July and August in 1938–1947, the latest published figures, and about 70 percent in the first 6 months of the marketing year—from July through December.

Commercial marketing of wheat begins at the local mills or elevators, which are located usually along railroads in grain-producing areas.

The elevators provide facilities for marketing, conditioning, and storing wheat. Their storage capacity generally is from 15,000 to 50,000 bushels.

Wheat Acreage by Regions

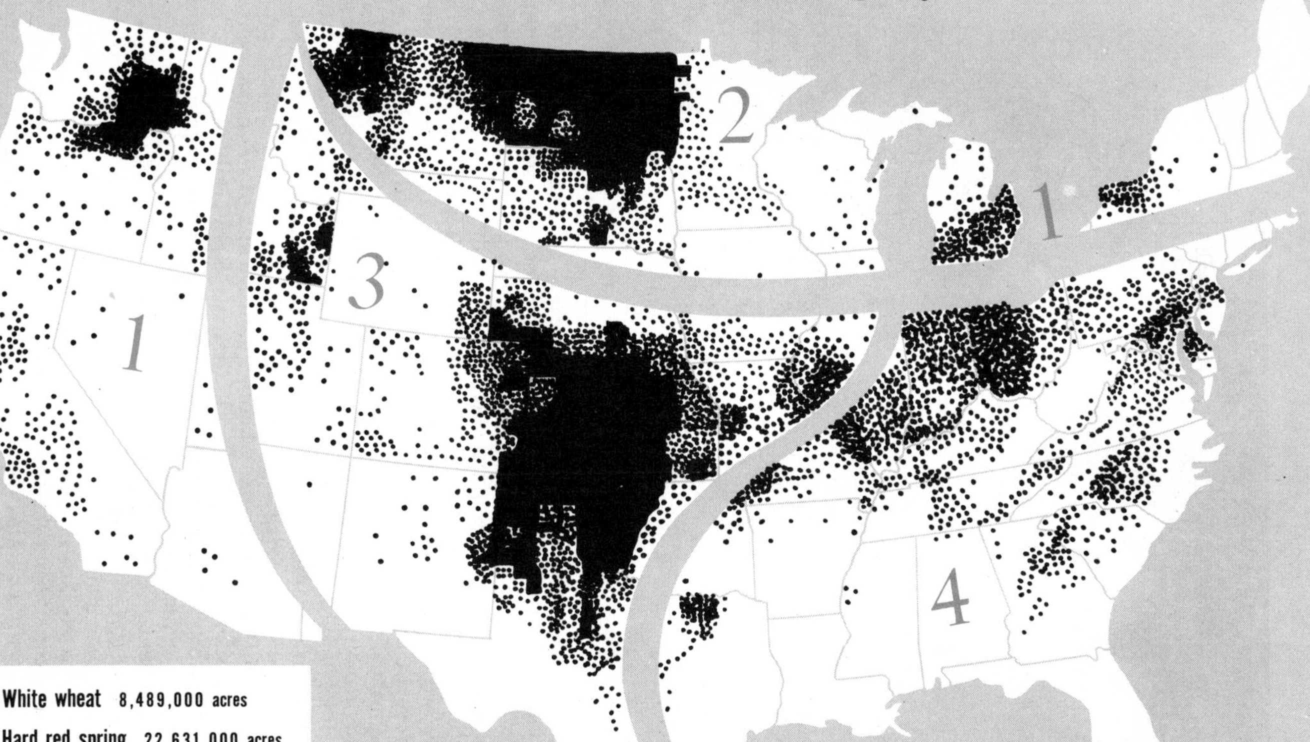

1 **White wheat** 8,489,000 acres
2 **Hard red spring** 22,631,000 acres
3 **Hard red winter** 41,645,000 acres
4 **Soft red winter** 12,166,000 acres

Each dot represents 5,000 acres (1949)

United States Wheat Production, 1919-53

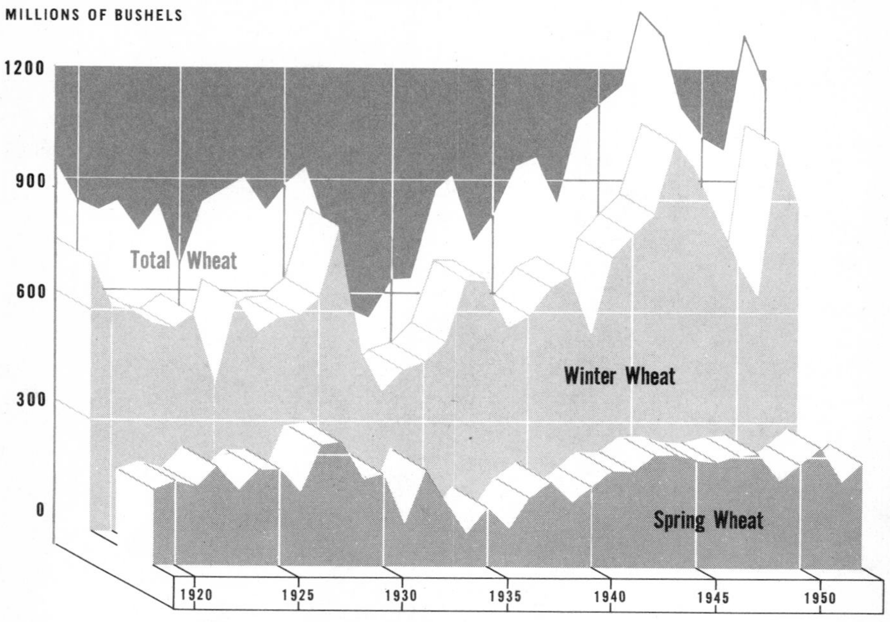

The wheat may be hauled directly to the local elevator from the farm as it is harvested, or it may first be binned on the farm. The dry summers in the Far West favor the local storage. But humid conditions elsewhere, especially in the South, mean heat and insect damage, which are unfavorable for storage except under ideal conditions of warehousing.

The high moisture content of grain harvested by combines makes it necessary to provide facilities for drying. Not many farmers have driers, so they take their grain to an elevator where it can be conditioned by mixing with dry grain or by running it through grain cleaners, which remove some of the moisture before it is sent on to the terminal market or mill. If the elevator has a drier, the grain may be dried and placed immediately in storage.

Wheat as it comes from the combine or thresher usually contains considerable amounts of weed seeds, trash, or other foreign material, which must be cleaned out before the grain can be milled or processed. Grain that contains 2 to 3 percent or more of screenings usually should be cleaned before it is sold. The cleaned grain brings a higher price, the screenings may have feed value, and freight costs are cut.

Most of the wheat handled by country elevators goes to terminals or subterminals for further distribution, or to processing plants. Some movement is direct to mills or other processing plants. Most of the movement to terminals is by rail, although in some areas motortrucks carry considerable quantities.

Terminal markets provide many services and facilities for marketing—weighing and inspection services; drying, cleaning, and storage facilities; trading-floor privileges, market quotations, services of salesmen and com-

Exports of United States Wheat

INCLUDING GRAIN EQUIVALENT OF FLOUR

Year beginning July

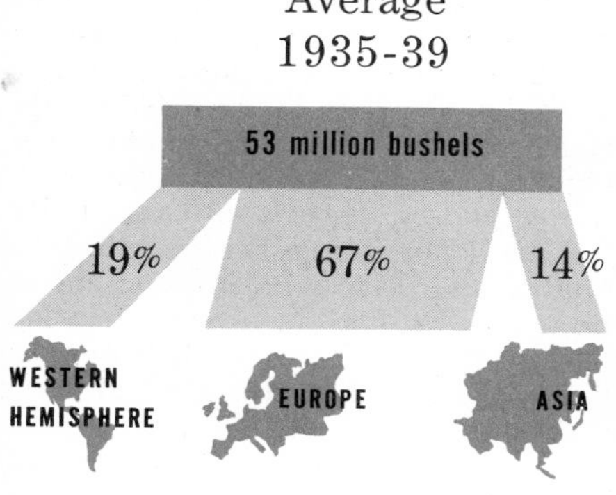

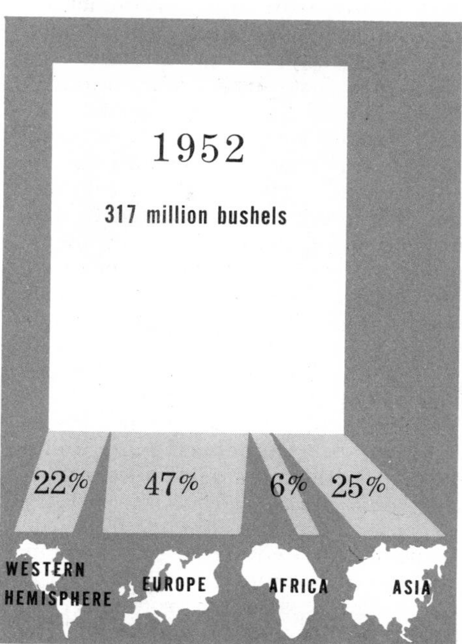

mission merchants; and services of financing, insurance, and forwarding agencies.

The primary function of terminal-market grain elevators is about the same as that of country elevators; that is, to receive, store, and distribute. The principal difference is in the handling and storage capacity of the plants. Also, terminal elevators usually hold grain in store for longer periods. A representative public grain elevator in a terminal market such as Kansas City, Minneapolis, or Buffalo can receive 15,000 bushels or more of grain an hour and load out 20,000 bushels or more. The storage capacity of individual elevators ranges from about a million to much more than 10 million bushels.

All grain shipped in interstate or foreign commerce to or from a point at which a licensed inspector is located must be officially inspected and graded if the grain is to be merchandised by grade. The inspection is done under the United States Grain Standards Act. The State and commercial grain-inspection departments now operate under it, and it provides in part for the establishment of official grain standards, the Federal licensing and supervision of the work of grain inspectors, and the entertaining of appeals from the grades assigned by inspectors.

Wheat is divided into 7 main classes, which are divided further into 15 subclasses. Identification of the different classes and subclasses is based on color, texture, and size and shape of kernel. Official wheat classes are as follows: Hard red spring, durum, red durum, hard red winter, soft red winter, white, and mixed. The grade determination is based on such factors as test weight per bushel, damaged kernels, moisture, and foreign material.

Before the Grain Standards Act was passed, many grade names and terms were in use, with little consistency or uniformity. Uncertainty, confusion, and frequently monetary losses resulted. The first official grain standards of the United States, promulgated in 1917, have been revised to keep abreast of changing conditions in production, harvesting, and marketing. The grades, implemented by the inspection service which applies them, provide a common language between buyers and sellers. Thus they can deal with confidence as to quality even when they are miles apart and without having the samples of wheat before them.

Flour mills obtain their wheat mainly from terminal and subterminal markets, although a substantial quantity comes directly from the country elevators and often directly from the farmers. The estimated 1,800 flour mills in this country on January 1, 1951, had total flour-producing capacity of 1.3 million hundredweight each 24 hours. A trend toward larger units but a smaller number of mills has been apparent since 1900 and has continued since 1951.

Buffalo, Kansas City, and Minneapolis, in that order, are the leading flour-producing centers. Kansas, Minnesota, and New York are the leading flour-producing States. The Southwest, which includes mills in Kansas, Oklahoma, and Nebraska, and in Kansas City and St. Joseph, Mo., is the principal flour-producing area.

Shifts in the geographic center of the flour-milling industry have occurred now and then since early in the nineteenth century, chiefly as a result of changes in population, shifts in wheat-producing areas and types of wheat produced, technological advances in milling methods, and changes in freight rates.

The price paid for wheat to producers in any locality at a given time is determined by many factors. Among them are: The quality of the wheat; character of the local market, whether it is in an area of surplus or deficiency production; distance to markets and cost of transportation; the time in relation to the season; effectiveness of price-support programs; financial conditions and prices of other commodities; and the total supply available for world markets in relation to consumer demands.

Similar conditions govern prices paid at principal central and export markets. Market prices are based on class and grade. Quality factors, including protein content (which does not enter into grade determination), frequently bulk large in milling value. The highest prices in the hard-wheat classes are usually paid for wheats of highest protein content. In the soft-wheat classes, highest prices usually are paid for softness of texture, a quality associated with low content of protein. Test weight is also an important quality factor in determining value, because it is indicative of flour yield.

Prices are generally lowest in the surplus-producing areas, which are less advantageously located with respect to the large markets, and highest in deficit areas, which are less favorably located with respect to supplies.

Cash prices of wheat are usually lowest following harvest and highest from January through May. In every marketing year from 1939–1940 to 1952–1953, cash prices of hard winter wheat averaged lowest in June, July, or August. In 11 of the 14 years, however, prices reached the highest levels for the season in the January–June period.

Prices to growers have averaged 1 to 7 cents below the effective loan rates in 7 of the 15 years since the loan program was started in 1938 (the effective rate before 1951–1952 was the announced loan rate; beginning with that year it was the announced rate with deduction for storage). But in 8 of the 15 years prices averaged 1 to 46 cents above the loan rate. The year in which prices averaged 7 cents below the loan rate, year-end carryover stocks

Distribution of United States Wheat

YEAR BEGINNING JULY

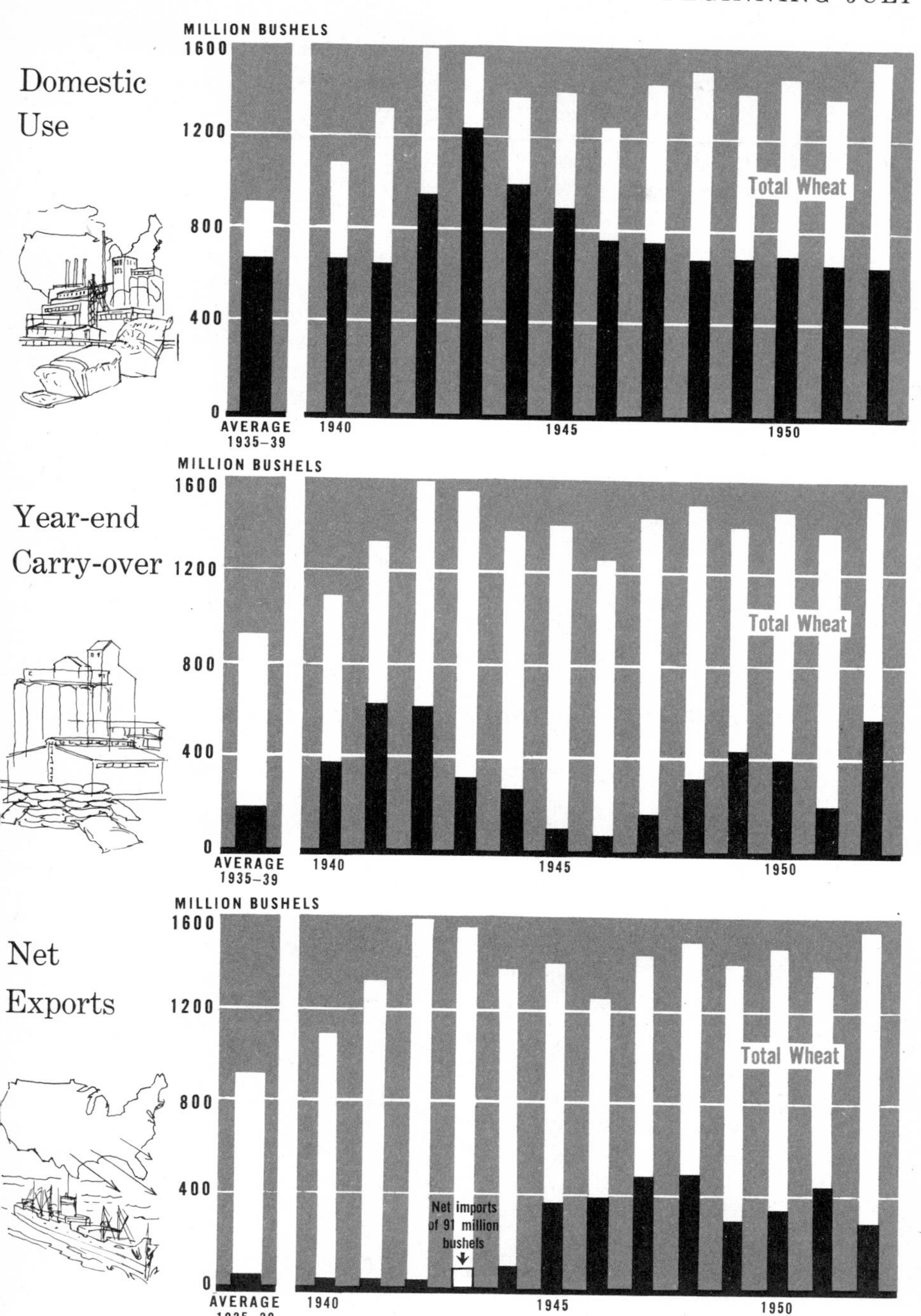

United States Wheat Acreage, Yield, and Production 1919-54

YEAR OF HARVEST	ALL WHEAT		
	1,000 acres seeded	*Bushels per seeded acre*	*1,000 bush[illegible] produced*
1919	77, 440	12. 3	952, 09[illegible]
1920	67, 977	12. 4	843, 27[illegible]
1921	67, 681	12. 1	818, 96[illegible]
1922	67, 163	12. 6	846, 64[illegible]
1923	64, 590	11. 8	759, 48[illegible]
1924	55, 706	15. 1	841, 61[illegible]
1925	61, 738	10. 8	668, 70[illegible]
1926	60, 712	13. 7	832, 21[illegible]
1927	65, 661	13. 3	875, 05[illegible]
1928	71, 152	12. 9	914, 37[illegible]
1929	67, 177	12. 3	824, 18[illegible]
1930	67, 559	13. 1	886, 52[illegible]
1931	66, 463	14. 2	941, 54[illegible]
1932	66, 281	11. 4	756, 30[illegible]
1933	69, 009	8. 0	552, 21[illegible]
1934	64, 064	8. 2	526, 05[illegible]
1935	69, 611	9. 0	628, 22[illegible]
1936	73, 970	8. 5	629, 88[illegible]
1937	80, 814	10. 8	873, 91[illegible]
1938	78, 981	11. 6	919, 91[illegible]
1939	62, 802	11. 8	741, 21[illegible]
1940	61, 820	13. 2	814, 64[illegible]
1941	62, 707	15. 0	941, 97[illegible]
1942	53, 000	18. 3	969, 38[illegible]
1943	55, 984	15. 1	843, 81[illegible]
1944	66, 190	16. 0	1, 060, 11[illegible]
1945	69, 192	16. 0	1, 107, 62[illegible]
1946	71, 578	16. 1	1, 152, 11[illegible]
1947	78, 314	17. 4	1, 358, 91[illegible]
1948	78, 345	16. 5	1, 294, 91[illegible]
1949	83, 905	13. 1	1, 098, 41[illegible]
1950	71, 287	14. 3	1, 019, 38[illegible]
1951	78, 048	12. 6	980, 81[illegible]
1952	78, 337	16. 6	1, 298, 95[illegible]
1953[1]	78, 741	14. 8	1, 168, 53[illegible]
1954[2]	63, 232	14. 2	900, 98[illegible]

[1] Preliminary.

[2] December 1 estimate of seeded acreage and April 1 indicated production of winter wheat plus spring wheat acreage indications as of March 1 and an approximate production, assuming yields are average.

WINTER WHEAT			SPRING WHEAT		
1,000 acres seeded	*Bushels per seeded acre*	*1,000 bushels produced*	*1,000 acres seeded*	*Bushels per seeded acre*	*1,000 bushels produced*
51,391	14.6	748,460	26,049	7.8	203,637
45,505	13.5	613,227	22,472	10.2	230,050
45,479	13.3	602,793	22,202	9.7	216,171
47,415	12.1	571,459	19,748	13.9	275,190
45,488	12.2	555,299	19,102	10.7	204,183
38,638	14.8	573,563	17,068	15.7	268,054
40,922	9.8	400,619	20,816	12.9	268,081
40,604	15.6	631,607	20,108	10.0	200,606
44,134	12.4	548,188	21,527	15.2	326,871
48,431	12.0	579,066	22,721	14.8	335,307
44,145	13.3	587,057	23,032	10.3	237,126
45,248	14.0	633,809	22,311	11.3	252,713
45,915	18.0	825,315	20,548	5.7	116,225
43,628	11.3	491,511	22,653	11.7	264,796
44,802	8.4	378,283	24,207	7.2	173,932
44,836	9.8	438,683	19,228	4.5	87,369
47,436	9.9	469,412	22,175	7.2	158,815
49,986	10.5	523,603	23,984	4.4	106,277
57,845	11.9	688,574	22,969	8.1	185,340
56,464	12.1	685,178	22,517	10.4	234,735
46,154	12.3	565,672	16,648	10.5	175,538
43,536	13.6	592,809	18,284	12.1	221,837
46,045	14.6	673,727	16,662	16.1	268,243
38,855	18.1	702,159	14,145	18.9	267,222
38,515	14.0	537,476	17,469	17.5	306,337
46,821	16.1	751,901	19,369	15.9	308,210
50,463	16.2	816,989	18,729	15.5	290,634
52,227	16.7	869,592	19,351	14.6	282,526
58,248	18.2	1,058,976	20,066	14.9	299,935
58,332	17.0	990,141	20,013	15.2	304,770
61,177	14.0	858,127	22,728	10.6	240,288
52,399	14.1	740,682	18,888	14.8	278,707
55,784	11.6	646,325	22,264	15.0	334,485
56,730	18.7	1,059,558	21,607	11.1	239,399
56,838	15.4	877,511	21,903	13.3	291,025
46,575	14.6	677,981	16,657	....	223,000

increased from 307 million to 425 million bushels. Of the 8 years in which prices averaged above the loan rate, the smallest amount was 1 cent in 1950–1951, when exports were above those of the previous year and stocks less, but still above average, and the largest was 46 cents in 1947–1948, when exports were very large and the carryover was below average.

In 1947–1948 the strong foreign demand for our wheat resulted from short crops in many importing countries. Beginning in 1945, large exports, influenced by the various foreign aid programs, became the chief price factor. Removal in June 1946 of price ceilings, which had been in effect for 30 months, permitted prices to advance. With the harvest of the near-record crop in 1948 and subsequent large crops here, together with relatively large harvests in importing countries, supplies in this country increased, and the loan program again became an important price factor, as it had been in 1938–1944.

General financial conditions and prices of other commodities not only influence the rate of the loan, because that rate is based on the prices farmers pay, but they also influence the relationship of market prices to the loan rate.

The outstanding problem before our wheat growers is how to avoid accumulations of burdensome surpluses. This is because of the large productive capacity that has been built up. Prospects are that exports of wheat in future years will be smaller than exports in the 7 years following the Second World War.

Our supplies of wheat go to satisfy domestic uses and exports, and what is left constitutes the carryover. The amount of wheat used domestically in the 5 years ended with 1952–1953 did not vary much from the average of about 675 million bushels. It consists of quantities used for food, feed, seed, and alcohol. Its use for food has remained fairly constant. Per capita consumption has declined but has been about offset by the increase in population. The milling and baking industries have been alive to the problem of declining per capita consumption. They are cooperating with the Department of Agriculture in studying the factors that underlie consumer preferences with a view to halting the downward trend.

In the 5 years ending with 1952–1953, the use of wheat for feed averaged about 100 million bushels, with little variation. But much larger quantities were fed in years when wheat prices were competitive with corn. Large quantities were used during the Second World War for feed, because supplies of feed grains were short and wheat was sold by the Commodity Credit Corporation at prices competitive with corn. Large quantities of wheat were imported in 1943–1944 and the following year for this purpose.

The amount used for seed varies within a narrow range, depending on acreage. The amount used for industrial purposes is usually insignificant except when there were wartime subsidy payments.

Because of the likelihood that domestic use of wheat will increase very little unless its use as feed is increased, it seems clear that continued exports on a high level afford the chief means of avoiding accumulation of excessive stocks of wheat.

The United States was the leading exporter of wheat, including flour and other products in terms of wheat, in each year from 1945–1946 to 1951–1952. In 1952–1953 exports from Canada again exceeded those from the United States, as was the pattern before 1945–1946.

Approximately 46 percent of the 7-year total world trade has come from this country. Included among the factors responsible for this position are: An abnormal world demand for wheat, especially during the immediate postwar years; a willingness on the part of the United States Government to assume responsibility for many of these requirements (approximately 55 per-

Kansas City Wheat Prices and Loan Rates

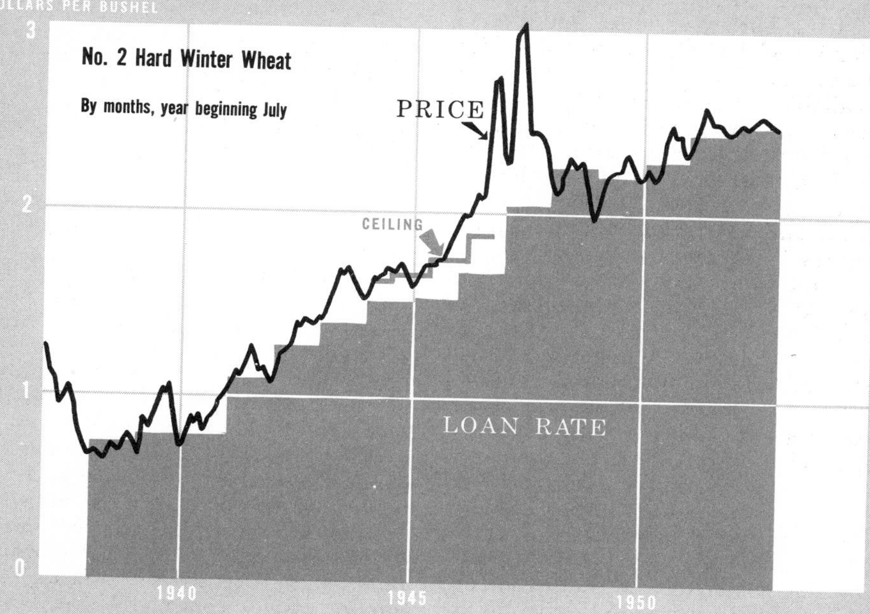

cent of the total) through various foreign aid programs; the ability of our wheat farmers to produce, aided by generally favorable weather and the incentives of the domestic price-support program; and the capacity of private enterprise—the grain trade, milling industry, and the transportation system—all cooperating with the Federal Government, to move unprecedented quantities of wheat and wheat products.

By the end of June 1952, our total exports for the 7 years that began in July 1945 had reached 2.9 billion bushels—an annual average of about 415 million bushels. The alltime peak was reached in 1948–1949, when exports totaled 503 million bushels—the largest quantity of wheat ever moved in a single year by an individual exporting country. Exports that year exceeded domestic consumption for food by more than 30 million bushels.

Western Europe in the 7 years took 64 percent of our total exports, Asia 22 percent, Latin America 11 percent, and Africa 3 percent. Western Germany has been the largest market, followed by Japan, Italy, and the Low Countries. Other sizable markets included Greece, the United Kingdom, France, Austria, and India.

Our exports during the 1952–1953 marketing season totaled 317 million bushels, a decline of 160 million bushels, from the 475 million bushels a year earlier but well above the longtime average of about 210 million bushels. Our smaller exports in 1952–1953 reflected mainly the record world wheat harvest in 1952. Much of the increase was in other exporting countries—an alltime record crop in Canada, the largest crop since 1940–1941 in Argentina, and an above-average crop in Australia. Minor exporting countries such as Turkey, France, and French North Africa also reported gains. Those increases in supplies of wheat available for export, together with an easier supply position in many important deficit areas, resulted in a decline in total world trade in wheat in 1952–1953 of about 8 percent from the record level of more than a billion bushels in 1951–1952.

In the future our wheat exports will depend largely on the outcome of world harvests and international conditions. Continued large exports will also depend upon finding some method (such as the International Wheat Agreement) of bridging the price gap and competing effectively whenever domestic price-support programs hold prices in this country above those prevailing in world markets. However, if international tensions do not increase, it is not to be expected that exports in the future will average as high as in the years following the war.

To meet the extraordinary demands during the war and rehabilitation following the war, wheat production in this country was greatly increased. Thus with average or better weather, our farmers in 1954 found themselves with a very large productive capacity, geared to a large export market. With that market declining, there is need to make adjustments to meet the changed situation. (*Robert E. Post*, *Edward J. Murphy*.)

On June 22, 1954, the Secretary of Agriculture announced a national wheat acreage allotment of 55 million acres for 1955 (the level specified in the controlling legislation under conditions of excessive supply); and announced that in 1955 wheat growers and others would have to comply with all acreage allotments established for a farm in order to be eligible for price support on any crop produced on the farm. Estimates then were that about 1,900 million bushels of wheat would be available for the 1954–1955 marketing year.

Fruits and Vegetables

Among fruits and vegetables we include more than 200 separate farm commodities and their products. Most of them are perishable, seasonal in production, subject to use in a number of different ways, and variable in the markets they have.

Some of the fruits and vegetables are quickly maturing annuals, such as green beans, spinach, and radishes. Some, like tree fruits, are perennials, requiring several years after planting time before they produce a crop. Production ranges from highly specialized crops to those grown as a part of general farming. Marketing practices also vary widely. The degree of perishability differs and determines whether the crops must be marketed within a few days after harvest or can be stored for several months. Because of perishability, the balance between supply and consumption must be maintained on a current basis, and there is little opportunity, except in the case of processed products, to balance supplies from one season to the next.

The basic characteristics of fruits and vegetables are not altered very much between the producer and the consumer. Fresh apples and lettuce as purchased by the consumer are in the same form as when they were harvested. Even a processed product such as quick-frozen green peas is not basically changed.

From the consumer's viewpoint, many fruits can be substituted readily for one another; various vegetables likewise tend to be substituted for one another. Also, among many, such as

Principal Marketing Channels

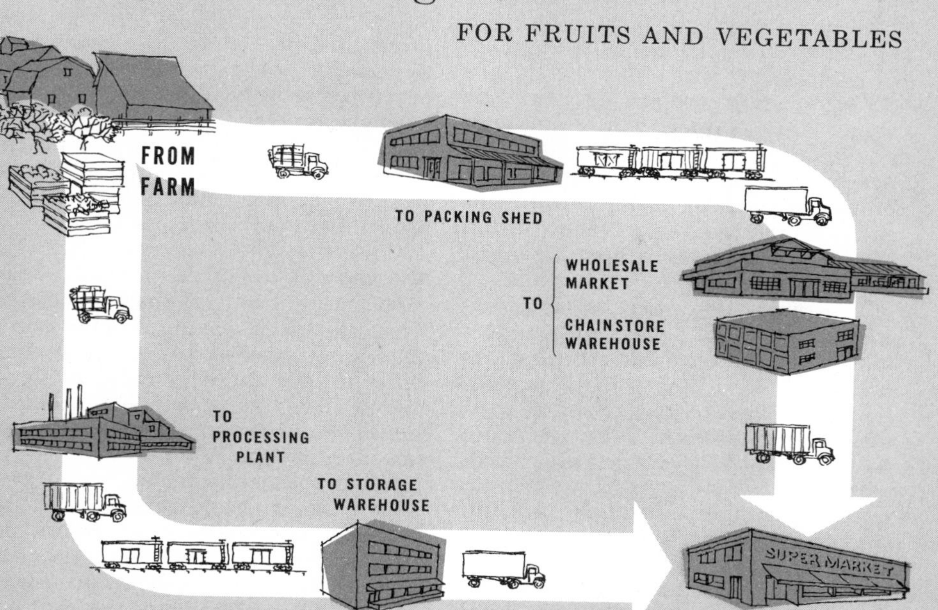

oranges, broccoli, or green beans, there is a high degree of competition between the fresh and processed forms of the same commodity. The consumers' demand for individual fruits and vegetables therefore tends to be more elastic than for a great many other farm products.

Relatively high costs for packing, containers, transportation, and handling, particularly for products from areas distant from consuming centers, make for high marketing margins and prices to consumers that are relatively unresponsive to changes in the farm prices.

A sharp increase in per capita consumption of fruits and vegetables in the past several decades reflects changed habits of eating which have resulted, in part, from rising incomes and recognition of the importance of these foods in the diet. The increase has not been uniform. In fact, the per capita consumption of such products as apples, potatoes, and sweetpotatoes actually has declined, but the use of citrus fruits has tripled, that of carrots has quadrupled, and that of lettuce has nearly doubled.

Total production of fruits, tree nuts, commercial vegetables, potatoes, and sweetpotatoes in 1951 and 1952 averaged about 46 million tons, valued at 3.1 billion dollars. Fruits and tree nuts accounted for 17 million tons and 37 percent of the value, all commercial vegetables 18 million tons and 41 percent of the value, potatoes and sweetpotatoes 11 million tons and 22 percent of the value. Most of the value is in the form of cash income, although for some crops a part is the value of produce used on farms where it was produced. Cash income from fruits and vegetables amounts to about 9 percent of total cash income received by farmers from the sale of agricultural products.

The leading crops, according to value, are potatoes, worth annually about 600 million dollars; tomatoes, nearly 250 million; and apples and oranges, valued at nearly 200 million each. Others having a value of 100 million or more are grapes, peaches, and lettuce.

The production of fruits and commercial vegetables (except potatoes and sweetpotatoes) has increased on both a total-volume and per capita basis. The level of production of commercial vegetables in 1952 was about double that of the 1918–1922 period, when official estimates of these crops were first compiled. Fruit and tree nut production is nearly double the level of 30 years ago. Potatoes show only a moderate increase in total production. Sweetpotatoes have declined to about one-half of the 1918–1922 level.

The production of commercial vegetables has increased on a per capita basis about 50 percent; that of fruits and tree nuts, 30 percent. Potatoes have declined about one-fifth. The per capita production of sweetpotatoes is only about a third of the 1918–1922 level. The level of per capita production in 1948–1952 was about 225 pounds of commercial vegetables, 150 pounds of potatoes, 14 pounds of sweetpotatoes, 225 pounds of fruits, and 2.5 pounds of almonds, filberts, pecans, and English walnuts combined.

Increased demand is the basic reason for the increased output, but a combination of factors made possible the expansion: The greater acreages of many crops, higher yields, greater use of fertilizer and lime, more effective pest controls, more irrigation, and the development of better varieties. For some crops, such as potatoes, shifts to higher yielding areas have helped to raise the average yield. Primarily because of the marked upward trend in acreage of citrus fruits, which produce relatively high yields per acre compared with other fruits, total fruit production has increased, while the acreage devoted to fruit has declined; many of the smaller, lower yielding apple and peach orchards have been pulled out. Large commercial orchards now produce the bulk of the apple and peach crops under conditions where it is possible to maintain better quality and to produce at lower costs per unit.

Marketing and processing facilities also have improved. Expanded transportation facilities and the advances in refrigeration, packaging, and in merchandising have combined with the trend toward more efficient production to place these commodities on the family dinner table in greater quantity and in better condition.

One of the significant features of the commercial fruit and vegetable industry, from a marketing standpoint, is the fact that such large quantities of these commodities come from areas located at considerable distances from the large eastern and midwestern consuming centers. With the growth of the processing industries and expanded transportation facilities, especially in the field of truck transportation—better roads and more trucks—and with the increased use of refrigeration in both rail and truck transportation, such factors as climate and soil largely have determined the location of commercial producing areas.

More than half of the fruit tonnage of the United States is produced in the 11 Pacific Coast and Rocky Mountain States; 45 percent is produced in California alone. About 40 percent of the total is produced in the Atlantic Coast States. Citrus fruit grown in Florida accounts for 30 percent of the national output for all fruits. Less than a tenth comes from the Central States. Washington, the leading apple State, ranks third in total fruit production, followed by New York, Michigan, and Virginia.

Fruit growers in the Central and Eastern States are nearer the big markets, but their fruit crops are more vul-

Marketing of Vegetables and Fruits

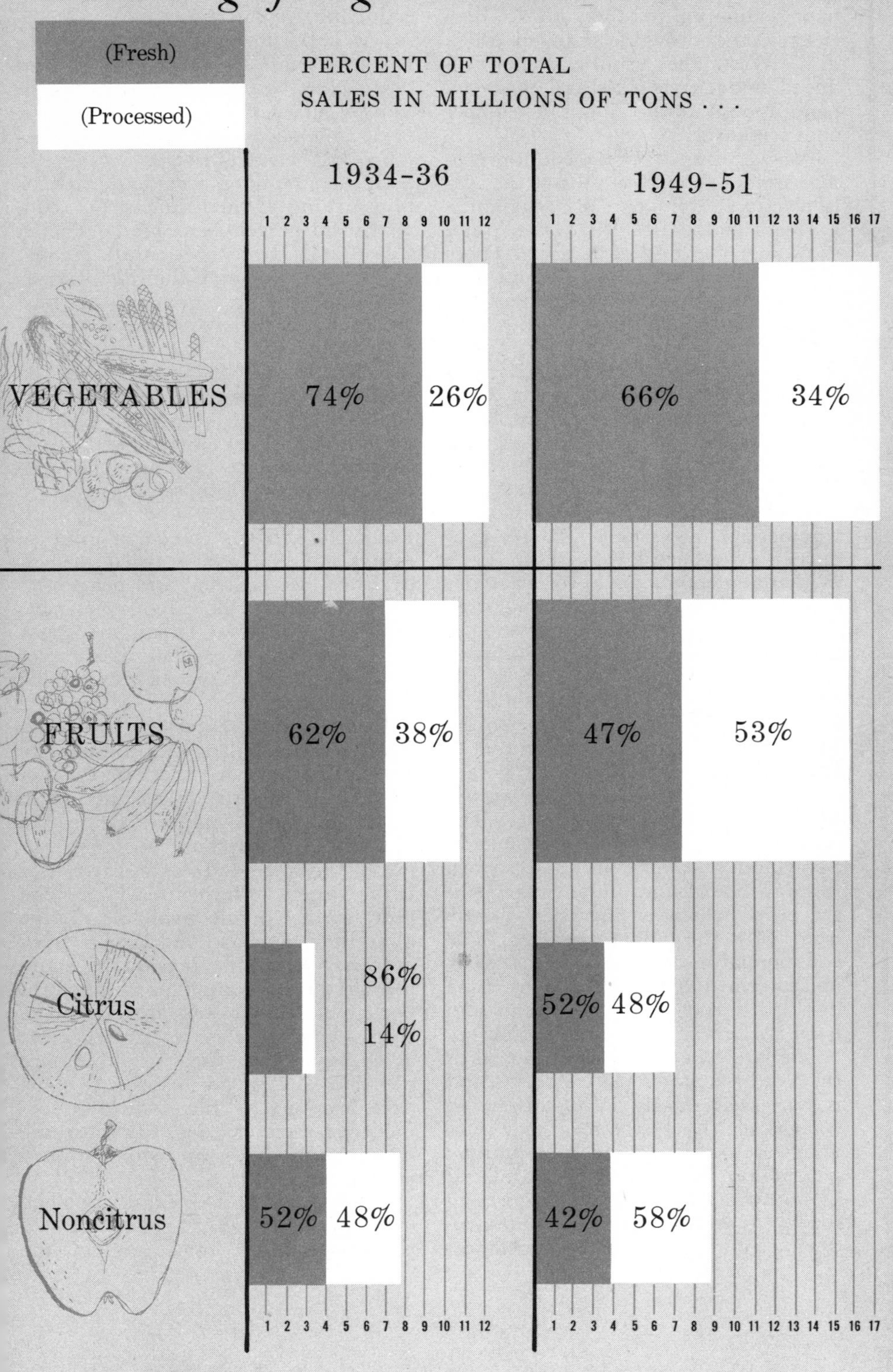

nerable to damage from frosts, freezes, poor pollination weather, storms, hurricanes, and droughts than are those in the West. They usually are not produced under irrigation and must depend upon natural rainfall. Yields per acre are lower.

The western part of the country produces more than two-fifths of the Nation's total tonnage of vegetables. Farmers in the Atlantic Coast States grow nearly a third of the total. Those in the Central States grow about one-fourth. California grows about 30 percent of the Nation's total. Other leaders are Florida, New York, Texas, Wisconsin, New Jersey, Arizona, Michigan, and Indiana. Florida, California, Arizona, and Texas specialize in the growing of fresh vegetables for the winter market. Wisconsin, Indiana, Illinois, Minnesota, and Maryland specialize in producing vegetables for commercial processing. Large producers of vegetables for both fresh market and commercial processing are California, New York, and New Jersey.

Potato harvest is under way somewhere in every month of the year. It starts in Florida and Texas about the first of the year. The States south of Virginia and from the Atlantic to the Pacific (including the southern half of California) produce the early potato crop, which is harvested and marketed from January through June. The States from the New Jersey-Delaware-Maryland-Virginia area westward through Kansas supply an intermediate crop, which is harvested mostly from July through September. The commercial production in the early and intermediate States has more than doubled during the past 30 years and is an important part of the total crop.

The late potato crop is produced in the Northern States and California and is harvested mostly in October and November. Late potatoes make up about four-fifths of the total annual production. Most of them are placed in storage and are the chief source of supply in winter. The chief late-producing States, in order of importance, are Maine, Idaho, New York, Colorado, and North Dakota.

The important sweetpotato-producing areas embrace the South Central States, the Atlantic coast as far north as New Jersey, and parts of California. Louisiana accounted for about one-fourth of the crop in 1952.

Of the 26 million acres under irrigation in the United States in 1949, nearly 80 percent was in the Pacific Coast and Rocky Mountain States; 25 percent was in California. Irrigation has enabled growers to take advantage of the favorable soil and climate in these States to make the growing of fruits and vegetables one of the leading industries of the West.

The dried fruit industry in California is an example. Hot, dry weather is essential to the development, harvesting, and drying of those crops. If rain occurred in summer and early fall, California growers could not produce raisins and dates, and dried prunes, apricots, figs, peaches, and pears.

Consequently, those industries have grown up in areas which are practically devoid of rainfall in summer and fall. Irrigation supplies the needed soil moisture.

About three-fifths of our fruits and tree nuts, one-half of our commercial vegetables, and one-third of the potato crop are grown on irrigated land.

Of tremendous importance in the marketing of the country's large output of fruits, vegetables, and tree nuts is the variety of forms in which those products are made available. Large quantities move to market as fresh produce. A sizable portion of many reaches the foodstore in processed form —canned, dried, and frozen. Some crops—peaches, cherries, strawberries, and asparagus, for example—are plentiful in fresh form for only short periods each year; but since large segments of these crops go to processors, these commodities are available on a year-around basis.

About 45 percent—nearly 3,300,000 tons—of the 1951–1952 citrus crop was processed. More than half of the

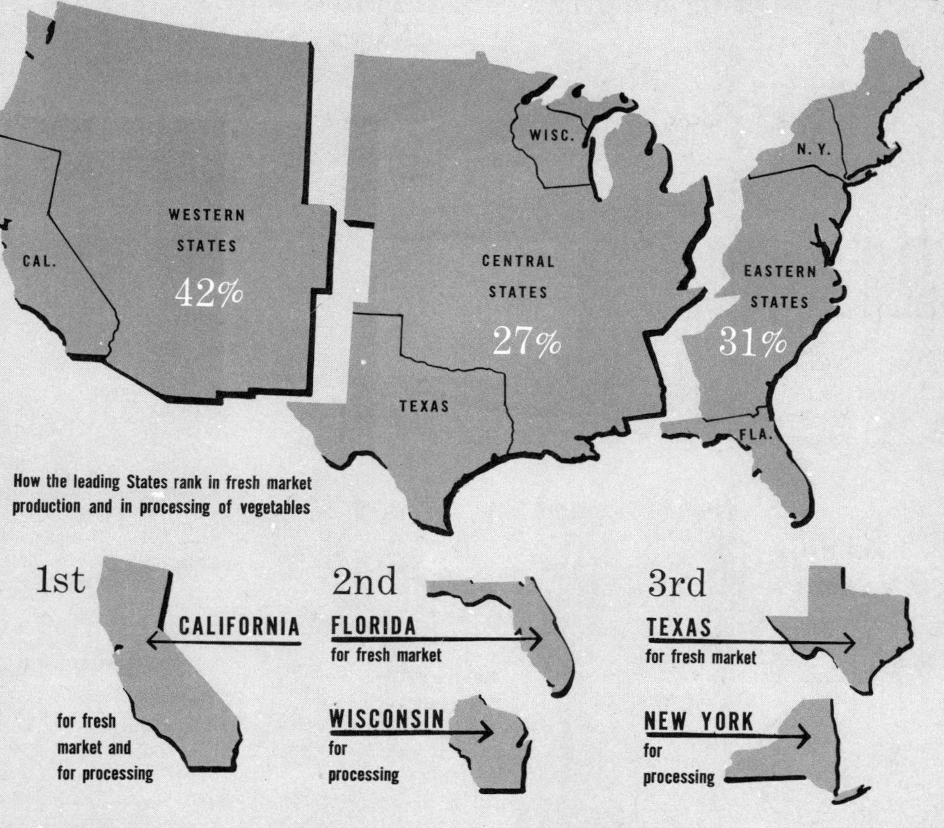

Florida citrus harvest was used for canning and freezing. Of the orange crop in Florida, about 40 percent was used for frozen juice concentrate and 20 percent for other processing, mostly canned juice. About 40 percent of the 1951–1952 crop of Florida grapefruit was processed.

About 27 percent of the citrus production in California in 1951–1952 was processed—nearly a fourth of the oranges and about a third of the lemon crop. Processing of grapefruit in California is relatively unimportant.

Nearly 60 percent of noncitrus fruit production in 1951 was processed—17 percent was canned, 18 percent was dried, and 17 percent consisted of California grapes crushed for making wine and brandy. About half of the peaches and pears produced in 1951 was processed, mostly canned. One-fourth of the commercial apple crop was used for canned, dried, and frozen apples and for cider, vinegar, and apple juice. Nearly two-fifths of the strawberry crop was processed—mostly frozen. About 85 percent of the 1951

Where the Consumer's Dollar Goes

FOR SELECTED FRESH FRUITS AND VEGETABLES

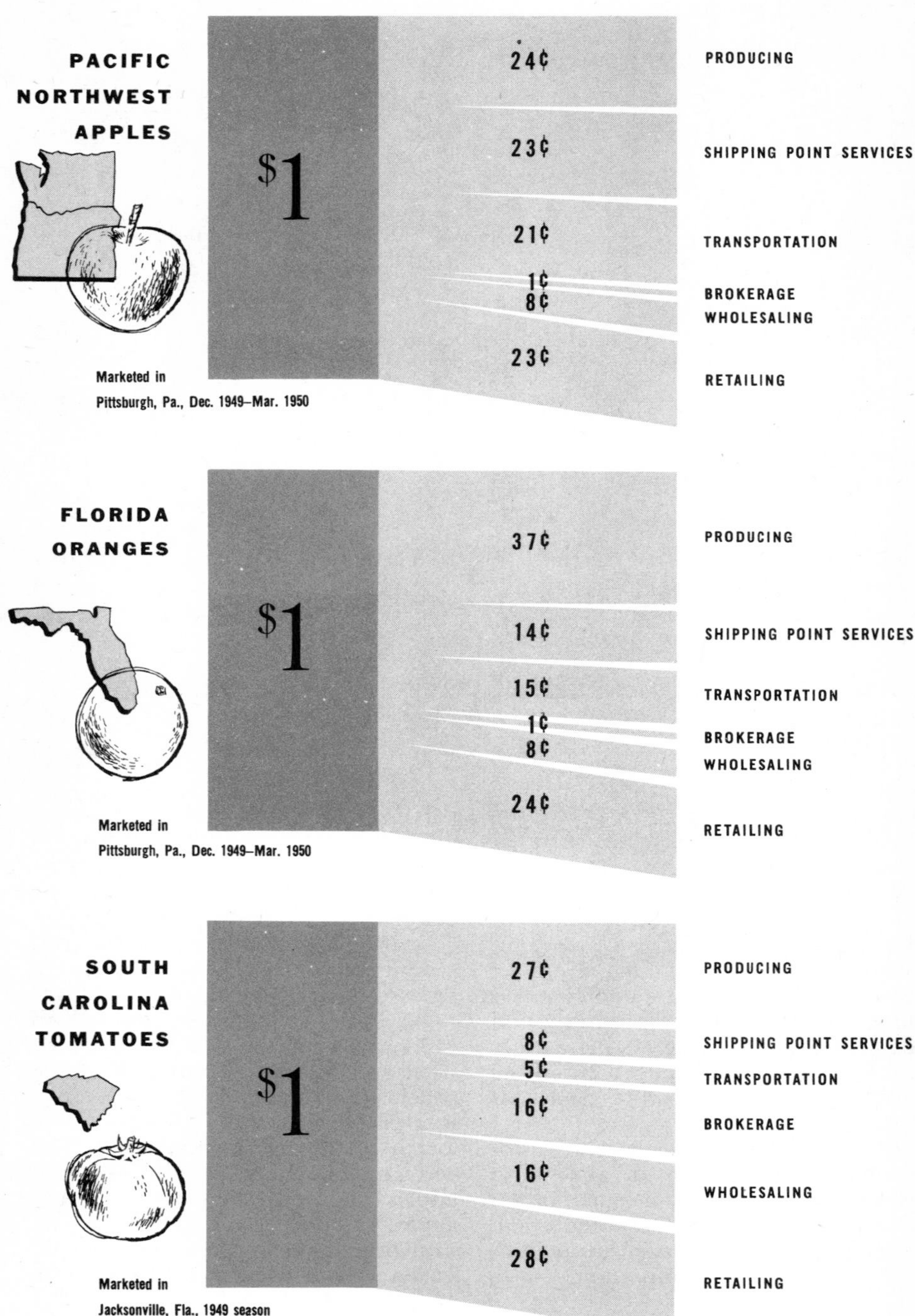

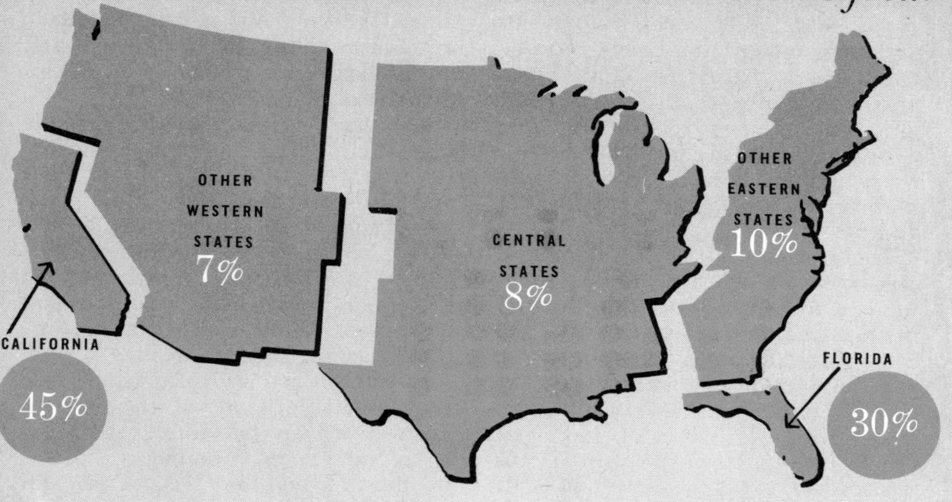

crop of sour cherries was marketed as canned and frozen cherries.

Dried fruits are produced chiefly in California. Fruits used for drying, including fruit from areas outside California, comprised more than one-sixth of the total production of noncitrus fruits on a fresh equivalent basis in 1951. Total production of dried fruit was nearly 500,000 tons. About half was raisins.

Since the mid-1930's the sales of noncitrus fruits, on a tonnage basis, have increased about a fifth—the rate of the increase of population. But during the same period a change occurred in the marketing pattern. The amounts marketed through processors increased about 40 percent, but sales on the fresh market declined slightly. Canners in 1953 handled twice as much fruit as in 1934–1936; the amount used for juice, wine, jellies, and preserves has almost doubled.

The freezing industry has become a major outlet in marketing strawberries and sour cherries, but the freezing of other noncitrus fruits has not yet achieved major proportions. The tonnage of noncitrus fruits used for drying has declined moderately, but dried fruits still are important in the overall fruit marketing picture.

More than 35 percent of the 1951 crop of English walnuts and about 75 percent of the pecans were marketed as shelled nuts.

While our population was increasing about 40 percent between 1920 and 1950, the production of commercial vegetables for the fresh market nearly doubled and the tonnage marketed through commercial processors for canning and freezing about tripled. Before the Second World War, about two-thirds of the production of commercial vegetables was sold on the fresh market, and one-third was processed. Wartime conditions stimulated the demand for both fresh and processed vegetables. During the war more than two-fifths of the total production of commercial vegetables was canned or frozen. This ratio dropped slightly in the years immediately following the war, but in 1951 and 1952 the ratio again exceeded two-fifths of the total.

The leading vegetables grown for commercial processing are tomatoes, green peas, sweet corn, snap beans, asparagus, green lima beans, broccoli, and spinach. Nearly all of the green peas, about nine-tenths of the green lima beans, four-fifths of the tomatoes, two-thirds of the sweet corn and asparagus, and about half of the broccoli, snap beans, and spinach go to canners and freezers.

The frozen pack of vegetables increased from about 150 million pounds in 1942 to nearly 900 million pounds in 1952. Although the quantity frozen is only a small percentage of the aggregate production of all the vegetables, freezing has become a very important outlet for a number of individual crops. Two-thirds of the crop of brussels sprouts, more than one-half of the green lima beans and broccoli, one-fourth of the cauliflower, green pea, and spinach crops, and one-tenth of the asparagus production were frozen in 1952.

As production has shifted to specialized areas, often at considerable distances from markets, a greater proportion of the consumer's dollar has been used to pay the costs of marketing, including greater transportation and handling charges. Also, as the products have been subjected to more processing or preparation before sale to the consumer, the proportionate costs of marketing have increased. Thus, today the producer receives, on the average, a little more than one-third of each dollar spent by the consumer for fruits and vegetables.

In preparing fruits and vegetables for the fresh market, practically all of the grading or sorting, much of the packing, and a considerable amount of the handling in packinghouses have required extensive hand labor. Growers and shippers—acutely aware of the need for reducing the cost of preparing and packaging their products if prices are not to rise to levels that will discourage consumption—are giving increasing attention to development of cheaper and improved containers and more efficient methods of packing and handling. As a result, the use of mechanized grading and sorting methods, automatic filling of containers, and mechanically powered handling equipment is growing rapidly.

Another development has been the invention of elaborate mobile packing machines—small-scale packing sheds on wheels—that are used for the packing of such fresh vegetables as lettuce and celery in the field at time of harvest, thus eliminating the need for an extra handling when these products are moved from the field through the usual packing sheds.

In the marketing of processed fruits and vegetables, one of the notable trends has been the shift toward packaging in smaller containers. Canners of most fruits and vegetables, for example, are putting up a major part of their packs for retail sale in cans that are smaller than formerly were considered standard. A similar development has been taking place in the packaging of frozen fruits and vegetables. The reasons given for this shift to smaller sizes are better adaptation to consumer needs and less consumer resistance to the unit prices at which they are sold.

Only a relatively few of the many kinds of fresh and processed fruits and vegetables produced in this country are important in international trade. In the years just before the Second World War, slightly more than one-tenth of our fruit production was exported. In the years since, the exports have averaged well under one-tenth of our production. In the prewar period, more than one-third of our dried fruit production was exported, about one-seventh of our canned fruit packs, and about one-twelfth of our fresh fruit.

Imports of fruits just before the Second World War amounted to about one-seventh of domestic production and since then have declined to about one-tenth. Bananas represent the bulk of the imports. Although imports of all other fruits are small in total, the imports of such commodities as dates and dried figs are large in relation to domestic production.

Western Europe, particularly the United Kingdom, in the period prior to the war, was the main export market for many of our fruits and fruit products. Certain varieties and sizes of apples and winter pears and a portion of the dried and canned fruit packs were produced especially for the European markets.

Fresh apples and pears were exported principally to the United Kingdom; that trade, disrupted during the war, has shown little recovery since. Canned fruits, such as fruits for salad, peaches, pears, and apricots, were exported in considerable volume, especially to the United Kingdom, before the war, but this outlet has disappeared almost entirely. Since the war there has been a slight increase in exports to non-European countries but the volume is relatively small. Large amounts of raisins and dried prunes, together with smaller amounts of dried apricots, peaches, pears, and apples were exported before the war, principally to Europe. In the years since the war exports of raisins and dried prunes have been maintained near prewar levels but only because of Government export subsidies. Exports of other dried fruits have declined sharply.

Citrus fruits and products were exported in sizable volume, especially to Canada before the war, and this trade has continued to grow in the years since the war. The United Kingdom took a considerable volume of our exports of citrus fruit and products before the war. This market has disappeared almost entirely, but there has been some increase in exports to other European countries, such as Belgium and the Netherlands, and to non-European countries.

Imports of tree nuts before the war amounted to almost as large a volume as was produced in this country, but now, because of increased domestic production, they represent a smaller percentage, although the volume imported is about the same. Cashews and Brazil nuts are the two most important imports. We export few tree nuts.

Foreign trade in vegetables is much less important than for fruits. Exports of canned vegetables represent only a small part of production. Exports of fresh vegetables have increased sharply. Almost all of this volume goes to Canada, principally during the winter and spring months. Canada, in turn, ships us both certified seed and table-stock potatoes, rutabagas, and some summer vegetables. In winter we import tomatoes, green peppers, and cucumbers from Mexico and Cuba. Onions, garlic, and cabbage are imported from overseas in years of limited domestic production and relatively high prices. (*Reginald Royston, Arthur E. Browne.*)

Sugar

Each person in the United States consumes an average of about 95 pounds of cane and beet sugar each year. The major use of sugar is to sweeten foods such as ice cream, baked goods, beverages, and candy. A small amount of sugar is consumed directly as such.

The total annual consumption of refined sugar in the United States amounts to about 7.6 million tons. The sources are the sugar beet regions of the Midwest and West, the sugarcane areas of Louisiana, Florida, Puerto Rico, and Hawaii, and the foreign sugarcane areas, principally Cuba and the Philippines. Continental and offshore domestic areas supply about 53 percent of total consumption; the rest is imported.

A fairly complex marketing structure carries sugar in its final form to the consumer from the farms where sugarcane and sugar beets are grown.

Cane sugar, which forms the bulk of domestic consumption, undergoes two refining processes before distribution to end users. The first refining process is done by factories in production areas where raw sugar is made from sugarcane. In a few instances, the second refining operation is done at the same plant, but most raw sugar is further processed by large refineries in major port cities in the United States. Thus sugarcane is sold by farmers to raw-sugar mills, which manufacture raw sugar from the cane and sell their output to refineries. Refiners perform the final processing necessary and act as primary distributors of sugar to industrial users, who use sugar in their operations, and to wholesale and retail buyers, who sell sugar to institutional and household consumers.

The development of the separate phases of processing and marketing came about for several reasons. The manufacture of raw sugar from cane, which is seasonally produced, extremely bulky in relation to value, and highly perishable, by mills located in production areas permits the second refining operation to be performed on a volume year-around basis by a relatively few large-scale refineries located in consuming areas. The complete manufacturing process performed at one factory would require great capital outlay, highly skilled labor, and adequate fuels. In the infancy of the sugar industry, those requirements were lacking in some of the production areas. Some marketing advantages accrue also to the location of refiners, who are primary distributors, in consuming areas.

Processing of beet sugar, because of the nature of the extraction methods, is an integrated operation at the factory located in the beet-growing region. Those processors are faced with the problem of seasonal use of costly facilities, but they have the advantage of location in areas where most of the beet sugar is consumed.

Another factor contributing to the complexity of the marketing structure is the way sugar is used. More and more manufactured sugar-containing products are bought; consequently there is a decline in direct sugar purchases by consumers for use in baking, canning, and other home uses. The industrial use of sugar has increased since 1935 from about 28 percent of total sugar marketed to slightly more than 51 percent in 1953. Conversely, sugar purchases for household, restaurant, and institutional usage have shrunk from about 72 percent of total marketings to about 49 percent.

Increased industrial use has been particularly notable in the beverage, baking, ice cream, canning, bottling, and frozen-food industries. Considerable quantities of sugar, most of which has already undergone two refining processes, consequently enter other manufacturing processes. The shift to industrial usage has come about because of the willingness of consumers to pay for additional marketing services embodied in finished products.

The greatest problem faced by domestic producers and processors over the years has been the achievement of relatively stable prices high enough to maintain a healthy industry.

The most important external factor contributing to that problem has been world market conditions. Sugar is one of the commodities on which many governments have placed tariffs, internal taxes, certain controls of supply, consumer subsidies, and other trade restrictions. Some countries have set up the restrictions for revenue purposes. Others use them to protect high-cost domestic industries. Uncertainty as to supplies in wartime motivates to a large extent the maintenance of sugar industries by many countries through various control measures. Sugar production is an industry that has a high capital investment and heavy fixed costs. Output cannot be adjusted readily to changes in de-

Entries and Marketings of Sugar in Continental United States by Area of Origin, in Thousands of Tons

Year	*Main-land beets*	*Main-land cane*	*Hawaii*	*Puerto Rico*	*Virgin Islands*	*Cuba*	*Philip-pine Islands*	*Other coun-tries*	*Total*
Average 1935–39	1,469	451	963	908	5	1,992	970	53	6,811
1944	1,155	515	802	743	3	3,618	....	106	6,941
1945	1,043	417	740	903	4	2,803	....	87	5,996
1946	1,379	445	633	867	5	2,282	....	46	5,657
1947	1,574	383	842	969	3	3,943	....	45	7,758
1948	1,656	455	714	1,013	4	2,927	252	62	7,084
1949	1,487	558	769	1,091	4	3,103	525	51	7,588
1950	1,749	518	1,145	1,053	11	3,264	473	61	8,274
1951	1,730	460	941	959	6	2,947	706	13	7,762
1952	1,560	552	972	983	6	2,980	860	51	7,964

mand and price. These also are factors which occasion the establishment of controls.

International trade barriers have two major effects on marketing sugar. The amount of sugar exported to countries or areas in which it enjoys no preference amounts to only about 10 percent of the world's total production and consumption of sugar. This limited amount constitutes the world free sugar market, to which Cuba is the chief supplier. It more nearly represents a residual supply, which completes the requirements of deficit-supply countries not filled by producers within the protective systems of such countries. This characteristic leads to instability in the world sugar market and makes prices in that market highly susceptible to the full inflationary and deflationary effects of changes in world production and consumption. Even small changes have significant effects because of the narrowness of the free world market.

High tariffs, internal taxes, and other barriers have resulted in high prices to consumers in many countries. In many instances they bear no relationship to prices received by exporters of sugar. High retail prices have tended to restrict consumption. Although per capita consumption in the United States is relatively high while prices to consumers are relatively low, the reverse situation prevails in many countries.

Some protection has been given the United States sugar industry against the instability of the world market.

281437°—54——29

Channels of Sugar Distribution : United States

ALL FIGURES EXPRESSED AS PERCENT OF TOTAL VOLUME
"A" REPRESENTS LESS THAN 0.5 PERCENT

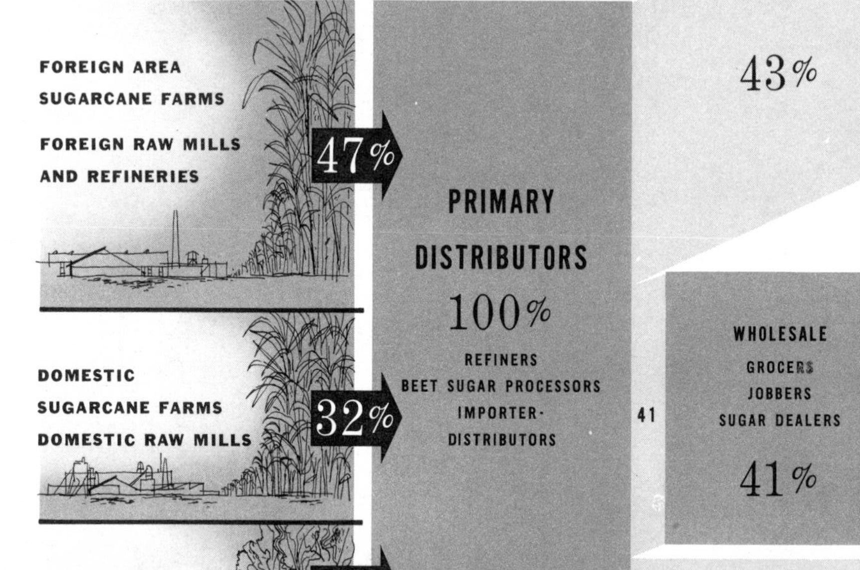

For many years a tariff system applied to sugar imports. Its net result was to encourage domestic production, while at times Cuba, the principal supplier, was obliged to reduce her export prices to disastrously low levels. Recurrent market crises led to the adoption of the Jones-Costigan Sugar Act in 1934. The Sugar Act of 1948, as amended, still maintains the general features of the first sugar act.

The Sugar Act is designed to maintain a healthy and competitive domestic sugar industry of limited size and to improve our import trade. As stated in the act, the objective is to achieve prices that will not be excessive to consumers and will fairly maintain and protect the domestic industry.

Provisions are included in the act to insure that a fair share of the consumer's dollar goes to growers and to workers in the beet and cane fields. To achieve the objectives, sugar requirements of consumers for the following year are determined by the Secretary of Agriculture each December; quota provisions for foreign and domestic areas to fill the requirements are administered; and conditional payments are made to domestic growers. The act contains an amendment to the Internal Revenue Code providing for an excise tax of one-half cent a pound, raw value, on the manufacture or importation of sugar. Tax collections have exceeded payments to growers by 15 to 20 million dollars a year.

It would be just about impossible, short of rigid controls, to isolate the United States sugar market from the world market, but the Sugar Act has reduced the impact of world market conditions on domestic prices. Since its inception in 1934, United States sugar prices have been much more stable, which has been beneficial to the domestic industry, and have shown a much less proportionate increase than have the prices of most other food products which has benefited consumers.

While sugar legislation provides a buffer against world market conditions, it is not a substitute for efficient marketing practices nor is it a cure-all for problems affecting price which are prevalent in all phases of the domestic marketing structure.

Cane and beets have to be marketed and processed shortly after harvest. Farmers must sell their crop at harvesttime with only moderate regard for price. To pay the growers, raw mills market the bulk of their raw-sugar production during and shortly after the processing season. Heavy volume of selling during this period in the past often has depressed prices more than if more orderly marketing methods were followed.

Farmers and mills therefore adopted a variety of settlement methods. Average prices for periods of 2 weeks to 12 months, depending on area and individual contractual arrangements, are used often in settlements between cane growers and processors. The common settlement practice for sugar beets is on the basis of net proceeds from sugar sales. As to raw cane sugar, many mills have attempted to hedge average settlements by corresponding arrangements to sell raw sugar. For example, sales of raw sugar often are made on various average price bases. This in effect removes such sellers from a bargaining position and reduces the volume of sugar as well as the number of sellers acting as a register of raw sugar values. There are indications that the raw-sugar market has become quite narrow, and at times small isolated transactions in raw sugar have a significant effect on the raw-sugar price level. Thus, these attempts to reduce market risks have given rise to other problems.

Problems affecting price also abound in the marketing of refined sugar. One is price resistance in the area of industrial usage. Retail prices of some products, among them soft drinks and candy, so-called "nickel" items, vary little. Other problems relate to longstanding sales practices, such as guarantees to buyers against price declines and bookings in advance of price increases. Such protection against both price declines and increases concentrates market risk on sellers of refined sugar.

RESEARCH financed with funds made available under the Research and Marketing Act of 1946 is delving into sugar-marketing problems to ascertain their fundamental causes and what practices can be put into effect to eliminate them. Considerable research also is being directed toward the development of more profitable market outlets for molasses and bagasse, the principal sugar byproducts. The sugar industry is exploring the possibilities of reducing marketing costs by widespread adoption of liquid and dry sugar and bulk handling methods. The United States Government in its negotiations with other countries on the provisions of an International Sugar Agreement is striving to reduce trade barriers on sugar so that world consumption can be increased and the world "free" market can become larger and more stable. The combined results should make for more sound and efficient sugar marketing. (*Marshall E. Miller.*)

Tobacco

The American farmer markets an average of more than 400 hours of labor in the tobacco he sells from an acre of land. It takes about a minute to examine and bid on that amount of tobacco at auction.

Some 850,000 farm families in 1953—roughly 1 out of every 7—in the continental United States and Puerto Rico marketed 2.1 billion pounds of tobacco, grown on 1.7 million acres. More than 90 percent of the tobacco was bought by about 20 major firms and their affiliates.

Americans paid around 5.2 billion dollars at retail for tobacco products in 1953. More than 1.6 billion dollars went for Federal tobacco taxes. Estimated State and municipal taxes amounted to more than 500 million dollars. Payments for transportation, processing and storage of leaf, manufacturing, distribution, imported leaf, and materials other than tobacco amounted to about 2.3 billion dollars. This figure includes profits of those engaged in the marketing process after purchase of leaf tobacco. United States farmers received approximately 800 million dollars from domestic manufacturers for the 1953 crop. In addition, they received around 300 million dollars for tobacco sold for foreign use.

About 25 percent of the United States crop is exported to foreign countries. The remainder is used by United States manufacturers. Foreign tobaccos imported in 1953 for blending with domestic tobaccos totaled about 7 percent of our consumption.

The manufacture of tobacco products of uniform quality depends on careful selection and blending of many different kinds and qualities of tobacco grown in different areas of this country and, for the large bulk of our products, in foreign countries.

Tobacco grown in this country and Puerto Rico is divided under Government standards into 6 major classes covering 26 types and a miscellaneous class covering minor types. Some types are divided into more than 100 grades and qualities. The different classes and types of domestic tobaccos can be grouped into those used primarily for cigarette and pipe and "roll-your-own" mixtures (flue-cured, Burley and Maryland types); chewing tobacco and snuff (fire-cured and dark air-cured types); and cigars (filler, binder and wrapper types).

The Tobacco Industry in the United States

APPROXIMATE
1951–53 AVERAGE

As tobacco progresses from farm to final product there is shrinkage due to loss of moisture, stemming, etc. Weights depicted are farm sales basis except at retail.

PRODUCED IN UNITED STATES
2250 MIL. LBS.

FLUE-CURED BURLEY AND OTHER

IMPORTS
105 MIL. LBS.
Cigar tobacco
Cigarette leaf

LEAF MARKETING

93% AT AUCTIONS

7% FARM AND OTHER

PROCESSING AND STORAGE
By manufacturers, dealers, and growers' cooperative associations

REDRYING
PACKING
AGING
STEMMING

UNMANUFACTURED
EXPORTS
550 MIL. LBS.

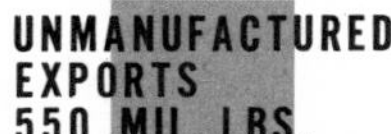

FLUE-CURED 80%

OTHER TYPES 20%

MANUFACTURE
1805 MIL. LBS.
81% Cigarettes
9.5% Cigars
7% Smoking and chewing
2.5% Snuff

EXPORT

16 Billion cigarettes
6 Mil. lbs. smoking and chewing

WHOLESALERS
JOBBERS
CHAINS

FOREIGN COUNTRIES
Dealers, manufacturers, government monopolies

550 Mil. lbs. unmanufactured
16 Billion cigarettes
6 Mil. lbs. manufactured smoking and chewing

RETAIL OUTLETS,
OVERSEAS FORCES
410 Billion cigarettes
6 Billion cigars
95 Mil. lbs. smoking tobacco
83 Mil. lbs. chewing tobacco
39 Mil. lbs. snuff

Leaf tobacco is sold on the basis of physical inspection. There are no tobacco exchanges. The market is seasonal. Price information in most areas is that reported by Federal-State tobacco market news service from actual sales of tobacco.

The systems through which United States farmers sell their tobacco include auction markets; "barn door," or country, buying; sales by cooperatives and private dealers after delivery of tobacco by growers; and the "hogshead" market for Maryland tobacco at Baltimore. A substantial part of the cigar wrapper tobacco is grown by cigar manufacturers or under contracts with them.

More than 90 percent of our 1953 tobacco crop was sold on 171 "loose leaf" auction markets. Sales are conducted in large, one-story warehouse buildings with skylights spaced across the roof to provide light. In 1953 there were 940 such warehouses, covering an area of more than 1,000 acres.

Before taking his tobacco to the auction, the farmer sorts it into lots based on color and other factors relating to grade and quality. Each lot of tobacco at the auction warehouse is placed on a separate basket or tray and weighed. A ticket on each basket shows the weight and the name of the grower and includes space for the Government grade, the price bid, and the buyer's grade.

The auction sale usually begins about 9 a. m. Federal inspectors enter the grade of the tobacco on each basket ticket ahead of the auction. The warehouseman, who acts as a commission merchant, makes the starting bid on each basket of tobacco. The auctioneer calls the bids. Usually 6 to 10 buyers participate in each auction sale. The ticket marker records the price bid and the buyer's name and grade on the ticket. Sales usually are made at the rate of 350 to 400 baskets an hour. The farmer can obtain payment for his tobacco at the warehouse office within a few minutes after the auction.

The farmer, who usually observes the sale of his tobacco, has a right—used seldom—to reject the bid on any basket of his tobacco.

About 4 percent of the 1953 tobacco crop was sold at the "barn door," about 2 percent through cooperatives or private dealers after delivery to warehouses by growers, and about 0.2 percent through the Baltimore "hogshead" market.

"Barn door" sales are made by individual negotiation between the farmer and the buyer. If deliveries are made to cooperatives or private dealers, the cooperative or dealer negotiates the sale on behalf of the farmer. On the Baltimore market the tobacco is packed in the hogshead by or for the farmer. Samples, drawn from each hogshead, are displayed by the grower cooperative or the commission merchant. Buyers inspect the samples and submit sealed bids. The farmer or his representative may reject the bids.

A farmer who rejects the sale of a basket of tobacco on the auction market runs the risk of a lower bid when it is reoffered. A farmer who rejects an offer for tobacco at the farm runs the risk that he will receive no other offer for some time. Although some growers of cigar tobacco and some Maryland growers hold their crops over from one year to another, to do so generally is not practical. The grower therefore is under pressure to sell at the price offered.

With the development of Federal price-support programs, loans have been made available for the various grades of tobacco at fixed rates. In areas served by the auction markets, a grower usually takes advantage of the loan if the buyer does not bid more than the loan. In other areas the grower usually sells before he knows the loan rates or prices. At best, he can only obtain an indication of the loan rate based on grading of samples. Final grades for loan purposes can be determined only after delivery of the tobacco to designated warehouses where it can be inspected fully.

Tax Receipts from Tobacco Products, and Farmers' Cash Receipts from Tobacco FISCAL YEARS 1935–53

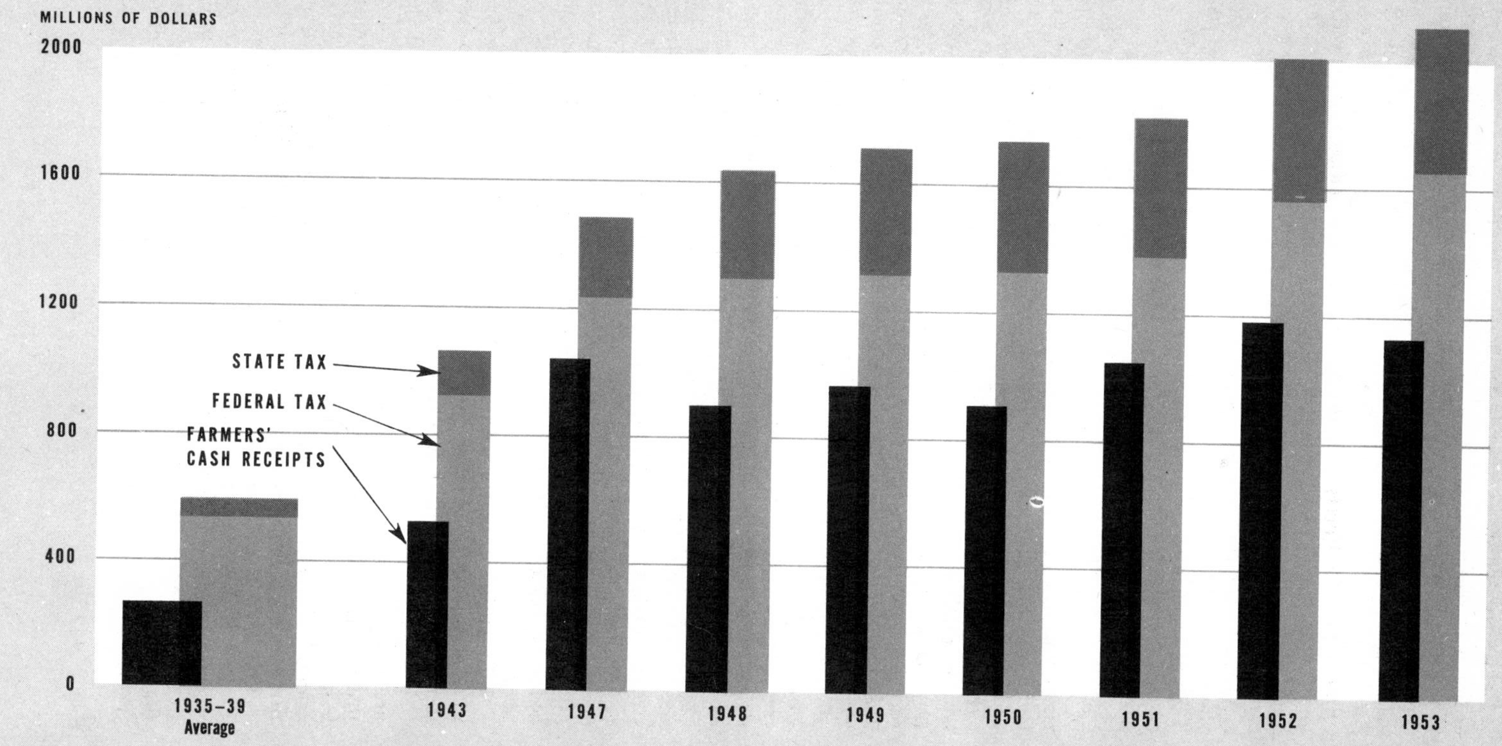

Each grower who places tobacco under loan usually becomes a member of a grower association, which makes the loans under contract with Commodity Credit Corporation. The association is responsible for having the tobacco processed, packed, and stored, and for its sale. Tobacco placed under loans from the 1951, 1952, and 1953 crops averaged 277 million pounds.

Most tobacco is in a semiperishable condition when it is sold by farmers. Therefore, it must be moved promptly to central plants for handling and processing. Before tobacco can be placed in storage for necessary aging of about 2 years it must contain the right amount of moisture. Air-drying, fermentation, and steam redrying are used to fix the percentage of moisture.

In the steam redrying process, moisture is removed from the leaf and then put back in proper amounts. Steam redrying machines are used for the cigarette and smoking tobaccos (except for most Maryland tobacco) and part of the chewing and snuff tobaccos. Most of the chewing and snuff tobaccos are air-dried. Maryland tobacco dries on the farm and usually is packed as delivered by farmers. Most of the cigarette, smoking, and chewing and snuff tobaccos after processing are packed in hogsheads that hold 800 to 1,500 pounds. Cigar leaf tobaccos are conditioned by fermentation. Nearly all of the cigar tobacco is packed in bales or boxes weighing 150 to 400 pounds.

Substantial amounts of tobacco used in the cigarettes in this country are stemmed at the redrying plants before being packed for storage. The stems are not removed from the remainder until the tobacco is moved forward from storage for manufacture. Tobacco purchased for export usually is not stemmed before shipment abroad.

The flavor, aroma, and quality of United States tobaccos are prized in many countries. United States exports of tobacco annually range from 450 to 600 million pounds (farm-sales weight). Tobacco frequently has ranked third among our agricultural exports. Exports before the Second World War amounted to about one-third of the crop each year. Postwar exports have been a little above the prewar exports, but represent only about one-fourth of the crop, as domestic use has increased much more than exports. About 75 percent of our exported tobacco goes to countries of Western Europe, with small amounts to other European countries, about 15 percent to countries in the Far Pacific and Asia, and about 10 percent to countries in Africa and South America.

The upward trend in smoking of cigarettes of the United States "blended" type and of the English "straight Virginia" (flue-cured) type has made flue-cured the main export tobacco. Average exports of flue-cured at 433 million pounds (farm weight) during the 5 marketing years ending with 1953 were almost 20 percent above the prewar level. The total United States exports for the 5 years, averaging about 530 million pounds, exceeded prewar levels by about 14 percent. Burley exports at around 35 million pounds now equal nearly 3 times the small prewar figure. Dark-fired and air-cured tobaccos have lost ground and exports at around 43 million pounds now average just over half as much as before the war. Exports of cigar wrapper and binder and of Maryland tobacco are larger than before the war.

Foreign markets for United States tobacco in the postwar period have been affected adversely by foreign restrictions imposed primarily to save dollar exchange. Governments of tobacco-importing countries have been loath to reduce total imports because tobacco products are a major source of revenue. This has led them to favor other tobaccos even where preference of their domestic trade is for United States leaf. These policies along with favorable worldwide tobacco prices in recent years have encouraged expansion of tobacco production in foreign

Tobacco Production Within States According to Primary Manufacturing Use

Average 1950–52 crops

STATE	PRODUCTION 1,000 LBS.	PRIMARY MANUFACTURING USE		
		CIGARETTES AND SMOKING TOBACCO	CHEWING TOBACCO AND SNUFF*	CIGARS AND SCRAP CHEWING TOBACCO
		Percent	Percent	Percent
North Carolina	931,322	100		
Kentucky	434,550	90	10	
Virginia	175,813	91	9	
South Carolina	166,320	100		
Tennessee	143,475	78	22	
Georgia	121,505	99		1
Pennsylvania	49,528			100
Maryland	40,377	100		
Florida	28,706	83		17
Ohio	26,889	67		33
Wisconsin	25,406			100
Connecticut	25,204			100
Indiana	14,096	99	1	
Massachusetts	10,934			100
Missouri	5,330	100		
West Virginia	4,103	100		
Alabama	539	100		
New York	460			100
Minnesota	433			100
Louisiana	198	100		
Kansas	150	100		
Total U. S.	2,205,338	90	4	6

*Excluding scrap chewing tobacco.

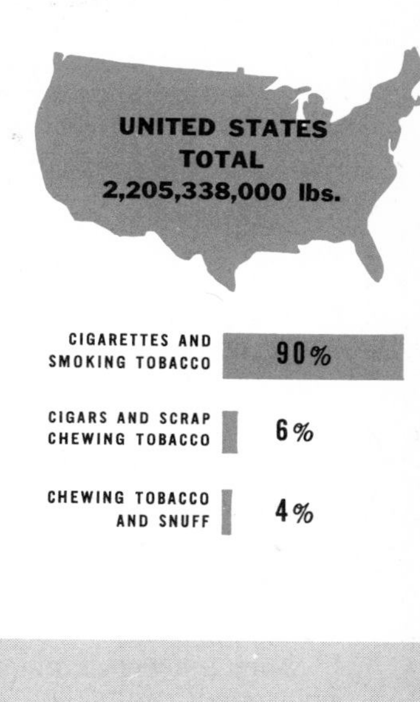

Tobacco Harvested

Acreage 1949

ONE DOT=1,000 ACRES

(County Unit Basis)

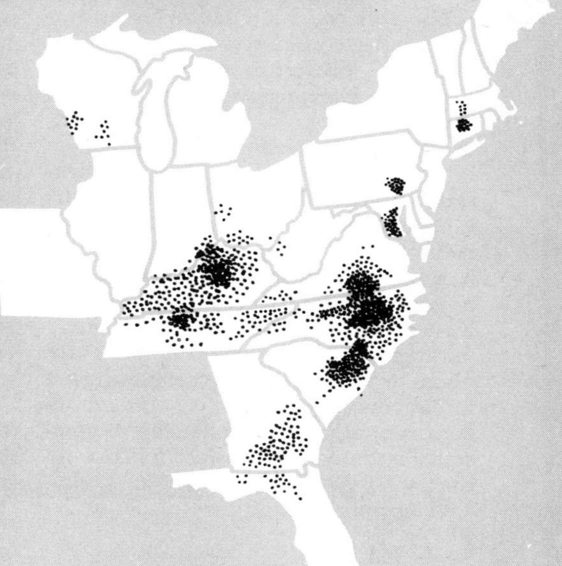

UNITED STATES TOTAL 1,532,298 acres

producing areas. Consequently, United States tobacco faces increasing competition in world markets.

About 93 percent of the tobacco used by American manufacturers is grown in this country. The rest consists of types imported primarily for blending with domestic tobaccos. This country usually ranks second or third among the world's importers. United States imports for consumption in 1953 were 105 million pounds. About three-fourths of United States imports are aromatic (oriental) cigarette tobacco, mainly from Turkey, Greece, and Syria, with smaller imports from several other countries. A fourth is cigar tobacco, mainly from Cuba, with small amounts from the Philippines and Indonesia.

The United States import duties on cigarette leaf and cigar wrapper have been reduced one-half and one-third, respectively, since 1947. A restrictive quota arrangement on Cuban tobacco was eliminated, and its preferential-duty status continued.

More tobacco is manufactured and consumed in the United States than in any other country, both in total quantity and per capita. With only about 6 percent of the world's population, the United States consumes nearly a fourth of the world's tobacco.

The tobacco manufacturing industry can be considered in three broad segments—cigarettes and smoking; cigars; and chewing and snuff. Several companies make more than one product.

More than 98 percent of the cigarette manufacture in the United States is concentrated in six companies. One factor in this concentration probably is the cigarette machine. Highly significant also are heavy investment in inventories of leaf tobacco sufficient for manufacturing requirements for about 2 years and large expenditures for advertising. Labor cost in manufacturing relative to the value of cigarettes is among the lowest for any industry.

Consumer expenditure of about 4.4 billion dollars in 1953 for cigarettes in the United States compares with total expenditures of 5.2 billion dollars for all tobacco products. The Federal Government and 41 State Governments collected about 2 billion dollars in taxes on cigarettes, compared with a total on all tobacco products of about 2.2 billion dollars.

Total output of cigarettes in the United States in 1953 was 423 billion —of which 16 billion were exported. In 1953, daily consumption of cigarettes averaged nearly 10 for each person, 15 years and older—more than twice as many as before the war.

In recent years there has been a steady and substantial gain of the "king size" cigarettes, which are about one-fifth longer and contain about one-sixth more tobacco than the standard size. There also has been a rapid gain in sales of filter tip cigarettes, although they still are a small part of total output.

Cigar manufacturing in the United States has shifted largely from hand to machine processes, but the shift has been slower and less complete than in the case of cigarettes. The greatest difference in mechanization of cigarette and cigar manufacture is the continuous feeding of tobacco and paper through the cigarette machine, whereas each cigar must be made individually through the machine from the leaf for the filler, the leaf for the binder, and the leaf for the wrapper. The output of a cigarette machine is 1,200 to 1,400 a minute. The output of a cigar machine is about 10 to 12.

In 1953, nearly 60 percent of the cigars were made by 8 companies, another 30 percent by some 40 companies, and the rest by a few hundred small firms. The manufacture of cigars employs about 40 percent more workers than does the manufacture of cigarettes.

Consumers spend about 560 million dollars annually for around 6 billion cigars. Around 50 million dollars represent taxes to the Federal Government and to 11 State Governments.

Tobacco Products in the United States 1934-53 UNSTEMMED PROCESSING-WEIGHT EQUIVALENT

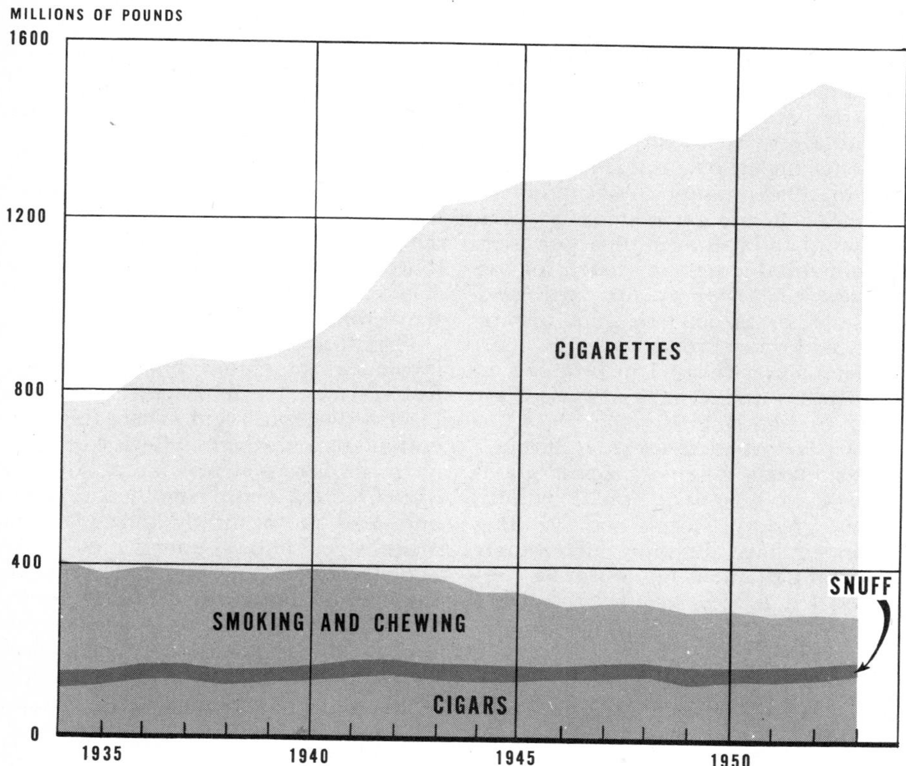

Total consumption of cigars in 1953 was about 14 percent above the 1935–1939 average, but consumption per person was down about 5 percent and was only about two-thirds of the 1925–1929 average.

Smoking tobacco, chewing tobacco, and snuff have been declining in relative importance over a considerable period of years. Output of smoking tobacco in this country in 1953 was 86 million pounds compared with an average of 161 million in 1925–1929. Similar output figures for chewing tobacco are 83 and 197 million pounds. The 1953 output of snuff was 39 million pounds, only a little below the 1925–1929 average. Annual tax receipts from smoking, chewing, and snuff are about 20 million dollars.

Historically in this country taxes are levied on cigarettes with rates fixed on a per thousand basis. Taxes on cigars are levied on the basis of variable rates per thousand depending upon the prices at which the cigars are manufactured to retail. Taxes on smoking and chewing tobaccos and snuff are levied with rates fixed on a per pound basis. The current Federal tax rate on cigarettes is $4.00 per thousand. On cigars the rates vary from $2.50 per thousand for those retailing at 2½ cents each or less to $20.00 per thousand on those retailing for more than 20 cents each. On smoking and chewing tobacco and snuff the rate is 10 cents per pound. Taking into account the tobacco contained in the various products the approximate tax rates per pound would be $1.89 on cigarettes, 44 cents on cigars, and 18 cents on smoking, chewing, and snuff combined.

About 250 million pounds of stems and scrap and damaged tobacco which are not suitable or not needed for use in tobacco products are processed annually for use in fertilizers, insecticides, and other products. Some stems from tobacco are used in products in this country and some are exported for use in foreign countries.

Tobacco products are sold through approximately 4,500 wholesalers and more than a million retail outlets. Chain grocery stores and vending machines have become increasingly important channels for consumer purchases. (*J. E. Thigpen*, *A. G. Conover*.)

Cotton

The marketing of an average United States cotton crop involves the distribution and utilization of some 6 or 7 billion pounds of fiber and 10 or 11 billion pounds of seed produced on about 1,100,000 farms in 17 or 18 States. It includes hundreds of processes and thousands of consumer items used by every individual and every segment of industry in this country and by many in foreign lands.

The fiber provides about 70 percent of the textile products manufactured in the United States, and sizable proportions of those in Europe, Japan, and other foreign areas. The seed provides nearly a third of the Nation's requirements for edible vegetable oil, a fifth of the protein feed consumed by our livestock, and large amounts of raw material for the domestic chemical industry.

No other agricultural product involves so many separate qualities, end products, and separate marketing phases or steps. Consequently, the marketing of cotton takes a larger share of the consumer's dollar and leaves to the farmer a much smaller share than for most farm products.

The first important steps in the movement of cotton fiber and seed from farmers to final consumers take place at the cotton gin. There the seed cotton goes through a series of mechanical processes, which separate the fiber from the seed. From the gins fiber and seed move mostly through separate steps and channels and into widely different markets and uses. As the fiber, or lint cotton, is 6 to 7 times as valuable as the seed sold, even though it is equivalent to less than 60 percent of the weight of the seed, it is given primary attention.

The various marketing transactions and services relating to American cotton fiber and fiber products are often included under five groups: Merchandising of the raw fiber; manufacturing of yarns and fabrics; manufacturing or fabricating apparel, household and other consumer items; wholesaling; and retailing.

The transactions and services considered here as merchandising cover such services as marking or tagging, weighing, compressing, storing, loading and transporting, sampling for and determining quality, buying and selling, assembling, financing, and hedging. Many of them are done by or at the direction of cotton merchants or shippers, and account for the designation of merchandising, but merchan-

The United States Consumer's Cotton Dollar

WHERE IT GOES, BY PERCENTAGES

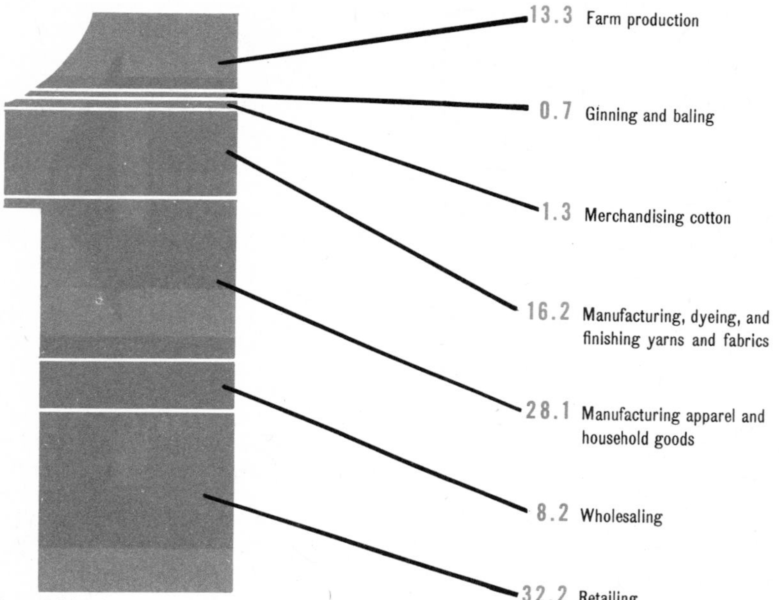

13.3 Farm production

0.7 Ginning and baling

1.3 Merchandising cotton

16.2 Manufacturing, dyeing, and finishing yarns and fabrics

28.1 Manufacturing apparel and household goods

8.2 Wholesaling

32.2 Retailing

Based on official and other data, and partly estimated (1950)

dising also includes the services of many other business organizations and of a few Government agencies. The activities collectively are concerned with the movement of hundreds of different qualities of lint cotton, from our 7,300 gins to 1,600 domestic spinning and weaving mills and to many such mills abroad.

After the lint cotton reaches the spinning mills, many of which are also weaving mills, it goes through a series of complicated manufacturing processes that convert the raw fiber into yarn. The types, sizes, and qualities of yarns produced determine the number of processes involved and the quality of fiber that can be used most advantageously. For single or unplied yarns, the number of processes range from 4 to 16; most yarns require 8 to 12 processes. The processes in the order in which the fiber moves through them are opening, cleaning, carding, or carding and combing, drawing, roving, spinning, spooling or winding, and warping or beaming.

The weaving of cotton yarns into fabrics also involves a number of processes. Ordinarily they include slashing and drawing in the warp, combining the warper beams into a single sheet for weaving, coating the yarns with sizing, and the actual weaving. Because of differences in the type of weave, width of fabric, warp and filling ends to the inch, and the size and quality of yarns used, there are thousands of different constructions and qualities of woven cotton fabrics. Woven fabrics are usually rolled automatically by the loom into large rolls, which may be sewed into even larger rolls. The fabrics are then cleaned and inspected, after which they are either transferred directly to the finishing plant or baled for shipment.

Some 5 to 10 percent of the cotton yarn produced in the United States goes into knit goods. Knit goods are made by the formation of connected loops produced on a series of needles. Variations in the types of machines, needles, and knitting principles used and the variations in the sizes and types of yarns result in hundreds of different kinds and qualities of knitted cotton products.

Most cotton goods come from the looms or from the knitting machines as gray goods and in most instances are subsequently dyed or otherwise finished before they are ready for the ultimate consumer. Some fabrics are made entirely or partly of dyed yarns and may or may not be used without additional finishing. The chief methods of finishing gray goods include bleaching, mercerizing, dyeing, and printing. The several hundred separate establishments engaged in dyeing and finishing textiles provide a wide variety of designs, styles, and finishes, which are performed by a diversity of processes. Many fabrics require a dozen or more separate operations.

Cotton textiles are used in a large number of products, which can be divided into three broad groups—clothing or apparel, household, and industrial. For such household items as sheets, pillowcases, and tablecloths, relatively little further processing is involved. For products generally included in the industrial-goods group, which includes fabrics or cords for such things as machinery belts, tarpaulins, bags, upholsteries, tires, and footwear, additional processing is usually done by firms outside the textile industry.

Probably the largest amount of cotton fiber goes into cutters goods, which are mainly for wearing apparel and household items produced by the textile establishments that cut and sew purchased fabrics. Their methods of fabricating cotton textiles vary considerably. Some of the key steps include cutting the material, sewing or joining the parts, pressing and folding, and boxing for shipping. In making dresses and other items of women's apparel, one of the important and expensive steps is designing.

Most cotton fiber products are distributed through a big number of wholesaling and retailing agencies.

Even though many manufacturers provide their own wholesaling services, large proportions of the products move through separate wholesalers. Wholesale services include storage; assembling and delivering the types, sizes, and quantities of items desired by retailers and others; and financing the movement of the goods.

RETAILING is the final stage in the marketing of raw and processed cotton fiber. A retailer's functions include assembling of varied stocks of goods, storage, financing, selling, and (in some instances) delivery and consumer credit. Through his direct contacts with consumers, the retailer also collects and passes back to processors and other distributors information on the consumers' desires, preferences, and practices, which serves as guides for future production.

The costs of moving the raw and manufactured cotton fiber from the farm to the ultimate consumer in this country represent a large share of the consumer's dollar.

For cotton clothing and household items, which account for almost three-fourths of domestic consumption, it is estimated that on the average about 85 to 90 cents of the consumer's dollar go for marketing services, including less than 1 cent for ginning. The remaining 10 to 15 cents represent the share going to farmers for the raw fiber.

A further breakdown shows that, of the five groups of services involved, merchandising of raw fiber and wholesaling of the manufactured goods re-

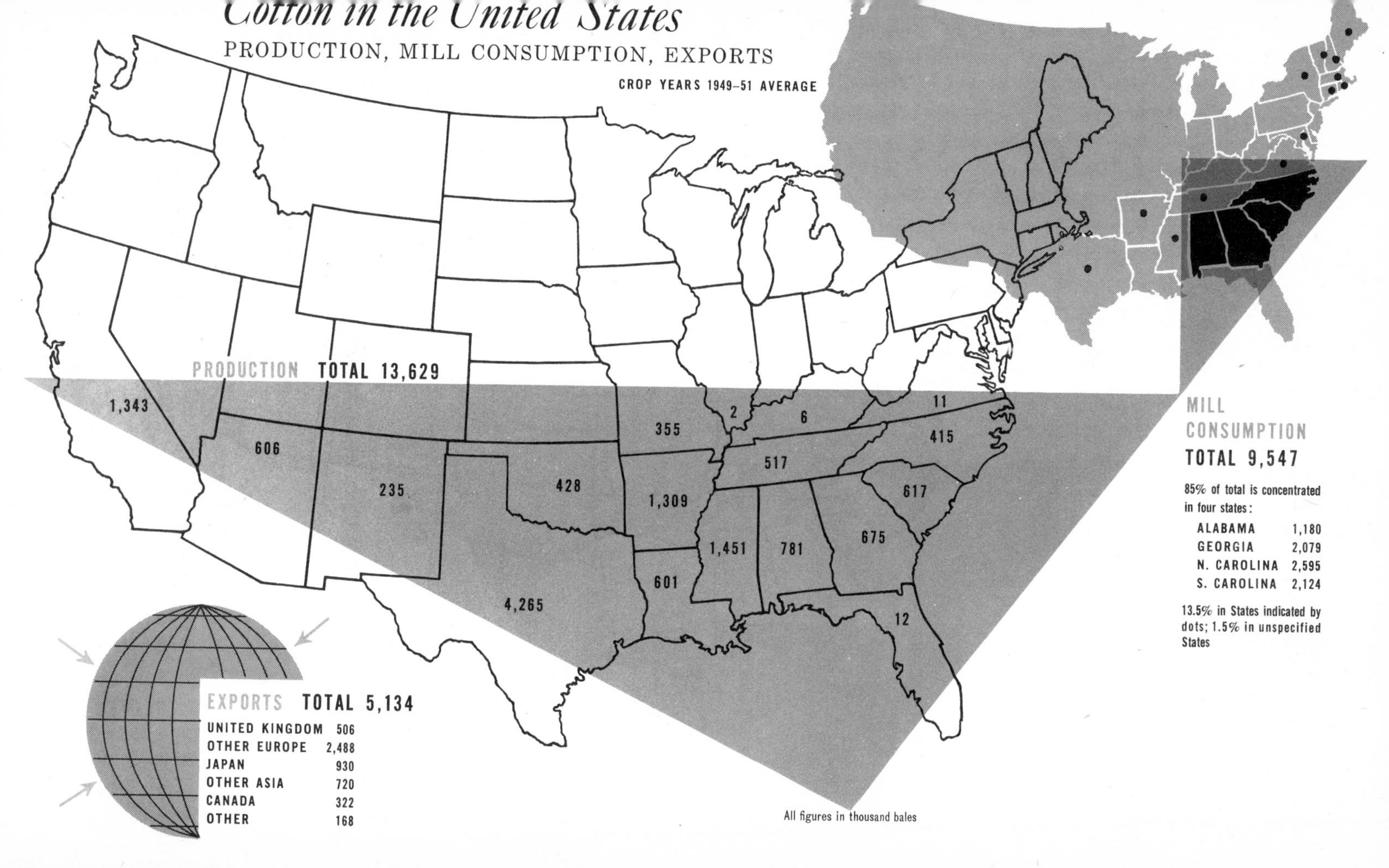
Cotton in the United States
PRODUCTION, MILL CONSUMPTION, EXPORTS
CROP YEARS 1949–51 AVERAGE
PRODUCTION TOTAL 13,629
1,343
606
235
428
4,265
355
1,309
601
2
6
517
1,451
781
11
415
617
675
12
MILL CONSUMPTION
TOTAL 9,547
85% of total is concentrated in four states:
ALABAMA 1,180
GEORGIA 2,079
N. CAROLINA 2,595
S. CAROLINA 2,124
13.5% in States indicated by dots; 1.5% in unspecified States
EXPORTS TOTAL 5,134
UNITED KINGDOM 506
OTHER EUROPE 2,488
JAPAN 930
OTHER ASIA 720
CANADA 322
OTHER 168
All figures in thousand bales

ceived the smallest proportions of the consumer's dollar. The other three broad phases—manufacturing, dyeing, and finishing of the yarns and fabrics; manufacturing or fabricating the apparel and household goods; and retailing—each accounted for much larger proportions and collectively represented about four-fifths of the dollar.

The costs for cotton in industrial products are so completely intertwined with costs of other materials and services that it is difficult to determine the farmer's share or any other division of the consumer's dollar. There is no question, however, but that the cost of the raw cotton also represents a small proportion of cotton's part of the final consumer's products.

Unlike cotton fiber, most of the cottonseed is sold by the farmer to the ginner, who in turn sells it directly to cottonseed processors. At the processing plants the seed is cleaned, delinted, and hulled, and the resulting flaked meat is separated from the hulls. These processes give two of the four original products obtained from cottonseed—linters, the short fuzz or fibers remaining on the seed coat after ginning, and hulls, the stiff outer coating of the seed. The other two products—oil and cottonseed cake or meal—are obtained from the flaked meat through mechanical or solvent extraction processes.

In mechanical extraction, which in 1953 accounted for about four-fifths of the cottonseed processed, the meats are rolled into flakes and cooked with or without pressure. The oil is then extracted from the meat by hydraulic or screw presses. The resulting cake is either ground into meal or cracked into smaller pieces, and the meal is often further processed into cubes or pellets.

Solvent extraction is rapidly increasing in importance because it takes less work and gives a greater proportion of oil. In the process the flaked meats are exposed to chemical solvents, which dissolve out the oil. The oil is separated from the solvent by distillation.

Oil is by far the most valuable of the cottonseed products. After it is extracted, it is processed mainly into such edible products as shortening, cooking oils, salad oils, salad dressing, and margarine. The major processing steps are refining, bleaching, winterizing, hydrogenation, deodorization.

Meal or cake, the second most valuable cottonseed product, and hulls are used primarily as feed for livestock. They need little additional processing.

Linters have a wider variety of uses than any of the cottonseed products. The most important use is as chemical cellulose, for which they are cooked or digested with chemicals, bleached, washed, and dried. The resulting linter pulp, which is practically pure cellulose, then goes into many uses, mainly as rayon, plastics, film, explosives, paper, and lacquers. The longest lengths and highest grades of linters are spun into coarse yarns. Others serve as a filler in bedding, furniture, and automobiles.

Since shortly after the First World War a combination of far-reaching developments has caused greater attention to be given to the various problems associated with the marketing of American cotton. Cotton farmers were severely affected in the 1920's by heavy losses because of insects and relatively high production and living costs. Depression in the 1930's again reduced prices of cotton and other farm products to a far greater extent than prices of things farmers purchased. Cotton farmers were hit especially hard by the increasing competition from synthetic fibers and other competing products and by reductions in foreign outlets, which for many years took more than half the domestic production of lint cotton. Consequently they joined with other groups in requesting additional assistance from the Government. It was primarily the seriousness of the problem of finding adequate markets at satisfactory prices that later caused the cotton industry to develop a coordinated program on behalf of all groups

Consumption of Cotton by End Use, U.S., 1952

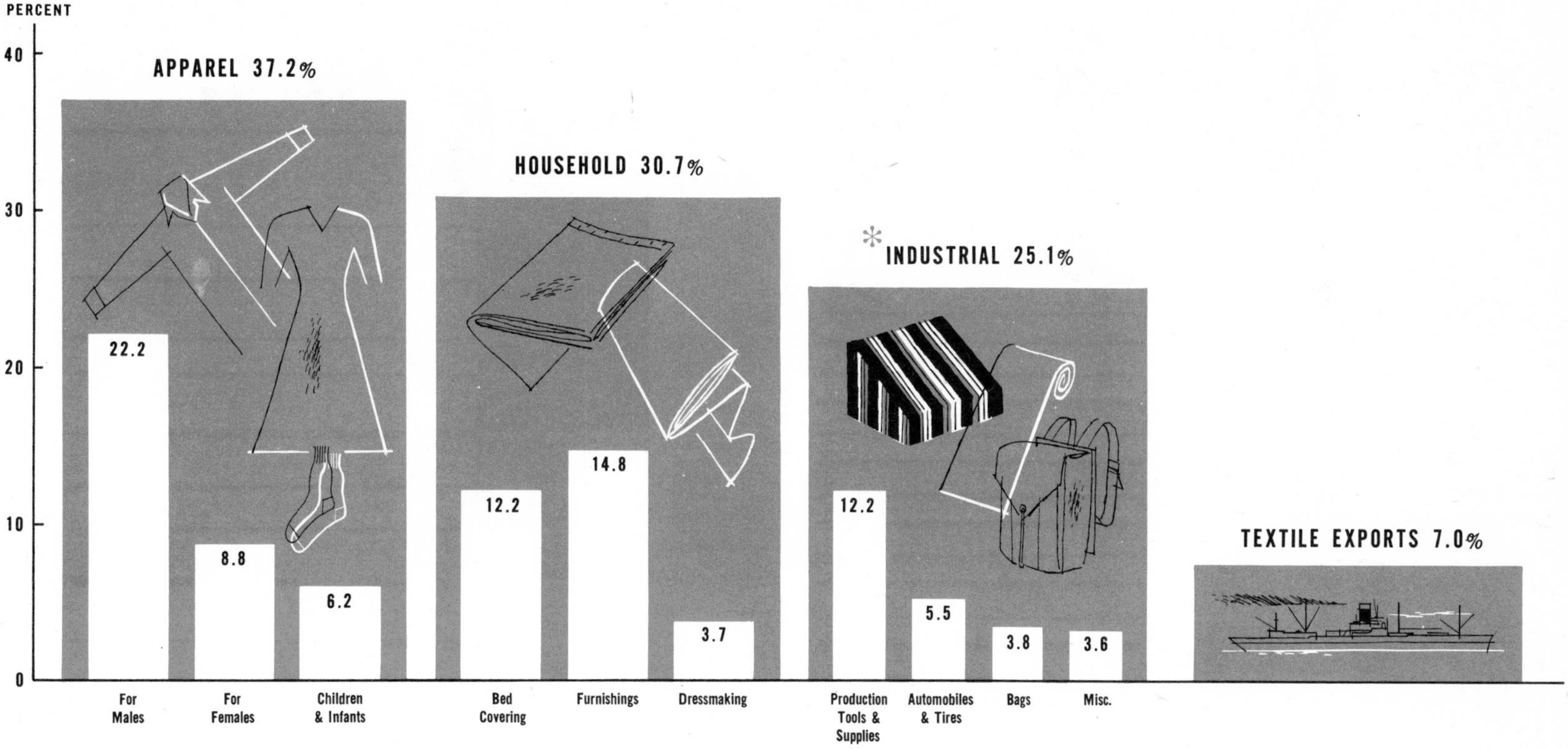

PERCENT

40
30
20
10
0

APPAREL 37.2%

For Males	For Females	Children & Infants
22.2	8.8	6.2

HOUSEHOLD 30.7%

Bed Covering	Furnishings	Dressmaking
12.2	14.8	3.7

*** INDUSTRIAL 25.1%**

Production Tools & Supplies	Automobiles & Tires	Bags	Misc.
12.2	5.5	3.8	3.6

TEXTILE EXPORTS 7.0%

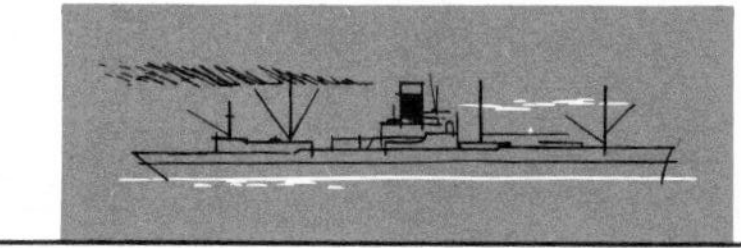

* Production tools . . . Items used in production of goods and services

Production supplies . Items used as auxiliary material in production of noncotton goods

Miscellaneous . . . . Includes sporting goods, mattress felts, medical supplies, and canvas goods

Seed Cotton

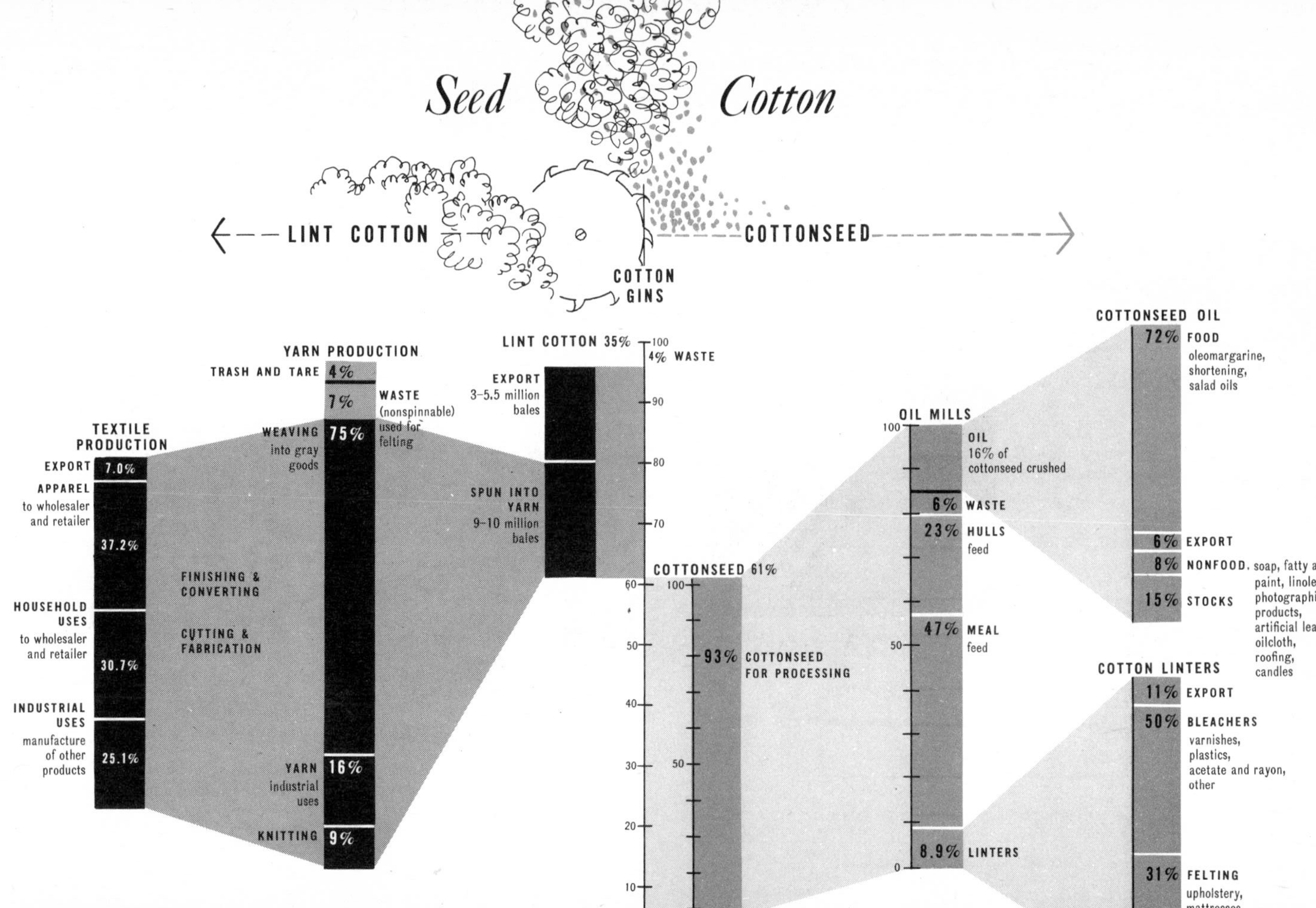

LINT COTTON
COTTONSEED
COTTON GINS
TEXTILE PRODUCTION
EXPORT 7.0%
APPAREL to wholesaler and retailer 37.2%
HOUSEHOLD USES to wholesaler and retailer 30.7%
INDUSTRIAL USES manufacture of other products 25.1%
FINISHING & CONVERTING
CUTTING & FABRICATION
YARN PRODUCTION
TRASH AND TARE 4%
WASTE (nonspinnable) used for felting 7%
WEAVING into gray goods 75%
YARN industrial uses 16%
KNITTING 9%
LINT COTTON 35%
4% WASTE
EXPORT 3–5.5 million bales
SPUN INTO YARN 9–10 million bales
COTTONSEED 61%
93% COTTONSEED FOR PROCESSING
OIL MILLS
OIL 16% of cottonseed crushed
6% WASTE
23% HULLS feed
47% MEAL feed
8.9% LINTERS
COTTONSEED OIL
72% FOOD oleomargarine, shortening, salad oils
6% EXPORT
8% NONFOOD. soap, fatty acids, paint, linoleum, photographic products, artificial leather, oilcloth, roofing, candles
15% STOCKS
COTTON LINTERS
11% EXPORT
50% BLEACHERS varnishes, plastics, acetate and rayon, other
31% FELTING upholstery, mattresses

directly concerned with raw cotton fiber and cottonseed and financed by them.

Since the middle 1920's few promising means of improving the situation have been left untried. The losses in markets and the accumulation of surplus stocks meant that greatest effort was directed toward improving the market situation. Among the developments were additional and more timely market information, including Government estimates of the quality of the crop and the carryover; research to improve ginning services; research to develop and encourage more efficient marketing methods, procedures, and processes and to provide new and expanded uses; market price supports, acreage allotments, and marketing quotas; and loans, grants, and other aid and assistance to foreign countries to strengthen the export markets.

Most groups directly concerned with cotton have been giving special attention to the various properties of cotton and how they can be utilized to better advantage. As a result, the precision measurements of fiber fineness and strength are now used commercially to a considerable extent in the marketing of cotton. By the use of laboratory measurements of cotton fiber properties and of yarns and fabrics, some of the larger merchants are now helping their customers determine the most desirable qualities of cotton for making particular products, a service similar to one the producers of synthetic fibers have provided for a number of years. Many cotton mills are also giving increasing attention to this method of providing better quality control and of increasing their processing efficiency.

Despite the large amount of effort that has been made to improve and utilize more effectively the various fiber properties and to increase the efficiencies and reduce the costs of the ginning, merchandising, manufacturing, and other marketing services involved, American cotton has been barely holding its own in the battle for domestic and foreign markets. The total domestic mill consumption of cotton has tended to increase since 1930, but when reduced to a per capita basis, it has not shown an upward trend. During this period, the favorable influence of increasing economic activity and higher consumer incomes on per capita consumption of cotton has been counterbalanced by per capita gains in consumption of synthetic fiber, paper, and plastics. As a result, consumption of cotton per person in 1952 was only slightly higher than it was in the late 1920's.

Exports of our cotton have declined since 1930 because many of the same competitive forces in our own markets are found also in foreign markets and because of foreign competition and efforts of other countries to conserve dollars by limiting imports.

There is a greater realization than ever before that producers, consumers, and providers of marketing services are all affected by the cost and efficiencies involved from the time the soil is prepared for planting until the finished cotton products reach the consumer. The cotton industry realizes that reductions in any or all of those costs, particularly if quality improves, will enable our cotton to gain or maintain larger domestic and export markets with resulting benefits to all groups. (*Maurice R. Cooper, Frank Lowenstein.*)

Fats and Oils

Large amounts of fats and oils are used in foods, paints for houses and automobiles, sizing for clothes and

Comparative Costs in Processing the Two Major Oilseeds and One Minor Oil Crop

AVERAGE FOR MILLS FOR 1948–49

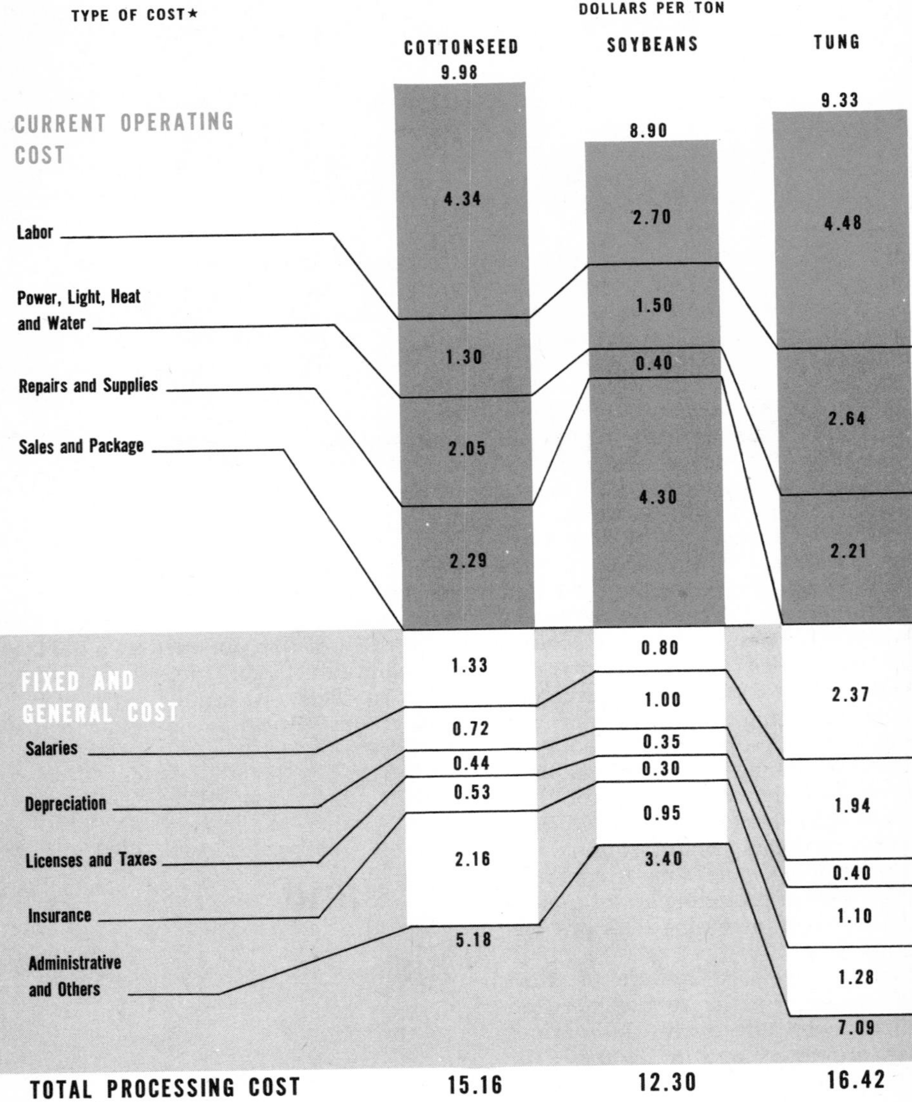

★ Soybeans processed by screw-press process 55.3 percent, by solvent extraction 39.6 percent, by hydraulic-press process 5.[illegible] percent. Cottonseed, primarily hydraulic-press process. Tung mills, screw-press operations only.

UNITED STATES FOREIGN TRADE IN

Fats, Oils and Oil-bearing Materials

(Oil equivalent)

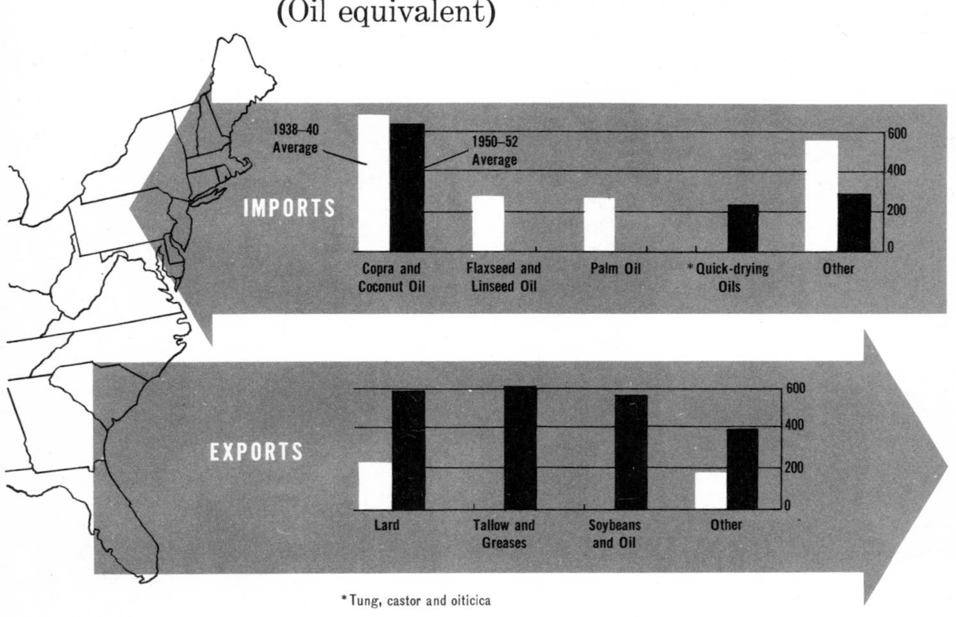

other textiles, and in soaps, linoleums, lubricants, plastics, steel rolling, medicinal and cosmetic materials, and in scores of other products.

The production of fats and oils from domestic materials has increased by more than a third since the late 1930's, in keeping with sharp increases in soybeans, flaxseed, lard, and the inedible tallow and grease from slaughter of livestock. The United States therefore has shifted from a net importer to a substantial net exporter.

Domestic oilseeds worth more than 1.3 billion dollars are crushed for oil and meal each year in nearly 600 mills throughout the country. Domestic animal fats, including butter, are valued at an equal amount.

In terms of value, more than half of the oilseeds are soybeans, produced mainly in the Midwest. Cottonseed forms one-third. The remainder includes flaxseed, mainly from Minnesota and North Dakota; corn germs, a byproduct of the cornstarch industry; peanuts crushed for oil; and tung nuts. The last are grown in a strip 100 miles wide along the Gulf of Mexico. Some castor beans have been produced domestically, chiefly in the Southwest and California, since 1951. Safflower, sunflower, sesame, and rapeseed are produced in small amounts.

More than 60 percent of the fats and oils we use are consumed as food. Butter and most of the lard are used in the same form as produced. Cottonseed and soybean oils are used mainly in shortening and margarine and as salad and cooking oils. Other important edible oils are corn, peanut, and olive. Coconut oil, mainly from the Philippines, is used chiefly as a quick-lathering oil in soap and synthetic detergents and for other specialized industrial uses. It is

Fats and Oils Used in Specified Products (1950-52 Average)

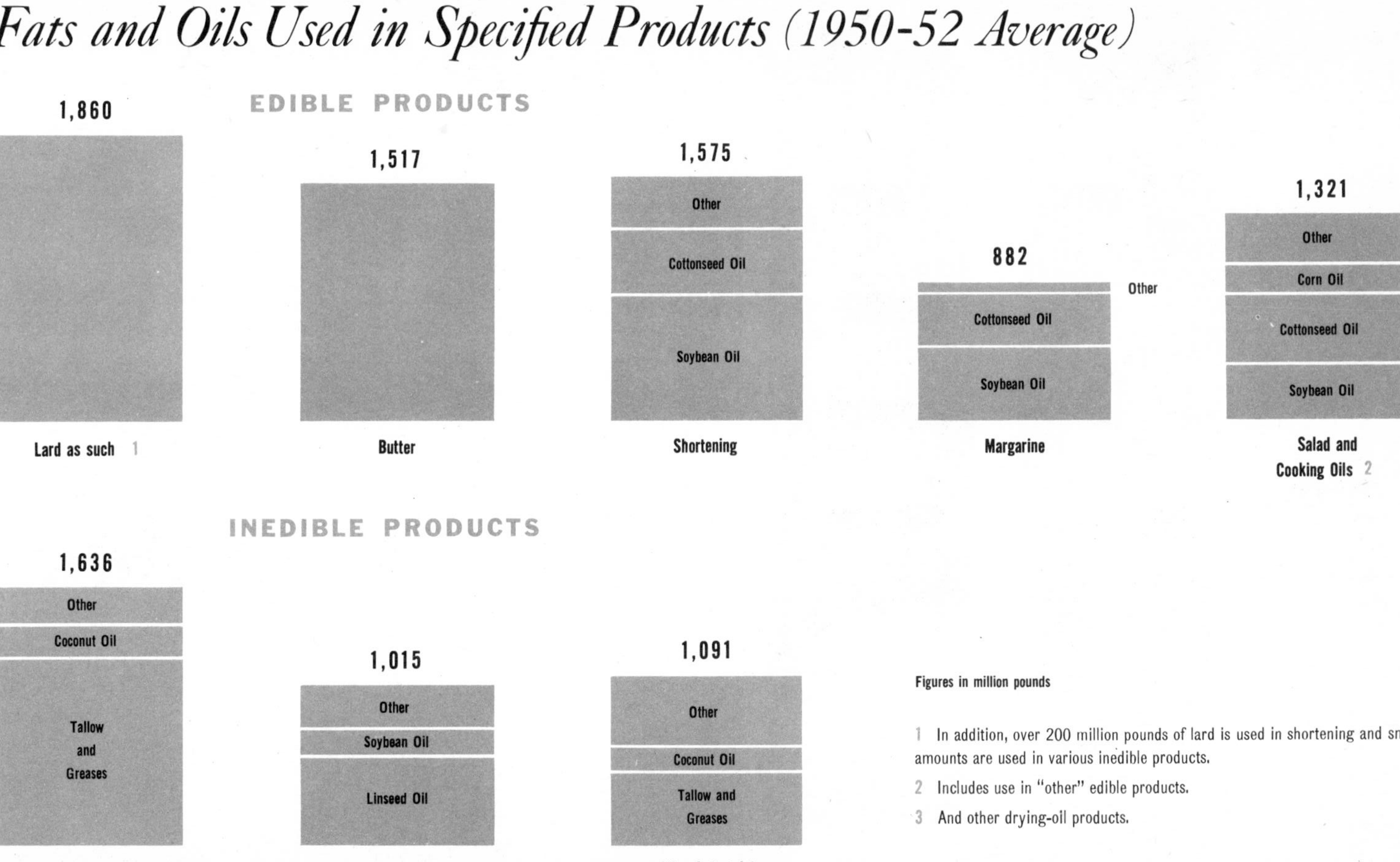

Figures in million pounds

1 In addition, over 200 million pounds of lard is used in shortening and small amounts are used in various inedible products.

2 Includes use in "other" edible products.

3 And other drying-oil products.

Oil Mills, 1953, CRUSHING *MAJOR VEGETABLE OILSEEDS

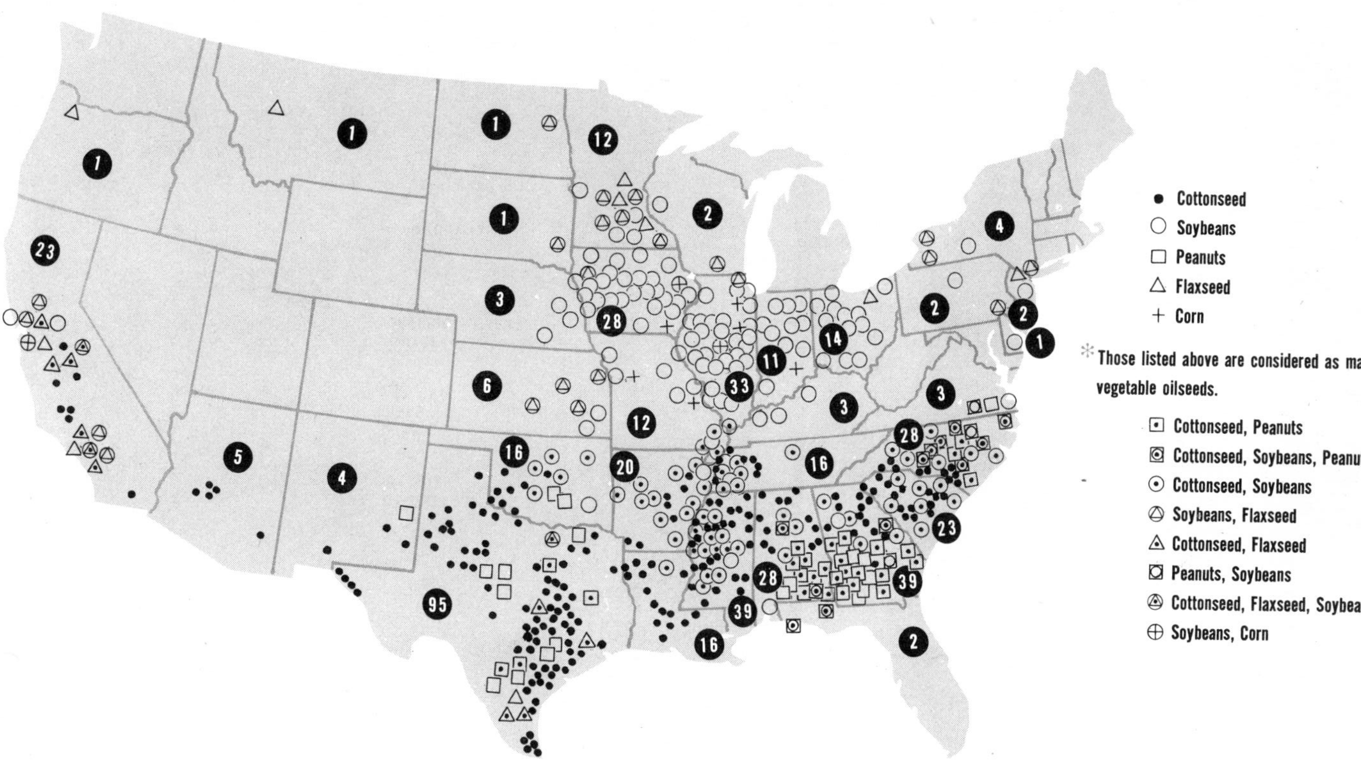

Figures indicate total number of mills in each State. United States total, 494. Nineteen mills crush both major and minor vegetable oilseeds.

Flow Chart for Soybeans and Soybean Oil

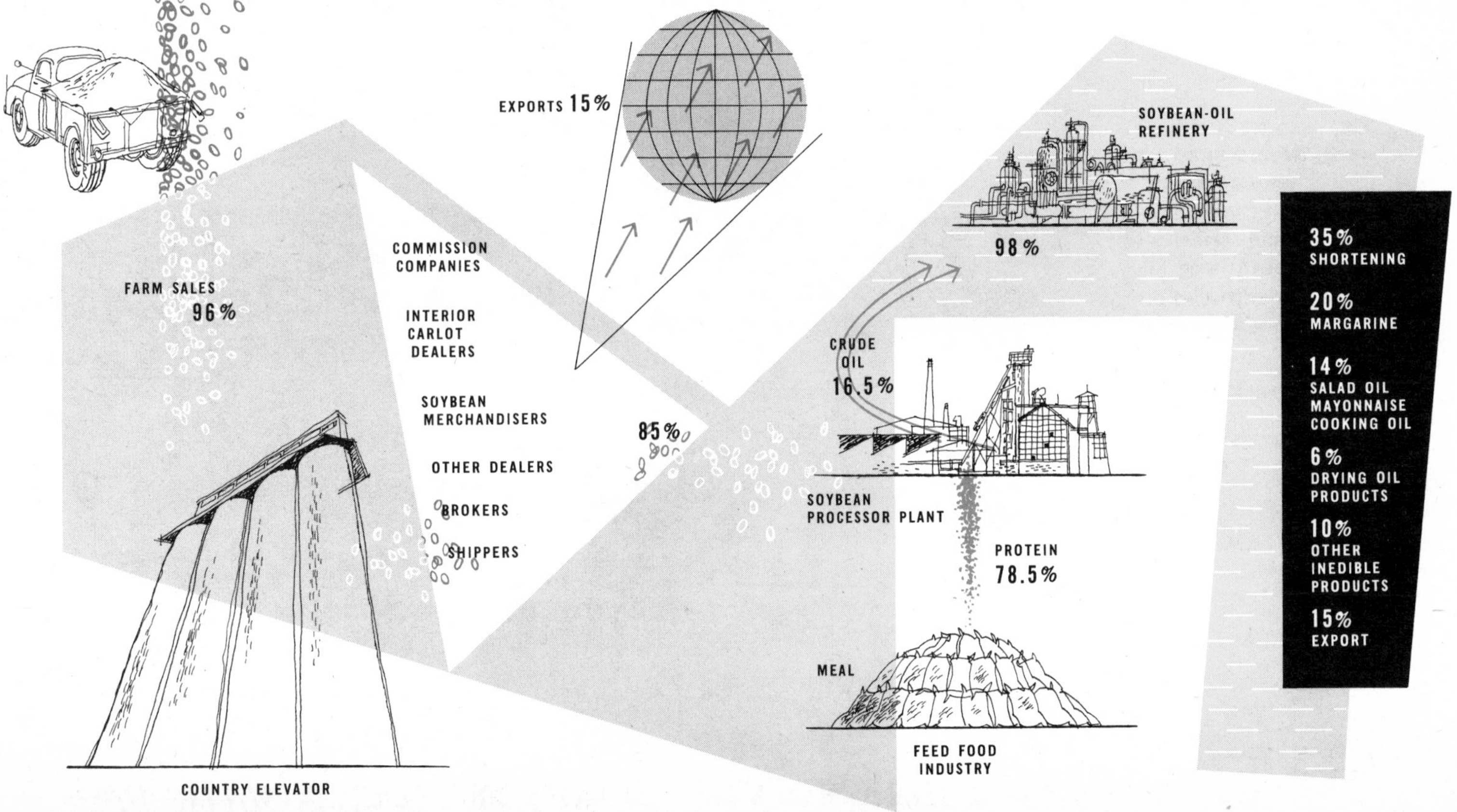

FARM SALES 96%

COUNTRY ELEVATOR

COMMISSION COMPANIES

INTERIOR CARLOT DEALERS

SOYBEAN MERCHANDISERS

OTHER DEALERS

BROKERS

SHIPPERS

EXPORTS 15%

85%

SOYBEAN PROCESSOR PLANT

CRUDE OIL 16.5%

PROTEIN 78.5%

MEAL

FEED FOOD INDUSTRY

SOYBEAN-OIL REFINERY

98%

35% SHORTENING

20% MARGARINE

14% SALAD OIL MAYONNAISE COOKING OIL

6% DRYING OIL PRODUCTS

10% OTHER INEDIBLE PRODUCTS

15% EXPORT

used also in sugar coatings by confectioners and bakers and in sweetened wafer fillings.

Major soap oils, other than coconut, are tallow and grease and "foots," the residue left after oil refining. Linseed oil (from flaxseed) is the major drying oil. It is used in paints and varnishes, printing ink, synthetic resins, linoleum, oilcloth, and numerous other products. Substantial amounts of soybean oil and such quick-drying oils as tung, dehydrated castor, and oiticica are used similarly.

Before the Second World War the major fat exported was lard. Copra and coconut oil dominated imports. Imports of flaxseed, chiefly from Argentina, exceeded domestic production in most years before 1940.

The major factors that put this country in a net exporting position in fats and oils after the war were the expansion of domestic production of oilseeds and animal fats, increasing consumption of fats and oils in surplus-producing countries such as India, a cutting-off of international supplies of Manchurian soybeans and Chinese tung oil from Asia, and international restrictions on the catching of whales. At the same time the increasing use of products made from substitute raw materials, such as rubber-base paints and synthetic detergents, has reduced the domestic demand for some fats and oils.

Soybeans are the country's largest oilseed crop. Normally at harvesttime, prices of soybeans are depressed, freight cars are scarce, and handling facilities at the country and terminal elevators are congested. Increased storage by farmers would have earned for them extra profits in 3 out of 4 postwar years. For example, peak soybean prices averaged 20 percent more than prices at harvest over the first 4 years after the Second World War.

About 90 percent of the soybeans go through country elevators. Movement from there to oil mills is usually by rail, but trucking has become feasible in some places. Railroads give most soybean oil mills a processing-in-transit privilege, which provides the soybean industry with advantageous rates on soybeans and products and permits mills to procure beans and sell meal at a distance on a more favorable basis.

Most soybeans are processed by the solvent method, which recovers more oil than the older screw-press method. Hydraulic mills, which are relatively inefficient for processing soybeans, do process small amounts in the South.

Of the 1951 crop, 74 percent was processed by the solvent method, 25 percent by screw press, and 1 percent by hydraulic mills.

About 190 mills with a monthly capacity of slightly more than 28 million bushels processed soybeans from the 1951 crop; 57 of them also processed cottonseed, 7 flaxseed, and 3 corn germs. Approximately half of the mills were located in the four major soybean-producing States. Crops in 1952 and 1953, with more than 200 million bushels available for processing, required less than three-fourths of this capacity.

The widely varying processing costs for soybeans appear to be closely associated with the volume processed, as is generally true for all oilseeds.

The first of several marketing problems is to maintain outlets against the inroads of synthetic products, particularly in soaps and cleaners, paints and varnishes, and emulsifiers. The production of vegetable and animal fats and oils has increased without an accompanying increase in demand since the end of the Second World War. Research has been undertaken on the economic possibilities of using more oils in livestock feeds and the chemical industries, on the technical aspects of agricultural fats in synthetic detergents and emulsifiers, and on the advantages and disadvantages of specific oils in the drying-oil field.

Another problem is the maintenance of quality of the various fats and oils from producer to finished product. Examples are the maintenance of quality of lard and prevention of reversion of the flavor of soybean oil.

A study of physical and chemical characteristics of soybeans related to outturn values indicated that variation in soybeans of the 1950 crop was equivalent to 60 cents in outturn value; split and damaged soybeans contained more oil per bushel than did whole beans, but the oil in such beans deteriorated faster in storage; and that moisture and foreign material alone would give an evaluation more equitable than the customary discount schedule or the "grading" methods of most country elevators.

Wide fluctuations in prices after the Second World War tended to discourage use of inedible tallow and grease in the development of new products. Their markets have suffered as a result of increased raw materials and better extraction methods at a time when their markets were being invaded by synthetics. Government agencies and private industry have started research in their expanded use in synthetic detergents, plastics, plasticizers, lubricants, and other products. Low prices have made them a worldwide bargain. Exports totaled 433 million pounds in 1949, 748 million in 1952, and 1,197 million in 1953, compared with less than 100 million a year in the preceding 2 decades.

Relative amounts of cottonseed and soybean oil in margarine and shortening largely depend on the relative prices of the two oils. The quantity of soybean oil converted for use in drying oils depends mainly on the relative price of linseed oil. The supply of peanut oil is especially unstable. Competition of azelaic acid from animal fats and sebacic acid from castor oil for use in special lubricants depends on relative prices and upon physical availability. A study of interchangeability must continually evaluate the needs of our expanding economy, including limited but highly critical needs, such as aviation requirements for specialized products. (*C. B. Gilliland*, *Richard J. Foote*.)

Wool

Wool is produced on approximately 285,000 farms and ranches in the United States. Farm flocks of fewer than 300 sheep account for more than one-third of the total domestic clip. About 70 percent of our shorn wool comes from the Western States and Texas. Texas alone accounts for some 20 percent of the total. Other leading producers are Wyoming, California, Montana, Utah, Colorado, New Mexico, Idaho, Ohio, Minnesota, South Dakota, Iowa, Missouri, New York, Pennsylvania, Kentucky, and Tennessee.

Western wools are known in the trade as Territory wools. Wools from Texas are known as Texas wools. Those produced in other parts of the country are called Fleece wools.

About a third of the sheep in Texas are shorn both in the spring and the fall. Some sections of California also produce two clips a year, but the rest of the sheep in the country are shorn only once, in the spring or early summer.

The fleeces mostly are tied with paper twine as shorn, on the ranch or farm, generally packaged in burlap bags 6 or 7 feet long, and sent to market. Bags of wool may weigh 100 to 350 pounds, depending on where the wools were produced, the grade, and the method and care used in packaging.

Our total annual production now is about 270 million pounds, of which 85 percent is shorn from live sheep. The rest is pulled from pelts of slaughtered animals.

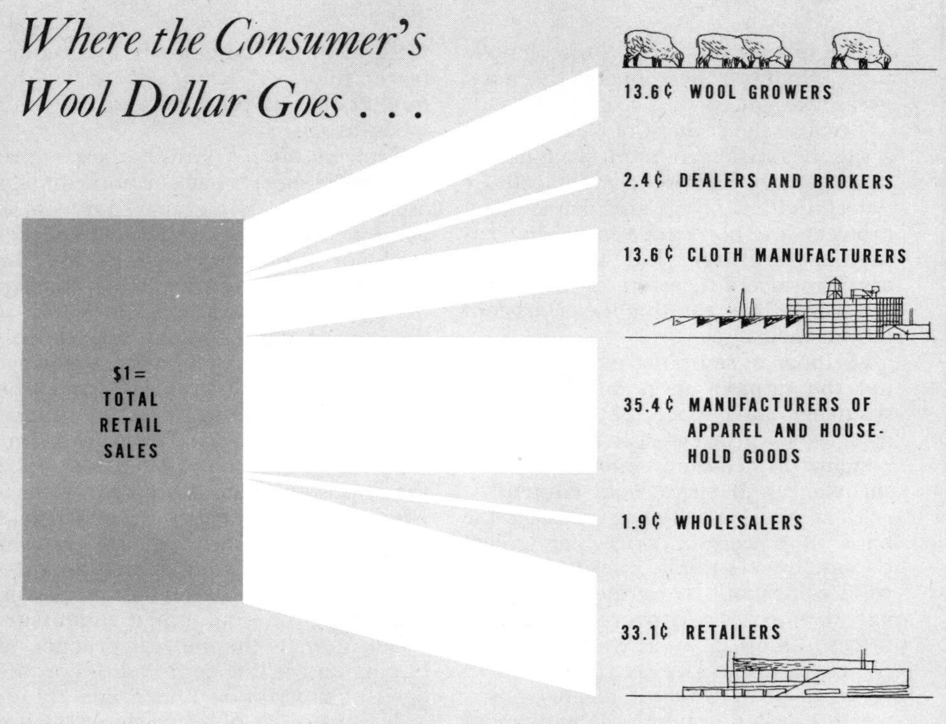

Wool is classified in the market primarily on the basis of its fineness and staple length. Strength, color, crimp, softness, and uniformity also influence its value and utility. Wool varies widely in fineness and staple length. In the marketing process it is customary to group like fleeces together. Such grading may be done occasionally on the ranch, but generally grading is performed in a warehouse where space, better handling facilities, and trained graders are available. The purpose of grading is to improve the marketability of wool by providing manufacturers and buyers with uniform lots, for which they are willing to pay higher prices. When a manufacturer acquires ungraded, mixed wool he buys it at a price that takes into consideration the costs he will have to incur in separating the wools he wants from the wools that are unsuited to his needs and may have to be resold at a loss.

Fineness, staple length, and other characteristics vary greatly between fleeces. The wool in the same fleece is not all of uniform quality. Wool from the back of the sheep is finer than wool from the britch. Before processing, therefore, each fleece in each grade lot may need to be separated into its constituent qualities, a process known as sorting.

Wool as it comes from the sheep is known as grease wool, wool in the grease, or raw wool. Such wool contains a certain amount of impurities, including grease, dirt, suint, and vegetable matter—components that are referred to as shrinkage. Depending on the breed of sheep, the area, and the husbandry, shrinkage will vary between lots of wool from 30 percent to more than 70 percent of the total grease weight.

Because the content of clean wool is a significant determinant of value, an important problem concerns accurate determination of the shrinkage. Most growers are not experienced in estimating shrinkage, but most buyers are. Producers therefore are at a disadvantage in evaluating the clean content in their clips.

Methods of sampling wool and testing the samples in a laboratory for shrinkage have been developed, but most wool growers still sell without benefit of accurate information on shrinkage and clean wool content.

Most growers sell their clips on the basis of a certain price per grease pound. Buyers think in terms of clean wool values, but by estimating shrinkage they readily convert clean wool prices to a grease basis by multiplying the clean wool price by the estimated yield of clean wool. If clean wool is worth 1 dollar a pound and a given lot of grease wool is estimated to shrink 50 percent, the grease-wool price is 50 cents a pound. If the shrinkage is estimated to be 55 percent, the grease-wool price would be 45 cents a pound. Methods by which shrinkage can be determined economically and accurately are therefore highly important to wool growers. Some growers have commercial laboratories sample and test their wool for shrinkage before offering it for sale.

Another marketing problem concerns the determination of fiber fineness, length, and other characteristics that establish value and usefulness of wool. Generally they are determined entirely by eye, and because experienced wool men do not always agree on quality and grade, most wool growers are at a disadvantage also in this determination. Techniques and procedures for sampling and testing for quality factors are available, but few wool manufacturers use them when buying raw wool.

The basic marketing problem for wool growers therefore is to become better informed about shrinkage, the quality of their product, and how and when to sell.

Growers often contract their entire clip on the sheep's back or immediately after shearing. Sometimes the wool is consigned to a local dealer, warehouseman, or cooperative association for sale. Again, the grower may consign his wool to a central market dealer. If the grower sells his wool on the sheep's back or immediately after shearing, the sale is made "as is," and the grower relies on competition among buyers for a fair price. If a grower consigns his wool it may be sold "as is" if the clip is considered uniform. Otherwise it probably will be graded before sale. In either instance, the grower depends on the competence and the integrity of the consignee in preparing and selling the wool to best advantage.

Contrary to the general practice of buying and selling commodities on the basis of description and grade standards, most sales of domestic wools are made on inspection. Each time a lot of wool changes hands, the buyer inspects it because he must satisfy himself that the wools are suitable for his particular purpose. Because all buyers do not see the same quality factors in a particular lot of wool, a given lot may be called one grade in one transaction and a somewhat different grade in another.

Standards for fineness of grades of grease wool have been developed by the Department of Agriculture for use as guides in grading fleeces and for sorting. The established grades are on a visual basis and the grade of any given lot of wool is determined by comparison with the official samples. Even though a physical sample of each grade is available, however, it often is difficult to make precise comparisons. With the present broad grade classes and the relatively little knowledge of wool qualities on the part of most growers, market news and price reports for wool sometimes are confusing and do not always serve as an effective guide to growers in

Grease Wool Production in the United States

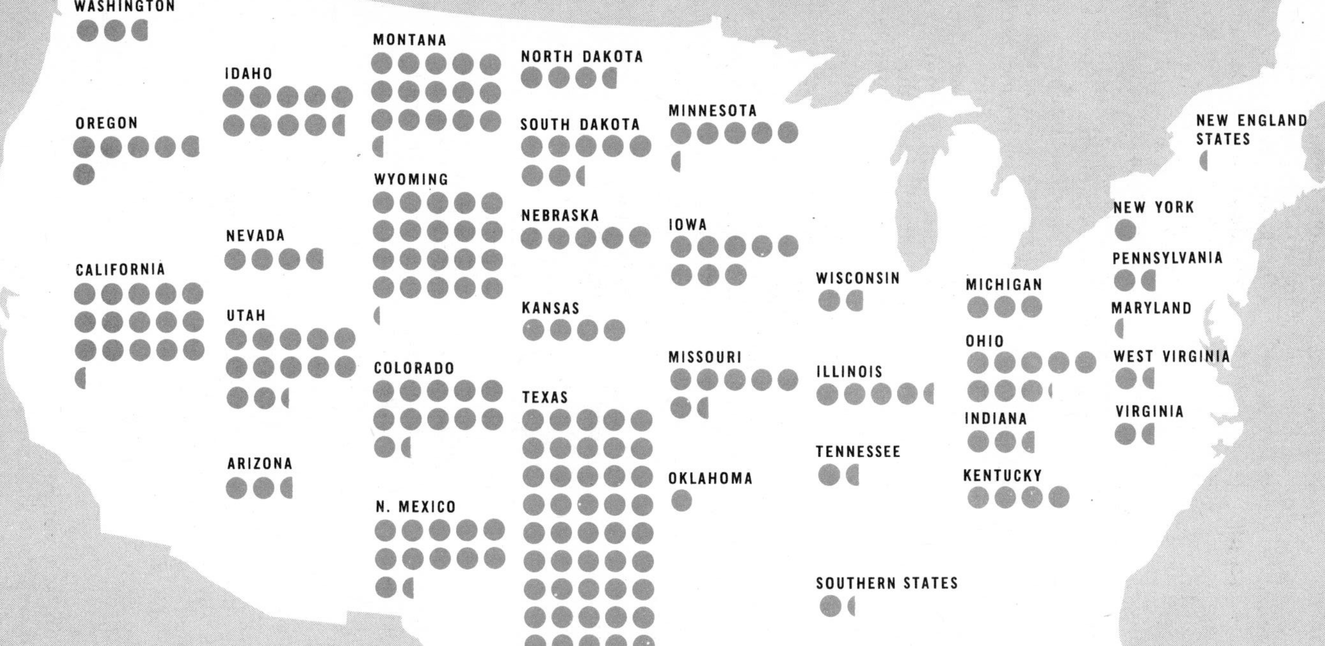

determining their marketing policies.

Wool top—wool after it has been washed, carded, and combed—is more uniform than the original raw wool. The specifications for fineness of grades of top can be expressed in precise terms. Combing is a process whereby the carded wool is passed through a machine which blends and parallelizes the fibers. Since grease wool generally is subjected to grading and some sorting before combing, there is a problem in relating grease-wool grade specifications to those developed for wool top.

The major domestic trade center for wool is Boston. Most market quotations are based on Boston prices. Buyers purchasing wool in the country deduct the freight to Boston in computing the prices they pay growers for their wools at their farms and ranches.

Among other market centers are Philadelphia, Chicago, San Francisco, and Portland. Philadelphia is regarded sometimes as the major market for scoured wool. With the exception of Portland, these market centers have little or no wool manufacturing except for small knitting and specialty-fabric mills. A large proportion of the wool has been and now is processed by mills in New England and the Middle Atlantic areas, although there has been a considerable movement of wool manufacturing to Southeastern States.

Middlemen between grower and manufacturer include the local buyers, warehousemen, cooperative marketing associations, regional wool dealers, order buyers, and merchants at terminal markets. The dealers, buyers, and merchants generally sell to other middlemen or manufacturers. Some dealers and merchants handle wool for growers on consignment. Wool warehousemen and cooperative marketing associations usually act as the agents for the growers and handle and sell their wool on a consignment commission basis.

Manufacturers commonly employ their own buyers, but sometimes they place orders with buyers who ar known as order buyers and who pur chase wool mostly from growers an warehousemen for manufacturers' ac counts. Some order buying is done o a brokerage basis; the manufacture pays the buyer a commission. Mor often the manufacturer gives the orde buyer a price limit and the order buye makes his margin of profit by pur chasing wool at prices less than th agreed price.

Growers often are faced with a prob lem in determining what type c sales agency to use in marketing thei wool. Until such time as clips and lo of wool can be sampled and tested fo all quality factors and transactions ca be based upon accurate description, i is desirable from the growers' stand point to have as many buyers as pos sible compete for the business.

Wool can be stored for several year with little deterioration if it is pro tected against the elements and insec damage. Large clips of wool seldon are stored on the farm or ranch. Im mediately after shearing, wool eithe is shipped from the producing area o stored in a local warehouse. In som States, the local warehouseman ofte stores wool at a small cost if the lot i consigned to him for sale. Other loca and central market handlers charg a fee of about 30 cents a bag a mont for storage.

The domestic market may be in active for months and only small ton nages may be sold, within narrov price ranges, to mills and top makers

Then overnight the market migh burst into activity; millions of pound might be sold in a few days, with a types of buyers and sellers participat ing. A dull market is not necessarily lower market, and an active marke does not always mean higher prices A steady and reliable market, with a even flow of wool to manufacturers an top makers throughout the year, woul be of benefit to wool growers.

Wool is made into yarns and the into different types of fabrics. Wool that are made into top before spinnin

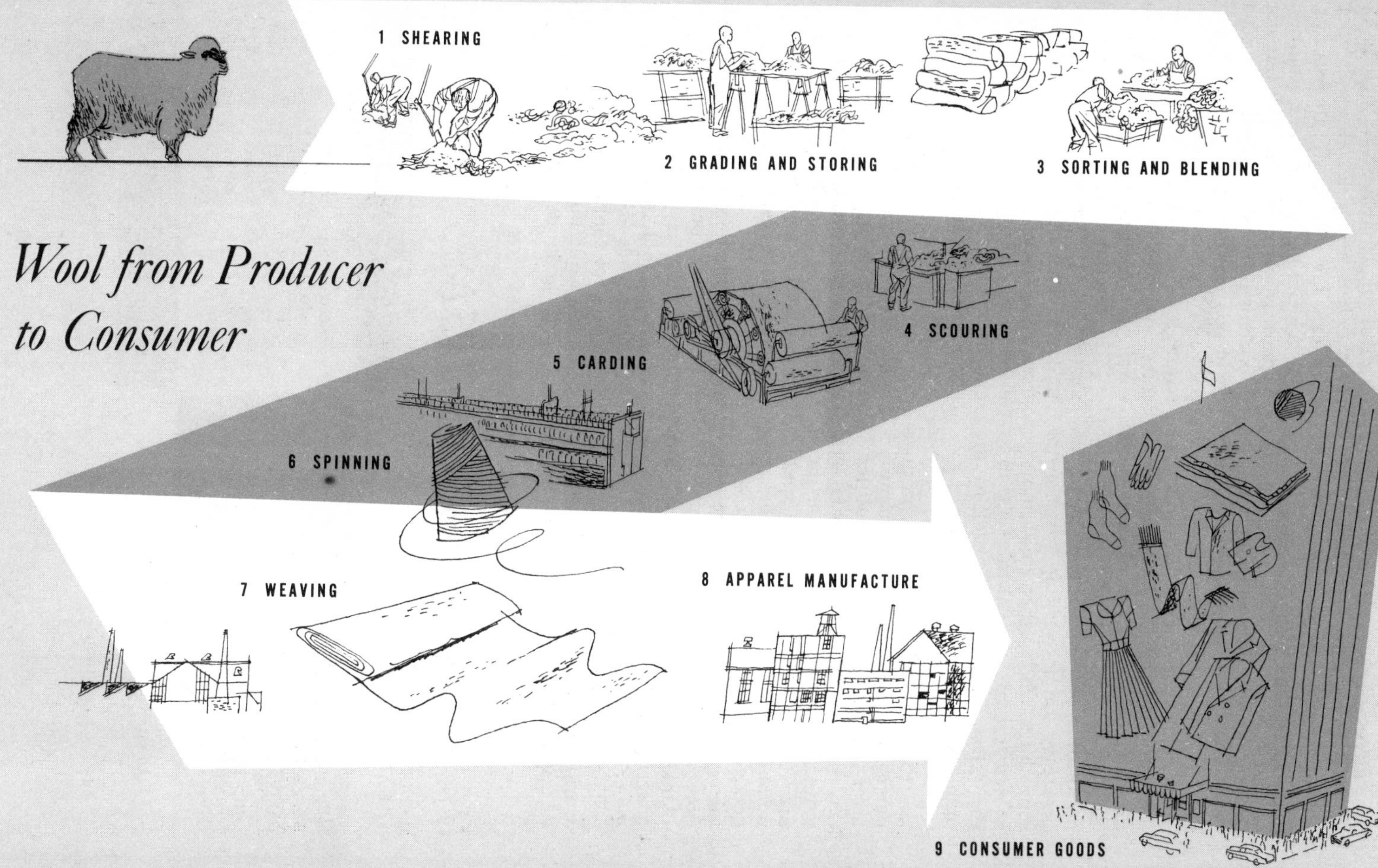
Wool from Producer to Consumer
1 SHEARING
2 GRADING AND STORING
3 SORTING AND BLENDING
4 SCOURING
5 CARDING
6 SPINNING
7 WEAVING
8 APPAREL MANUFACTURE
9 CONSUMER GOODS

are said to be processed on the worsted system. Wools that are merely carded and then spun into yarn are processed on the woolen system.

Top makers purchase grease wool, convert it into top in their own or another mill, and sell tops. Some mills specialize in custom combing. Other mills make yarn; they acquire wool top and carry out the spinning operations. Textile mills processing wool may be specialized to the extent of performing only one of the operations necessary for converting grease wool into cloth, while other mills may be geared to carry out all the steps from the purchase of grease wool to the manufacture and sale of fabrics.

Manufacturers try to buy wool that has the qualities needed to produce particular types of fabrics. A manufacturer may blend different qualities of raw wool or he may mix wool and cotton or wool and some artificial fiber. Wool mills sell fabrics to apparel manufacturers who make up consumer goods for distribution through wholesalers and retailers. Almost the entire domestic clip is used for apparel or blankets. Wools for carpets and floor coverings are of the coarser grades and generally are imported.

The domestic price for wool reflects world supplies and demand. Imports of apparel wools have been subjected to a duty that has been as high as 34 cents a clean pound for all wools finer than 44's. The 1953 tariff rate was 25.5 cents a clean pound for these qualities. Apparel wools finer than 40's but not finer than 44's had a duty of 17 cents a clean pound; those not finer than 40's paid 13 cents a clean pound. Imported scoured wools carried slightly higher rates. Wools imported for use in carpets were duty-free.

Most foreign clips are graded and partly sorted, and the lots are quite uniform. They also generally are free from black fibers, so that the tops processed from them are suitable for any end use.

Domestic clips are not uniformly well prepared for market. Therefore the cost of converting them into top generally is higher than the cost of converting foreign grease wool. Domestic wools (because of breeding) often contain black fibers (which show up in pastel or light shades) so that the top has a more restricted range of uses.

Consequently, one of the marketing problems is to determine the economic feasibility of better preparation of clips by growers before sale, by exercising care in handling black fleeces, by eliminating all tags, off sorts, and locks of wool containing nonscourable branding paint, and by offering a more uniform and attractive product to

World Production of Wool, 1951-53

MILLIONS OF POUNDS GREASE BASIS	1951	1952	1953[1]
Argentina	420.0	407.0	420.0
Australia	1,080.0	1,280.0	1,310.0
New Zealand	406.7	418.0	421.0
Union of South Africa	240.0	256.8	268.0
United States	251.4	266.0	271.3
Uruguay	187.4	190.0	195.0
Other countries	1,464.5	1,512.2	1,531.0
Estimated world total	4,050.0	4,330.0	4,416.3

[1] Subject to revision.

mills and manufacturers. For individual small operators, the cost involved in better preparation probably would not return a profit. Such small clips, however, might be pooled into sufficient quantities to make better preparation feasible. Large sheep ranchers should find it advantageous to market their clips on the basis of uniformity in fineness and length of staple. Black wool, tags, and rejects always should be packaged separately, regardless of size of the clip.

Because of high labor costs in preparing wool for manufacture, the old type of meticulous sorting of domestic wools no longer is practiced except in special cases. In its place a procedure known as trap sorting has been substituted, whereby only tags, off sorts, and any clearly unsuitable portions of the fleece are removed prior to processing. Such work normally is performed in the mill. Even without the higher cost of preparing domestic wool for manufacture, however, foreign wools still enjoy a competitive advantage, primarily because of the wider range of end uses and the fact that extra time and money need not be spent in eliminating black fibers from the fabrics.

No significant difference in basic quality between foreign and domestic wools has been determined.

The Federal Government has employed several means of supporting wool prices, in addition to tariff legislation. The "Buy American Act" of 1933 and the Berry Amendment to the Defense Appropriations Act of 1952 required that preference be given to domestic wools in the manufacture of wool items for the Armed Forces. The Government wool purchase plan, initiated in 1943, was aimed at securing an adequate supply and efficient distribution of wool to meet wartime needs.

After the war, a purchase program was directed toward supporting the price of wool and halting the downward trend in sheep numbers in this country which had started in 1942. Then the Agricultural Act of 1949 directed the Secretary of Agriculture to support domestic wool prices up to 90 percent of parity to encourage a domestic production of 360 million pounds of shorn wool. The quantity of wools purchased by the Government under the programs has ranged from nothing to practically 100 percent of the domestic clip.

In 1952 the wool price-support activity was changed from purchase to a nonrecourse loan program. Under that plan, clips and lots of wool are appraised by the Government, and growers obtain a loan reflecting 90 percent of the parity price as defined for the particular grade and quality offered. (*H. H. Hulbert*, *P. L. Slagsvold*.)

Eggs and Poultry

The average American family in 1953 ate 150 dozen eggs, the annual yield of 11 chickens; 20 broilers and 8 other chickens; a turkey; and perhaps a duck or a goose or a guinea. That supply amounted to about 400 eggs a person and about 36 pounds of poultry meat.

Chickens were kept on 78 percent of the 5.4 million farms enumerated in the 1950 Census of Agriculture, and at one season or another of the year most of those farms had eggs or chickens to sell. The number of farms reported as having chickens on hand was 4.2 million, compared with 3.6 million having one or more milk cows, 3.4 million growing corn for grain, and 3.8 million that had vegetable gardens.

But relatively few farms—only 173,000—can be called specialized poultry farms. Sixty-five percent of the eggs sold in the United States come from

281437°—54——31

Marketing Channels for Chickens

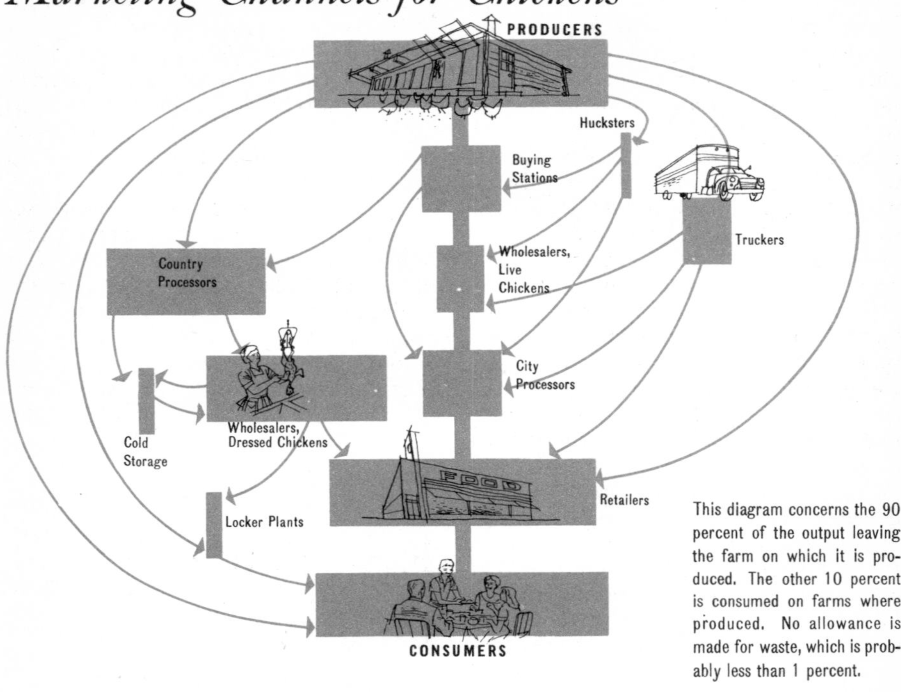

This diagram concerns the 90 percent of the output leaving the farm on which it is produced. The other 10 percent is consumed on farms where produced. No allowance is made for waste, which is probably less than 1 percent.

flocks of fewer than 400 layers. Such flocks typically round out the operations on general farms and by themselves are not large enough to support a family. Specialized poultry meat production, of broilers or turkeys, is more typically a large-scale operation than is egg production.

More than one-tenth of the eggs produced on farms in the United States, about 25 percent of the chickens (exclusive of broilers), and 1 percent of the turkeys are used on the farms that produce them. There is also a considerable production of nonfarm—backyard—chickens and eggs, estimated at about one-tenth of that produced on farms. Most of this backyard output probably is eaten by the families producing it, or, if it is marketed, it is delivered to the consumer through simple and direct marketing channels.

To get eggs, chickens, and turkeys from producer to consumer is often a matter of matching supply and demand over a wide area as well as over the entire year. The spanning of time and place poses problems in preserving quality as well as of mere holding or transit.

Generally the areas of greatest concentration of human population do not coincide precisely with the areas of heaviest production. Further, production of eggs and most poultry meats varies seasonally, whereas the demands for eggs and chicken are fairly uniform throughout the year. Also, the consumer prefers to buy poultry products in a somewhat more highly processed or closely graded form than that in which farmers usually sell them.

Changes in the marketing problems for eggs and poultry have dovetailed with changes in production practices. Some of the developments in produc-

Distribution of Eggs Produced on Farms

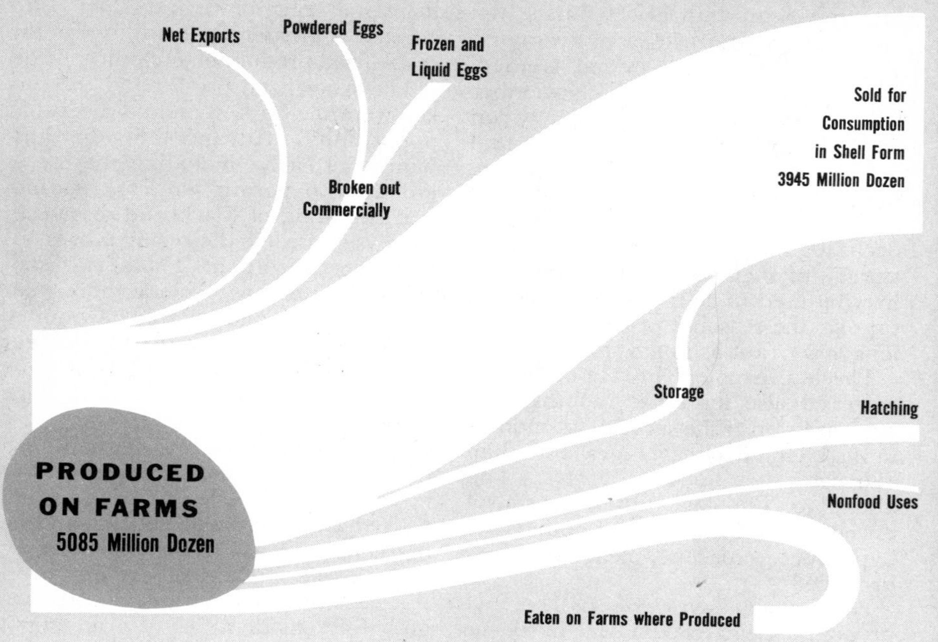

tion practices have in themselves been adaptations to a marketing problem, and it is well to review them in order to show what their effects are.

In a natural environment, the hen would lay some eggs in the spring and sit on them herself. Then her chicks, hatched in the spring, would have the benefit of the milder seasons for their growth and development before they were challenged by the first winter. Of course this natural cycle was somewhat upset, to man's advantage, when chickens were domesticated and at least partly relieved of the responsibility of scrounging for their own feed and shelter. It was upset further by systematic breeding to intensify the characteristics which make the hen economically worth while, as well as by the pathologists' efforts to preserve her from the diseases that plagued her when she roamed at will and from others that appeared when she was crowded into flocks of hundreds or thousands.

Enough of this natural cycle still persists—peak egg production and hatchings in spring and growth of young chickens in summer and fall—so that it is a dominant influence in the poultry industry. But commercial poultrymen are adapting their operations to take advantage of its economic consequences.

In the 1920's they began to take advantage of the discovery that the daily duration of light is the regulator of the bird's egg-laying process. Accordingly they put their layers under electric lights in the fall and winter. Artificial illumination for layers now is standard practice; with other innovations, it has boosted egg production per layer in November from 3 or 4 eggs during the 1920's to 12 in 1952.

Egg prices in November therefore are not so high now as they used to be in comparison with prices during the rest of the year. Instead of averaging 42 percent above the annual average, as they did in the 1920's, November egg prices to farmers now typically run at about 17 percent above the annual average. The seasonal variation in egg prices has been similarly affected at all levels of trade. As a further result, a declining phase of egg marketing is the storage of shell eggs for consumption in what used to be the months of short supply; the seasonal price changes no longer warrant as much storage.

The improvement in rate of lay has occurred also for other months. The present layer, if she survives 12 months in the laying flock, averages more than 180 eggs; her ancestor in 1925 laid about 90. For each dozen eggs produced, therefore, fewer pounds of byproduct chicken meat are now produced.

Poultry meat was essentially a byproduct of egg production until the early 1930's. The cockerels that were hatched with the pullets intended for egg production, and adult birds that had outlived their usefulness in the laying flocks, were the sources of Sunday chicken dinners. Their production was highly seasonal and was only modestly supplemented by roasting chickens that were grown especially for their meat, or by turkeys. No separate figures are available for roasting chickens, although in 1930 the turkey supply was less than 2 pounds per capita, compared with about 20 pounds of chicken.

As egg production per bird increased, the supply of byproduct chicken meat accompanying each dozen of eggs produced decreased. The relative decline in the supply of poultry meat was accentuated by the sexing of baby chicks. Sexed chicks are pullets and cockerels separated at hatching time according to sex, so that buyers who prefer only pullets need not rear the cockerels as well. The baby cockerels of the specialized egg-producing breeds often are destroyed rather than raised for meat. That development and the increased egg production per bird created a greater opportunity for the specialized production of poultry meat.

The specialized broiler and the turkey were the birds chosen to meet that opportunity. Advances in the husbandry of each—including the use of vitamins to permit winter brooding, and subduing of blackhead disease in turkeys—assisted their first moves toward specialization. Those two specialized birds now provide more than half of our annual supply of poultry meat. They have placed poultry meat in a marketing position where it must be thought of as an everyday dish rather than as a Sunday treat.

Most poultry products, eggs and live poultry in particular, require little or no commercial processing before being cooked and consumed—they could be marketed directly to the consumer by the appropriately located producer. But because of the nature, time, place, and different densities of production, and other factors, for most of the products it is more practical to depend for the processing and marketing upon a number of handlers between the producer and the consumer, each performing a service and adding to the price spread between the farm price and the consumer price. In 1953 the producers got an average of 73 percent and 53 percent, respectively, of the consumers' expenditures for eggs and poultry.

Most eggs receive no processing other than cleaning and sorting for quality and size before being packed in cases or cartons by the producers or market agencies and sold as shell eggs. A small portion of these shell eggs, particularly those intended for cold storage, however, are dipped in a tasteless, odorless oil to help preserve quality by sealing the pores of the shell, and another portion of the output is broken-out commercially, for use as liquid, frozen, or dried egg.

Large volumes of the eggs and poultry produced do not enter commercial

Regional Production of Eggs, Broilers, and Turkeys—1952

IN RELATION TO POPULATION

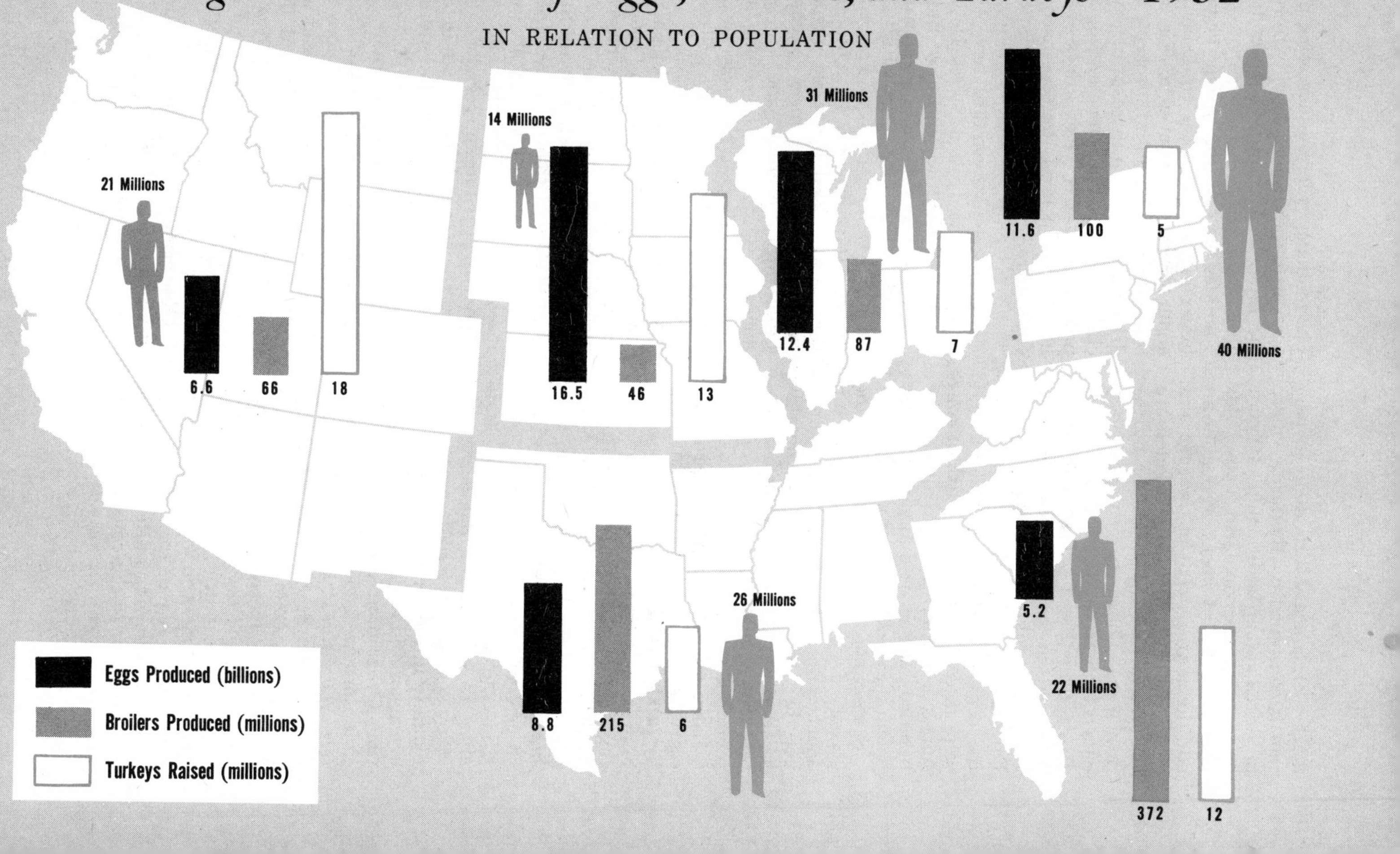

21 Millions
6.6
66
18

14 Millions
16.5
46
13

31 Millions
12.4
87
7

11.6
100
5
40 Millions

26 Millions
8.8
215
6

22 Millions
5.2
372
12

Eggs Produced (billions)
Broilers Produced (millions)
Turkeys Raised (millions)

market channels. More than 10 percent is consumed on the farms where produced and an additional 10 percent in or near the nonfarm households having backyard flocks. Probably an additional 10 percent of the eggs and 5 percent of the poultry marketed are sold directly to the consumer by the producer. Those percentages vary widely by States and regions. In August 1948, fewer than 1 percent of the eggs produced in Iowa, a heavy surplus State, were sold directly to consumers. During the same month, 33 percent of the eggs produced in Rhode Island were thus sold. The products not consumed on the farms or sold directly are handled by one or many middlemen before they reach the consumer.

Several considerations influence the choice of commercial channels and agencies through which producers market their eggs and poultry—notably location in relation to important centers of consumption and type of farm production.

Large quantities of poultry products, especially eggs, are sold to retail stores by producers. In the 12 Northeastern States producers sold 30 percent of the eggs they marketed in August 1948 to retailers. In 14 North Central States the producers sold 36 percent to retail stores—in 4 of those States more than 50 percent.

Several other outlets may be available. In some areas hatcheries take many eggs for flock replacement, particularly in the spring months, and on a year-around basis for broiler production. Other producer outlets, varying in importance geographically, are hotels, restaurants, bakeries, hucksters, local produce dealers, cooperative associations, country receivers, packers, and city receivers.

Most of the eggs sold by the producers to country retail stores and eggs entering commercial channels otherwise may pass through several or all of the following in their route from the producer to the consumer: Huckster, local assembler, processor, wholesaler, cold storage, jobber, and retailer. The tendency is for an increasing proportion to move more directly toward the retail outlet, through fewer handlers.

Besides the eggs that reach the consumer in shell form, the equivalent of about 40 eggs a person a year is used commercially in liquid, frozen, and dried forms. Eggs in those forms—used chiefly by bakers, confectioners, and producers of dry cake mixes—enter households in forms unrecognized by consumers.

GRADES AND STANDARDS have been set up by the United States Department of Agriculture and most States. The use of Federal grades is voluntary. In 1953 about 10 percent of all shell eggs sold were graded by Federal or Federal-State graders. In most areas they were graded for resale purposes rather than for producer payment. Few States require payment to producers on a grade basis, but most States require that eggs sold to consumers shall be on a grade basis—usually on a State grade basis.

Many eggs from farm flocks, particularly in the north central and southern regions, are still sold by producers on a current-receipt basis. A survey of egg marketing in the North Central States in 1948 showed that 59 percent of the eggs sold by producers in the area were marketed without grading. The range among the 13 States surveyed was from 29 to 78 percent. However, an increasing number of the larger and more aggressive assemblers are now paying the producers according to their own grades or those of the State or Federal Government. This is true more particularly in the northeastern and western regions, where specialized flocks are common and egg-marketing cooperatives have set the pattern of paying producers according to egg quality and size.

Ohio is one of the leading States in using Federal-State egg grades. In 1950, 26 percent of Ohio eggs marketed were officially graded and inspected. Similar information is not

Progress in Broiler Production in the Shenandoah Valley, 1947-52

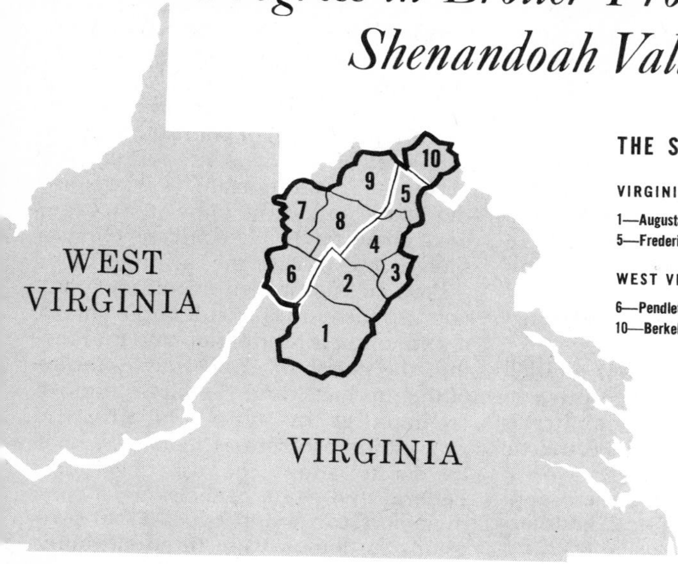
WEST
VIRGINIA
VIRGINIA
1
2
3
4
5
6
7
8
9
10

THE SHENANDOAH VALLEY AREA

VIRGINIA COUNTIES

1—Augusta; 2—Rockingham; 3—Page; 4—Shenandoah; 5—Frederick.

WEST VIRGINIA COUNTIES

6—Pendleton; 7—Grant; 8—Hardy; 9—Hampshire; 10—Berkeley.

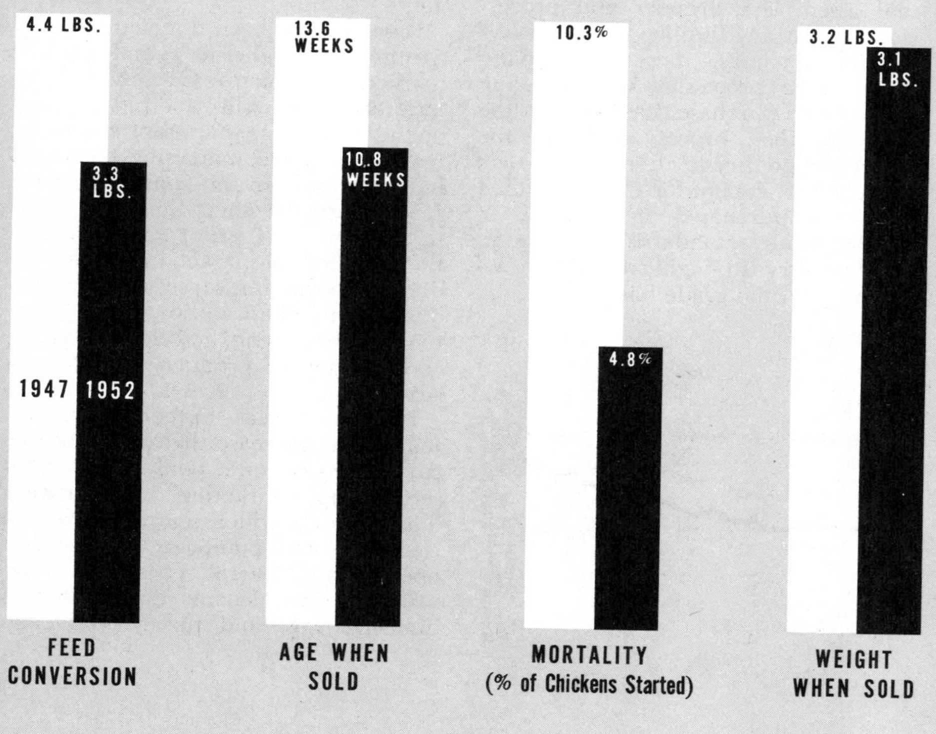
4.4 LBS.
3.3 LBS.
1947
1952
FEED CONVERSION
13.6 WEEKS
10.8 WEEKS
AGE WHEN SOLD
10.3%
4.8%
MORTALITY (% of Chickens Started)
3.2 LBS.
3.1 LBS.
WEIGHT WHEN SOLD

available for other States or regions, but a survey in 1948 showed that 95 percent of the New England buyers used Federal or State quality grades as a criterion for judging value when purchasing eggs from farmers. On the other hand, in the Middle Atlantic States only 47 percent of the dealers bought eggs from farmers on either their own or Federal or State grades. Most eggs marketed by producers in the Southern States are paid for on an ungraded basis. In 1950, 90 percent of the southern producers reported selling eggs on this basis.

Poultry, except that which is retailed live, requires somewhat more processing than eggs. While little poultry is sold other than live by producers, little is sold live to the consumer.

In the marketing chain, there generally are fewer buyers and handlers of poultry than of eggs, because farm-flock poultry is marketed mostly in the fall and the year-around volume is inadequate to sustain small specialized marketing agencies. Local handlers may assemble the live farm-flock poultry for reselling to local or terminal assemblers, dressers, and processors. In heavy broiler- and turkey-producing areas, there are usually some large processors with dressing plants who purchase directly from the growers, then process and sell the processed poultry to either wholesalers or retailers. Except for turkeys, which often are purchased on the basis of United States standards and grades, little poultry is bought from the growers on a formal grade basis.

Egg Production per Bird, 1925-53

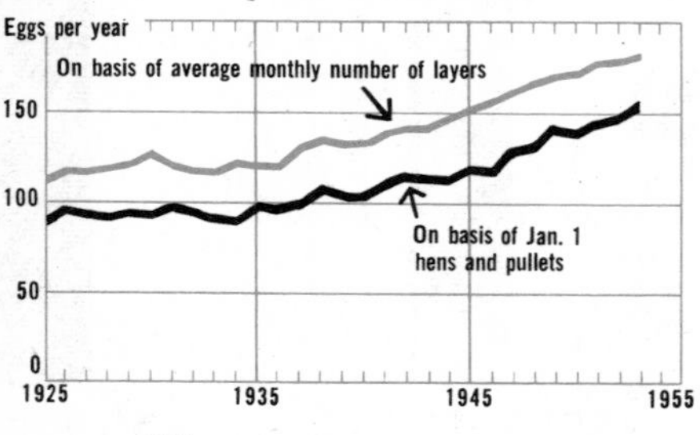

More and more poultry is being sold each year in drawn or ready-to-cook form, whole or cut up, fresh or frozen. Large volumes of poultry, particularly fowl, are canned.

With the seasonal leveling out of overall production of poultry meat, the cold-storage holdings of poultry are becoming less important. Turkeys are the most important class in storage; next come fowl. The bulk of these is slaughtered during the fall months.

Problems in marketing poultry products are the natural result of the varied nature of their production and marketing, the perishable and fragile nature of the products, and the large number of handlers by type and number.

A major problem is the slowness of buyers to adopt the use of grades. Federal and State agencies have conducted research and educational programs to demonstrate the desirability of paying producers on the basis of grades. This gives them an incentive to produce the most desirable qualities and sizes of eggs and poultry. Use of grades likewise helps in merchandising the products at later stages of marketing.

Research has been directed towards a number of other egg and poultry marketing problems: Overcoming deterioration in quality and physical loss on the farm and in marketing channels; reduction in the marketing costs and in the producer-and-consumer price spreads; greater short-time and long-time stability of prices; reduction in the number of market channels; reduction in the time lapse between production and consumption; more effective merchandising; and closer seasonal coordination of production and consumption.

In many areas farmers have attempted to increase their share of the consumer's egg and poultry dollar by setting up marketing cooperatives. There are 150 widely scattered specialized egg- and poultry-marketing cooperatives of several types, in a wide range of sizes, located chiefly in the intensive egg- and turkey-producing sections. About 650 other farm cooperatives, such as cooperative creameries, handle eggs and poultry as a sideline. Cooperatives handle less than 10 percent of the poultry products, but many of the organizations are important pace setters and innovators in marketing eggs and poultry.

Our international trade in poultry products is now relatively unimportant. Exports of dried egg in the late 1940's and early 1950's were an aftermath of price-support operations.

The interest in activities to support egg prices in many of the years up to 1950 illustrated one of the pressing marketing problems in the poultry industry—to avoid the wide year-to-year swings in returns from egg production. The swings cause farmers to enlarge or reduce their flocks, depending on whether current conditions are favorable or unfavorable. Such annual adjustments by farmers usually have been too extreme and therefore have failed to result in a stable industry. As a result, the swings have perpetuated themselves through a chain of actions and reactions. (*Edward Karpoff, John J. Scanlan.*)

Dairy Products

One-sixth of every food dollar spent by nonfarm consumers is for dairy products. A little less than half of that outlay goes to the marketing and processing agencies and the rest goes to farmers.

Milk is produced in nearly every county of the United States. About 3,600,000 farmers were milking at least one cow at the time of the 1950 census; 2 million of them reported sales of dairy products, and the rest used all the milk at home. Sales of whole milk were reported by 1,097,000 farms; sales of farm-separated cream by 862,000, and butter by 121,000.

In the 15 years ending in 1953, farm milk production in the United States ranged from 107 billion to 121 billion pounds. To obtain that huge amount, farmers milked 22 to 26 million cows twice a day, and got an average of about 5,000 pounds a year from each cow.

The annual production is somewhat more than 700 pounds of milk for each person in the United States—about 100 pounds per capita less than a decade earlier.

Fresh milk is a favorable medium for bacterial growth if it is not carefully handled. The earliest governmental regulation in the milk industry was primarily concerned with protecting consumers against fraud and adulteration, but the realization of the dangers of infected milk led to the broadening of the scope of regulation to cover factors influencing health and sanitation.

A standard milk ordinance was requested from the United States Public Health Service in earlier years to overcome the wide variations among local regulations. The first ordinance was published in 1924, and an accompanying code was published in 1927. The ordinance had been adopted by 1,575 municipalities and 405 counties by March 1, 1954. It is used as the standard of milk served on interstate carriers and has been incorporated into Federal specifications. An important effect of the standard is to facilitate the shipment and acceptance of milk from one area to another.

In earlier days, when most families had a cow or two, the location of milk production varied directly with the distribution of the population. Specialization in production of milk and factory dairy products brought important regional differences in production. Since 1925 the east north central region has consistently marketed a larger

Dairy Products

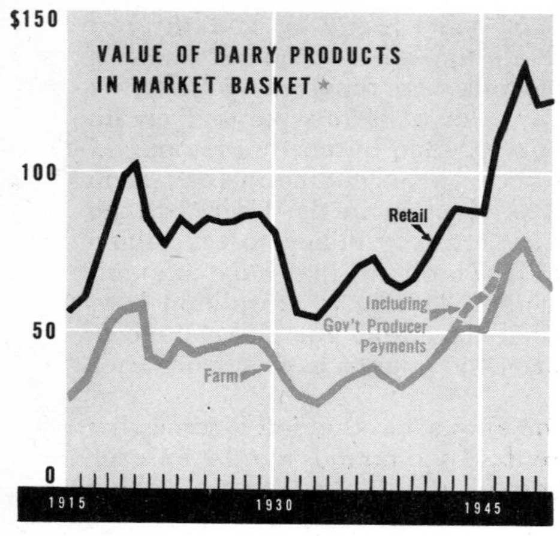

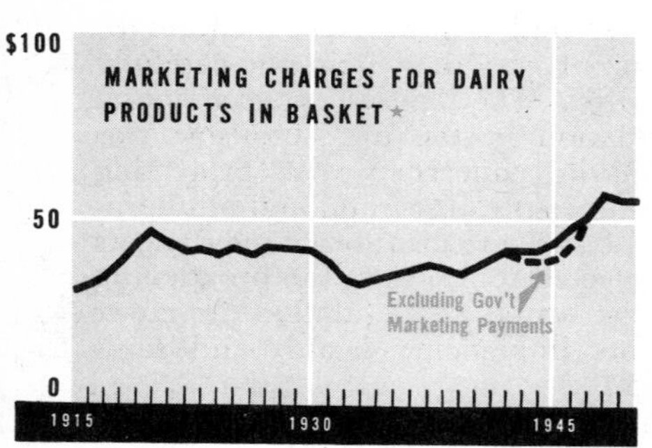

* Retail cost of average annual quantity purchased per family of 3 average consumers, 1935-39, and farm value of equivalent quantities of milk, butter, and butterfat.

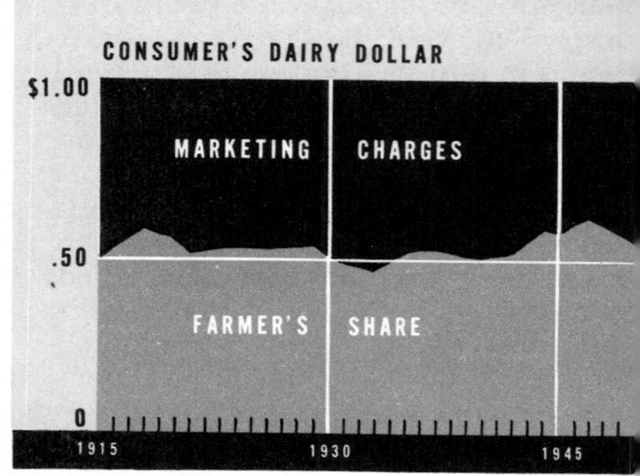

proportion of the Nation's milk than any other region—about a third of the milk and cream delivered to plants and dealers in the United States. Next in importance are the West North Central States, with nearly one-fourth of the marketings. Other regions accounted for the following percentages: North Atlantic, 16 to 19 percent; the Western States, 12 percent; the South Central States, 9 percent; and the South Atlantic States, 5 percent.

Because of its perishability and comparative bulkiness, milk for fluid use tends to be obtained from nearby sources. In any given area milk for fluid consumption gets first call on the available supply because it brings the highest average price. The greater the distance from major markets, the greater the tendency for the milk to be used in production of a high value product per unit of weight. Accordingly 70 percent of the manufactured dairy products come from the North Central States.

With a larger population in comparison to the milk supply and a higher average consumption of liquid milk per person, an increase has occurred in the percentage of total milk used in fluid outlets. Of the milk and cream produced by farmers in 1953, 47 percent was used by consumers in liquid form, a gain of 6 percentage points over 1935. The change lowered the proportion of milk used in making factory products from about 55 percent in the 1920's and 1930's to about 50 percent in later years.

Milk production usually shows substantial seasonal variation but milk consumption is about the same in all months. Therefore some city markets must bring in "outside" milk during months of lowest production, usually late fall and early winter. Interregional shipments of milk, however, are comparatively small, partly because of the high freight rate in relationship to the value of the product.

Because the production of milk varies seasonally and factory uses of milk absorb the excess over fluid needs, there is pronounced seasonal variation in the total production of manufactured dairy products. But the consumption of the products is rather steady throughout the year. Most processed dairy products may be stored only from the seasonal surplus—spring and summer—to the following winter. The manufacturing and storing of dairy products offer a problem to operators of marketing and processing agencies. It is hard for them to gage demand and supplies so as to establish prices that will give a desirable balance between production and accumulation in storage during the into-storage season and consumption of stored products during the deficit out-of-storage season of the year.

Milk going into commercial channels annually since 1940 amounted to the equivalent of 90 billion to 100 billion pounds. In 1952, marketing reached 77 billion pounds as whole milk delivered to plants and dealers; the equivalent of a little less than 20 billion pounds in the form of farm-separated cream; and 3.5 billion to 4 billion pounds retailed by farmers directly to consumers as milk and cream. Out of the 77 billion pounds of whole milk delivered to plants and dealers, 41 billion pounds were used to meet requirements of fluid milk and cream. Fluid milk requires less processing than many other foods. It undergoes only pasteurization, refrigeration, and sometimes homogenization and the addition of vitamin D.

The consumption of fluid milk and cream per person in the United States changed little until the 1940's. During the Second World War, because of shortages of some other foods and the relatively low retail prices of whole milk, the use of fluid milk went up substantially. The consumption of fluid cream declined after the war, but the consumption of liquid skim milk and other liquid products made from skim milk increased.

Consumption of milk fat per person declined from 32 pounds annually during the late 1930's to 27 pounds in the early 1950's. The amount consumed through different dairy products shifted far more than the figures indicate. Except for 3 percent fed to calves, all the milk fat produced is used as human food. Consumption of milk fat in butter declined from around 14 pounds in most years before 1940 to less than 7 pounds per person in 1953. Nearly half the decline in butterfat consumed as butter was absorbed through the increased consumption of fluid milk, cheese, and ice cream. Butter now takes about 25 percent of the milk fat produced in the United States, compared with about 45 percent two decades earlier.

In the period that per capita consumption of butter has declined nearly 50 percent, consumption of margarine more than doubled, but consumption of the two items combined is no greater than consumption of butter alone in earlier years. Among many reasons for the increase in the use of margarine were the removal of Federal taxes on its production and distribution and the removal of restrictions governing its sale in individual States. Other considerations in the decline in demand for butter were an apparent general lessening in demand for table spreads and a conscious effort on the part of consumers to eat less fat.

The consumption of solids-not-fat increased from 40 pounds a person in the 1930's to 50 pounds in 1946; then it declined slightly. The consumption of all dairy products which contain solids-not-fat increased over prewar—

whole milk, skim milk drinks, cottage cheese, cheese, ice cream, and nonfat dry milk solids. Sales of nonfat dry milk solids in consumer packages, generally 1 pound each, increased from 2 million pounds in 1948 to 94 million in 1953. This pattern of consumption is significant: Whereas solids-not-fat and milk fat are produced in a rather fixed ratio, the trend in milk fat consumption is downward, while the trend in consumption of solids-not-fat is upward.

Of the nonfat portion of milk, a large percentage is still used for nonfood purposes. Much of it is retained on farms and therefore does not enter commercial channels. A substantial increase occurred, however, in the proportion of this component of milk marketed. More than 70 percent of the production has been used for food in recent years, compared with 50 percent two decades earlier.

Milk used in manufacturing is produced under two different circumstances. A substantial part is produced near city markets as an excess over current fluid milk requirements. In some markets less than one-half of the milk meeting sanitary requirements for fluid purposes is channeled to that outlet; the balance is sufficient to produce more than one-third of the total of manufactured dairy products in the United States. Items made from this milk consist mainly of ice cream and bulk condensed milk; some part of it is made into butter and dried milk during one season or another. The other milk used in manufacturing is supplied by farmers who have only a manufacturing outlet or whose milk is not eligible for anything except use in manufacturing.

Of the milk fat used in making creamery butter, about two-thirds is still supplied by farm-separated cream. Cream sold by farmers declined nearly 50 percent from the mid-1930's to 1953. The decline reflected a reduction in milk output in the farm-separated cream areas of the country and an increase in sales of whole milk by farmers in most States. Most of the solids-not-fat produced on farms selling cream does not get into commercial channels but is used for feeding hogs, poultry, and other livestock.

While the North Central States account for about 70 percent of the total United States quantity of milk used in manufacturing, there is substantial variation among the products as far as the contribution of each region is concerned.

The north central region in 1952 produced 75 percent of the country's cheese, 83 percent of the creamery butter, 74 percent of the dry whole milk, 73 percent of the nonfat dry milk, and 58 percent of the evaporated milk. The contribution of the region to the United States total of each product (except evaporated milk) was larger in 1952 than in 1929. Because of its bulky nature and strict requirements for refrigeration, production of ice cream is concentrated near the consuming areas. Regional shifts in output of ice cream therefore have followed geographical changes in population.

Dairy products are manufactured in about 10,000 plants that are scattered throughout the States. Many individual plants are operated by one parent firm. The largest concentration of ownership exists in the evaporated milk industry, and probably the least in the manufacture of butter and nonfat powdered milk. Since 1939, production of all of the principal manufactured dairy products except butter increased. The number of processing plants dropped because of improvements in transportation, more complete use of plant capacity, and replacement of small plants by larger ones, particularly the multiple-product type of plant.

The numbers of creameries and cheese factories declined considerably. A striking change in the structure of the dairy processing industry was the rapid increase in number of plants making nonfat dry milk solids during the Second World War. Production of nonfat dry milk solids increased from

Milk Production per Capita, 1952

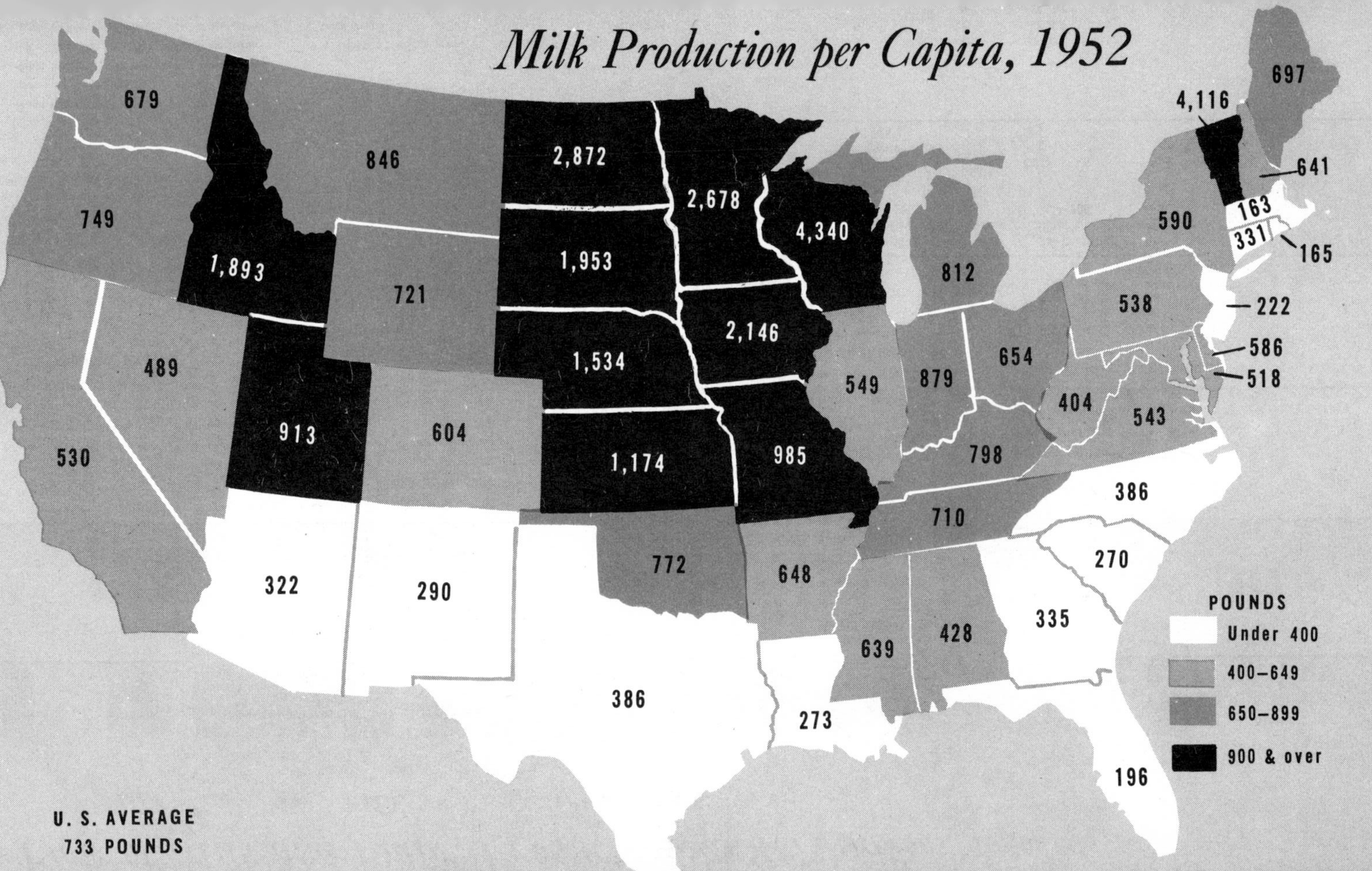

Flow of Milk and Dairy Products, 1953 *(In millions of pounds)*

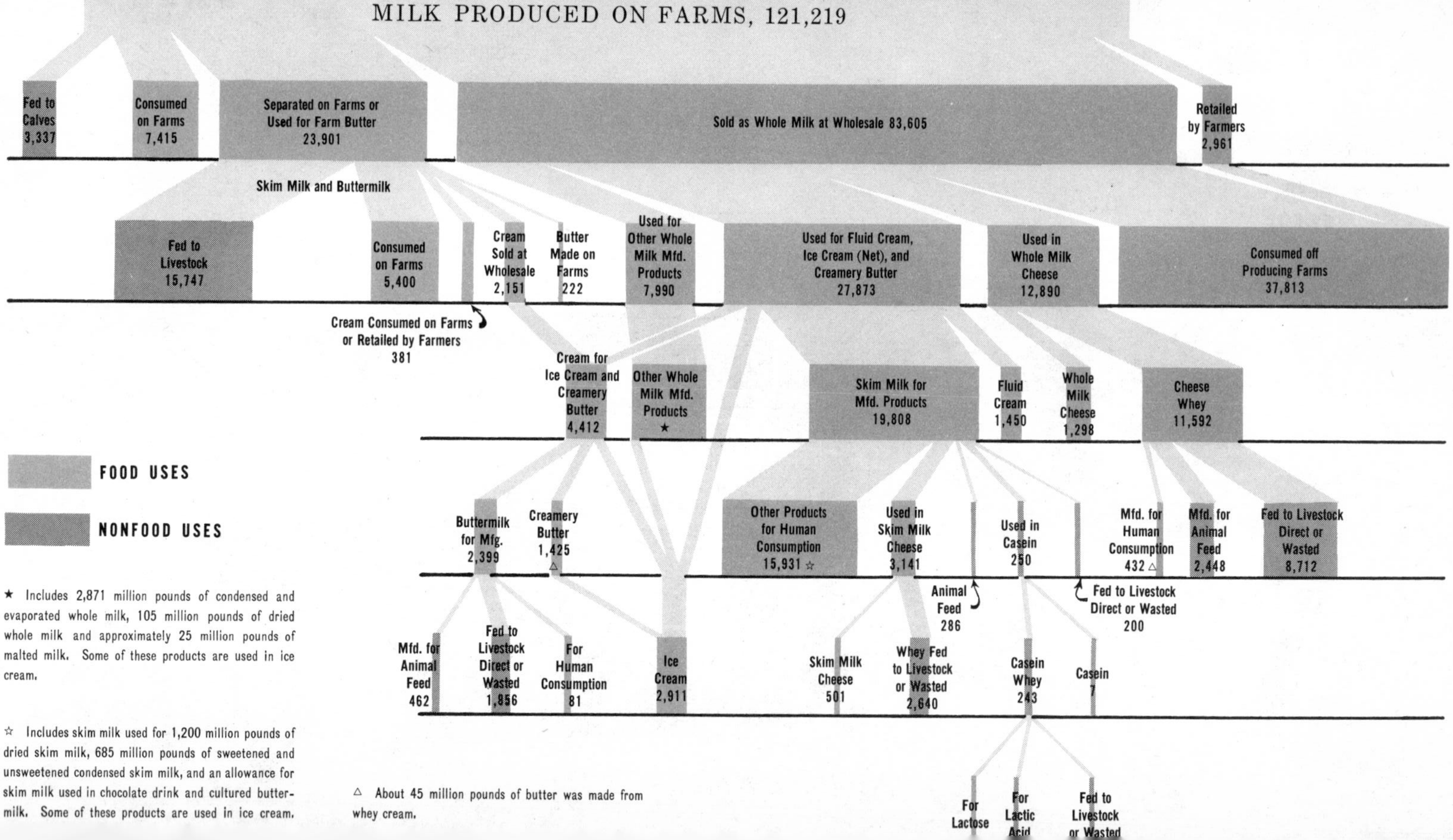

MILK PRODUCED ON FARMS, 121,219

Fed to Calves 3,337
Consumed on Farms 7,415
Separated on Farms or Used for Farm Butter 23,901
Sold as Whole Milk at Wholesale 83,605
Retailed by Farmers 2,961

Skim Milk and Buttermilk

Fed to Livestock 15,747
Consumed on Farms 5,400
Cream Sold at Wholesale 2,151
Butter Made on Farms 222
Used for Other Whole Milk Mfd. Products 7,990
Used for Fluid Cream, Ice Cream (Net), and Creamery Butter 27,873
Used in Whole Milk Cheese 12,890
Consumed off Producing Farms 37,813

Cream Consumed on Farms or Retailed by Farmers 381

Cream for Ice Cream and Creamery Butter 4,412
Other Whole Milk Mfd. Products ★
Skim Milk for Mfd. Products 19,808
Fluid Cream 1,450
Whole Milk Cheese 1,298
Cheese Whey 11,592

Buttermilk for Mfg. 2,399
Creamery Butter 1,425 △
Other Products for Human Consumption 15,931 ☆
Used in Skim Milk Cheese 3,141
Used in Casein 250
Mfd. for Human Consumption 432 △
Mfd. for Animal Feed 2,448
Fed to Livestock Direct or Wasted 8,712

Animal Feed 286
Fed to Livestock Direct or Wasted 200

Mfd. for Animal Feed 462
Fed to Livestock Direct or Wasted 1,856
For Human Consumption 81
Ice Cream 2,911
Skim Milk Cheese 501
Whey Fed to Livestock or Wasted 2,640
Casein Whey 243
Casein 7

For Lactose
For Lactic Acid
Fed to Livestock or Wasted

FOOD USES

NONFOOD USES

★ Includes 2,871 million pounds of condensed and evaporated whole milk, 105 million pounds of dried whole milk and approximately 25 million pounds of malted milk. Some of these products are used in ice cream.

☆ Includes skim milk used for 1,200 million pounds of dried skim milk, 685 million pounds of sweetened and unsweetened condensed skim milk, and an allowance for skim milk used in chocolate drink and cultured buttermilk. Some of these products are used in ice cream.

△ About 45 million pounds of butter was made from whey cream.

366 million pounds in 1941 to 643 million in 1945 and in 1953 exceeded 1.2 billion pounds.

In pricing, milk offers an unusual problem among livestock products because of its perishability, the frequency of its marketing, and its widely dispersed sources of supply. Market prices for butter and nonfat dry milk solids have made milk fat the more valuable component of milk. Milk as produced contains on the average 2.25 pounds of solids-not-fat for every pound of fat. Milk fat from 100 pounds of milk has been worth two to three times as much as the nonfat, but because of the increasing trend in use of solids-not-fat, increased emphasis has been given to that component in pricing of milk. This component of milk offers consumers a cheap source of high-quality protein and some other food nutrients. Consumers, however, buy individual dairy products for the particular want-satisfying qualities of the product, rather than for the quantities of the different milk solids contained in it.

Regardless of whether milk is sold for manufacturing or for fluid use, it must be sold by a prearranged pricing procedure, as raw milk does not lend itself to dealing on an "offer and acceptance" basis. Firms making processed dairy products base their purchase prices for milk largely on the basis of returns for the finished products that they sell nationally.

Wholesale markets for most dairy items are scattered over the country. Even in the largest wholesale markets, trading is light in relation to the total supply. But prices established through a series of adjustments tend to approximate an equilibrium so that the total national supply normally moves into consumption. Manufactured dairy products are not so perishable as to prevent shipment between important wholesale markets. Through such shipments, the prices in the individual wholesale markets tend to be the same except for customary freight differentials.

Pricing milk used in fluid consumption is a more delicate task than pricing the product used in manufacturing. Several price-making bodies or procedures govern the pricing and marketing of fluid milk. They include (1) simple negotiations between dealers and farmers or between dealers and representatives of farmers, (2) State milk-control agencies, which may set prices at various stages of distribution from farmers to consumers, and (3) Federal milk marketing orders, which establish only minimum prices to producers.

After the Second World War there was a shift to the use of pricing formulas that employed more general types of economic indicators. The specific formulas were introduced after long study by economic technicians, and the Federal marketing orders using them were promulgated after public hearings. Regardless of the pricing procedure used, the returns to farmers invariably are based on prices for milk in the different classifications of use.

The Federal Government first entered fluid milk pricing in 1933 and 1934, issuing licenses regulating the handling of milk in about 50 markets. Following passage of the Agricultural Adjustment Act of 1935, the role of the Federal Government in pricing milk was conducted through the establishment of milk marketing orders. Forty-nine milk marketing orders were in operation by 1953; through them prices and other conditions for sale of milk by producers were established in the marketing areas covered. Marketing orders may be issued only after petitions of dairy farmers, public hearings, and approval by at least two-thirds of the dairy farmers affected by the order. The order may be amended or discontinued by a two-thirds vote of the dairy farmers affected by it. Approximately one-third of the milk consumed in fluid form is channeled through markets with Federal orders and a substantially greater proportion of the Nation's milk supply for fluid use is indirectly affected by the orders.

At various times since the early

Geographical Distribution of Milk Sales and Proportion Used in Manufacturing by Regions, Selected Years

Region	*Percentage of United States milk marketed by farmers as whole milk and farm-skimmed cream*				*Percentage of total United States milk used in whole milk products*				*Percentage of milk ma by farmers as whole and farm-skimmed cr in each region used factory products*			
	1929	*1935*	*1945*	*1951*	*1929*	*1935*	*1945*	*1951*	*1929*	*1935*	*1945*	
	Pct.	*Pct.*	*Pct.*	*Pct.*	*Pct.*	*Pct.*	*Pct.*	*Pct.*	*Pct.*	*Pct.*	*Pct.*	
North Atlantic.......	16.8	17.4	16.6	18.4	6.1	5.4	7.5	8.8	23.9	21.0	26.9	2
North Central East...	31.2	31.8	33.3	32.7	34.0	36.3	38.4	37.8	71.9	76.8	68.2	6
North Central West..	29.6	28.7	25.5	23.4	40.6	38.3	33.0	33.1	90.4	89.6	76.6	7
South Atlantic.......	2.5	2.5	3.7	5.0	.9	1.0	2.0	2.5	24.7	27.2	32.9	2
South Central.......	7.6	7.3	8.9	8.9	5.5	6.4	8.2	7.4	47.1	59.0	54.1	4
Western...........	12.3	12.3	12.0	11.6	12.9	12.6	10.9	10.4	69.5	68.6	53.7	5
United States......	100.0	100.0	100.0	100.0	100.0	100.0	100.0	100.0	66.0	67.2	59.2	5

1930's, the Federal Government has intervened in the pricing of manufactured dairy products. A purchase and diversion program was organized in the interest of achieving higher prices for milk and farm-separated cream that go into the making of manufactured dairy products. In recent years the Secretary of Agriculture has been required by law to support the prices of milk and butterfat at a level between 75 and 90 percent of parity. Purchases of manufactured dairy products under this program tend to stabilize prices of fluid milk as well as those of the entire manufacturing milk category.

About half of the expenditures by consumers for dairy products goes to producers. The other half goes for marketing, processing, and other services. Wages and salaries take between 20 and 25 percent of the consumer's dollar spent for the four major dairy products; costs of buildings and equipment take around 6 percent. Of the total cost involved in moving the annual quantity of dairy products from farms to consumers, 11 percent goes for processing, 4 percent for wholesaling, 23 percent for retailing, and 6 percent for all other marketing costs, including transportation.

Combined costs of retailing and wholesaling are lowest for butter and evaporated milk—about 20 percent of the consumer's dollar for each. Retailing and wholesaling expenses for fluid milk (not including plant costs for pasteurizing and bottling) are approximately 30 percent, and retailing and wholesaling expenses for American cheese about 35 percent of the consumer's dollar.

Innovations offer prospects for re-

Geographical Distribution of Manufactured Dairy Products Output, 1929 and 1951

Region	*Production in each region as a percentage of United States total production*											
	Creamery butter		*Total cheese*		*Evaporated milk*		*Dry whole milk*		*Nonfat dry milk solids for human consumption*		*Ice cream*	
	1929	*1951*	*1929*	*1951*	*1929*	*1951*	*1929*	*1951*	*1929*	*1951*	*1929*	*1951*
	Pct.	*Pct.*	*Pct.*	*Pct.*	*Pct.*	*Pct.*	*Pct.*	*Pct.*	*Pct.*	*Pct.*	*Pct.*	*Pct.*
orth Atlantic	1.6	2.3	11.9	10.0	7.1	2.4	46.2	18.5	23.9	15.8	37.1	31.1
orth Central East	27.1	26.4	70.3	62.8	58.8	48.5	38.9	59.2	33.4	44.4	25.6	22.7
orth Central West	51.2	55.7	4.9	12.1	5.3	9.7	5.1	14.9	7.3	26.7	10.7	9.9
outh Atlantic	.7	1.0	.3	.2	1.0	5.7	6.0	.....	1.4	1.6	7.4	11.5
outh Central	6.5	5.9	2.9	8.4	6.0	14.8	.4	.....	3.0	1.1	7.8	11.8
Vestern	12.9	8.7	9.7	6.5	21.8	18.9	3.4	7.4	31.0	10.4	11.4	13.0
United States	100.0	100.0	100.0	100.0	100.0	100.0	100.0	100.0	100.0	100.0	100.0	100.0

Number of Plants Making Manufactured Dairy Products, 1939 and 1951

Manufactured products	*1939*			*1951*		
	Plants	*Total output*	*Average output per plant*	*Plants*	*Total output*	*Average output per plant*
	Number	*1,000 pounds*	*1,000 pounds*	*Number*	*1,000 pounds*	*1,000 pounds*
utter, creamery	4,646	1,781,737	383	2,879	1,202,981	418
merican cheese, whole milk	2,284	537,298	235	1,592	873,080	548
vaporated whole milk, case goods	143	2,170,601	15,179	120	2,896,386	24,137
onfat dry milk solids, human consumption	258	267,860	1,038	461	702,465	1,524
ry whole milk	57	24,472	429	67	131,017	1,955
		1,000 gallons	*1,000 gallons*		*1,000 gallons*	*1,000 gallons*
e cream, wholesale	4,202	278,532	66	3,180	517,343	163

Civilian Consumption of Dairy Products, Milk Solids, and Margarine

POUNDS PER CAPITA

	Average		*1950*	*1951*	*1952*	*1953* [1]
	1935–39	*1947–49*				
Butter	16.8	10.5	10.6	9.5	8.6	8.6
American cheese	4.0	5.2	5.4	5.0	5.3	4.7
Other cheese	1.5	1.7	2.2	2.1	2.2	2.3
Evaporated and condensed milk	16.5	19.8	19.8	18.0	17.4	17.1
Dry whole milk	0.12	0.33	0.28	0.27	0.44	0.25
Ice cream, product weight	9.8	18.5	17.0	17.1	17.6	17.8
Ice cream, net milk used	24.6	47.0	44.4	44.1	46.7	47.2
Fluid milk and cream	330	359	349	352	352	352
Total milk	791	732	731	707	694	689
Nonfat dry milk solids	1.9	3.1	3.6	4.2	4.6	4.2
Milk fat	31.2	29.2	29.0	28.0	27.3	27.1
Milk solids-not-fat	39.6	46.6	46.4	46.6	47.3	46.5
Margarine	2.8	5.5	6.0	6.5	7.8	8.1

[1] Preliminary.

ducing the costs of handling, transporting, or manufacturing milk and dairy items.

One is the bulk-tank method of storing and transporting milk. It involves use of a bulk-type tank on the farm where the milk is cooled and stored until collected by a bulk type of milk truck. It was used first in California in 1938, in Connecticut in 1948, and in a number of other areas by the early 1950's. It reduces costs and makes possible the delivery of milk of higher quality.

In 1953 the Department of Agriculture announced perfection of a procedure for shortening the time of production of Cheddar cheese, a process that will permit a plant to double its daily output.

A concentrated fresh milk was made available to several fluid milk markets in 1951. It could be processed in surplus milk-producing areas and sold in areas of deficit supply, and seemed to offer a saving. In a number of markets in which it was first introduced, however, the raw milk from which it was made was priced the same as fresh milk used for fluid consumption, thus lessening the economic advantage.

Vending machines may increase sales of fluid milk and reduce costs of distribution. They are of four main types—a dispenser used in eating places, which eliminates the cost and handling of containers; a type that dispenses small cartons to consumers for on-the-spot consumption; one that vends quart-size containers for home use; and an outdoor, high-volume type, which vends milk in quart and half-gallon containers for home use.

Paper containers for fluid milk are the predominant method of packaging milk in many areas, particularly for store distribution. Their per-unit cost exceeds that for glass but they need not be returned. Milk keeps better in them, and they permit a wider distribution of milk from processing points.

The substitution of vegetable fats for milk fats in foods caused concern in the dairy industry in the early 1950's. There already had been a sharp decline in use of milk fat as a spread, and prices of milk fat were high in relation to prices of vegetables fats. Opportunities appeared for reducing the costs of food by substituting the lower-cost product. A few States permitted the production and sale of "filled" milk, which is evaporated milk. This milk fat is replaced by vegetable fat. Frozen desserts resembling ice cream also use vegetable fat in place of milk fat and have become a significant factor in a number of markets. The practice of substituting vegetable fat for milk fat in such products promises to grow even more rapidly than has the substitution of margarine for butter. That is to be expected, for the decision to substitute vegetable fat for milk fat in these foods is made by a limited number of food processors rather than by millions of consumers individually.

Our imports of dairy products, measured on a fat-solids basis, have seldom exceeded 1 percent of the domestic production. Exports normally have been smaller than imports, so that there has been a slight net import balance. During the Second World War and for several years following, however, the pattern was reversed, as exports under various aid programs reached 6 percent of domestic production and took one-half or more of dry milk. Exports by 1952 had declined to the lowest level since 1940 and imports had increased so that there was a small export balance. Imports recently would have been greater had there not been import controls on individual dairy products.

Large amounts of most manufactured dairy products are sold by other dairy exporting countries at prices considerably less than the equivalent prices received in recent years by United States dairy farmers.

Cheese has been the most important single dairy item imported by the United States. That is because some types of cheese are made only in certain countries and they are available to consumers in the United States only if they are imported. (*Herbert C. Kriesel, Max K. Hinds.*)

Livestock

The United States ranks well above all other countries in total output of meat. Nearly all of its production is consumed by its own population. The output in the past decade made possible an average yearly consumption of 136 to 154 pounds per capita. In 1953 the average was approximately 154 pounds; in 1952 the average was about 144 pounds.

Meat is the most important item in the food budget. Expenditures for meat amount to 25 percent or more of the total cost of all food of the American people, and average 5½ percent of total disposable income (the amount remaining after payment of taxes). The retail value of the per capita meat consumption in 1953 was about 83 dollars. For that sum the consumer got in terms of carcass weight (before shrinkage resulting from cutting, trimming, and evaporation) 63 pounds of pork, 77 pounds of beef, 9 pounds of veal, and 5 pounds of lamb. Actual purchase weights were less.

About 60 cents out of every dollar consumers spend for meat goes back to the livestock producer. To the value he receives from the meat is added the income from hides, pelts, fats, and other byproducts. Together, cash receipts of 10,335 million dollars were returned to farmers for the meat animals they marketed in 1952. This was almost a third of farmers' receipts from all sources.

Most of the beef, veal, lamb, and mutton reaches the consumer within a short time after slaughter. Much of the pork also is sold quickly, although several pork products are cured and then moved along more slowly. Peak loads of meat in commercial freezer and cooler storage seldom amount to more than 3 percent of the annual commercial output of beef and veal, 4 percent of lamb and mutton, and 8 percent of pork—the equivalents of only 10, 15, and 30 days' supplies of the respective meats.

Considerable amounts of meat—although a small part of the total supply—are made into sausages, frankfurters, sandwich meats, and other products. More of them go into cans now than a few years ago. From an annual rate of 300 to 500 million pounds before the war, the output of canned meat jumped to 2 billion pounds in 1943. It was 1,437 million pounds in 1953. The total production of carcass meat was 25 billion pounds that year.

Range, pasture, and hay are primary feeds for raising sheep and cattle. Corn and other concentrate feeds are the diet for hogs, and they will put finish on cattle and sheep.

First-ranking grazing and pasture area is that large territory known as the Great Plains, which slopes east from the Rockies and is bracketed on the north by Canada, on the south by the Gulf of Mexico, and on the east by the western edge of the Corn Belt (about the 97th meridian). The region is primarily a breeding ground. Each year it sends hundreds of thousands of feeder cattle and sheep east. It also feeds many animals to part or full finish, slaughtering some locally but shipping more of them east or west for slaughter. In January 1954 the six States from North Dakota to Texas had 28 percent of the Nation's cattle, 28 percent of its sheep, and 12 percent of its hogs.

The mountain West has a similar position as a cradle for feeder cattle and sheep as well as a producer of many grass-fat and some grain-fed animals, but its carrying capacity is below that of the Plains. In 1954 it had 11 percent of all cattle and 35 percent of all sheep. Few hogs are raised there.

The area ranking first in raising hogs and feeding cattle and sheep is the Corn Belt. The 8 States from Ohio to Minnesota produce three-fifths of the United States corn crop. In 1953 those States raised about 69 percent of all the pigs. On January 1, 1954, they had 55 percent of all the cattle and 36 percent of all the lambs that were on feed in feed lots. Those States also have large numbers of cattle and sheep for breeding. In 1954 they had 14 percent of all the beef cows.

Progress toward more productive pastures and better adapted breeds has boosted the cattle industry of the South and Southeast. Large acreages of cropland in the area have been shifted from cultivated crops to grassland. The region ships out a few feeder cattle but the greater part of its production is slaughtered locally as grass-fat cattle. It ranks next to the Corn Belt in production of hogs. It has 22 percent of the population of the United States, but it has 19 percent of the cattle, 6 percent of the sheep, and 18 percent of the hogs. Inshipment of beef is not so great as the figures suggest; people in the South eat less beef per capita than do those in other regions, but more pork.

The Northeastern States are the big deficit region into which meat pours, chiefly from the Midwest. With 28 percent of the population and an above-average income per person, the States from Maryland to Maine have less than 10 percent of the country's livestock.

On the Pacific coast a growing cattle industry has failed to keep up with an even faster growing population. The region in 1954 with 10 percent of the population had only 6 percent of the Nation's cattle. It had 10 percent of the sheep. Both range and irrigated land are used in the production of cattle and sheep. There is much dry-lot feeding on beet pulp, barley, and a variety of other feeds that substitute for the Corn Belt's plentiful corn.

Regional Production of Cattle and Calves, 1952

MILLIONS OF POUNDS, LIVE WEIGHT

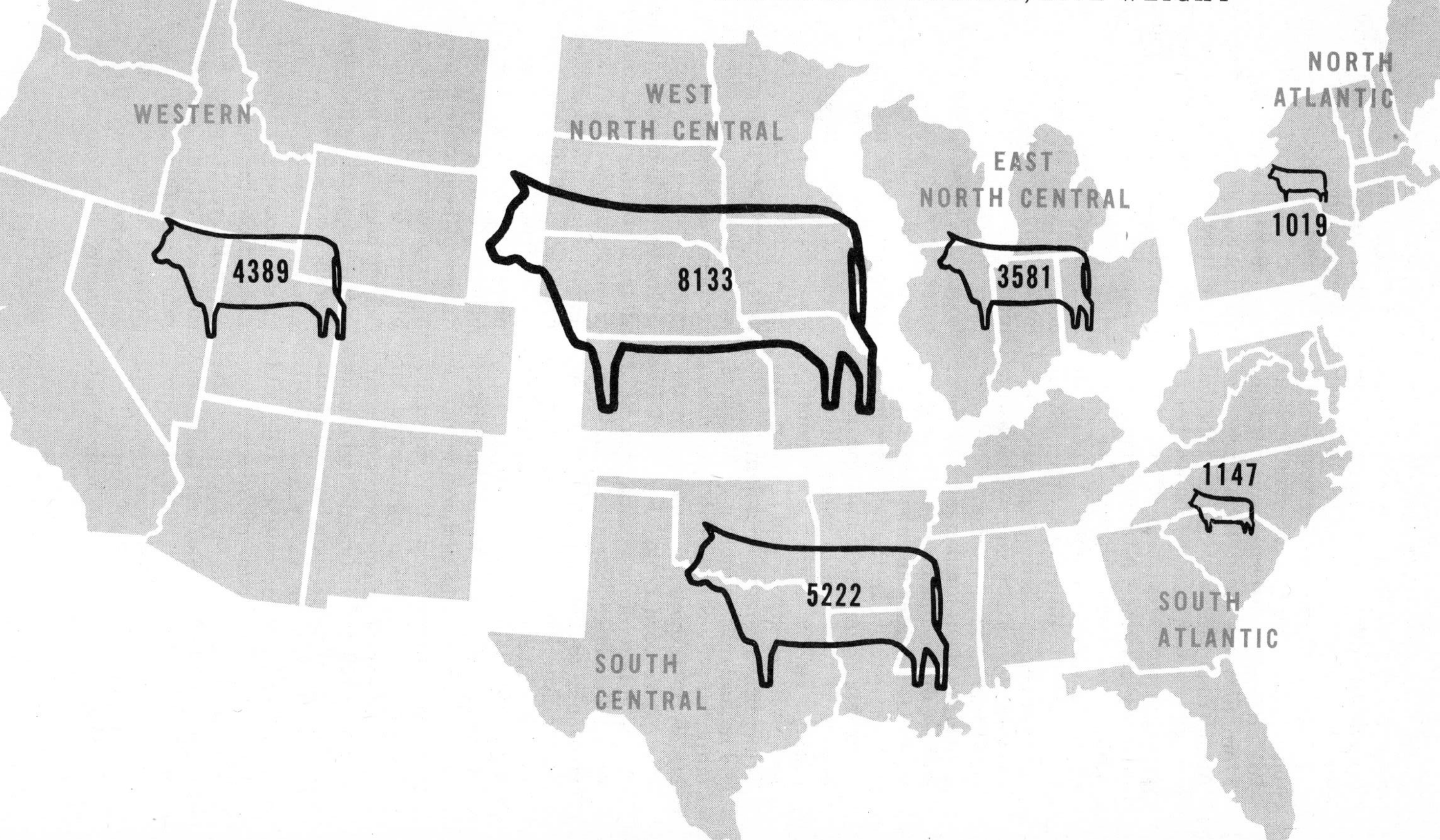

The quantity of meat produced varies both seasonally and from year to year. Not all the ingenuity of man has erased fully the synchronism of the seasons and the life cycle in livestock production. Spring still is the time of most births, summer of grazing, and fall and winter of intensive feeding. More pigs are born in March and April than in any other months. Crowded into 3 months, November to January, is fully a third of the year's total hog slaughter. A second slaughter peak occurs in early spring. Slaughter of all cattle considered together is fairly evenly distributed throughout the year because feeding operations act as a leveler of supplies, withdrawing cattle marketed off grass in the fall and delivering them for slaughter the next spring. But in this process the composition of slaughter and the beef supply changes greatly. In the fall more grass cattle are slaughtered and the lower grades of beef are in more plentiful supply. In the spring and summer well-finished cattle and Choice and Prime beef are more abundant.

The annual production of hogs and output of pork rise and fall irregularly, largely in response to changes in the size of the corn crops. The ratio between prices of hogs and prices of corn, alternately favorable and unfavorable to hog production, is the mechanism that keeps the hog production in line with the corn supply. When corn loan programs are in effect, however, the production of hogs and of pork is less closely tied to the size of each year's corn crop. It is governed more by the relation of demand for pork to loan or release prices for corn.

The production of cattle and output of beef go through long cyclical variations. Because of the heavy investment required for raising cattle and the long life span of the species, changes in demand for beef or in the supply of range, pasture, and crop feed are manifest in slow and prolonged upswings and downswings in cattle numbers and beef supply.

Sheep production and annual output of lamb also experience cyclical fluctuation, chiefly according to altering conditions in producing areas and shifting competitive relationships.

Meat is a heterogeneous commodity. Red meat comprises beef, veal, lamb, mutton, and pork, each of which is retailed in a wide assortment of cuts. Meats also vary over a range of grades, since they are derived from live animals varying greatly in quality, conformation, and finish. Standard grade names established by the Department of Agriculture have provided an identification terminology for transactions in all livestock except hogs, even though actual sales usually are made by inspection of each lot offered. New grades were set up in 1952 for hogs, but these animals still are sold more according to weight than by grade. There also are Federal grades for meat. Any inspected and some noninspected packers can have meat graded by Federal graders by asking for and paying the costs of the service. Substantial quantities of all meats except pork are so graded. Much meat is sold by description alone rather than by personal inspection at the time of sale.

Grades for livestock and meat, as for all farm commodities, differentiate the products in a way that facilitates trade and rewards the producer who supplies the kind and qualities desired by consumers. The increasing consumer preference for lean over fat pork, for instance, can be reflected back to producers of hogs only if a distinction is made between fat and lean hogs and a higher price paid for the leaner ones. Selling hogs by the new live hog grades is one proposed method for doing that. Another is selling by carcass grade and weight, a system whereby the return to the producer for each hog is determined from the value of its carcass.

Finally, meat comes from numerous suppliers. About 4 million farms and ranches produce cattle and 3 million produce hogs. A little more than 300,000 produce sheep. The slaughtering industry has considerable concentra-

Income per Person and Retail Value of Meat Consumed 1920-53

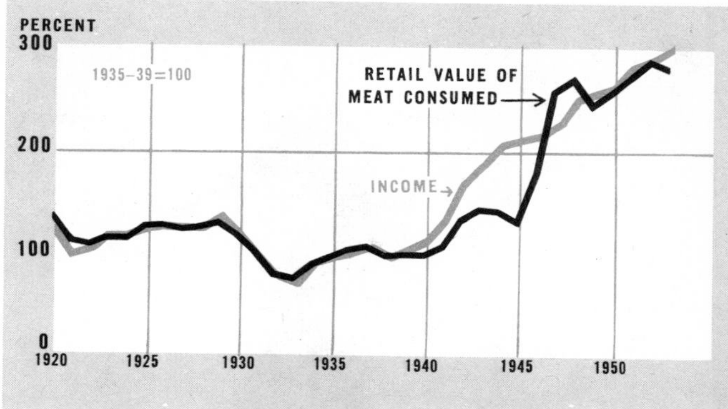

Meat Consumption per Person 1900-53

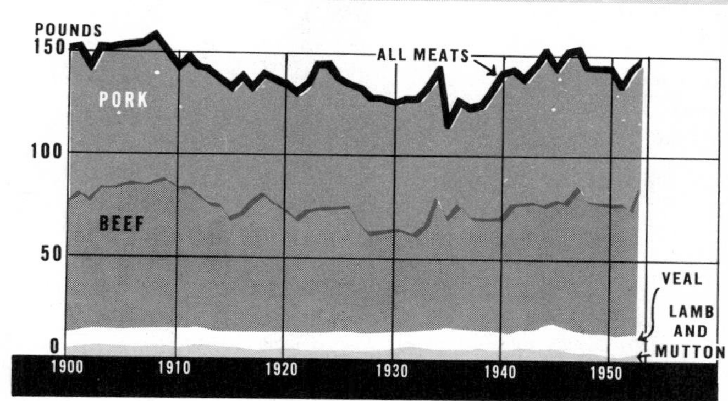

tion among a few large packers and several dozen firms of intermediate size, but even so it includes a total of 1,250 wholesale slaughterers, 2,200 local smaller concerns classed as slaughterers, and 11,000 still smaller operators designated as butchers. Meat wholesalers are many and retailers legion.

Livestock marketing agencies are equally diverse. Notwithstanding many changes in the livestock marketing system over the years, terminal public markets still are of considerable importance. In 1950 federally inspected packers reported that they obtained 75 percent of their cattle, 57 percent of their calves, 40 percent of their hogs, and 57 percent of their sheep and lambs at the 65 stockyards markets operating under Federal supervision.

Direct buying of livestock has grown in volume and is the predominant means of marketing hogs in many areas of the North Central States.

Livestock auctions experienced a spectacular expansion after 1930, until they numbered about 2,400 in 1949. In the South and Southeast about two-thirds of the livestock is sold at these auction markets.

In addition to these outlets, local markets and local dealers and buyers probably numbering in the tens of thousands are available in all parts of the country. Local dealers, livestock auctions, terminal markets, and direct sales to packers were each of about equal importance as livestock outlets for farmers and ranchers in the Mountain States and Pacific Coast States in 1949. (*Charles A. Burmeister, Harold F. Breimyer.*)

Food Production

POPULATION CENTERS OF 100,000 AND OVER

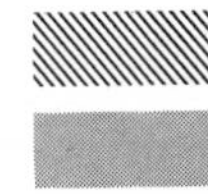

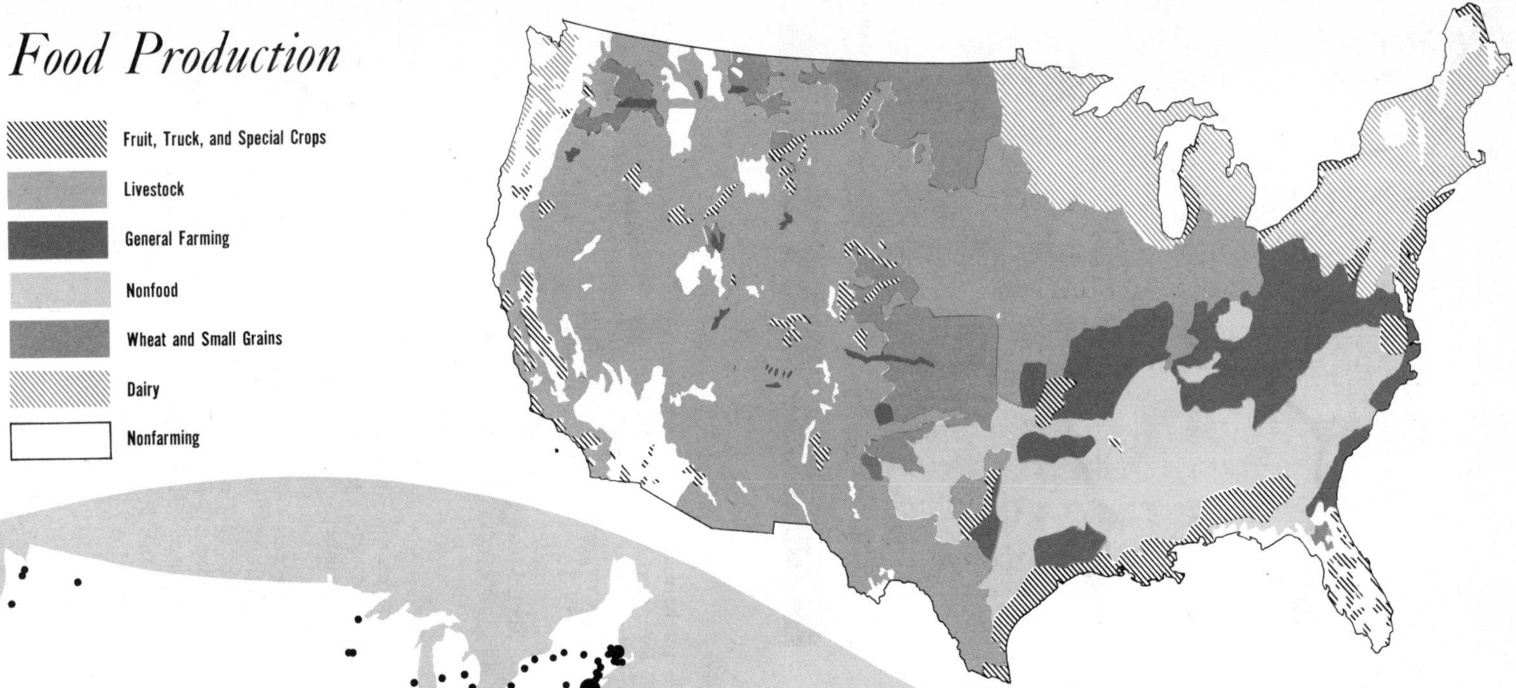

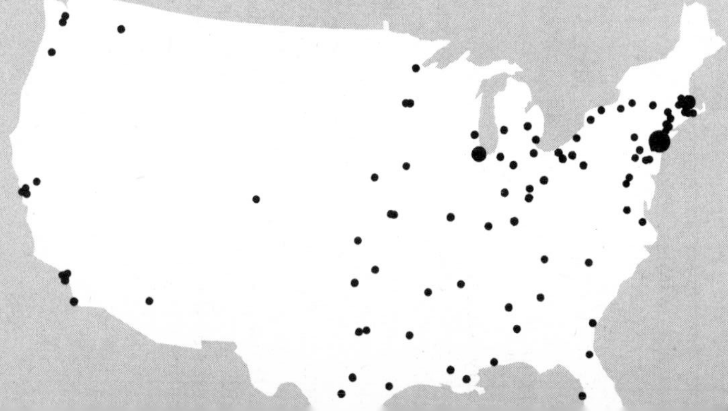

Major Consuming Centers

The Contributors

Martin A. Abrahamsen, Chief, Farm Supplies Branch, Purchasing Division, Farmer Cooperative Service.

Don S. Anderson, Acting Director, Livestock and Dairy Division, Commodity Stabilization Service.

Merritt W. Baker, formerly Deputy Director, Fruit and Vegetable Branch, Production and Marketing Administration.

W. Edwards Beach, Director, Trading and Reports Division, Commodity Exchange Authority.

L. A. Bevan, Director of Extension Service, University of New Hampshire.

M. C. Bond, Professor of Marketing, Cornell University.

Neil H. Borden, Professor of Advertising, Harvard University Graduate School of Business Administration.

Harold F. Breimyer, Head, Livestock Section, Statistical and Historical Research Branch, Agricultural Economics Division, Agricultural Marketing Service.

R. G. Bressler, Jr., Director, Giannini Foundation of Agricultural Economics, University of California.

Neil Brooks, Associate Solicitor in Charge of Appellate Litigation, Office of Solicitor.

Arthur E. Browne, Assistant to the Director, Fruit and Vegetable Division, Agricultural Marketing Service.

James W. Browning, Assistant to the Administrator, Commodity Stabilization Service.

Max E. Brunk, Professor of Marketing, Cornell University.

Charles W. Bucy, Associate Solicitor in Charge of Marketing and Regulatory Laws, Office of the Solicitor.

Marguerite C. Burk, Head, Food Consumption Section, Statistical and Historical Research Branch, Agricultural Economics Division, Agricultural Marketing Service.

Charles A. Burmeister, formerly Livestock Analyst, Livestock Branch, Production and Marketing Administration.

C. J. Carey, Deputy Director, California State Department of Agriculture.

L. C. Carey, Head, Standard Container Section, Regulatory Branch, Fruit and Vegetable Division, Agricultural Marketing Service.

Russell L. Childress, Fruit and Vegetable Marketing Economist, Division of Agricultural Economics, Federal Extension Service.

Donald E. Church, Chief, Transportation Division, Bureau of the Census.

Faith Clark, Food Economist, Home Economics Research Branch, Agricultural Research Service.

Forrest Clements, Stewart, Dougall and Associates; formerly Head, Market Surveys Section, Market Development Branch, Marketing Research Division, Agricultural Marketing Service.

Malcolm Clough, Agricultural Economic Statistician, Statistical and Historical Research Branch, Agricultural Economics Division, Agricultural Marketing Service.

Robert H. Cole, Assistant Professor of Marketing, University of Illinois.

Jessie V. Coles, Professor of Home Economics, University of California.

A. G. Conover, Head, Tobacco Section, Statistical and Historical Research Branch, Agricultural Economics Division, Agricultural Marketing Service.

Paul D. Converse, Professor of Marketing, University of Illinois.

M. J. Cook, Chief, Packers and Stockyards Branch, Livestock Division, Agricultural Marketing Service.

Maurice R. Cooper, Head, Fibers Section, Organization and Costs Branch, Marketing Research Division, Agricultural Marketing Service.

Charles W. Crawford, Commissioner of Food and Drugs, United States Department of Health, Education, and Welfare.

E. C. Crittenden, Consultant, National Bureau of Standards, United States Department of Commerce.

William C. Crow, Chief, Transportation and Facilities Branch, Marketing Research Division, Agricultural Marketing Service.

Ted C. Curry, Chief, Regulatory Branch, Fruit and Vegetable Division, Agricultural Marketing Service.

D. B. DeLoach, Chief, Organization and Costs Branch, Marketing Research Division, Agricultural Marketing Service.

Ralph L. Dewey, Assistant Dean, Graduate School, and Professor of Economics, The Ohio State University.

George A. Dice, Assistant to Deputy Administrator for Marketing Services, Agricultural Marketing Service.

Edward A. Duddy, Professor of Marketing (Emeritus), University of Chicago.

William H. Elliott, Head, Handling and Facilities Research Section, Transportation and Facilities Branch, Marketing Research Division, Agricultural Marketing Service.

Gertrude G. Foelsch, Agricultural Economist, Organization and Costs Branch, Marketing Research Division.

Richard J. Foote, Assistant Chief for Commodity Research, Statistical and Historical Research Branch, Agricultural Economics Division.

Karl A. Fox, Chief, Statistical and Historical Research Branch, Agricultural Economics Division, Agricultural Marketing Service.

Edward E. Gallahue, Marketing Specialist, Vegetable Branch, Fruit and Vegetable Division, Agricultural Marketing Service.

Kelsey B. Gardner, Chief, Business Administration Branch, Management Services Division, Farmer Cooperative Service.

C. B. Gilliland, Head, Special Crops Section, Organization and Costs Branch, Marketing Research Division.

E. T. Grether, Dean and Flood Professor of Economics, School of Business Administration, University of California.

Sidney N. Gubin, Staff Assistant to the Director, Price Division, Commodity Stabilization Service.

Harold Hedges, deceased; formerly Chief, Cooperative Research and Service Division, Farm Credit Administration.

Floyd F. Hedlund, Deputy Director, Fruit and Vegetable Division, Agricultural Marketing Service.

Joseph F. Herrick, Jr., Agricultural Economist, Transportation and Facilities Branch, Marketing Research Division, Agricultural Marketing Service.

Louis F. Herrmann, Head, Dairy Section, Organization and Costs Branch, Marketing Research Division, Agricultural Marketing Service.

Omer W. Herrmann, Agricultural Attaché, American Embassy, Paris, France.

G. E. Hilbert, Director, Utilization Research, Agricultural Research Administration.

Max K. Hinds, Dairy Marketing Economist, Division of Agricultural Economics, Federal Extension Service.

Donald E. Hirsch, Chief, Dairy Branch, Marketing Division, Farmer Cooperative Service.

R. W. Hoecker, Head, Wholesaling and Retailing Section, Transportation and Facilities Branch, Marketing Research Division, Agricultural Marketing Service.

A. C. Hoffman, Vice President for Purchasing, Kraft Foods Company.

Budd A. Holt, Assistant Chief, Transportation and Facilities Branch, Marketing Research Division, Agricultural Marketing Service.

Sidney S. Hoos, Professor of Agricultural Economics, University of California, and Economist, California Agricultural Experiment Station.

L. D. Howell, Agricultural Economist, Organization and Costs Branch, Marketing Research Division, Agricultural Marketing Service.

William J. Hudson, Chief, Economics and Statistics Branch, Traffic Management Division, General Services Administration.

H. H. Hulbert, Agricultural Economist, Livestock and Wool Branch, Marketing Division, Farmer Cooperative Service.

L. S. Hulbert, Attorney-at-Law and Legal Consultant for American Institute of Cooperation.

H. S. Irwin, formerly Agricultural Economist, Food Distribution Branch, Production and Marketing Administration.

O. B. Jesness, Head, Department of Agricultural Economics, University of Minnesota.

Harold D. Johnson, Transportation Economist, Transportation and Facilities Branch, Marketing Research Division.

Thew D. Johnson, Agricultural Economist, Transportation and Facilities Branch, Marketing Research Division.

Edward Karpoff, Head, Poultry and Egg Section, Statistical and Historical Research Branch, Agricultural Economics Division, Agricultural Marketing Service.

Joseph G. Knapp, Administrator, Farmer Cooperative Service.

Theodore J. Kreps, Professor of Business Economics, Graduate School of Business, Stanford University.

Herbert C. Kriesel, Head, Dairy Section, Statistical and Historical Research Branch, Agricultural Economics Division, Agricultural Marketing Service.

Don C. Leavens, Office of the Undersecretary for Transportation, United States Department of Commerce.

Paul P. Logan, Director of Research on Food and Equipment, National Restaurant Association.

W. F. Lomasney, Food Merchandising Specialist, Division of Agricultural Economics, Federal Extension Service.

Frank Lowenstein, Head, Cotton and Other Fibers Section, Statistical and Historical Research Branch, Agricultural Economics Division, Agricultural Marketing Service.

Lorenzo B. Mann, Chief, Frozen Food Locker Branch, Purchasing Division, Farmer Cooperative Service.

Andrew W. McKay, formerly Assistant to the Chief, Cooperative Research and Service Division, Farm Credit Administration.

J. M. Mehl, Administrator, Commodity Exchange Authority.

George L. Mehren, Professor of Agricultural Economics, University of California, and Economist, California Agricultural Experiment Station.

Trienah Meyers, Assistant Head, Market Surveys Section, Market Development Branch, Marketing Research Division.

Henry Miller, Assistant General Counsel, Federal Trade Commission.

Marshall E. Miller, Agricultural Economist, Organization and Costs Branch, Marketing Research Division.

James A. Mixon, Director, Distribution Research and Development, National Wholesale Frozen Food Distributor's Association.

Edward J. Murphy, Director, Grain Division, Agricultural Marketing Service.

Sterling R. Newell, Director, Agricultural Estimates Division, Agricultural Marketing Service.

L. J. Norton, Professor of Agricultural Economics, University of Illinois.

Kenneth E. Ogren, Head, Marketing Information and Statistics Section, Organization and Costs Branch, Marketing Research Division, Agricultural Marketing Service.

Warren W. Oley, Director, Division of Markets, New Jersey Department of Agriculture.

Allen B. Paul, The Brookings Institution.

W. T. Pentzer, Head, Section of Quality Maintenance and Improvement, Biological Sciences Branch, Marketing Research Division, Agricultural Marketing Service.

Robert E. Post, Head, Grain and Feed Section, Statistical and Historical Research Branch, Agricultural Economics Division, Agricultural Marketing Service.

Margaret R. Purcell, Transportation Economist, Transportation and Facilities Branch, Marketing Research Division, Agricultural Marketing Service.

David A. Revzan, Professor of Business Administration, School of Business Administration, University of California.

Shelby A. Robert, Jr., Head, Product Development Section, Market Development Branch, Marketing Research Division, Agricultural Marketing Service.

Harold B. Rowe, The Brookings Institution.

Reginald Royston, Chief, Fruit and Vegetable Statistics Branch, Agricultural Estimates Division.

Donald M. Rubel, Director, Fruit and Vegetable Division, Foreign Agricultural Service.

J. K. Samuels, Director, Marketing Division, Farmer Cooperative Service.

John J. Scanlan, Chief, Poultry Branch, Marketing Division, Farmer Cooperative Service.

Frances Scudder, Federal Extension Service; formerly State Leader of Home Demonstration Agents, New York.

Geoffrey Shepherd, Professor of Agricultural Economics, Iowa State College.

P. L. Slagsvold, Agricultural Economist, Food and Materials Requirements Division, Commodity Stabilization Service.

Herman M. Southworth, Research Assistant, Office of the Administrator, Agricultural Marketing Service.

Hazel K. Stiebeling, Director, Human Nutrition and Home Economics Research.

Donald R. Stokes, Agricultural Economist, Transportation and Facilities Branch, Marketing Research Division.

Jesse W. Tapp, Executive Vice President, Bank of America.

J. E. Thigpen, Director, Tobacco Division, Commodity Stabilization Service.

J. Murray Thompson, Director, Price Division, Commodity Stabilization Service.

Robert M. Walsh, Chief, Market Development Branch, Marketing Research Division, Agricultural Marketing Service.

William B. Ward, Head, Department of Extension Teaching and Information, Cornell University.

Chester R. Wasson, Leo Burnett, Inc.

Frederick V. Waugh, Director, Agricultural Economics Division, Agricultural Marketing Service.

Gertrude S. Weiss, Assistant Chief, Home Economics Research Branch, Agricultural Research Service.

O. V. Wells, Administrator, Agricultural Marketing Service.

Bennett S. White, Associate Chief, Organization and Costs Branch, Marketing Research Division.

John A. Winfield, Director, Division of Markets, North Carolina Department of Agriculture.

Frederick C. Winter, Associate Professor of Industrial Engineering, Columbia University, and Consultant, Transportation and Facilities Branch.

John C. Winter, Head, Transportation Section, Transportation and Facilities Branch, Marketing Research Division, Agricultural Marketing Service.

Index